SELF-CATERING

Houndapitt Farm Cottages

English Tourist Board
COMMENDED

Set in 150 acres of farmland with magnificent views of the sea. One mile from award winning beach and heritage coastline. This attractive development will sleep 2 to 9 in a high standard of accommodation.
- Coarse fishing • Shetland pony rides
- Farm pets • Adventure playground
- Nearby indoor heated pool

Terms include electricity, heating.
(Sorry, we do not allow pets.)

Detailed Colour Brochure from:
Mr & Mrs F. S. Heard, Houndapitt Farn., Sandymouth, Bude EX23 9HW. Tel: 01288 355455

BOARD

Owned and managed since 1927 by four generations of the young family. The Bristol continues to be one of Newquay's leading hotels. Enjoy traditional hospitality and dine in our Rosette awarded restaurant. We are the ideal centre from which to discover the many excellent golf courses in Cornwall.

☆☆☆

NARROWCLIFF • NEWQUAY • CORNWALL TR7 2PQ
www.cornwall-online.co.uk/hotelbristol

The BRISTOL *Newquay*

Tel: 01637 875181

Best Western

BOARD

TREGIDDLE FARM

Gunwalloe, Helston, Cornwall. TR12 7QW

Telephone 01326 572726

Tregiddle Farm is situated on the Lizard Peninsula. The farmhouse has beautiful views across open country to the golf course and sea. Easy access to many beaches and attractions. There are two double rooms, one with four poster bed and one single.

Breakfast includes farm fresh eggs and home made bread. There is an award winning inn overlooking the sea close by, which serves bar snacks and has an extensive table menu.

Proprietors: Mrs Christine Hosking   **BED AND BREAKFAST FROM £15.00**

BOARD SELF-CATERING

16th/17th Century cottage in pretty hamlet near St. Agnes. A short walk leads to National Trust valley to Chapel Porth beach. Old Inn Cottage has two double bedrooms each with four poster bed, one twin bedded room, all with washbasins; one single bedroom, bathroom, toilet, large cosy sitting room, TV, books, open fireplace, oak beams; dining room. (Self catering available. Details on request.) Off road parking. Regret not suitable for tiny children. No smokers or pets. Bed and Breakfast from £15.50 per person.

Mrs V. Maltwood, Old Inn Cottage, Mingoose, Mount Hawke, Truro, Cornwall. TR4 8BX   Telephone 01209 890545

SELF-CATERING

The Cabin and The Barn
Little Crugwallins Farm, Burngullow, St Austell, Cornwall PL26 7TH

Ideally situated in Mid-Cornwall near the Lost Gardens of Heligan with easy access to North and South coasts, two newly refurbished cottages sleeping two and five. Set on our peaceful five acre smallholding with the freedom of our fields and large secluded gardens.

- ○ tastefully furnished
- ○ bed linen supplied
- ○ short breaks available
- ○ full central heating included
- ○ ample parking – space for trailers
- ○ B&B in farmhouse

For further information see classified entry in Cornwall – St Austell

Tel or Fax: 01726 63882

SELF-CATERING

Friesian Valley Cottages
Mawla, Redruth, Cornwall TR16 5DW
Telephone: 01209 890901

On the Atlantic Coast, between Newquay and St. Ives. Charming luxury cottages, elegantly furnished and surrounded by fields. Two miles to sandy beaches of Portreath, Porthtowan and the NT Coastal Path. Games room, launderette and cosy bar. Sleep 2 to 6 persons. *Terms from £120 to £480 per week.*

SELF-CATERING

Picturesque group of 17th century cottages overlooking beautiful National Trust valley, some with sea views. All our cottages are individually furnished and equipped to a very high standard. All have colour TV, etc. Cottages are warm and comfortable and are open all year. Wonderful walks, peace and quiet and unspoilt beaches nearby.

English Tourist Board Member. ♙♙-♙♙♙♙ Commended
Please write or phone for our free colour brochure.

Mr & Mrs D. Clough, Courtyard Farm, Lesnewth, Near Boscastle, Cornwall PL35 0HR   Telephone: 01840 261256 Fax: 01840 261794

SELF-CATERING

ST. MARGARET'S PARK HOLIDAY BUNGALOWS
POLGOOTH, ST. AUSTELL, CORNWALL PL26 7AX

Family owned and run small park, set in six acres of tranquil lovely grounds and offering good quality accommodation of varying sizes, sleeping from up to eight persons to small self-contained units for two. The attractive timber Bungalows are all detached, many on level ground with parking outside or nearby, some of the smaller units on the valley sides nestling among the trees. Two Bungalows have wheelchair access and partially adapted toilet facilities. All properties are well equipped including colour TV, microwave ovens and outside furniture. We have a children's playing field, launderette and payphone in the park and the Polgooth Inn and village shop are a short stroll away. Safe, sandy beaches 3 miles, famous gardens and fishing ports locally and an excellent location to tour all Cornwall. Well controlled pets allowed. Open March to December.

Phone: 01726 74283 or Fax: 01726 71680 for Brochure

Derwent Manor

Portinscale, KESWICK, Cumbria, England, CA12 5RE

Derwent Manor

Luxury Lakeland Holiday Cottages and Apartments

This former gentleman's country residence now provides some of Lakeland's finest self-catering accommodation amid tranquil surroundings on the fringe of a picturesque village. Wander down to the shores of Lake Derwentwater through 16 acres of private, unspoilt meadows - a recognised conservation area, or stroll along footpaths and over the River into the market town of Keswick.

Our tastefully converted one or two bedroomed self-catering apartments and cottages are all superbly appointed and offer a uniquely high standard of facilities. Fully fitted feature kitchens (many with dishwashers), independent central heating, remote control teletext colour televisions with video player, CD player and direct dial telephone, whilst the bedrooms are complete with hairdryer, trouser press and radio alarms.

Your accommodation comes complete with welcoming tea tray, bouquet of fresh flowers, fruit basket, beds made and towels supplied. Even fresh milk in the fridge, and to be sure your holiday starts with a sparkle, a bottle of chilled Champagne.

But that's not all.

On your first evening with our compliments, you may have dinner at the adjacent award winning and highly commended Derwentwater Hotel. Likewise, breakfast on your departure morning is also included, and there is more, ample free parking, takeaway meal and grocery delivery service, and a special welcome for pets.

For that really special occasion try our Glaramara Cottage, which is tucked away in the corner of the grounds and enjoys king size, half tester bed making an ideal romantic hideaway.

*Derwent Manor ...
an unrivalled location
with quality accommodation
and a range of
services and facilities
seldom matched.*

*Call us now for
our full colour brochure
on 017687 72211.*

BOARD

REDMAYNE, GRASMERE, CUMBRIA

LA22 9QY   Tel: (015394) 35635

Superb elevated private situation. Redmayne enjoys breathtaking views of the Lake and mountains, only five minutes walk from Grasmere Village amenities. Spacious luxury en-suite double bedrooms have colour television, hospitality tray and many thoughtful extras. Bed and Breakfast from £22 - £26. Regret no children or pets. Exclusively for non smokers. Private enclosed parking.

 E.T.C. ◆◆◆◆ *Guest Accommodation*

BOARD

Littletown Farm, situated in a peaceful part of the beautiful Newlands valley has all the facilities of a small hotel. Although fully modernised, the farmhouse retains a traditional character with comfortable lounge, diningroom and licensed bar. Most bedrooms are en suite with tea-making facilities, heating and washbasins. Traditional four-course dinner served six nights a week. Excellent walking and climbing nearby. The market towns of Keswick and Cockermouth and the Lakes are all within easy distance. Ample parking.

Newlands, Keswick, Cumbria CA12 5TU
Tel: 017687 78353   Fax: 017687 78437

Dinner Bed & Breakfast from £38 to £42 per person
Bed and Breakfast from £26 to £30 per person. SAE please

BOARD

The Ferndale Hotel

Lake Road, Ambleside, Cumbria LA22 0DB

Tel: 015394 32207

The Ferndale Hotel is a small, family run Hotel where you will find a warm, friendly welcome and personal attention at all times. Offering excellent accommodation with good home cooked English or Vegetarian breakfast. Our nine attractive bedrooms have all been individually decorated and furnished, each with full en suite facilities, colour television and tea/coffee making tray. Full central heating throughout, several rooms having views of the fells, and including ground floor bedrooms. The Ferndale is open all year round with a car park, is licensed, offers packed lunches, hair dryer, clothes/boot drying and ironing facilities. A wide choice of places to dine, within minutes' walking distance, ranging from excellent pub food to superb restaurants of many varied cuisines will complete your day.

Bed and Breakfast £17.50 - £24.00 pppn. Weekly £115 - £150 pp. **Please phone for brochure.**

SELF-CATERING

ETB 4 Keys Commended

PETS WELCOME

Fishing, Walking, Pure Escapism

Tranquil quality cottages overlooking two modest lakes amid Lakeland's beautiful Eden Valley countryside, only 30 minutes' drive **equidistant** from Ullswater, North Pennines, Hadrian's Wall and Scottish Borders. You will find beds freshly made up for your arrival, tranquillity and freedom in your surroundings, and good coarse and game fishing at hand. Accommodation is clean, well equipped and maintained; laundry area; **PETS WELCOME.**

Exceptional wildlife and walking area. **NO SILLY RULES.** Relax and escape to **YOUR** home in the country – why settle for less! Telephone or SAE for details.

Crossfield Cottages, Kirkoswald, Penrith CA10 1EU. 7 days 8am - 10pm Tel: 01768 896275 (Fax available)
24 hour Brochure Line: 01768 898711 (manned most Saturdays)

THE GATE HOTEL & ORCHID SIAM RESTAURANT

An attractive family-run business on the outskirts of Appleby in easy reach of the town centre with its shops, castle and swimming pool and approximately one mile from the golf course. It is tastefully decorated with panelling from the steam ship 'The Berengaria'. A traditional log fire enhances the warm and friendly service offered all year round. Our rooms are en suite and well furnished with colour TV and tea/coffee trays. There is ample parking, a pleasant enclosed garden and play area. Pets welcome by arrangement. Specialising in Thai food we also offer conventional English food. Licensed. Bed and Breakfast from £17.50 to £27.50 per person; Evening Meal from £4.95 to £10.95.

THE GATE HOTEL, BONGATE, APPLEBY CA16 6LH TEL: 017683 52688; FAX: 017683 53858

Betty Fold, Hawkshead Hill, Ambleside LA22 0PS

Betty Fold is a large country house in its own spacious grounds with magnificent views and set in the heart of the Lake District National Park. The quaint village of Hawkshead is nearby and Coniston and Ambleside are within four miles; the beauty spot of Tarn Hows is 20 minutes' walk away. As well as being a Guest House, Betty Fold offers self-catering accommodation for up to four persons; there is "Garden Cottage" in the grounds and "Letterbarrow View", a self-contained flat, both suitable for four persons. All accommodation is centrally heated and facilities such as linen, colour TV and cots are provided, also heating, power and lighting. Pets welcome. Terms approximately £260 to £360 per week, in main season Special Packages from November to Easter. Dinner available in Guest House.

Telephone: (015394 36611)

COMMENDED

Fellside Farm
Near Wastwater, The Lake District
Enquiries to: Mrs S Capstick, Whicham Hall, Whicham Valley, Silecroft, Cumberland LA18 5LT
Tel: 01229 772637

Sleeps seven plus baby, on a working farm Situated in a peaceful unspoilt part of the Lake District, we offer a truly "get away from it all" holiday.
Lounge with open fireplace or electric fire, playroom with table tennis equipment.
Kitchen with oil fired Rayburn which runs central heating, electric cooker, fridge/freezer. three large double bedrooms and cot and highchair. Bathroom with airing cupboard. two w.c, one upstairs and one downstairs. Large playsafe garden. Ample parking. Electricity and coal all inclusive. 10 minutes to Wastwater. 13 miles to Coniston. Local shop and Post Office 15 minute walk.
Price per week:
from £130 short break to £400 high season.

SANDOWN
Lake Road, Windermere, Cumbria LA23 2JF Tel: 015394 45275

Superb Bed and Breakfast accommodation. All rooms en suite with colour TV and tea/coffee making facilities. Situated two minutes from Lake Windermere, shops and cafes. Many lovely walks. Open all year. Special out of season rates, also two-day Saturday/Sunday breaks. From £30 per person, excluding Bank Holidays. Well behaved dogs welcome. Each room has own safe private car parking. SAE or telephone for further details

Proprietors: Irene and George Eastwood

Home Sweet Holiday Home

There's no better way to experience the charms of North Devon than from the comfort and luxury of a Marsdens holiday cottage.

Our acclaimed full colour brochure includes properties each personally inspected by our staff, as well as graded by the Tourist Board, and most are commended for quality.

Romantic whitewashed cottages nestling in the heart of North Devon's idyllic countryside and Exmoor ....secluded beach houses just a stone's throw away from some of Britain's most spectacular and unspoilt coastlines.... whatever your idea of a perfect holiday, we can help make it a reality.

And, as an extra bonus, our prices will come as a pleasant surprise too. Little wonder, then, that so many of our customers come back for more.

Call now for your free colour brochure.

MARSDENS
COTTAGE HOLIDAYS

01271 813777

2 The Square, Braunton,
North Devon, EX33 2JB.
Fax:(01271) 813664.
email: holidays@marsdens.demon.co.uk
Web site: www.marsdens.co.uk

"Easily the best choice of cottages in Devon..."

...and comfortably the best value you'll find anywhere !

Contact us now for a free copy of our guide to the 500 best value cottages around Devon's unspoilt National Trust Coast. Choose from Spring and Autumn breaks in delightful Exmoor farm cottages from only £89 to luxury beachside homes with swimming pools at over £890 per week in Summer.

All are regularly inspected and guaranteed to offer first class value.

North Devon Holiday Homes

19 Cross Street, Barnstaple EX31 1BD
Tel:(01271) 376322 (24 hrs) Fax:(01271) 346544
www.northdevonholidays.co.uk

*E*njoy a family holiday in the beautiful setting of our 18th century hotel, enveloped by six acres of glorious gardens. We are situated in the beautiful countryside not far from the beach. Our aim is to give you and your children a totally relaxing and stress free stay whether swimming in our heated pools or playing in our large indoor games room. We want you to experience peace of mind within our safe environment. Our superb food and evening entertainment, along with different activities for all age groups and baby listening facilities adds the perfect touch to a total family holiday. Our award winning hotel has family rooms and two room suites. All are with ensuite and have tea making facilities, colour TV and baby listening intercoms.

For a Relaxing Family Holiday

Radfords Country Hotel

Set amongst beautiful Devon countryside, in six acres of grounds, with playground. Come and relax, we cater for every member of the family, even ted!

- ❖ Excellent ensuite accommodation family rooms or two bedroom suites.
- ❖ 3 heated swimming pools.
- ❖ Playgroup three mornings a week.
- ❖ Supervised play 5 evenings.
- ❖ Toddlers playroom and soft play area.
- ❖ Superb food.
- ❖ Varied entertainment programme.
- ❖ Evening baby listening.
- ❖ Launderette.
- ❖ Flexible mealtimes.
- ❖ Easy reach beach, town, Dartmoor.
- ❖ All inclusive terms.

Contact Janet and Terry Crump, Radfords Country Hotel, Dawlish, Devon, EX7 0QN

Telephone: 01626 863322

Dunscombe Manor
"For peace and tranquillity"

- ✦ *Bedrooms en suite.*
- ✦ *Quiet courtyard.*
- ✦ *Peaceful garden.*
- ✦ *Ample parking.*

Newly converted Farm Buildings comprising one and two bedrooms. Tastefully furnished and equipped to a high standard. The thatched Farmhouse is at the head of a wooded coombe leading to the coastal footpath and Weston Mouth beach providing the key to unlock a National Trust area of outstanding natural beauty, rich in wildlife, flora and fauna. The location is adjacent to the internationally renowned Donkey sanctuary.

Regret no smoking inside the apartments. No pets.

For colour brochure:

Dunscombe Manor, Sidmouth, Devon EX10 0PN
Telephone and Fax: 01395 513654

BOARD

Upton House   Cullompton, Devon EX15 1RA

We will welcome you to this beautiful 300 year old farmhouse, charmingly furnished with oak panelled walls and lovely inglenook fireplaces in is tranquil parkland setting. Lovely garden with superb views. All bedrooms are spacious, tastefully decorated en suite with all facilities. We have a picturesque coarse fishing lake on this 180 acre organic farm. We are ideally placed for exploring Devon National trust properties and North and South coasts. Just one-and-a-half miles from junction 28, MT

Telephone 01884 33097   *English Tourism Council* ◆◆◆◆

BOARD

MAELCOMBE HOUSE

Idyllically situated in a classified area of outstanding natural beauty. Nestled in a private bay beneath wooded cliffs, well away from the bustle of busy tourist spots. Spectacular walking, climbing, sailing, golfing and riding in the area. We also have a fine all weather tennis court. All set in extensive tropical gardens overlooking the sea, one minute from the beach. Three luxury self-contained and well-equipped apartments, each sleeping up to six. East Prawle is one mile distant, Kingsbridge and Salcombe are nearby with excellent facilities. Camping and B&B also available. Please ring for full colour brochure.

Sally and Peter Barber, Maelcombe House, East Prawle, Near Kingsbridge, Devon TQ7 2DE
Tel: 01548 511521   Fax: 01548 511501

BOARD SELF-CATERING

FARM & GUESTHOUSE
Doddiscombsleigh, Exeter, Devon EX6 7RF
Telephone 01647 252058
GREAT LEIGH   **Fax: 01647 253008**

S ituated in the beautiful picturesque Teign Valley, where peace and solitude rule, but only a few miles from Exeter and Dartmoor. The farm owns 170 acres of land completely surrounding it. Rough shooting is avaliable and fishing in the River Teign. Golf is also available nearby. The spacious rooms, all with en suite facilities are beautifully converted in an old stone barn retaining much of the Old World charm. There is a games room housing a full size snooker table.
There are also three self contained cottages with open fires and magnificent views. Pets allowed.

2 Double/2 Twin Bedded rooms. All en suite with TV and tea-making facilities, hairdryers and shoe cleaning kits. £25/£30 per person for a double room Single £35/£40 per person. Open all the year round.

PUBLISHER'S NOTE

While every effort is made to ensure accuracy, we regret that FHG Publications cannot accept responsibility for errors, omissions or misrepresentations in our entries or any consequences thereof. Prices in particular should be checked because we go to press early. We will follow up complaints but cannot act as arbiters or agents for either party.

Flear Farm Cottages

Discover nine superb cottages set in 75 acres of a beautiful South Devon valley - just five miles from the sea. As well as peace and quiet, we offer a 40ft indoor heated swimming pool, sauna, all weather tennis court, large indoor and outdoor play areas.

Non-smokers only. Children and dogs welcome. Log fires and full central heating - perfect for off-season breaks

ꕥꕥꕥꕥ to ꕥꕥꕥꕥ Highly Commended

East Allington, Totnes, South Devon TQ9 7RF
e-mail: www.flearfarm.co.uk

'Phone (01548) 521227 or Fax (01548) 521600 For our Colour Brochure

LYME BAY HOLIDAYS

FREE BROCHURE

Lyme Regis, Charmouth and West Dorset

**LYME BAY HOLIDAYS, (FHG)
BOS HOUSE, 44 CHURCH STREET
LYME REGIS, DORSET DT7 3DA**

ALL PROPERTIES TOURIST BOARD INSPECTED

100 + PROPERTIES

Tel: (01297) 443363 (24hrs)

Fax: (01297) 445576 (24hrs)

KIMMERIDGE FARMHOUSE
✦ ✦ ✦ *Bed & Breakfast* ✦ ✦ ✦

Relax and take a well earned break in our period 14th Century farmhouse with views of Kimmeridge Bay across 700 acres of farmland. There are many spectacular walks either along the coastal paths or inland over the Purbeck Hills surrounding the ruins of Corfe Castle.

Spacious and attractively furnished en suite rooms with colour television, beverage tray and full central heating for those off-season breaks. A delicious homecooked breakfast of your choice and a warm welcome assured. For further details please contact:

Mrs Annette Hole ✦ **Tel: 01929 480990**
Kimmeridge, Wareham, Dorset BH20 5PE

*Bed & Breakfast from £21 per person
Open all year except Christmas Day
Evening Meal by arrangement (Oct-Mar)*
ETC ◆◆◆◆ *Gold Award*

BOARD

A historic country hotel whose heritage dates to the 13th Century situated in the heart of the Forest of Dean, close to the Wye Valley.

The hotel retains many of its original features, including beams, timber panelling and oak spiral staircases. Fourteen en suite bedrooms are located throughout the hotel grounds. Within the house are two four-poster bedrooms and additional double and twin rooms. All bedrooms are en suite and have with colour TV, direct dial telephones and tea and coffee making facilities. Our red rosette candlelit restaurant is renowned for its quality cuisine and friendliness of service.

Tudor Farmhouse Hotel is the ideal retreat to relax and unwind.

The Tudor Farmhouse & Restaurant
Clearwell, near Coleford, Gloucestershire GL16 8JS
Freephone: 0800 7835935 • Fax: 01594 833046
E-mail: reservations@tudorfarmhse.u-net.com • website: www.tudorfarmhousehotel.co.uk

BOARD

AA Harts Lodge
◆◆◆◆
242 Everton Road
Everton, Lymington, Hampshire SO41 OHE

Bungalow (non smoking), set in three acres. Large garden with small lake and an abundance of bird life. Quiet location, convenient for A337. Three miles west of Lymington. Friendly welcome and high standard. Accommodation comprising double, twin and family en suite rooms, each with tea/coffee making facilities and colour TV. Delicious four-course English breakfast. The sea and forest are five minutes away by car. Horse riding, golf and fishing are nearby. The village pub, serving excellent homemade meals is half-a-mile away. Children and pets welcome. Bed and Breakfast from £20 per person.

Telephone: 01590 645902

BOARD

Our Bench
Guest House

Tel & Fax: 01590 673141
www.newforest.demon.co.uk/bench.htm

Proprietors: Roger and Mary Lewis

✦ Walking Disabled Welcome.
✦ Indoor Heated pool, Jacuzzi and Sauna.
✦ Non-Smokers only.
✦ No Children or Pets.
✦ National Accessibility Scheme three.
✦ Optional Evening Meals.
✦ Quiet Situation between New Forest and Coast.
✦ Large Bungalow and Garden.
✦ Four course breakfast special diets catered for.
✦ Mountain bikes available.

9 Lodge Road, Pennington, Lymington. SO41 8HH

SELF-CATERING

Langstone Court Farmhouse

14th Century farmhouse. Lounge and dining room each measure 15 x 18 feet. Farmhouse wing sleeps 15 plus cots, Cidermill flat sleeps 5-7 plus cot or can be let as one unit sleeping up to 22 plus cots. Very popular for hen parties, birthdays and family get-togethers.

Two ground floor bedrooms, 1 double, 1 single. Central heating, log fires, laundry, payphone, bike storage, dishwashers. Set in beautiful Herefordshire Countryside. Large groups please book early. Short Breaks available all year except August.

Tel: 01989 770774
Colour brochure: Lesley Saunders, Dales Barn, Langstone, Llangarron, Ross-on-Wye HR9 6NR

Moor Court Farm

Stretton Grandison, Near Ledbury, Herefordshire HR8 2TR. Telephone: 01531 670408

Relax and enjoy our attractive 15th century timber-framed farmhouse with its adjoining oast-houses, whose picturesque location will ensure a peaceful stay. The Godsall family run a traditional hop and livestock farm situated in the beautiful countryside of Herefordshire being central to the local market towns, with easy access to the Malverns, Wye Valley and Welsh Borders. Guests will enjoy spacious bedrooms, all with en suite facilities, their own oak-beamed lounge, dining room and the peaceful setting of the garden or walks through surrounding woods and farmland with their rural views. Fishing is available in our own pool and there are stables on the farm.

Bed & Breakfast from £19.00; Evening Meal £12.50. Residential licence.

ETC ◆◆◆◆

Come and stay on a farm in

THE LUNE VALLEY

This lovely area of North Lancashire and South Cumbria is known for its stunning countryside and unspoilt villages. There is a variety of farmhouse accommodation to stay in, including self-catering and B&B. Excellent location for visiting The Lake District, Yorkshire Dales, Forest of Bowland, Historic Lancaster and the nearby coast.

See Board, Self-Catering and Caravan Sections – **LUNE VALLEY, LANCASHIRE**

For general information on the Lune Valley, please telephone:
Lancaster Tourist Information Centre on **01524 32878**

River Lune near Arkholme

Rakefoot Farm

Tel: Chipping 01995 61332 or 0589 279063   Chaigley nr. Clitheroe BB7 3LY

Working family farm peacefully situated in the beautiful countryside of Ribble Valley at the foot of Bowland, with panoramic views (3 miles Chipping, 8 miles M6 J31a). Warm welcome whether on holiday or business with refreshments on arrival.

BED & BREAKFAST and SELF CATERING

available in renovated 17th Century farmhouse and traditional stone barn conversion. Superbly furnished, wood burning stoves, central heating, exposed beams and stonework. Most bedrooms en suite, some ground floor. Excellent home cooked meals, laundry, pubs/restaurants nearby. Indoor/outdoor play areas, garden and patios. Dogs by arrangement.

Self Catering properties sleeping 2 to 8 (3 interconnect, sleeping 16) £75-£420 weekly. Short Breaks available.

Shrublands Farm

Shrublands farm is a working arable farm in the village of Northrepps, two and a half miles south-east of Cromer and 20 miles north of Norwich. This is the ideal situation for exploring the wonderful coast of North Norfolk, National Trust properties and The Norfolk Broads. The Victorian/Edwardian house has three bedrooms, all with private facilities, colour TV, and tea and coffee making facilities. There is full central heating and plenty of parking space. Evening meals by arrangement. This is a non-smoking house. Children over 12 years. Sorry, no pets. Prices: £21- £27 per person per night.

ETC ◆◆◆◆ **AA**

Mrs Ann Youngman, Shrublands Farm, Northrepps, Cromer, Norfolk NR27 0AA
Tel and Fax: (01263) 579297 e-mail: youngman@farming.co.uk Website: www.broadland.com/shrublands

Church Farm Cottages

Mrs G. V. Howes, Church Farm Cottages,
Brisley, Dereham, Norfolk NR20 5LL
Tel & Fax: 01362 668332

Peace and tranquillity in two owner-supervised cottages between Dereham and Fakenham. Kept to a very high standard of cleanliness and comfort. They have full oil-fired central heating, log fires, colour TV, video, washing machine, dishwasher, fridge freezer, microwave, tumble dryer, outside drying etc. Both also have lawned gardens and plenty of parking space. Open all year. Linen, logs and heating are included in price. Sorry no pets.

Weekly price: £165 – £321 for two or £185–£342 for four. £227–£384 for five.
Short breaks available from October to April from £99 for two to £230 for five.

♈ to ♈♈♈♈
APPROVED

✓✓✓✓
Excellent

'Luxury lodges and Woodland Cottages in a peaceful country setting'

★ Touring ★ walking ★ cycling ★ boating
★ bird-watching ★ fishing ★ exploring local
nature reserves ★ tourist attractions.   **Gold**

Short breaks and longer stays all year round. May to September: *Swimming, lawn tennis, mini-golf, family pub, summer time apartments award winning touring park and more!....*

Clippesby Holidays, Clippesby Hall, Clippesby, Norfolk NR29 3BL
Telephone: 01493 367800   Fax: 01493 367809
E-mail: holidays@clippesby.ndirect.co.uk
Website: clippesby.ndirect.co.uk   **COLOUR BROCHURE**

BOARD

Red House Farm

Enjoy a farmhouse Bed and Breakfast at Red House Farm, a late Victorian farmhouse in Longdon-on-Tern, a small village between the historic county town of Shrewsbury and Telford.

- Friendly welcome • Spacious rooms
- Home comforts • Families welcome
- Local pubs serving good food
- Bed & Breakfast from £18 per person
- Reductions for Children

Visit the world famous Ironbridge Gorge with its industrial museums

Contact Mrs Mary Jones, Red House Farm, Longdon-on-Tern, Wellington, Telford Shropshire TF6 6LE
Tel: 01952 770245 • *Website: www.go2.co.uk/RedHouseFarm*

SELF-CATERING

GRANGE COTTAGES

Conversions from 17th Century Barns are set in the beautiful grounds (4½ acres) of this period house. Hundreds of trees and shrubs in the peaceful gardens which have a delightful duck pond. Four miles from the pretty market town of Ludlow. Wonderful views all around the area and many attractions and places to visit within a short distance. Quality cottages (sleep four) with quality fittings and outdoor furniture. Open all year round; central heated; double glazed.

- Small pets welcome • All weather tennis court (en-tout-cas) • Golf course – 2 miles
- Horse Racing – 2 miles • Cycle Hire – close by • Good walking country
- Three night breaks or longer – Arrive any day • Colour brochure.

Lower Hayton Grange, Lower Hayton, Ludlow, South Shropire SY8 2AQ
Tel: 01584 861296 Fax: 01584 861371

BOARD

Malt House Farm

Lower Wood, Church Stretton, Shropshire SY6 6LF
Prop. Mrs Lyn Bloor
Tel: (01694) 751379
AA ◆◆◆

Olde worlde beamed farmhouse situated amidst spectacular scenery at the lower slopes of the Long Mynd Hills. We are a working farm producing beef cattle and sheep. One double bedroom and one twin, both with en suite bathroom, colour TV, hairdryer and tea tray. Good farmhouse cooking is served in the dining room. Private guests' sitting room. Non-smoking. Regret no children or pets. Now fully licensed.

Bed and Breakfast from £18.50 pppn; Evening Meal from £15.00 pp.

BOARD

❖ ❖ LINE FARM ❖ ❖

Tunnel Lane, Orleton, near Ludlow, Shropshire SY8 4HY
Telephone: 01568 780400

Situated five miles south of Ludlow in glorious unspoilt open countryside. Spacious en suite bedrooms, friendly atmosphere, beautiful gardens with panoramic scenery and delicious breakfasts. All this makes Line Farm somewhere truly special to stay. Contact Mrs Lewis

NO SMOKING ESTABLISHMENT AA ◆◆◆◆

SELF-CATERING

BOARD

BOARD SELF-CATERING

Walburn Hall

Walburn Hall is one of the few remaining fortified farmhouses dating from the 14th century. It has an enclosed courtyard and terraced garden. Accommodation for guests includes two double (one with four poster) and one twin bedroom all with en suite facilities. The guests' lounge and dining room have beamed ceilings and stone fireplaces with log fires as required. Your stay at Walburn Hall in the heart of the

Yorkshire Dales of Swaledale and Wensleydale gives the opportunity to visit Richmond, Middleham and Bolton Castles and numerous Abbeys. York, Durham and Harrogate are one hour away. Sorry no pets. Non smoking. Bed and Breakfast from £23 per person. Open March - November. Self catering farmhouse available, sleeps seven plus cot. Brochure on request.

ETC ♦♦♦♦   **Mrs Diana Greenwood, Walburn Hall, Downholme, Richmond DLII 6AF Tel & Fax: 01748 822152**

Middle Farm is a peacfully situated traditional Dales farmhouse, with adjoining stable block for guests accommodation. Situated on the unclassified road linking Wensleydale and Wharfedale. Ideal place to escape the 'madding crowd'. Good base for walking and touring any of the Dales' many beauty spots. Noted for excellent home cooking, offering Bed and Breakfast with optional Dinner. Two double and one twin-bedded rooms all en suite. Separate lounge, dining room.
Guests' privacy assured. Pets and children welcome. Ample private off-road parking. Open all year round.

Middle Farm

Woodale, Leyburn, Coverdale, North Yorkshire DL8 4TY

Tel: 01969 640271

Brochure available on request.

Tom and Sandra Spashett

RED HOUSE FARM

Glaisdale, Near Whitby, North Yorkshire YO21 2PZ
Telephone/Fax: 01947 897242

Listed Georgian farmhouse featured in Houses of the North York Moors. Completely refurbished to the highest standards, retaining all original features. Bedrooms have bath/shower/toilet, central heating, TV and tea making facilities. Excellent walks straight from the doorstep. Friendly farm animals – a few cows, horses, geese and pretty free roaming hens. 1½ acres of gardens, sitting-out areas. Magnificent views. Interesting buildings – listed barns now converted to two holiday cottages. Games room with snooker table. Eight miles from seaside/Whitby. Village pubs within walking distance. Stabling available for horses/dogs. Non-smoking. Please phone **Tom** or **Sandra** for more information.

'Langber Country Guest House'

Ingleton, "Beauty Spot of the North" in the National Park area. Renowned for waterfalls, glens, underground caves, magnificent scenery and Ingleboro' Mountain (2,373 feet), an excellent centre for touring Dales, Lakes, coast and Three Peaks/National Park area. "Langber", a detached country house, is set amidst beautiful scenery with 4½ acres of fields and gardens. There are three family, three double or twin and one single bedrooms, some en-suite. Central heating, comfortably furnished throughout. Fire precautions. Babysitting offered. Open all year except Christmas and New Year. Highly Recommended. Reductions for children under 13 sharing parents' room. Good food and a warm welcome. SAE please.

Mrs Mollie Bell, Langber Country Guest House
Ingleton, North Yorkshire LA6 3DT (015242 41587).

BOARD

Banavie ETC ◆◆◆◆

Banavie is a large stone-built semi-detached house set in Thornton-le-Dale, one of the prettiest villages in Yorkshire with a stream flowing through the centre. Situated in an attractive part of the village off the main road, it is ideal for touring coast, moors, Castle Howard, Flamingo Park, Eden Camp, North Yorkshire Moors Railway and "Heartbeat" country. A real Yorkshire breakfast is served by Mrs Bowes herself which provides a good start to the day. One family en suite bedroom, two double en suite bedrooms, all with shaver points, colour TV and tea-making facilities. Dining room. Lounge with TV, central heating. Children and pets welcome; cot, high chair, babysitting. Own door keys. Car park. Cycle shed. Open all year. Bed and Breakfast (including tea and biscuits at bedtime) from £18.00. SAE, please.

Thornton-le-Dale has three pubs, two restaurants and fish and chip shop for meals. Welcome Host, Hygiene Certificate held.

Mrs Ella Bowes, Banavie, Roxby Road, Thornton-le-Dale, Pickering, North Yorkshire YO18 7SX • Tel: 01751 474616

BOARD

West's Caravan Park

**Killarney Road, Killorglin,
Ring of Kerry, SW Ireland
FREEPHONE 0800 374424
(from Britain): Tel: 00 353 66 9761240**

Modern, comfortable caravans and chalets, 2/3 bedrooms, full size cooker, fridge, hot water, shower and toilet. On family-run park situated on banks of River Laune overlooking Ireland's biggest mountain. TV lounge, pool table, table-tennis, laundry, payphone. Town one mile away. Ideal touring centre. Ferry and static caravan prices.

Mobile homes from £109 – £349

Also sites available for houses and twin units ½ mile from the town centre, overlooking sea.

CARAVANS

Dungannon Park CAMPING AND CARAVANNING

Dungannon Park is set in 70 acres of beautiful parkland surrounding an idyllic stillwater lake. It is situated in the heartland of Ulster, less than a mile from the motorway to Belfast and is within easy walking distance of the historic town of Dungannon. Relax and enjoy the many facilities and activities available:

◆ Twelve fully serviced caravan sites, tent access for up to eight tents
◆ Stillwater Rainbow Trout fly fishery ◆ 3 miles of scenic park walks ◆ Barbeque site & picnic area
◆ Modern visitor amenity, servicing all your needs ◆ Children's play area ◆ Disabled facilties & wheelchair friendly

TARIFF: Caravans £8.00 Tents £6.00 on site: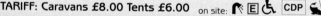

**For more information contact: Dungannon Park, Dungannon
District Council Tel: 028 87727327 or Fax: 028 87729169**

CARAVANS

NOTE

All the information regarding Golf Clubs in this guide is given in good faith in the belief that it is correct. However, the publishers cannot guarantee the facts given in these pages, neither are they responsible for changes in ownership or facilities, such as green fees, that may take place after the date of going to press. Readers should always satisfy themselves that the facilities they require are available and that the terms, if quoted, still apply.

SELF-CATERING

Discover this idyllic 17th century riverside millhouse and charming wool manager's cottage in superb waterfall valley between Porthmadog and Beddgelert. Mill (WTB 4 Dragons) with large character beamed livingroom, period furnishings, wood stove, central heating, colour TV. Luxury kitchen, modernised bathroom/cloakroom. Sleeps eight/10 in four bedrooms and self-contained annexe. Secluded terraces (barbecue/floodlighting) adjoin Mill pool and falls. Cottage (WTB 3 Dragons) sleeping four/six in two bedrooms, and self-contained gable annexe with similar facilities, is delightfully situated overlooking ancient fording bridge. Superb local scenery with Snowdon, Portmeirion, Ffestiniog Railway all nearby. Cottage Terms £175 to £390 and Mill £200 to £700 weekly. Brochure, photographs:-

Mr and Mrs O. Williams-Ellis, San Giovanni, 4 Sylvan Road, London SE19 2RX Tel: 020 86533118

Felin Parc Cottages

SELF-CATERING

Hendwr Scandinavian Lodges
in the beautiful Welsh Countryside

Solid Finnish timber lodges situated in parkland in a tree lined driveway at the foot of the Berwyn mountains. Each heated by electricity and fully furnished with three bedrooms, bathroom, fitted kitchen with electric cooker, fridge and breakfast bar.
Cool and airy in summer and cosy and warm in spring and autumn.
Spacious lounge with three piece suite and colour TV, opening on to a veranda. Well stocked farm shop, Laundrette, pay phone.

GRADE 1 2 3 4 5

J&D Hughes Hendwr Scandinavian Lodges Llandrillo, Corwen North Wales LL21 0SN • Telephone: 01490 440 210

BOARD

Awelon

Awelon once formed part of the estate of William Salisbury, translator of the New Testament into Welsh in the 16th century. With three-foot thick outer walls, it has now been modernised and is an attractive small guest house. Three bedrooms with en suite available with colour TV and teamakers; cosy lounge; central heating ensures a comfy stay. Private parking. Llanrwst, a busy market town at the centre of the beautiful Conway Valley, is close to Snowdonia, Bodnant Gardens and North Wales coast. A warm Welsh welcome awaits all guests. Bed and Breakfast from £16; en suite from £18.50. A good choice of Hotels, Pubs and Cafes available for evening meals in Llanrwst. All home cooking. Children and pets welcome.

Mrs Eleanore Roberts, Awelon, Plas Isa, Llanrwst LL26 0EE Tel: 01492 640047

SELF-CATERING

• MYDROILYN •

Stone farm buildings, recently converted into four cottages, providing modern standards of comfort in a traditional setting. Sleep 2/3 (terms £95 - £190) or 4/8 (£155 - £320). Gas, electricity, linen included. All have shower room; fully equipped kitchen; colour TV; shared laundry room; facilities for children. Secluded rural area, abundant with wildlife and flowers; five miles from sandy beaches, picturesque harbours of Cardigan Bay, National Trust coastal paths, breathtaking mountain scenery; birdwatching; fishing, pony trekking, steam railway nearby.

WTB and AA Approved   Open Easter to October

Gil & Mike Kearney, Hillside Cottages, Blaenllanarth, Mydroilyn, Lampeter, Ceredigion SA48 7RJ Telephone: Lampeter (01570) 470374

Our World by the Sea

Map Ref. H8

FOR INEXPENSIVE QUALITY

FEATURED BY **BBC**

DOLPHIN QUALITY
VERY GOOD

BEACH MODERN LUXURY HOLIDAY HOME *or Caravan*

With the beach moments from your door. An Award winning Park, in an area of outstanding natural beauty. This is a quiet secluded cove and Park with sub-tropical plants confirming Gulf Stream mild climate. Safe bathing, water sports, sea & river fishing. Ramble along the flat coastal strip. The local post office & shop is only 3 min. walk. Nearby restaurants, Bar Snacks, Take Aways, golf, pony trekking, three modern leisure centres, Nature Trails in the Historic Glynllifon Country Park. Tour beautiful Snowdonia and the famous Llŷn peninsula, beaches & Portmeirion. Featured by the BBC, Wales Tourist Board & British Holiday Home Parks. Families return to us year after year with the new Dual expressway making the journey so easy. Come & view anytime. All our Accommodation comprises Shower, W/basin & Toilet, 2 or 3 Bedrooms, Remote Control Colour TV, Well Heated, Free Electric & Gas, Fridge/Freezer, Cooker, Electric Blanket, Kettle, Hoover, Blankets, Pillows, Crockery, Cutlery, Cooking Utensils. Bring your own sheets, pillow cases & towels or own duvet. All have Heated Bedroom, Microwave & Toaster. Full Central Heating to 65° on Request. Some are double glazed. Try a "Super 12" Home which is 20% more spacious. Park next to your Accommodation. Try a £12 Minibreak Special. Holiday Home Caravans for sale on Park. Phone for our detailed Brochure.

SUPER 12 20% more spacious	2000	Model Type	Sleeps	Bed rooms	MAR	APRIL GF	BH	BH	MAY	BH	JUNE	JULY	AUGUST	BH	SEPTEMBER	OCTOBER	Model Type
	Week Commencing				25	1/8	15	22	29	6	13 20 27	3 10 17 24	1 8 15 22 29	5/12 19 26	2 9 16 23 30	7/14 21	
	Economy Standard Caravan	C	4-6	2	59	1/8	79	99	79	59	59 69 159	95 99 129 139	149 149 209 239 249	249 249 189	129 99 89 69	69 79	C
	Budget Holiday Home	D	4-7	2	69	75	95	139	99	85	95 99 199	139 149 159 169	179 189 209 289 299	299 299 249	169 149 119 99	89 79	119 D
	Budget Holiday Home	E	4-8	3	69	79	99	149	109	95	99 109 229	149 159 179 199	199 229 299 319 329	329 329 259	179 149 125 99	89 85	129 E
	Super Holiday Home	F	4-7	2	69	79	99	149	115	89	109 109 219	149 159 169 179	189 199 239 299 319	329 329 279	189 159 129 109	99 85	125 F
	Super Holiday Home	G	4-8	3	79	85	119	169	129	109	119 119 249	159 169 189 199	209 229 249 329 359	359 359 279	189 159 129 109	95 89	139 G
	UP MARKET PLUS Holiday Home	H	4-6	2	75	85	119	169	119	109	129 129 249	169 179 189 209	239 239 259 319 359	359 359 279	189 159 129 119	99 89	129 H
SUPER 12	Superior Holiday Home	I	4-8	2	75	85	119	169	129	109	129 129 249	169 179 189 209	239 239 259 319 339	359 359 269	179 159 129 119	99 89	129 I
SUPER 12	Superior Holiday Home	L	6-10	3	89	105	169	239	169	139	169 169 289	229 239 249 259	279 289 329 349 389	399 399 319	229 189 169 149	129 119	179 L

SUPER SHORT BREAKS – ANYTIME
3 nights weekend. **4/3** nights midweek,
HALF weekly price to next £ and add →
Other dates/nights by arrangement.
Phone for quotation.
ANY DATES TO SUIT YOU

NO HIDDEN EXTRAS. COME AND INSPECT ANYTIME & CHOOSE

10	15/20	25	40	25	40	25	15	20	20	45	25	25	30	30	30	40	45	45	50	40	40	30	25	20	15	35

Deposit £33 P.W., and Insurance £1 Nightly for Holiday Home. Cots & High Chairs £2 Nightly each.
Some Double Glazed. Over £6 persons £5 per night each. Full Central Heating to 65°
£5 Nightly Request. All prices inc. electric, piped gas & VAT @ 17½%.
Recent Model £5 Nightly. Dogs £3 Nightly.

INSTANT HOLIDAYS – ANYTIME

Should you be able to take a last minute break, please ring 01286 660400, and we will do our best to accommodate you – the same day if you wish.
MINIBREAK – A few days, week-end or mid-week
4-6 Berth FROM £10 per night per Holiday Home, Caravan
4-8 Berth FROM £12 per night per Holiday Home, Caravan
6-10 Berth FROM £14 per night per Holiday Home, Caravan

ANY 4 DAYS - BEACH MODERN LUXURY HOLIDAY HOME, ANY 3 NIGHTS. Extra nights available. FROM

	MARCH	APRIL	BERTH	MAY	BERTH	JUNE	BERTH	JULY	BERTH	AUGUST	BERTH	SEPTEMBER	OCTOBER
From		4-6 4-8 6-10		4-6 4-8 6-10		4-6 4-8 6-10		4-6 4-8 6-10		4-6 4-8 6-10		4-6 4-8 6-10	
	25	39 45 47	1	47 49 54	6	44 57 62	3	72 94 99	1	104 119 124	5	169 194 204	2 104 124 129	7 47 54 57
		8	49 57 59	13	44 67 69	10	75 99 104	8	104 124 129	12	169 194 209	9 89 114 114	14 49 57 62
				15th	59 69 75	20	54 69 74	17	89 104 114	15	124 144 159	19 169 194 209	16 74 89 92	21 75 94 99
				22nd	89 109 115	27th	124 144 159	24	99 114 119	22	164 184 194	147 174 179	23 59 74 79
				29th	64 74 79				29	169 194 204		30	54 64 64

EASTER WEEK-END
19th April to 26th April

MAY DAY BANK HOLIDAY WEEK-END
28 APRIL-4 MAY 4-6 Berth 4-8 Berth 6-10 Berth
Any 3 nights FROM £64 £74 £79

WHIT BANK HOLIDAY WEEK-END
26 MAY-1 JUNE 4-6 Berth 4-8 Berth 6-10 Berth
Any 3 nights FROM £124 £144 £159

AUGUST BANK HOLIDAY WEEK-END
25 AUG-31 SEPT 4-6 Berth 4-8 Berth 6-10 Berth
Any 3 nights FROM £144 £174 £179

Easter Week-End
4-6 4-8 6-10
From Berth Berth Berth
2 nights £49 £79 £89
3 nights £89 £109 £115
4 nights £118 £145 £149
Also "Super 12" 20% more spacious. Villa chalets & Executive Bungalows.

Also "Super 12" 20% more spacious. Villa chalets & Executive Bungalows.

BOARD

Gwarmacwydd

Gwarmacwydd is a country estate of over 450 acres, including two miles of riverbank. See a real farm in action, the hustle and bustle of harvest, newborn calves and lambs. Children are welcomed. On the estate are five character stone cottages, Tourist Board Grade 4. Each cottage has been lovingly converted from traditional farm buildings, parts of which are over 200 years old. Each cottage is fully furnished and equipped with all modern conveniences. All electricity and linen included. All cottages are heated for year-round use. Colour brochure available.

Mrs Angela Colledge, Llanfallteg, Whitland, Pembrokeshire. SA34 0XH

Tel: 01437 563260 Fax: 01437 563839

BOARD

Braich Goch Inn & Restaurant
Corris, Near Machynlleth, Powys SY20 9RD

Set in beautiful surroundings in the foothills of Snowdonia on the A487. Ideally situated for touring, steam train enthusiasts, birdwatching, rambling, fishing. Golf, horse riding and clay pigeon shooting all well catered for. World famous Centre for Alternative Technology and King Arthur's Labyrinth (new attraction) close by. Bedrooms en suite or with private facilities; licensed restaurant with extensive menu; cheerful beamed bar is a meeting place for friendly locals. Pets most welcome.

B&B £21–£25pp (double or twin); Autumn and Winter Breaks phone for details.

Tel/Fax: 01654 761229

 Commended

BOARD SELF-CATERING

UPPER GENFFORD FARM
GUEST HOUSE • SELF-CATERING

Set amongst the most spectacular scenery of the Brecon Beacons National Park, Upper Genfford Farm is an ideal base for exploring the Black Mountains, Wye Valley and the Brecon Beacons, an area of outstanding beauty, rich in historical and archaeological interest, with Roman camps and Norman castles. Picturesque mountain roads will lead you to reservoirs, the Gower coast with its lovely sandy beaches and Llangorse Lake – well known for all kinds of water sports.

The charming Guest House accommodation includes one double and one twin-bedded rooms, both with en suite facilities. They are beautifully decorated and furnished, including tea/coffee making facilities, central heating, colour TV and hairdryer. The cosy lounge has a wealth of personal bric-a-brac, maps and paintings. Very much a home from home, with colour TV and books. Guests are made welcome with home-made cakes and tea on arrival. The local pub and restaurant is nearby and Hay-on-Wye, 'The Town of Books', is a short distance away.

Our self-catering cottage is fully-equipped with fridge-freezer, electric cooker, microwave, and oil-fired Rayburn for cooking. There is a cosy, comfortable lounge with colour TV, open log fire (logs provided), pretty bathroom and two attractive bedrooms (one with two single beds, the second with one double and one single). Ample parking in attractive patio adjacent to the cottage. Play area for Children, also a friendly pony.

Bed & Breakfast from £18 to £20 per person.

Terms from £150 to £180 weekly.

MRS PROSSER, UPPER GENFFORD FARM GUESTHOUSE, TALGARTH, BRECON LD3 0EN

AA
♦♦♦
Guest Accommodation

TELEPHONE: 01874 711360

AA
QQQQ

Awarded Plaque of Recommendation from the Welsh Tourist Board
Nominated "Landlady of the Year" 1999   Winner of FHG Diploma

LOCHMEYLER FARM

Guest House

Tel: 01348 837724
Fax: 01348 837622

Mrs Morfydd Jones
Llandeloy,
Pen-y-Cwm,
Near Solva,
St. Davids,
Pembrokeshire
SA62 6LL

A warm welcome awaits you at Lochmeyler, a 220 acre dairy farm in the centre of the St David's Peninsula. It is an ideal location for exploring the beauty of the coast and countryside.

There are 16 bedrooms, eight of them in the adjacent cottage suites. All are en-suite, non-smoking, luxury rooms with colour TV, video and refreshment facilities. Optional evening dinner with choice of menu including vegetarian. Children are welcome and there is a children's play area. Dogs free. Kennel facilities are free for owners wishing to leave their dogs during the day. Well behaved dogs

can sleep in bedrooms providing they have their own bedding on the floor.

Open all year. Credit cards accepted. Colour brochure on request.

RAC ♦♦♦♦♦   ★★★★ FARM   GOLD

DAILY RATES
Bed & Breakfast per person per night • min £20 - max £25
Optional evening dinner £12.50
Children half price sharing family room.

SCOTLAND
Counties

SHETLAND ISLANDS

WESTERN ISLES

HIGHLAND

MORAY

ABERDEENSHIRE

ABERDEEN CITY

ANGUS

PERTH AND KINROSS

DUNDEE CITY

ARGYLL AND BUTE

STIRLING

FIFE

9

2 6 8
1 3 5 7 10 11 E. LOTHIAN
4 12

NORTH AYRSHIRE

S. LANARKSHIRE

EAST AYRSHIRE

BORDERS

SOUTH AYRSHIRE

DUMFRIES AND GALLOWAY

1. Inverclyde
2. West Dunbartonshire
3. Renfrewshire
4. East Renfrewshire
5. City of Glasgow
6. East Dunbartonshire
7. North Lanarkshire
8. Falkirk
9. Clackmannanshire
10. West Lothian
11. City of Edinburgh
12. Midlothian

©MAPS IN MINUTES™ (1998)

Balmoral Estates

Off the A93, between Ballater and Braemar

Grounds and Exhibitions

Open daily to the Public between 10.00 a.m. to 5.00 p.m.

Monday 17th April 2000 until Monday 31st July 2000

**GARDENS ~ COUNTRY WALKS ~ GIFT SHOPS ~ CAFETERIA
PONY TREKKING ~ PONY CART RIDES** (when ponies available)

**EXHIBITION OF PAINTINGS AND WORKS OF ART
AND TARTAN COLLECTION IN THE CASTLE BALLROOM**

(The remainder of the Castle is closed to the Public)

**EXHIBITION OF CARRIAGES, COMMEMORATIVE CHINA,
PHOTOGRAPHIC COLLECTION AND A DISPLAY OF WILDLIFE IN
THEIR NATURAL HABITAT IN THE CARRIAGE HALL**

**Regional Car Park near Main Gate
Enquire at Main Gate for Disabled Access**

Admission Charges

Adults ~ £4.00   Senior Citizens ~ £3.00   Children (5 to 16) ~ £1.00

For further details please contact

The Estates Office, Balmoral, Ballater, Aberdeenshire, AB35 5TB

Telephone (013397) 42334 Fax (013397) 42271

E-Mail~info@balmoral-castle.co.uk   Internet~www.balmoral-castle.co.uk

SELF-CATERING

The Estate lies along the beautiful Deveron River and our traditional stone cottages nestle in individual seclusion. Visitors can explore one of the ancient baronies of Scotland. The sea is only nine miles away, and the market town of Turriff only two miles, with its golf course, swimming pool, etc. Places of interest including the Cairngorms, Aviemore, picturesque fishing villages and castles, all within easy reach on uncrowded roads. See our Highland cattle.

Terms: from £145 weekly. Special Winter lets. 10 cottages sleeping 6-9. Children and reasonable dogs welcome. STB Inspected.

For a brochure contact: **Mrs P. Bates, Holiday Cottages, Forglen Estate, Turriff, Aberdeenshire AB53 4JP Tel: 01888 562918/562518; Fax: 01888 562252**

BRECHIN CASTLE CENTRE

Haughmuir, by Brechin, Angus
Tel: 01356 626813

One of the largest tourist attractions in Angus and a great day out for all the family.

~ **HIGH QUALITY GARDEN CENTRE** *and* **COFFEE SHOP** ~
~ **COUNTRY PARK** *with* ~ **ORNAMENTAL LAKE** ~ *picnic and enjoy the tranquillity;*
walk around the park to the **FARM,** *touch the animals* ~ **SUMMER EVENTS** ~
Brochure on request

SELF-CATERING

COLOGIN FARM HOLIDAY CHALETS
Oban

All Scottish Glens have their secrets: let us share ours with you – and your pets !

- Tranquil country glen, just 3 miles from Oban
- Free fishing and dinghy use on our hill loch.
- Excellent walks for you and your dogs.
- Home-cooked food and licensed bar in our converted farm-yard byre.
- A safe haven for pets and children.
- A friendly, family run complex with a good range of facilities.

PETS WELCOME

Our cosy holiday chalets, set on an old farm in a peaceful private glen, can sleep from two to six people in comfort. They all have private parking, central heating, colour TV and bed linen.

Call now for our colour brochure and find out more:

MRS LINDA BATTISON, COLOGIN FARMHOUSE, LERAGS GLEN, BY OBAN, ARGYLL PA34 4SE

**Tel: Oban (01631) 564501 Fax: (01631) 566925
E-mail: cologin@oban.org.uk**

STB ★★ Self Catering

Open all year round.
Rates from £120 to £420 per week.
Autumn Gold breaks and
mid-week deals also available.

The Highland Estate of Ellary and Castle Sween

OFFERS

★ PEACE
★ SECLUSION
★ VARIETY OF INTERESTS

★ FREEDOM
★ HISTORY
★ OUTSTANDING SCENERY

This 15,000-acre Highland Estate lies in one of the most beautiful and unspoilt areas of Scotland and has a wealth of ancient historical associations within its bounds. There is St. Columba's Cave, probably one of the first places of Christian Worship in Britain, also Castle Sween, the oldest ruined castle in Scotland, and Kilmory Chapel where there is a fascinating collection of Celtic slabs.

There is a wide range of accommodation, from small groups of cottages, many of the traditional stone-built estate type to modern holiday chalets, super luxury and luxury caravans at Castle Sween.

Most of the cottages accommodate up to six, but one will take eight.

All units fully equipped except linen. Television reception is included in all but one cottage where reception is not possible.

Ellary is beautiful at all times of the year and is suitable for windsurfing, fishing, swimming, sailing and the observation of a wide variety of wildlife; there are paths and tracks throughout the estate for the visitor who prefers to explore on foot, and guests will find farmers and estate workers most helpful in their approach.

For further details, brochure and booking forms, please apply to:

ELLARY ESTATE OFFICE, by LOCHGILPHEAD, ARGYLL PA31 8PA
Tel: 01880 770232/770209 or 01546 850223
Fax: 01880 770386 Website: www.ellary.com

 # Rockhill Farm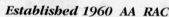
Country Guest House
with Self-Catering Cottage and Bungalow
Ardbrecknish, By Dalmally, Argyll PA33 1BH   Tel: 01866 833218

Established 1960 AA RAC

17th Century Guest House in spectacular waterside setting
on Loch Awe with breathtaking views to
Ben Cruachan and towards Glencoe, where comfort,
peace and tranquillity reign supreme.

- Small private Highland estate breeding Hanoverian
competition horses. • 1200 metres free trout fishing.

- 5 delightful rooms with all modern facilities.
First class highly acclaimed home cooking with much
home grown produce.

- Wonderful area for touring the Western Highlands,
Glencoe, the Trossachs and Kintyre. Castles, gardens and all
kinds of attractions to visit. Ideal for climbing, walking, bird
and rare animal watching. Boat trips locally and from Oban
(30 miles) to Mull, Iona, Fingal's Cave and other islands.

- SELF CATERING.
Secluded, clean, comfortable, well equipped peaceful
waterside bungalow and cottage on Loch Awe side.
Both sleep seven. Outstanding views over loch.

- *Early booking discount scheme.*

Poltalloch Estate • Loch Crinan

STB ★★★★

A selection of charming self-catering cottages, each unique in its history and character, and enhanced by the natural beauty of Loch Crinan. All have been attractively modernised and furnished, with care taken in the retention of many traditional and historically interesting features. The cottages offer varying accommodation for two to five persons in comfort. Eating out is no problem with many good restaurants in the area. Salmon fishing, hill walking and safe, sandy beaches can all be enjoyed on the estate. Terms and further details on application. SAE requested.

Contact: Susan Malcolm
Duntrune Castle,
Kilmartin, Argyll PA3I 8QQ
Telephone: 01546 510283

ELERAIG HIGHLAND CHALETS
near Oban, Argyll, gateway to the Highlands and islands

In the breathtaking scenery of a private glen within 1800-acre working sheep farm. The chalets are ideal for a holiday with dogs (& cats). Widely spaced, sleeping four to seven. Parking by each chalet. Cots and high chairs available. By Loch Tralaig. Free fishing and boating. Peace and tranquillity are features of this walkers' and birdwatchers' paradise. Riding, golf, watersports and evening entertainment available locally. Open March to October.

From £205 weekly per chalet, including electricity.
Colour brochure from resident owners:
Anne and Robin Grey, Eleraig Highland Chalets,
Kilninver, by Oban, Argyll PA34 4UX
Tel/Fax: 01852 200225 · Web: www.scotland2000.com/eleraig

Scottish Tourist Board ★★ SELF CATERING

HIGHLAND HIDEAWAYS   Argyllshire

This is one of several high quality self-catering properties of individual character we have to offer in outstanding coastal, town and country locations in Argyll including the Oban area and around Loch Awe. Sleeping 2 to 12 from £130 to £950 per week. Up to STB 4 star grade.

For further derails contact:
Highland Hideaways,
5/7 Stafford Street, Oban, Argyll PA34 5NJ
Tel: 01631 562056 Fax: 01631 566778
E-mail: ADEA@obanestates99.freeserve.co.uk

SELF-CATERING

STABLE COTTAGE

Warm, comfortable, stone cottage sleeping four plus cot/childbed in a secluded glen 18 miles south of Oban. Within a regional scenic area, an ideal base for exploring Argyll and the Islands. Fishing, walking, watersports, golf, pony trekking, birdwatching, gardens all nearby. Sorry, no pets. Short breaks.

£162-£291 per week. Discounts for two. Colour brochure.

Contact: Mrs G.H Dalton, Maolachy, Lochavich, by Taynuilt, Argyll PA35 1HJ. Tel 01866 844212. Fax: 01866 844295

SELF-CATERING

Hunter Holiday Cottages

Rosewell, Edinburgh

Hunter Holiday Cottages offer a range of cottages in beautiful countryside only eight miles from Edinburgh city centre. These superior cottages are recently renovated, have all modern facilities and sleep six to eight plus. They provide the ideal base for the perfect Scottish holiday from their location in Midlothian's historic countryside. There is easy access to Scotland's capital and the major routes to the rest of Scotland. For more information visit our website. Also B&B, £20-£25 per night

Contact Duncan Hunter   Tel: 0131 448 0888 Fax: 0131 440 2082
E-mail: hunter@holidaycottages.demon.co.uk   Website: www.holidaycottages.demon.co.uk

PUBLISHER'S NOTE

While every effort is made to ensure accuracy, we regret that FHG Publications cannot accept responsibility for errors, omissions or misrepresentations in our entries or any consequences thereof. Prices in particular should be checked because we go to press early. We will follow up complaints but cannot act as arbiters or agents for either party.

SELF-CATERING

SELF-CATERING

SELF-CATERING

SELF-CATERING

Newmill Farm

Mrs Ann Guthrie, Newmill Farm, Stanley, Perthshire PH1 4QD
Telephone: (01738) 828281 E-mail:guthrienewmill@sol.co.uk

STB ★★★ B&B

Newmill Farm is situated only six miles from Perth, in 330 acres of lovely farmland. There are twin, double and family rooms available (most en suite); lounge, sittingroom, diningroom; bathroom, shower room and toilet. The many castles and historic ruins around Perth are testimony to Scotland's turbulent past. Situated at the "Gateway to the Highlands" the farm is ideally placed for those seeking some of the loveliest unspoilt scenery in Western Europe. Many golf courses and trout rivers nearby. Bed and breakfast from £18, Evening meal on request. Reductions and facilities for children. Pets welcome.

Mains of Murthly
Aberfeldy PH15 2EA

Two beautifully situated holiday cottages on a working farm, overlooking Aberfeldy, one-and-a-quarter-miles from town.

- Fully equipped for three to five persons.
- Hire service available • Children welcome.
- Pets accepted • Ample parking.

Fishing available on private stretch of River Tay. Golf courses nearby and new recreation centre with swimming pool in Aberfeldy. Available all year, with terms from £150.

Further details contact Mrs J.M. McDiarmid, Tel/Fax (01887 820427)

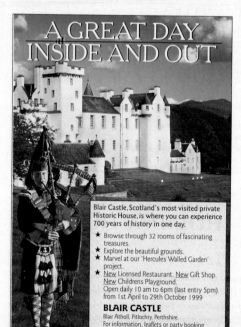

A GREAT DAY
INSIDE AND OUT

Blair Castle, Scotland's most visited private Historic House, is where you can experience 700 years of history in one day.

★ Browse through 32 rooms of fascinating treasures.
★ Explore the beautiful grounds.
★ Marvel at our 'Hercules Walled Garden' project.
★ New Licensed Restaurant. New Gift Shop. New Childrens Playground.
Open daily 10 am to 6pm (last entry 5pm) from 1st April to 29th October 1999

BLAIR CASTLE
Blair Atholl, Pitlochry, Perthshire.
For information, leaflets or party booking information, telephone: **01796 481 207**

Website: www.blair-castle.co.uk

Other FHG holiday and accommodation guides

FHG Publications have a large range of attractive holiday accommodation guides for all kinds of holiday opportunities throughout Britain. Our guides are available in most bookshops and larger newsagents, but we will be happy to post you a copy direct if you have any difficulty. Below are just two of our guides. For full details of all our publications see back of this book.

BED AND BREAKFAST STOPS.
Over 1000 friendly and comfortable overnight stops. Non-smoking, Disabled and Special Diets Supplements.

SELF-CATERING HOLIDAYS in Britain
Over 1000 addresses throughout for Self-catering and caravans in Britain.

FHG PUBLICATIONS
ABBEY MILL BUSINESS CENTRE
SEEDHILL, PAISLEY, SCOTLAND PA1 1TJ
(TEL: 0141-887 0428; FAX: 0141-889 7204)

THE ASSOCIATION OF SCOTLAND'S SELF CATERERS

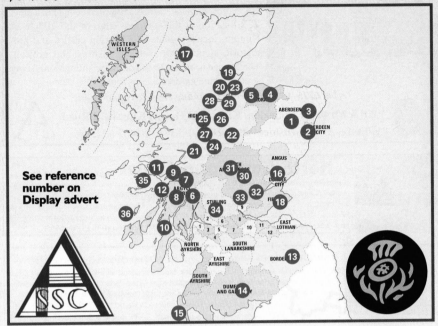

See reference number on Display advert

Selected Self-Catering Holidays in Scotland

Members of the ASSC are committed to high and consistant standards in self catering. Contact your choice direct and be assured of an excellent holiday.

Brochures: 0990 168 571 • Web site: www.assc.co.uk

Owner-Operators ready to match our standards and interested in joining are requested to contact our Secretary for information – 0990 168 571

DYKESIDE AND TANAREE COTTAGES (SLEEP 4 AND 6)

STB ★★★★ SELF-CATERING. A warm welcome awaits you at Logie Newton Farm, eight miles east of Huntly. Two charming single-storey cottages are available, both extremely well equipped including colour TV, video, payphone, etc. The farm has its own walks, children's lead rein pony rides, stone circles and Roman Camp Site. For further information and bookings please contact:
Mrs Rhona Cruickshank, LOGIE NEWTON FARM, by Huntly, Aberdeenshire AB54 6BB. Tel: 01464 841229. Fax: 01464 841277.

1

THE ROBERT GORDON UNIVERSITY   TEL: 01224 262134 FAX: 01224 262144

Kepplestone

The Robert Gordon University in the heart of Aberdeen offers a wide variety of accommodation to visitors from June through to August. Aberdeen is ideal for visiting Royal Deeside, Castles and historical buildings, playing golf or touring the Malt Whisky Trail. The city itself is a place to discover and Aberdonians a friendly and welcoming people. We offer self-catering accommodation for individuals or for groups of people at superb rates. Each of our flats is self-contained, centrally heated and fully furnished and suitable for children and disabled guests. All flats have colour TVs and some have microwave facilities. Bed linen and cooking utensils are all provided as is a complimentary 'welcome pack' of basic groceries. Towels available on request. Each residence has laundry and telephone facilities as well as ample car parking.

King Street

2

Contact: The Robert Gordon University, Business and Vacation Accommodation, Customer Services Dept, Schoolhill, Aberdeen. AB10 1FR

THE GREENKNOWE

A comfortable, detached, renovated cottage in a quiet location at the southern edge of the village of Kintore. Ideally situated for touring castles and prehistoric sites or for walking, fishing and golfing. The cottage is on one level with large sittingroom facing south and the garden. Sleeps four.

Terms £225–£350 per week including electricity and linen.

Mr & Mrs P.A. Lumsden, Kingsfield House, Kingsfield Road, Kintore, Aberdeenshire AB51 2UD. Tel/Fax: 01467 632366

North East Farm Chalet *Near Keith and Elgin*

One 'A' frame chalet on working farm. 'Habitat' furnished, fully equipped for 2–6 people, colour TV, bed linen, duvets. Beautiful rural location in Moray – famous for flowers – district of lowlands, highlands, rivers, forests, lovely beaches, historic towns, welcoming people. Excellent local facilities. Moray golf tickets available. *From £170–£300 (January-December)* **Contact: Mrs. J.M. Shaw, Sheriffston, Elgin, Moray IV30 8LA Tel/Fax: (01343) 842695**

Tulloch Lodges - *Peace, Relaxation and Comfort in Beautiful Natural Surroundings*

One of the loveliest self-catering sites in Scotland. Modern, spacious, attractive and beautifully equipped Scandinavian lodges for up to six in glorious woodland/water setting. Perfect for the Highlands and Historic Grampian, especially the Golden Moray Coast and the Golf, Castle and Malt Whisky Trails. £195 - £540 pw. **Brochure:** Tulloch Lodges, Rafford, Forres, Moray IV36 2RU **Tel : 01309 673311 Fax: 01309 671515 Web: ww.assc.co.uk/tulloch** STB ★★★★ Self-catering

---

BRALECKEN HOUSE
A mid 19th Century stone building carefully restored to provide two

comfortable houses. Situated on private upland farm. Each comprises sitting room, fully fitted kitchen, two bedrooms, bathroom and shower room. Both are completely private or suitable for two families wishing to holiday together. Large parking area and garden. Children most welcome but regretfully no pets. Contact Mr and Mrs Crawford

Brenchoille Farm, Inveraray, Argyll PA23 8XN TEL: (01499) 500662

Mr & Mrs E. Crawford

Blarghour Farm

Loch Awe-side, by Dalmally, Argyll PA33 1BW
Tel: 01866 833246   Fax: 01866 833338

At Blarghour Farm one may choose from four centrally heated and double glazed holiday homes sleeping from 2 to 8 people, all enjoying splendid views of lovely Loch Awe. Kitchens are well appointed, lounges tastefully decorated and furnished with payphone, TV and gas fire, beds are made up and towels supplied while the two larger houses have shower rooms in addition to bathrooms, all with shaver points. The two larger houses are suitable for children and have cots and high chairs. No pets are allowed. Open all year. Centrally situated for touring. Illustrated brochure on request.

STABLE COTTAGE Warm, comfortable stone cottage sleeping four plus cot/ childbed in a secluded glen 18 miles south of Oban. Within a Regional Scenic Area, an ideal base for exploring Argyll and the Islands. Fishing, walking, watersports, golf, pony trekking, birdwatching, gardens all nearby. Sorry, no pets. Short Breaks. £162-£291 per week; discounts for two. **Colour brochure. Contact Mrs G H Dalton, Maolachy, Lochavich, by Taynuilt, Argyll PA35 1HJ. Tel: 01866 844212. Fax: 01866 844295.**

SHEPHERD AND STOCKMAN FLATS – DUMFRIES

Listed farm steading flats in peaceful pastoral valley surrounded by wooded hills and forest lanes. Two bedrooms each plus sofa bed and cot. TV, linen and central heating provided. Electricity metered. Outside facilities include drying room, bicycle shed, stable, dog run, barbecue and picnic area. Management is eco-sound and nature friendly. Lower flat and forest walks are wheelchair compatable. Village shop 1 1/2 miles, Thornhill nine miles, Dumfries 15 miles, Riding four miles, fishing two miles, Mountain bike course is two miles and Queensberry is five miles.

14

Contact: David and Gill Stewart,
Gubhill Farm, Ae, Dumfries DG1 1RL
Telephone: 01387 860648   E-mail: stewart@creaturefeature.freeserve.co.uk

---

HARBOUR ROW

Mull of Galloway, Wigtownshire

Row of five cottages and two houses completed in 1990 and designed to extend the village of Drummore. Patios at the rear benefit from the southerly exposure and open fires give evening relaxation.

Only yards from sand and sea.
Highest quality furnishings and equipment.
Garden with children's playground.
Open all year. Colour brochure.
Prices £195-£455
including linen and towels.

15

Contact Mrs Sally Colman, Harbour Row,
Cailiness Road, Drummore, Stranraer DG9 9QX
Telephone/Fax: 01776 840631

THE WELTON OF KINGOLDRUM by Kirriemuir, Angus DD8 5HY

Three luxurious self-catering properties on a secluded working farm, set in a spectacular setting with superb paronamic views. Ideal for hillwalking and bird-watching. An excellent base for golf, fishing, riding, skiing, shooting etc. and touring the glens, coast and castles.

DETACHED COTTAGE – STB ★★★★ DISABLED CATEGORY 3. SLEEPS 4.
SEMI-DETACHED BUNGALOW – STB ★★★ BEDROOMS EN SUITE. SLEEPS 4.
STUDIO FLAT – STB ★★★ EN SUITE. SLEEPS 2.

16

For further information and brochure contact Mrs Maureen Marchant.

Telephone / Fax: 01575 574743
e-mail: weltonholidays@btinternet.com
www.angusanddundee.co.uk/members/562.htm

OPEN ALL YEAR.   SHORT BREAKS AVAILABLE.   PRICES £150 - £320

Clashmore Holiday Cottages Our three croft cottages at Clashmore, are the ideal base for a holiday in the Highlands. They are cosy and fully equipped, with linen provided. Nearby there are sandy beaches, mountains and lochs for wild brown trout fishing. Children welcome but sorry no pets. Open all year, sleeping two-five £160-£320 per week.

**Contact Mr and Mrs Mackenzie, Lochview,
216 Clashmore, Stoer, Lochinver, Sutherland IV27 4JQ
Tel/Fax: 01571 855226 E-mail: clashcotts@aol.com**

17

---

*WHEN REQUESTING INFORMATION ABOUT
SELF-CATERING ACCOMMODATION,
A STAMPED, ADDRESSED ENVELOPE IS ALWAYS APPRECIATED*

THORNDENE

On the southern shore of the Tay estuary

NEWPORT-ON-TAY, FIFE

Thorndene is the secluded, self-contained west wing of a listed house in a 3-acre walled garden. Bright and sunny, on the ground floor with its own garden and entered by a paved courtyard, it is equipped to a high standard, fully carpeted, with central heating. Two double bedrooms (one with shower en suite), a single bedroom, large sittingroom, dining room, sun lounge, bathroom and shower, fitted kitchen with washing machine, dishwasher, microwave and breakfast bar. Sleeps 5-6. £170-£360 weekly.

Brochure requests and enquiries to Mr & Mrs Ramsay, Balmore, Newport-on-Tay, Fife DD6 8HH
Tel: 01382 542274   Fax: 01382 542927

18

CLUAINE LODGE

A comfortable modern bungalow within a secluded private garden, two acres with mature woodland all around. Near to Dornoch. One double and one twin bedded room, sleeps four. Living room with open fire, coal/logs provided. Well-equipped fully fitted kitchen. Full electric central heating, using night storage heaters. Bedding, towels provided. Colour TV, radios in bedrooms. Open all year, Pets by arrangement. NO SMOKING ONLY PLEASE Tariff: October-April from £170-£200, June-September £210-£250. Contact; Mrs E.A. Dunlop, Cluaine, Evelix, Dornoch, Sutherland IV25 3RD   **Tel/Fax: 01862 810276**

19

Scorrielea, Black Isle

Scorrielea is a well equipped traditional detached farm cottage situated in a large garden with parking for three cars surrounded by open farmland near to sandy beach and 18 hole golf course. Sleeps 6 plus cot. Accommodation on two floors comprises: on upper 2 twin bedrooms plus shower room. On ground floor 1 double bedroom, lounge, fully equipped kitchen, sun lounge, additional WC. Ideal base for exploring the Highlands (Inverness half-an-hour), observing dolphins, seals and other wildlife (Dolphin viewpoint nearby). Local walks, Pictish history. Open March-November. Brochure available. Contact Mrs L. Grant, Fasgadh, Ness Road, Fortrose, Ross-shire IV10 8SD Tel: 01381 620367

20

Pets Welcome! Free Fishing!

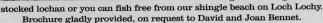

RIVERSIDE LODGES

INVERGLOY, SPEAN BRIDGE, INVERNESS-SHIRE PH34 4DY
TEL/FAX 01397 712684
e-mail: riverside.lodges@dial.dot.pipex.com
web: www.ykm09.dial.pipex.com

Peace and quiet are synonymous with Riverside, where our three identical lodges each sleep up to six people. Accessible from the A82 but totally hidden from it, our 12 acres of woodland garden front on Loch Lochy. Cots, linen, boat, fishing tackle, barbecue, all for hire. Pets welcome. There is a nominal charge for fishing on our stocked lochan or you can fish free from our shingle beach on Loch Lochy. Brochure gladly provided, on request to David and Joan Bennet.

21

Aviemore – DELL LODGES

For that special vacation enjoy the stunning beauty of the Highlands and the Cairngorm Mountains from our choice of cosy lodges and superbly appointed villas.
- Great locations ● Peaceful and relaxing setting ● Sky TV, video, payphone, barbecue
- Pets welcome. Mini breaks ● Many activities available ● Leisure pool and restaurants nearby ● Open all year. Free brochure ● Internet www.premiervacations.net
Premier Vacations 07000 2000 99 or 0131 221 9001
Fax: 07000 777577 e-mail: reservations@premiervacations.net

22

Laikenbuie Holidays, near Nairn

Watch deer and osprey on tranquil organic croft with beautiful outlook over loch amid birch woods. Free range hens, cows, sheep, fishing. Large warm lodge or residential caravan provide quality accommodation by the Moray Firth and its dolphins. Excellent holiday centre four miles from Nairn, safe for children, low rainfall, plentiful sunshine, sandy beaches. Near Loch Ness, Cairngorm mountains, Cawdor Castle. No smoking inside. Lodge £112-£468; Caravan £112-£300. www.bigfoot.com/~muskus or colour brochure:
Mrs Therese Muskus, Laikenbuie, Grantown Road, Nairn IV12 5QN Telephone: 01667 454630

23

The Farm Holiday Guide to

HOLIDAYS IN

ENGLAND, SCOTLAND, WALES, IRELAND

& THE CHANNEL ISLANDS

Farms, guest houses and country hotels;
cottages, flats and chalets; caravans and camping;
activity holidays; country inns.

CONTENTS

ENGLAND

CONTENTS

SCOTLAND

WALES

NORTHERN IRELAND

REPUBLIC OF IRELAND

FARM HOLIDAY GUIDE
ENGLAND, SCOTLAND, WALES, IRELAND
& THE CHANNEL ISLANDS

Welcome to the 53rd edition of Farm Holiday Guide, which covers the whole of the country.

We are pleased to offer for the Year 2000 holiday season, an interesting range of holiday opportunities of all sorts throughout Britain. Full board, bed & breakfast, self-catering; hotels, farms, guest houses, caravan parks and camping sites, not forgetting inns and activity entries . . . in the country, by the sea . . . for short breaks or annual holidays. Our Readers' Offer Vouchers for free or reduced rate entry to a range of popular holiday attractions start on page 43 and we hope that these will add to your holiday enjoyment.

Anne Cuthbertson
Editor

ISBN 185055 304 1
© IPC Magazines 2000
Cover photographs: Main picture – Picture Bank; smaller picture – Andy Wiliams
Cover design: Oliver Dunston, Link House Magazines

Maps: ©MAPS IN MINUTES™ (1998)

Typeset by FHG Publications Ltd. Paisley.
Printed and bound in Great Britain by William Clowes, Beccles, Suffolk.

Distribution. Book Trade: WLM, Unit 11, Newmarket Court, Newmarket Drive, Derby DE24 8NW
(Tel: 01332 573737. Fax: 01332 573399).
News Trade: Market Force (UK) Ltd, 247 Tottenham Court Road, London WIP 0AU
(Tel: 020 7261 6809; Fax: 020 7261 7227).

Published by FHG Publications Ltd., Abbey Mill Business Centre,
Seedhill, Paisley PA1 ITJ (Tel: 0141-887 0428 Fax: 0141-889 7204).
e-mail: fhg@ipc.co.uk

US ISBN 1-55650 872 7
Distributed in the United States by
Hunter Publishing Inc., 130 Campus Drive, Edison, N.J. 08818, USA

The Farm Holiday Guide is a Link House publication, published by
IPC Country & Leisure Media Ltd, part of IPC Magazines Group of Companies.

Woburn Safari Park

Woburn Park, Bedfordshire MK17 9QN

Tel: 01525 290407

One child FREE with two full-paying adults. Not valid for coach parties

READERS' OFFER 2000

valid 4th march to 29th October 2000

NOT TO BE USED IN CONJUNCTION WITH ANY OTHER OFFER

Bekonscot Model Village

Warwick Road, Beaconsfield, Buckinghamshire HP9 2PL

Tel: 01494 672919

One child FREE when accompanied by full-paying adult

READERS' OFFER 2000

valid February to October 2000

NOT TO BE USED IN CONJUNCTION WITH ANY OTHER OFFER

NEDDI Donkey Sanctuary

Lower Maidenland, St Kew, Near Wadebridge, Cornwall PL30 3HA

Tel: 01208 841710

One child FREE with each adult

READERS' OFFER 2000

valid during 2000

NOT TO BE USED IN CONJUNCTION WITH ANY OTHER OFFER

Windermere Steamboat Museum

Rayrigg Road, Windermere, Cumbria LA23 1BN

Tel: 015394 45565

Two for the price of one (adults) OR 25% off family ticket

READERS' OFFER 2000

valid March to October 2000

NOT TO BE USED IN CONJUNCTION WITH ANY OTHER OFFER

Treak Cliff Cavern

Castleton, Hope Valley, Derbyshire S33 8WP

Tel: 01433 620571

Individuals pay group rate

READERS' OFFER 2000

valid during 2000

NOT TO BE USED IN CONJUNCTION WITH ANY OTHER OFFER

Drive-through animal reserves
Large leisure area
All-inclusive price
NB: pets not allowed in Safari Park

Open:
4th March to 29th October 2000

Directions:
off Junction 13 of the M1

FHG PUBLICATIONS, ABBEY MILL BUSINESS CENTRE, PAISLEY PA1 1TJ

A magical miniature world of make-believe depicting rural England in the 1930's.
"A little piece of history that is forever England."

Open:
10am to 5pm daily 19th February to 31st October.

Directions:
Junction 16 M25, Junction 2 M40.

FHG PUBLICATIONS, ABBEY MILL BUSINESS CENTRE, PAISLEY PA1 1TJ

Visit the rescued donkeys, feed and groom them; donkey picnics. Assault course, bouncy castle.

Open:
one week before Easter to end October
10am to 5pm daily.
Winter hours by arrangement.

Directions:
follow brown and white signs from A39

FHG PUBLICATIONS, ABBEY MILL BUSINESS CENTRE, PAISLEY PA1 1TJ

World's finest steamboat collection and premier all-weather attraction. Swallows and Amazons exhibition, model boat pond, tea shop, souvenir shop. Free guided tours.

Open:
10am to 5pm 3rd weekend in March to last weekend October

Directions:
on A592 between Windermere and Bowness-on-Windermere

FHG PUBLICATIONS, ABBEY MILL BUSINESS CENTRE, PAISLEY PA1 1TJ

An underground wonderland of stalactites, stalagmites, rocks, minerals and fossils. Home of the unique Blue John stone – see the largest single piece ever found. Suitable for all ages.

Open:
March to October opens 9.30am,
November to February opens 10am.
Enquire for last tour of day and closed days.

Directions:
½ mile west of Castleton on A6187 (old A625)

FHG PUBLICATIONS, ABBEY MILL BUSINESS CENTRE, PAISLEY PA1 1TJ

FHG
READERS'
OFFER
2000

The Big Sheep

Bideford, Devon EX39 5AP

Tel: 01237 472366

Admit one child FREE with each paying adult

valid during 2000

NOT TO BE USED IN CONJUNCTION WITH ANY OTHER OFFER

FHG
READERS'
OFFER
2000

Plymouth Dome (and Smeaton's Tower)

The Hoe, Plymouth, Devon PL1 2NZ

Tel: 01752 600608

One child FREE with one full-paying adult

valid during 2000

NOT TO BE USED IN CONJUNCTION WITH ANY OTHER OFFER

FHG
READERS'
OFFER
2000

Killhope Lead Mining Centre

Cowshill, Upper Weardale, Co. Durham DL13 1AR

Tel: 01388 537505

One child FREE with full-paying adult (not valid for Park Level Mine)

valid April to October 2000

NOT TO BE USED IN CONJUNCTION WITH ANY OTHER OFFER

FHG
READERS'
OFFER
2000

NATIONAL WATERWAYS MUSEUM

Llanthony Warehouse, Gloucester Docks, Gloucester GL1 2EH

Tel: 01452 318054 e-mail: info@nwm.org.uk website: www.nwm.org.uk

20% off all museum tickets (Single)

valid during 2000

NOT TO BE USED IN CONJUNCTION WITH ANY OTHER OFFER

FHG
READERS'
OFFER
2000

Verulamium Museum

St Michael's, St Alban's, Herts AL3 4SW

Tel: 01727 751810

"Two for One"

valid from 1/8/00 until 31/12/00

NOT TO BE USED IN CONJUNCTION WITH ANY OTHER OFFER

"England for Excellence" award-winning rural attraction combining traditional rural crafts with hilarious novelties such as sheep racing and duck trialling. Indoor adventure zone for adults and children.

Open:

daily all year, 10am to 6pm

Directions:

on A39 North Devon link road, two miles west of Bideford Bridge

---

Award-winning centre sited on Plymouth's famous Hoe telling the story of the city, from the epic voyages of Drake, Cook and the Mayflower Pilgrims to the devastation of the Blitz. A must for all the family

Open:

daily all year except Christmas Day
(Smeaton's Tower closed October to Easter)

Directions:

follow signs from Plymouth City Centre to the Hoe and seafront

---

Britain's best preserved lead mining site – and a great day out for all the family, with lots to see and do. Underground Experience – Park Level Mine now open.

Open:

April 1st to October 31st
10.30am to 5pm daily

Directions:

alongside A689, midway between Stanhope and Alston in the heart of the North Pennines.

On three floors of a Listed Victorian warehouse telling 200 years of inland waterway history.
• Historic boats • Painted boat gallery
• Blacksmith • Archive film
• Hands-on displays
"A great day out"

Open:

10am to 5pm. Closed Christmas Day and Jan.1st/2nd

Directions:

Junction 11A or 12 off M5 – follow brown signs for Historic Docks. Railway and bus station 10 minute walk. Free coach parking.

The museum of everyday life in Roman Britain. An award-winning museum with re-created Roman rooms, hands-on discovery areas, AV, and some of the best mosaics outside the Mediterranean

Open:

Monday to Saturday 10am-5.30pm
Sunday 2pm-5.30pm

Directions:

St Alban's

Europe's finest collection of tigers, including Siberian, Royal Bengal, White and rare Chinese. Other big cats include leopard, black panther and jaguar; also collection of endangered primates.

Open:
Easter to end October 10am to 5pm
Phone for winter opening hours.

Directions:
on B3329 road (Sandown to Bembridge), along seafront towards the White Cliff

---

Over 3500 years of history vividly brought to life. Visit the hands-on 'Roman Encounters' and step into the 1940's Dover Street in 'Our Finest Hours'. New: The Dover Bronze Age Boat Gallery

Open:
April to October 10am to 5pm
November to March 10am to 3pm

Directions:
signposted from M2/A2 and M20/A20; brown/white signs on entering Dover

---

Enjoy a marvellous day out: feed the animals, tractor ride, indoor adventure play area, nature trail. Indoor and outdoor picnic areas, tea room, fine food and gift shop. Disabled access.

Open:
daily 10.30am to 5pm. Closed between Christmas and New Year's Day.

Directions:
M6 Junction 35; on B6254 at Arkholme, towards Kirkby Lonsdale.

The world's largest collection of Grand Prix racing cars – over 130 exhibits within five halls, including McLaren Formula One cars.

Open:
daily 10am to 5pm (last admission 4pm). Closed Christmas/New Year.

Directions:
2 miles from M1 (J23a/24) and M42/A42; to north-west via A50.

All-weather museum of science and working life. Loads of "hands-on" science fun indoors and out.

Open:
May to August 10am to 6pm
September to April 10am to 5pm
Closed 25/26 December

Directions:
10 minutes from Junction 22 M1 or Junction 13 M42/A42.

Large wildlife park with Reptile
Land, Tropical House, Insectarium,
Birds of Prey Centre, farm animals,
wallaby enclosure, llamas;
adventure playground, tea room
and gift shop.

Open:

daily from 10am
April to end October

Directions:

off A17 at Long Sutton

Lions, snow leopards,
chimpanzees, penguins, reptiles,
aquarium and lots more, set
amidst landscaped gardens.
Gift shop, cafe and picnic areas.

Open:

all year round from 10am

Directions:

on the coast 16 miles north
of Liverpool; follow the brown
and white tourist signs

Come to the world's greatest
medieval adventure and enter our
world of mystery and merriment.
Jump on the magical
'Travel Back in Time'
and ride in search of Robin.

Open:

daily 10am to 6pm
(last admission 4.30pm)

Directions:

near Nottingham Castle in city centre –
follow brown tourist signs

The largest motor museum in the
UK providing a unique insight into
the history of the motor vehicle.
Something for all ages to educate
and entertain. Full catering and
picnic area.

Open:

9.30 am to 5.30pm daily
(until 6.30pm in summer)

Directions:

Sparkford

---

* Britain's most spectacular caves
* Traditional paper-making
* Penny Arcade
* Magical Mirror Maze *

Open:

Summer 10am to 5pm; Winter 10.30am to
4.30pm. Closed 17-25 Dec

Directions:

from M5 J22 follow brown-and-white signs
via A38 and A371. Two miles from Wells.

The world's largest display of Royal Doulton figures past and present. Video theatre, demonstration room, museum, restaurant and shop. Factory Tours by prior booking weekdays only.

Open:
Monday to Saturday 9.30am to 5pm
Sundays 10.30am to 4.30pm
Closed Christmas week

Directions:
from M6 Junction 15/16; follow A500 to junction with A527. Signposted.

FHG PUBLICATIONS, ABBEY MILL BUSINESS CENTRE, PAISLEY PA1 1TJ

The story of the people and horses involved in racing from its royal origins to Lester Piggott, Frankie Dettori and other modern heroes. Millennnium Exhibition – The Essential Horse.

Open:
Easter to end October: Tuesdays to Saturdays; also Bank Holiday Mondays and Mondays in July and August.

Directions:
on High Street next to Jockey Club

FHG PUBLICATIONS, ABBEY MILL BUSINESS CENTRE, PAISLEY PA1 1TJ

18-hole American Adventure Golf set in ⅓ acre landscaped surroundings. Played on different levels including water features.

Open:
April until end October
10am until dusk

Directions:
on the seafront ¼ mile east of Eastbourne Pier.

FHG PUBLICATIONS, ABBEY MILL BUSINESS CENTRE, PAISLEY PA1 1TJ

Suitable for all ages. All-weather attractions include: Planet Earth and Dinosaur Museum, fabulous Botanical Garden, Living Rain Forest, indoor Oriental Garden, Newhaven Miniature Railway, Pleasure Gardens, Water Gardens, gift shops, Garden Centre, licensed Coffee Shop.

Open:
all year, except Christmas Day and Boxing Day.

Directions:
signposted off A26 and A259

FHG PUBLICATIONS, ABBEY MILL BUSINESS CENTRE, PAISLEY PA1 1TJ

---

100 acres of parkland, home to hundreds of duck, geese, swans and flamingos. Discovery centre, cafe, gift shop; play area.

Open:
every day except Christmas Day

Directions:
signposted from A19, A195, A1231 and A182

FHG PUBLICATIONS, ABBEY MILL BUSINESS CENTRE, PAISLEY PA1 1TJ

FHG

READERS' OFFER 2000

HATTON COUNTRY WORLD FARM PARK

Dark Lane, Hatton, Near Warwick, Warwickshire CV35 8XA

Tel: 01926 843411

Admit TWO for the price of one into Farm Park
(not valid Bank Holidays). Admission into Shopping Village free.

valid during 2000

NOT TO BE USED IN CONJUNCTION WITH ANY OTHER OFFER

FHG

READERS' OFFER 2000

LONGLEAT

Warminster, Wiltshire BA12 7NW

Tel: 01985 844400

£1 off Longleat Passport tickets, up to a max. of 6 per voucher

valid April to October 2000

NOT TO BE USED IN CONJUNCTION WITH ANY OTHER OFFER

FHG

READERS' OFFER 2000

Embsay & Bolton Abbey Steam Railway

Bolton Abbey Station, Skipton, N. Yorkshire BD23 6AF

Tel: 01756 710614

One adult travels FREE when accompanied by a full fare paying adult
(does not include Special Event days)

valid during 2000

NOT TO BE USED IN CONJUNCTION WITH ANY OTHER OFFER

FHG

READERS' OFFER 2000

Yorkshire Dales Falconry and Conservation Centre

Crows Nest, Giggleswick, Settle, North Yorkshire LA2 8AS

Tel: 01729 822832

One FREE adult admission with every full-paying adult

valid 1/4 to 30/9/2000 (not Bank Holidays)

NOT TO BE USED IN CONJUNCTION WITH ANY OTHER OFFER

FHG

READERS' OFFER 2000

Staintondale Shire Horse Farm

Staintondale, Scarborough, North Yorkshire YO13 0EY

Tel: 01723 870458

10% discount

valid during 2000 season

NOT TO BE USED IN CONJUNCTION WITH ANY OTHER OFFER

A totally unique blend of shopping and leisure. Hatton Farm Park has farm animals, pets' corner, nature trail, farming and falconry displays. Hatton Rural Craft and Shopping Village has the UK's biggest craft centre, discount shops, antiques, cafe/bar and soft play area. Free parking.

Open:
daily 10am to 5pm.
Closed Christmas Day and Boxing Day

Directions:
5 minutes from J15 M40, A46 towards Coventry, then just off A4177 Warwick to Solihull road

Longleat is probably best known for its Safari Park where your family can view the famous lions, tigers, wolves, giraffes, zebras and many more magnificent animals. Also Parrot Show, Pets' Corner, Mirror Maze, feeding sea lions on the Safari Boats, the 'World's Longest Hedge Maze' and Longleat House

Open:
April to October 10am to 6pm (all attractions); rest of year House open 10am to 4pm (except Christmas Day)

Directions:
just off the A362 between Warminster and Frome

Steam train operated over a 4½ mile line from Bolton Abbey Station to Embsay Station. Many family events including Thomas the Tank Engine take place during major Bank Holidays.

Open:
steam trains run every Sunday throughout the year and up to 5 days a week in summer. 11am to 4.15pm

Directions:
Embsay Station signposted from the A59 Skipton by-pass; Bolton Abbey Station signposted from the A59 at Bolton Abbey.

Award-winning bird of prey centre featuring free-flying demonstrations daily. 30 species on permanent display including the largest bird of prey in the world – the Andean Condor. Children's adventure playground. Tea-room and gift shop.

Open:
daily 10am to 5pm

Directions:
just outside Settle on the A65 Skipton to Kendal road.

Daily shows and demonstrations with our Shire horses, Shetland ponies, and Palomino horse (Western style). Fun and photo time; children can brush and groom the Shetland ponies.

Open:
from Spring Bank Holiday to mid-September Tues/Wed/Fri/Sun – 10.30am to 4.30pm (plus Bank Holiday Mondays)

Directions:
Off A171 between Scarborough and Whitby

FHG

READERS'
OFFER
2000

STORYBOOK GLEN

Maryculter, Aberdeen, Aberdeenshire AB12 5FT

Tel: 01224 732941

10% discount on all entries

valid until end 2000

NOT TO BE USED IN CONJUNCTION WITH ANY OTHER OFFER

FHG

READERS'
OFFER
2000

Inveraray Maritime Museum

Arctic Penguin, The Pier, Inveraray, Argyll PA32 8UY

Tel: 01499 302213

One child FREE with each full-paying adult

valid until end 2000

NOT TO BE USED IN CONJUNCTION WITH ANY OTHER OFFER

FHG

READERS'
OFFER
2000

JEDFOREST DEER & FARM PARK

Mervinslaw Estate, Camptown, Jedburgh, Scottish Borders TD8 6PL

Tel: 01835 840364

website: www.aboutscotland.com/jedforest/

One FREE child with two full-paying adults

valid May/June and Sep/Oct 2000

NOT TO BE USED IN CONJUNCTION WITH ANY OTHER OFFER

FHG

READERS'
OFFER
2000

CREETOWN GEM ROCK MUSEUM

Chain Road, Creetown, Near Newton Stewart,
Kirkcudbrightshire DG8 7HJ

Tel: 01671 820357

10% off admission prices

valid during 2000

NOT TO BE USED IN CONJUNCTION WITH ANY OTHER OFFER

FHG

READERS'
OFFER
2000

MYRETON MOTOR MUSEUM

Aberlady, East Lothian EH32 0PZ

Tel: 01875 870288

One child FREE with each paying adult

valid during 2000

NOT TO BE USED IN CONJUNCTION WITH ANY OTHER OFFER

28-acre theme park with over 100 nursery rhyme characters, set in beautifully landscaped gardens. Shop and restaurant on site.

Open:

1st March to 31st Oct:daily 10am-6pm
1st Nov to end Feb: Sat/Sun only 11am-4pm

Directions:

6 miles west of Aberdeen off B9077

FHG PUBLICATIONS, ABBEY MILL BUSINESS CENTRE, PAISLEY PA1 1TJ

A fascinating collection of Clyde maritime displays, memorabilia, stunning archive film and entertaining hands-on activities on board a unique three-masted schooner

Open:

daily 10am to 6pm April to September, 10am to 5pm October to March

Directions:

at Inveraray on the A83

FHG PUBLICATIONS, ABBEY MILL BUSINESS CENTRE, PAISLEY PA1 1TJ

Working farm with visitor centre showing rare breeds, deer herds, ranger-led activities and walks. Bird of prey displays and tuition. Corporate activities. Shop and cafe.

Open:

Daily: May-August 10am to 5.30pm; Sept/Oct 11am to 4.30pm

Directions:

5 miles south of Jedburgh on A68

FHG PUBLICATIONS, ABBEY MILL BUSINESS CENTRE, PAISLEY PA1 1TJ

STB award-winning museum designed to stimulate interest and wonder in the fascinating subjects of gems, crystals and mineralogy. Exciting audio-visual display.

Open:

Open daily Easter to 30th November; Dec/Jan/Feb – weekends only.

Directions:

7 miles from Newton Stewart, 11 miles from Gatehouse of Fleet; just off A75 Carlisle to Stranraer road.

FHG PUBLICATIONS, ABBEY MILL BUSINESS CENTRE, PAISLEY PA1 1TJ

Motor cars from 1896, motorcycles from 1902, commercial vehicles from 1919, cycles from 1880, British WWII military vehicles, ephemera, period advertising etc

Open:

daily October to Easter 10am to 5pm; Easter to October 10am to 6pm. Closed Christmas Day and New Year's Day

Directions:

off A198 near Aberlady. two miles from A1

FHG PUBLICATIONS, ABBEY MILL BUSINESS CENTRE, PAISLEY PA1 1TJ

Visitor Centre with Exhibition Room, factory tours, factory shop (children must be able to wear safety glasses provided), Crystal Shop, gift shop, coffee shop. Facilities for disabled visitors.

Open:

Visitor Centre open daily; Factory Tours weekdays (9am-3.30pm) all year, plus weekends (11am-2.30pm) April to September.

Directions:

10 miles south of Edinburgh on the A701 Peebles road; signposted a few miles from the city centre

FHG PUBLICATIONS, ABBEY MILL BUSINESS CENTRE, PAISLEY PA1 1TJ

Scotland's award-winning aquarium where you can enjoy a spectacular diver's eye view of our marine environment through the world's longest underwater safari. New 'Amazing Amphibians' display, behind the scenes tours. An unforgettable adventure whatever the weather

Open:

daily except Christmas Day and New Year's Day

Directions:

from Edinburgh follow signs for Forth Road Bridge, then signs through North Queensferry. From North, follow signs through Inverkeithing and North Queensferry.

FHG PUBLICATIONS, ABBEY MILL BUSINESS CENTRE, PAISLEY PA1 1TJ

Highland croft open to visitors for "hands-on" experience with over 35 different breeds of farm animals – "stroke the goats and scratch the pigs". Farm information centre and old farm implements. For all ages, cloud or shine!

Open:

daily mid-May to third week in September 10am to 5pm

Directions:

on A835 15 miles north of Ullapool

FHG PUBLICATIONS, ABBEY MILL BUSINESS CENTRE, PAISLEY PA1 1TJ

Beneath the heather and high in the glen, the secrets of the ancient Highlander live on. Experience through live performance the energy of the myths and legends which have governed the people here for centuries past.

Open:

daily April to October 10am to 4.30pm

Directions:

just off A82 opposite Ballachulish village, 15 mins south of Fort William

FHG PUBLICATIONS, ABBEY MILL BUSINESS CENTRE, PAISLEY PA1 1TJ

200-year old conservation village with award-winning Visitor Centre, set in beautiful countryside

Open:

daily all year round 11am to 5pm

Directions:

one mile south of Lanark; well signposted from all major routes

FHG PUBLICATIONS, ABBEY MILL BUSINESS CENTRE, PAISLEY PA1 1TJ

FHG

READERS'
OFFER
2000

MUSEUM OF CHILDHOOD MEMORIES

1 Castle Street, Beaumaris, Anglesey LL58 8AP

Tel: 01248 712498 website: www.nwi.co.uk/museumofchildhood

One child FREE with two adults

valid during 2000

NOT TO BE USED IN CONJUNCTION WITH ANY OTHER OFFER

FHG

READERS'
OFFER
2000

Pili Palas – Butterfly Palace

Menai Bridge, Isle of Anglesey LL59 5RP

Tel: 01248 712474

One child FREE with two adults paying full entry price

valid March to October 2000

NOT TO BE USED IN CONJUNCTION WITH ANY OTHER OFFER

FHG

READERS'
OFFER
2000

Alice in Wonderland Centre

3/4 Trinity Square, Llandudno, Conwy, North Wales LL30 2PY

Tel: 01492 860082

One child FREE with two paying adults

valid during 2000

NOT TO BE USED IN CONJUNCTION WITH ANY OTHER OFFER

FHG

READERS'
OFFER
2000

Celtica

Y Plas, Machynlleth, Powys SY20 8ER

Tel: 01654 702702

Child FREE when accompanied by full-paying adult

valid during 2000

NOT TO BE USED IN CONJUNCTION WITH ANY OTHER OFFER

FHG

READERS'
OFFER
2000

Big Pit Mining Museum

Blaenafon, Torfaen, South Wales NP4 9XP

Tel: 01495 790311

One FREE child with each full-paying adult

valid until end November 2000

NOT TO BE USED IN CONJUNCTION WITH ANY OTHER OFFER

Nine rooms in a Georgian house filled with items illustrating the happier times of family life over the past 150 years. Joyful nostalgia unlimited.

Open:
March to end October

Directions:
opposite Beaumaris Castle

Visit Wales' top Butterfly House, with Bird House, Snake House, Ant Avenue, Creepy Crawly Cavern, shop, cafe, adventure playground, picnic area, nature trail etc.

Open:
March to end October 10am to 5pm daily; November/December 11am to 3pm.

Directions:
follow brown-and-white signs when crossing to Anglesey; 1½ miles from Bridge

---

Walk through the Rabbit Hole to the colourful scenes of Lewis Carroll's classic story set in beautiful life-size displays. Recorded commentaries and transcripts available in several languages

Open:
10am to 5pm daily Easter to end October; closed Sundays November to Easter

Directions:
situated just off the main street, 250 yards from coach and rail stations

---

A unique theme attraction presenting the history and culture of the Celts. Audio-visual exhibition, displays of Welsh and Celtic history, soft play area, tea room and gift shop. Events throughout the year.

Open:
10am to 6pm daily (last admission to exhibitions 4.40pm

Directions:
in restored mansion just south of clock tower in town centre; car park just off Aberystwyth road

---

A unique underground tour of a real coal mine. The miners and engineers who maintain the pit also act as guides. They will lend you a helmet and lamp and take you down the 90m shaft in the pit cage to walk through the underground roadways. Children must be 5 years or over to go underground.

Open:
March to November. Underground tours 10am to 3.30pm (ring for details)

Directions:
Junction 26 off M4

ENGLAND
Board Accommodation

LONDON

See also Colour Display Advertisement

LONDON. Aaron House Hotel, 17 Courtfield Gardens, London SW5 0PD (020 7370 3991; Fax: 020 7373 2303} 👑. Originally a family home, Aaron House Hotel now has 23 rooms of character, most en suite and with TV and tea/coffee-making facilities. Centrally located but in a quiet residential area facing a garden square, Aaron House is only five minutes' walk from Earls Court Road Underground and from there to Heathrow Airport or the West End. An ideal base at modest price with a personal welcome from our friendly staff. Bed and Breakfast: Single Room from £35.00. Double from £50.00 inclusive.

BEDFORDSHIRE

SANDY. Mrs M. Codd, Highfield Farm, Great North Road, Sandy SG19 2AQ (01767 682332; Fax:

01767 692503). ◆◆◆◆◆ Tranquil welcoming atmosphere on attractive arable farm. Set well back off A1 giving quiet, peaceful seclusion yet within easy reach of the RSPB, the Shuttleworth Collection, the Greensand Ridge Walk, Grafham Water and Woburn Abbey. Cambridge 22 miles, London 50 miles. All rooms have tea/coffee facilities, most have bathrooms en-suite and two are on the ground floor. There is a separate guests' sittingroom with TV. Family room. Dogs welcome by arrangement. No smoking. Guestaccom "Good Room" Award. Most guests return! Prices from £25 per person per night.

BUCKINGHAMSHIRE

MILTON KEYNES. Mrs Christina Payne, Spinney Lodge Farm, Hanslope, Milton Keynes MK19 7DE

(01908 510267). 👑 *COMMENDED.* Spinney Lodge is an arable, beef and sheep farm. The lovely Victorian farmhouse with its large garden and rose pergola has en suite bedrooms with colour TV and tea-making facilities. Close to Woburn Abbey, Stowe Gardens and Silverstone; M1 Junction 15 eight minutes, 12 minutes to Northampton, 15 minutes Milton Keynes. Bed and Breakfast from £20 to £25; Evening Meal by arrangement. Open all year except Christmas.

Key to Tourist Board Ratings

👑 **The Crown Scheme**

The English Tourism Council (formerly the English Tourist Board) has joined with the AA and RAC to create a new, easily understood quality rating for serviced accommodation. **Hotels** will receive a grading ranging from **one to five STARS**. Other serviced accommodation such as **guest houses** and **B&B establishments** will be graded from **one to five DIAMONDS**. These ratings represent Quality, Service and Hospitality not just facilities.

NB.Some properties had not been assessed at the time of going to press and in these cases the publishers have included the old CROWN gradings.

 The Key Scheme

The Key Scheme covering self-catering in cottages, bungalows, flats, houseboats, houses, chalets, etc remains unchanged. The classification from **One to Five KEYS** indicates the range of facilities and equipment. Higher quality standards are indicated by the terms APPROVED, COMMENDED, HIGHLY COMMENDED AND DE LUXE.

CAMBRIDGESHIRE

CAMBRIDGE. Mrs Jean Wright, White Horse Cottage, 28 West Street, Comberton, Cambridge CB3

7DS (01223 262914). A 17th century cottage with all modern conveniences situated in a charming village four miles south-west of Cambridge. Junction 12 off M11 - A603 from Cambridge, or A428 turn off at Hardwick Turning. Accommodation includes one double room, twin and family rooms. Own sitting room with colour TV; tea/coffee making facilities. Full central heating; parking. Golfing facilities nearby. Excellent touring centre for many interesting places including Cambridge colleges, Wimpole Hall, Anglesey Abbey, Ely Cathedral, Imperial War Museum at Duxford, and many more. Bed and Breakfast from £20 per person. Children welcome.

CAMBRIDGE. Nick & Sylvia Lock, Goose Hall Farm, Ely Road, Waterbeach, Cambridge CB5 9PG (Tel

& Fax: 01223 860235). Situated between Cambridge and Ely, Goose Hall Farm offers a good central position for visiting the many attractions of East Anglia including stately homes such as Sandringham, Woburn Abbey, Wimpole Hall and Wicken Fen. The farmhouse and cottages are surrounded by high hedgerows enclosing meadows, red deer runs and a beautiful half-acre lake. High speed train to London's King's Cross in 55 minutes. Available in the modern centrally heated farmhouse are double and twin rooms en suite, also a triple room with private facilities. All bedrooms have colour TV, drink trays and radio alarms. Guest lounge has French doors opening onto patio and gardens. Self-catering cottages also available. Bed and Breakfast from £25 single, double/twin £42 and triple £52.

CAMBRIDGE. Cristina's Guest House, 47 St. Andrews Road, Cambridge CB4 1DH (01223

365855/327700; Fax: 01223 365855). ETC/AA ◆◆◆. Guests are assured of a warm welcome here, quietly located in the beautiful city of Cambridge, only 15 minutes' walk from the City centre and colleges. All rooms have colour TV, hairdryer, alarm/clock radio and tea/coffee making equipment, some rooms have private shower and toilet. Centrally heated with comfortable TV lounge. Private car park, locked at night. RAC Acclaimed. No smoking house.

CAMBRIDGE near. Mrs J.L. Bygraves, Elms Farm, 52 Main Road, Little Gransden SG19 3DL (01767

677459). Situated south west of Cambridge on B1046 from Junction 12 on the M11 or from A1 at St. Neots. Excellent touring centre for Cambridge, Duxford War Museum, Wimpole Hall, Woburn Abbey, Audley End House, Ely Cathedral, etc. Working arable farm with rural views and country walks around picturesque village. Recently renovated farmhouse offering a friendly atmosphere. Accommodation comprises one double, one twin with en suite facilities and one single bedrooms, all with colour TV, tea/coffee making facilities and central heating. Four pubs nearby for evening meals. Bed and Breakfast from £20 per person. No smoking.

When making enquiries or bookings,
a stamped addressed envelope is always appreciated.

CAMBRIDGE near. Mrs Sadler, Wallis Farm, 98 Main Street, Hardwick, Cambridge CB3 7QU (01954 210347; Fax: 01954 210988). ♛♛ *HIGHLY COMMENDED.* A warm welcome awaits you at our traditional Victorian farmhouse on our working farm in the picturesque village of Hardwick. We are seven miles from the university town of Cambridge and ideally situated for touring Cambridgeshire, Norfolk and Suffolk. All rooms are ground floor, en suite, twin/double, with four in a recently converted barn, furnished to a high standard. Large gardens and farmland which guests are welcome to use. All rooms have colour TV and tea/coffee facilities. Bed and Breakfast per night: single occupancy from £30 to £35; double room from £42 to £46. Ample parking. Children welcome.

CAMBRIDGE near. Vicki Hatley, Manor Farm, Landbeach, Cambridge CB4 4ED (01223 860165). Five miles from Cambridge and 10 miles from Ely. Vicki welcomes you to her carefully modernised Grade II Listed farmhouse, which is located next to the church in this attractive village. All rooms are either en suite or have private bathroom and are individually decorated. TV, clock radios and tea/coffee making facilities are provided in double, twin or family rooms. There is ample parking and guests are welcome to enjoy the walled gardens. Bed and Breakfast from £19 per person double, and £25 single.

ELY. Mrs Linda Peck, Sharps Farm, Twenty Pence Road, Wilburton, Ely CB6 3PX (01353 740360). Between Ely (six miles) and Cambridge (12 miles) our modern farmhouse offers guests a warm welcome and a relaxed atmosphere. All rooms have en suite or private bathrooms, central heating, colour TV, radio alarm, tea/coffee making facilities, hair dryer and views over surrounding countryside. Breakfast is served in the Conservatory, with home-made preserves and free range eggs. Special diets catered for. Disabled facilities. Ample parking. No smoking. Bed and Breakfast from £18.00.

HEMINGFORD GREY. Maureen and Tony Webster, The Willow Guest House, 45 High Street, Hemingford Grey, St. Ives (Cambs.) PE18 9BJ (01480 494748; Fax: 01480 464456). Large private house in the centre of this picturesque village. 100 yards from a much photographed section of the Great Ouse River, and oldest (1150) inhabited house in England. One mile from 15th century bridge west of St. Ives, 15 minutes' drive from Cambridge City Centre. Family rooms, twin rooms, doubles and singles. All bedrooms are en suite and have colour TV, tea/coffee making facilities, hairdryers, clock radios, central heating. Private parking. Guest phone. Bed and Breakfast from £21 including VAT (full English Breakfast). Sorry no pets or smoking. Ideally situated for north/south and east/west travel being only one mile from A14 dual carriageway connecting M1-A1 and M11.

WICKEN. Mrs Valerie Fuller, Spinney Abbey, Wicken, Ely CB7 5XQ (01353 720971). ♦♦♦♦ Working farm. Spinney Abbey is an attractive Grade II Listed Georgian stone farmhouse with views across pasture fields. It stands in a large garden with tennis court next to our dairy farm which borders the National Trust Nature Reserve Wicken Fen. One double and one family room, both en suite, and twin-bedded room with private bathroom, all with TV, hospitality tray, etc. Full central heating, guests sitting room. Regret no pets and no smoking upstairs. Situated just off A1123, half a mile west of Wicken. Open all year. Bed and Breakfast from £21 per person.

CHESHIRE

CHESTER. Mrs Anne Arden, Newton Hall, Tattenhall, Chester CH3 9NE (01829 770153; Fax: 01829 770655). 👑👑 *COMMENDED* A warm welcome to our part-16th Century oak-beamed farmhouse. Set in large well kept grounds, with fine views of historic Beeston and Peckforton Castles and close to the Sandstone Trail. Six miles south of Chester off A41 and ideal for Welsh Hills. Rooms are en suite or have adjacent bathroom. TV in bedrooms. Guests' own sitting room. Full central heating. Bed & Breakfast from £20 to £25.

CHURCH MINSHULL. Brian and Mary Charlesworth, Higher Elms Farm, Minshull Vernon, Crewe CW1 4RG (01270 522252). 👑👑 A 400-year-old farmhouse on working farm. Oak-beamed comfort in dining and sittingrooms, overlooking Shropshire Union Canal. No dinners served but four pubs within two miles. Interesting wildlife around. Convenient for M6 but tucked away in the countryside; from M6 Junction 18, off A530 towards Nantwich. Family room, double, twin and single rooms are all en suite, with colour TV and tea/coffee facilities. Well behaved pets welcome. Within 15 miles of Jodrell Bank, Oulton Park, Bridgemere Garden World, Stapeley Water Gardens, Nantwich and Chester. Bed and Breakfast from £20. Half price for children under 12 years.

CONGLETON. Mrs Worth, Sandhole Farm, Manchester Road, Hulme Walfield, Congleton CW12 2JH (01260 224419; Fax: 01260 224766). Beautiful country farmhouse situated two miles north of the market town of Congleton. Ideal for visiting the Peak District, the Potteries, Little Moreton Hall, Jodrell Bank and many other places of interest. Accommodation consists of 15 superb bedrooms in our converted stable block, all with magnificent en suite bathrooms. All rooms are centrally heated, double glazed and furnished to the highest standard; each has remote-control TV, hairdryer, trouser press, direct-dial telephone and tea/coffee facilities. Visitors' lounge with French windows opening onto a peaceful garden. In the main farmhouse are a further three bedrooms with private bathrooms, and elegant conservatory dining room seating up to 30 guests.

CONGLETON. Mrs Sheila Kidd, Yew Tree Farm, North Rode, Congleton CW12 2PF (01260 223569). ETC ◆◆◆◆. Discover freedom, relaxation, wooded walks and beautiful views. Meet a whole variety of pets and farm animals on this friendly working farm. Your comfort is our priority and good food is a speciality. Generous scrummy breakfasts and traditional evening meals. A true taste of the countryside -- just for you! Bed and Breakfast from £19; optional Evening Meal £10. Write or phone for a brochure.

CONGLETON. Dorothy and Joe Gilman, Pedley House Farm, Pedley Lane, Timbersbrook, Congleton CW12 3QD (01260 273650). A family family farm run on traditional lines with dairy cows, beef and sheep. The countryside is very beautiful with good walks nearby. Well situated for easy access to the Peak District and Staffordshire moorland; Alton Towers is 15 miles away ; Little Moreton Hall, Gawsworth Hall, Biddulph Grange Gardens, Macclesfield Silk Museum are all within a 10-mile radius and well worth visiting. Accommodation is offered in a family room with double and bunk beds, and a family room; bathroom; lounge with TV and tea-making facilities. Full English breakfast served using home and local farm produce whenever possible. Brochure with full details on request. Self-catering accommodation also available.

CREWE. Mrs Williamson, Snape Farm, Snape Lane, Weston, Near Crewe CW2 5NB (01270 820208).

ETC ◆◆◆ A warm welcome awaits you at our centrally heated farmhouse situated on a 150 acre beef and arable farm three miles from Crewe, a good centre for visiting Nantwich (five miles) and Chester or the Potteries. There is a separate guests' lounge with log fire and a snooker room. We have two twin rooms, one en suite, and one double room; all have colour TV, tea/coffee facilities, washbasin, hairdryer, electric blanket and heater. There are a wealth of gardens in the area for you to visit including Biddulph Grange, Arley Hall and the Dorothy Clive Gardens. For the younger visitor there is fishing in our pool or a game of croquet on the lawn. Horse riding nearby, also an open farm where you can watch the milking and pet the smaller animals.

CREWE. Little Heath Farm, Audlem, Near Crewe CW3 0HE (Tel & Fax: 01270 811324). ♛♛

COMMENDED. **Working farm.** Hilary and Bob Bennion welcome you to their warm and spacious farmhouse which is over 200 years old, with oak-beamed TV lounge and dining room, and furnished in traditional style. The accommodation consists of warm spacious no-smoking bedrooms, one double en suite, one double and one twin, all with washbasin and tea making facilities. Every effort is made to make your stay enjoyable, comfortable and relaxing. We provide a full farmhouse breakfast; in the evening a three-course meal of good country food with fresh meat and vegetables and locally baked bread. Little Heath makes an ideal base for visiting Cheshire, Shropshire and Staffordshire. Bed and Breakfast from £18 per person, Evening Meal available.

HYDE, near Manchester. Mrs Charlotte R. Walsh, Needhams Farm, Uplands Road, Werneth Low, Gee Cross, Near Hyde SK14 3AQ (0161-368 4610; Fax: 0161-367 9106). ETC/AA ◆◆◆. Working farm. A cosy 16th

century farmhouse set in peaceful, picturesque surroundings by Werneth Low Country Park and the Etherow Valley, which lie between Glossop and Manchester. The farm is ideally situated for holidaymakers and businessmen, especially those who enjoy peace and quiet, walking and rambling, golfing and riding, as these activities are all close by. At Needhams Farm everyone, including children and pets, receives a warm welcome. Good wholesome meals available in the evenings. Residential licence and Fire Certificate held. Open all year. Bed and Breakfast from £20 single minimum to £34 double maximum; Evening Meal £7. RAC Acclaimed.
e-mail: charlotte@needhamsfarm.demon.co.uk
website: www.needhamsfarm.demon.co.uk

KNUTSFORD. Virginia Brown, Pickmere House, Park Lane, Pickmere, Knutsford WA16 0JX (Tel & Fax: 01565 733433; Mobile 07867 533508). A Listed Georgian farmhouse in rural village close to Arley Hall and Tatton Park, two miles west of M6 Junction 19 on B5391 giving swift access to airport and all major north west towns and tourist attractions. Spacious en suite rooms with TV, tea/coffee trays and hairdryers, overlooking farmlands. Parking at rear. No smoking policy. Bed and Breakfast £22.50 to £32.50 single, £48 double/twin; Evening Meal by arrangement. Minibus groups by negotiation. AA Approved. Also Mews Cottage (two bedrooms, two bathrooms) available for self-catering lets.

MACCLESFIELD. Susan Brocklehurst, Hill Top Farm, Wincle, Macclesfield SK11 0QH (01260 227257).

Working farm. Overlooking the beautiful Dane Valley in this unspoilt region of the East Cheshire countryside, Hill Top is a working dairy and sheep farm situated in the tiny village of Wincle. Pretty bedrooms, a cosy television lounge and separate dining room, together with good food and a friendly service make this the ideal base from which to explore the Peak District National Park, either by car or as a walker. Bed and Breakfast from £19 per person. Evening meal also available.

MACCLESFIELD. Isobel and John Worthington, Carr House Farm B&B, Mill Lane, Adlington, Macclesfield SK10 4LG (01625 828337). ETC ◆◆◆. We

extend a warm welcome to you from our cattle and sheep farm. The accommodation is in the two-hundred-year-old farmhouse with garden setting. Ideally situated for Manchester Airport, Styal Cotton Mill, Macclesfield Silk Museum, stately homes and National Trust properties and for touring the peaks of Derbyshire and the plains of Cheshire. A cup of tea and a cake is offered on visitors' arrival, and served on the lawn, weather permitting. Rooms have individually controlled radiators and tea/coffee facilities. Full English breakfast is served in an attractive dining room overlooking the garden. Visitors' own lounge with log fires in the colder months. No pets, no smoking. Limited car storage. Good selection of local restaurants. Terms from £20 single, £32 double. Closed December and January.
e-mail: carrhousefarm@ukcomplete.co.uk

MACCLESFIELD. Mrs P.O. Worth, Rough Hey Farm, Leek Road, Gawsworth, Macclesfield SK11 0JQ (01260 252296). ♛♛ COMMENDED. Featured in "Which?"

B&B Guide. Delightfully situated overlooking the Cheshire Plain and on the edge of the Peak National Park, Rough Hey is an historic former hunting lodge dating from before the 16th century, tastefully modernised yet retaining its old world character. This 300 acre sheep farm consists of wooded valleys and hills with plenty of wildlife and lovely walks. In the locality there are numerous old halls and villages to visit. Double room en suite, twin room en suite and two single rooms, all with washbasins, TV and tea/coffee making facilities. Large comfortable lounge with TV. No smoking. A warm and friendly welcome is assured. Terms from £20.

LEA FARM

Mrs Jean E. Callwood, Lea Farm,
Wrinehill Road, Wybunbury, Nantwich CW5 7NS

Charming farmhouse set in landscaped gardens, where peacocks roam, on 150 acre dairy farm. Working farm, join in. Spacious bedrooms with washbasins, colour TV, electric blankets, radio alarm and tea/coffee making facilities. Family, double and twin bedrooms, en suite facilities. Luxury lounge, diningroom overlooking gardens. Pool/snooker; fishing in well stocked pool in beautiful surroundings. Bird watching. Children welcome, also dogs if kept under control. Help feed the birds and animals and see the cows being milked. Near to Stapeley Water Gardens, Bridgemere Garden World. Also Nantwich, Crewe, Chester, the Potteries and Alton Towers. Bed and Breakfast from £17 per person; Evening Meal from £11. Children half price. Weekly terms available.   **AA ◆◆◆**

Tel & Fax: 01270 841429

NANTWICH. Mrs West, Stoke Grange Mews, Stoke Grange Farm, Chester Road, Nantwich CW5 6BT (01270 625525). ETC ◆◆◆. Comfortable canalside

farmhouse B&B with en suite rooms, colour TV, tea/coffee facilities plus a four-poster bed. Balcony giving panoramic views of canal and countryside. Log burning fire in dining room and wonderful antique tapestry in the lounge. We also have a two bedroomed self-catering cottage with all mod cons in a converted barn across from the farmhouse. Shared garden. Pets corner. Meals can be obtained from two pubs in the village of Barbridge only a ten minute walk away along the canal or road. B&B from £25 single, £45 double. Self-catering from £200 per week.

FHG   Please mention *The Farm Holiday Guide* when enquiring
about accommodation featured in these pages.

NANTWICH. Caroline Hocknell, Poole Bank Farm, Wettenhall Road, Poole, Nantwich CW5 6AL (01270 625169). 👑👑 *COMMENDED.* A charming 17th century timbered farmhouse on 360 acre dairy farm set in quiet countryside two miles from the historic town of Nantwich. Ideal base for discovering the beautiful Cheshire countryside. Central for Chester and the Potteries. Comfortable attractive rooms, all with period furnishings. TV and tea/coffee making facilities. A warm welcome and an excellent breakfast are assured. Children welcome. Open all year. Bed and Breakfast from £15 to £18.

NORTHWICH. Mrs T.H. Campbell, Manor Farm, Cliff Road, Acton Bridge, Northwich CW8 3QP (Tel & Fax: 01606 853181). ETC ◆◆◆◆. *WELCOME HOST.* Peaceful, rural, elegantly furnished traditional country house with open views from all rooms. Situated away from roads down a long private drive, above the wooded banks of the River Weaver. Absorb the tranquillity of our garden providing access to a private path through our woodland into the picturesque valley. In the heart of Cheshire, we are an ideal location for business or pleasure. Within easy reach of Chester, Merseyside, Manchester/Liverpool Airports and the motorway network (M56 Junction 10). All rooms have en suite/private bathrooms and beverage trays. Guests' TV lounge. Ample safe parking. Bed and Breakfast from £20.

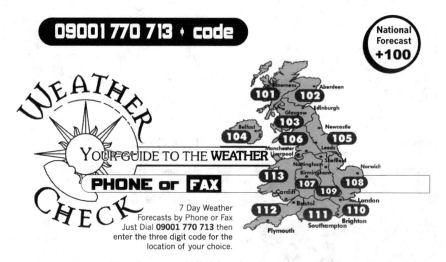

CORNWALL

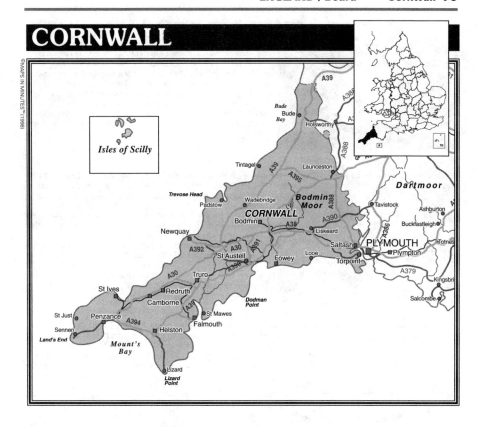

BODMIN. Mrs Joy Rackham, High Cross Farm, Lanivet, Near Bodmin PL30 5JR (01208 831341).

Cornwall Tourist Board *APPROVED*. **Working farm.** High Cross is a 91 acre Christian working stock farm situated in the village of Lanivet which is the geographical centre of Cornwall and ideally central to beaches on the North and South coast and the moor. Riding, fishing and cycle tracks are nearby. The bedrooms have washbasins and shaver points; separate lounge and dining room for guests. Traditional farmhouse cooking and a warm welcome awaits you. Bed and Breakfast £13 daily; Evening Meal optional. SAE please or telephone.

BOSCASTLE. Mrs Cheryl Nicholls, Trerosewill Farm, Paradise, Boscastle PL35 0DL (01840 250545).

Working farm. 👑👑👑 *HIGHLY COMMENDED*. Luxurious Bed and Breakfast accommodation in modern farmhouse on working farm, only short walk from the picturesque village of Boscastle. Rooms have spectacular coastal and rural views, all en suite with tea-making facilities. Colour TVs and telephones available if required. Four-posters, mineral water and bath robes. Licensed. Centrally heated. Seasonal log fires. Large gardens. Traditional farmhouse fayre. Feed the calves. Superb coastal and countryside walks. Specially negotiated rates for nearby golf and pony trekking. One way walks arranged. Packed lunches available. Spring and Autumn breaks. Strictly no smokers. Bed and Breakfast from £16. FHG Diploma Award 1995.

BOSCASTLE. Mrs Jackie Haddy, Home Farm, Minster, Boscastle PL35 0BN (01840 250195).

ETC ◆◆◆. Home Farm is a traditional 145 acre National Trust farm with outstanding views of Heritage coast, Boscastle village and harbour. National Trust footpaths surround the farm and we are within easy walking distance of Minster Church, Valency Valley and Boscastle village. Close to many beaches, golf courses, riding stables, fishing and cycle tracks. The farmhouse is set in its own walled garden offering quality accommodation, good home cooking, twin and double rooms with en suite, colour TV and tea making facilities. Children welcome - cot and high chair available. Tasteful furnishings and a warm welcome await you. Bed and Breakfast from £16.

BUDE. Mrs Sylvia Lucas, Elm Park, Bridgerule, Holsworthy EX22 7EL (01288 381231). 👑👑

COMMENDED. Elm Park is a 205 acre dairy, beef, sheep farm six miles from surfing beaches at Bude and ideal for touring Devon/Cornwall. Children are especially welcomed with pony rides and a tractor and trailer ride around the farm. There are spacious family rooms (two en-suite) and a twin-bedded room, all with colour TV and tea/coffee making facilities. Ample four-course dinners with freshly produced fare and delicious sweets. Games room with snooker, table skittles, darts, etc, and golf putting. Bed, Breakfast and Evening Meal, reasonable terms. Reductions for children and everyone is made welcome and comfortable. Brochure available.

BUDE. Jan and Paul Hudson, Little Bryaton, Morwenstow, Near Bude EX23 9SU (01288 331755).

OS Grid Reference 221156. Lovely old farmhouse in tranquil, peaceful setting, close to Heritage coastal footpath, surfing beaches, rocky coves, impressive cliffs and the seaside resort of Bude. Luxurious accommodation comprises two double bedrooms and one family suite, all with en suite bathrooms; central heating; colour TV and tea/coffee-making facilities. Guests have own private conservatory and diningroom. Bed and Breakfast from £17.50. Three course Candlelit Dinner from £9.50. Reductions for mini-breaks, weekly bookings and children. Cots and high chairs available. Open all year. ALSO highly recommended self-contained annexe beautifully equipped, oak-beamed. Sleeps two to four. Available all year. Telephone or e-mail us soon to book your holiday.
e-mail:little.Bryaton@dial.pipex.com.

BUDE. Mrs Pearl Hopper, West Nethercott Farm, Whitstone, Holsworthy (Devon) EX22 6LD (01288

341394). Working farm, join in. Personal attention and a warm welcome await you on this dairy and sheep farm. Watch the cows being milked, help with the animals. Free pony rides, scenic farm walks. Short distance from sandy beaches, surfing and the rugged North Cornwall coast. Ideal base for visiting any part of Devon or Cornwall. We are located in Cornwall though our postal address is Devon. The traditional farmhouse has washbasins and TV in bedrooms; diningroom and separate lounge with colour TV. Plenty of excellent home cooking. Access to the house at anytime. Bed and Full English Breakfast from £14, Evening Meal and pack lunches available. Children under 12 years reduced rates. Weekly terms available.

FALMOUTH. Celia and Ian Carruthers, The Clearwater, 59 Melvill Road, Falmouth TR11 4DF (01326 311344). AA Recommended. Enjoy quality bed and breakfast accommodation, in a perfect location. Clean, comfortable, tastefully decorated bedrooms with TVs and hot drink making facilities. Some en suites. Delicious home cooking. Close to excellent restaurants, idyllic walks, secluded coves, creekside pubs, watersports, ancient castles and country houses. Two minutes' walk to Falmouth's main beach. Drying and storage facilities for sailing, diving, walking gear, etc. Ample off-road parking and near railway station. We welcome guests for short or long stays almost all year, from a very reasonable £17 per night. Please call for a brochure, directions or to check availability.
e-mail: clearwater@lineone.net

FOWEY. Mrs S.C. Dunn, Menabilly Barton, Par PL24 2TN (01726 812844). Working farm. Menabilly Barton is a secluded farmhouse set in a wooded valley leading to a quiet sandy beach. Spacious dining room, lounge with TV, peaceful garden open during the day. Good traditional farmhouse food. Three large bedrooms, en suite available. Bathroom with shower, two toilets. Facilities for making drinks and microwave if required. Coastal walks, National Trust properties and Heligan Gardens all nearby. Local village pub serves good food. Historic port of Fowey three miles, North Coast only 40 minutes' drive. Bed and full English Breakfast. Reductions for children. Colour brochure on request.

HELSTON. Mrs P. Roberts, Hendra Farm, Wendron, Helston TR13 0NR (01326 340470). Hendra Farm, just off the main Helston/Falmouth road, is an ideal centre for touring Cornwall; three miles to Helston, eight to both Redruth and Falmouth. Safe sandy beaches within easy reach – five miles to the sea. Beautiful views from the farmhouse of the 60-acre beef farm. Two double, one single, and one family bedrooms; bathroom and toilets; sittingroom and two diningrooms. Cot, babysitting and reduced rates offered for children. No objection to pets. Car necessary, parking space. Enjoy good cooking with roast beef, pork, lamb, chicken, genuine Cornish pasties, fish and delicious sweets and cream. Open all year except Christmas. Evening Dinner, Bed and Breakfast from £120 per week which includes cooked breakfast, three course evening dinner, tea and home-made cake before bed. Bed and Breakfast only from £12.50 per night also available.

HELSTON. Mrs Penny Jenkin, Barton Farm, Gweek, Helston TR13 0QH (01326 573557). Barton Farm is a family-run dairy farm situated in a quiet location just above Gweek. The charming open beamed farmhouse is surrounded by gardens. The accommodation consists of three attractive bedrooms with tea/coffee facilities, clock, radio, hairdryer and heating. Two bathrooms/showers, dining room and open fired lounge with TV. A warm welcome, good food and comfort are a priority. Ideal for touring South West Cornwall including the beautiful Helford River and the Lizard. Excellent beaches and coastline to explore just a short drive away. Tourist attractions include the Seal Sanctuary, Flambards and Poldark Mine only five minutes away.

See also Colour Display Advertisement

HELSTON. Mrs Christine Hosking, Tregiddle Farm, Gunwalloe, Helston TR12 7QW (01326 572726). Tregiddle Farm is situated on the Lizard Peninsula. The farmhouse has beautiful views across open country to the golf course and sea. Easy access to many beaches and attractions. There are two double rooms, one with four-poster bed and one single. Breakfast includes farm fresh eggs and home-made bread. There is an award-winning inn overlooking the sea close by, which serves bar snacks and has an extensive table menu. Bed and Breakfast from £15.00.

LAUNCESTON. Hurdon Farm, Launceston PL15 9LS (01566 772955). AA/RAC/ETC ◆◆◆◆. Elegant Listed 18th century farmhouse, idyllically tucked away amidst our 500 acre mixed working farm. Centrally positioned on Devon/Cornwall border, it is ideally located for exploring the many attractions in both counties. Six luxurious and spacious en suite bedrooms, all with colour TV, radio, tea/coffee facilities and central heating. Comfortable guests' lounge. Superb English breakfasts and delicious four course dinners, freshly prepared and cooked, are served at separate tables in the dining room. Open May till November. Bed and Breakfast from £20.

LISKEARD. Mrs E.R. Elford, Tresulgan Farm, Near Menheniot, Liskeard PL14 3PU (Tel & Fax: 01503 240268). ETC ◆◆◆. Working farm, join in. Tresulgan is situated overlooking the wooded Seaton Valley where picturesque views can be seen from our pretty garden. The 17th century farmhouse still retains its character, with its original oak-beamed diningroom serving delicious meals. The three attractive and comfortable bedrooms are all en suite with colour TV and drink making facilities. The nearest beach is at Seaton, four miles away, and the popular fishing villages of Looe and Polperro six miles, with extensive water sport facilities, boat trips and mackerel fishing. Many tourist attractions for all ages and numerous gardens and National Trust attractions, breathtaking in the Spring. Friendly accommodation at an ideal location for exploring this most beautiful part of Cornwall. AA member. Colour brochure. website: www.tresulgan.co.uk

LISKEARD. Mrs Lindsay M. Pendray, Caduscott, East Taphouse, Liskeard PL14 4NG (Tel & Fax: 01579 320262). ETB Listed *COMMENDED.* **Working farm** Sweet dreams and restful nights broken only by the owl's hooting in the clear night sky. From Stargazers to Shellseekers, all the ingredients are here to match your mood. Attractive 17th century Listed farmhouse. Central heating log fires. Traditional Bed and Breakfast (from £17 to £21 non-smoking) served in large lounge/dining room; double room (en suite, toilet/shower), adjoining twin bedded room, ideal for families. The Pendrays have farmed Caduscott for over 70 years and will make every effort to ensure that you discover Cornwall e-mail: caduscott@farmline.com

LISKEARD. Mrs Stephanie Rowe, Tregondale Farm, Menheniot, Liskeard PL14 3RG (Tel & Fax: 01579 342407). ETC/AA ◆◆◆◆. Working farm, join in. Feeling like a break near the coast? Come and relax, join our family with the peace of the countryside — breathtaking in Spring — on a 200 acre mixed farm, situated near Looe between A38 and A390. See pedigree South Devon cattle and sheep naturally reared, explore the new woodland farm trail amidst wildlife and flowers. This stylish, characteristic farmhouse, which dates back to the Domesday Book, has featured in the Daily Telegraph, and is a Cream of Cornwall member, provides exceptional comfort with en suite suite bedrooms all with colour TV, tea/coffee facilities, lounge dining room with log fires. A conservatory to enjoy each day's warmth capturing a beautiful view over the farm, set in an original walled garden including picnic table, tennis court and play area. Special activities can be arranged — golf, fishing, cycling and walking. Home and local produce a speciality, full English Breakfast; try our delicious optional evening meal from £11. Bed and Breakfast from £20. Open all year. Self-catering character cottage also available (ꝗꝗꝗ *HIGHLY COMMENDED*). A warm welcome awaits you to discover the beauty of Cornwall. Please phone for a brochure and discuss your requirements.

LOOE. Mrs J.M. Gill, Cleese Farm, Nomansland, Looe PL13 1PB (01503 240224). Cleese Farm is a family run dairy farm situated two miles east of Looe just off the B3253 Plymouth to Looe road. The twin towns of East and West Looe are only one-and-a-half miles away, with narrow, winding streets, picturesque fishing port, famous banjo pier and golden sandy beach. Our farmhouse is set in beautiful unspoilt countryside overlooking the sea and mini-gorge of Morval. Ideal walking country and easy access to a wide range of activities and all the pleasures of the surrounding countryside and coast. The rooms are handsomely decorated in country-cottage style and have sea or valley views,TV's, washbasins, tea/coffee making facilities; bathroom includes shower; TV lounge. Ample parking. We offer a warm welcome and a friendly atmosphere. Bed and Breakfast from £16.

LOOE. Mrs Lynda Wills, Polgover Farm, Widegates, Looe PL13 1PY (01503 240248). Working farm.

Polgover Farm is situated in picturesque countryside, four miles from Looe on the B3252 and ideally situated to explore Cornwall and South Devon. Local attractions include horse riding, golf, fishing, water sports, Monkey Sanctuary and many beaches. There is always a warm welcome at Polgover's spacious 16th century Listed farmhouse, where you can have a peaceful and relaxing holiday. There are three tastefully decorated bedrooms, all with washbasins, colour TV and tea/coffee facilities. Guests' bathroom. Lounge with colour TV incorporating breakfast room with separate tables. Sorry, no pets. Open Easter to October. Ample parking. Bed and Breakfast from £16. Weekly and child reductions. Brochure available. Also luxury six-berth fully equipped self-catering caravan in its own garden available at the farm.

LOOE. Mrs D. Eastley, Bake Farm, Pelynt, Looe PL13 2QQ (01503 220244). ◆◆◆. Working farm.

This is an old farmhouse, bearing the Trelawney Coat of Arms (1610), situated midway between Looe and Fowey. There are three double bedrooms all with washbasin, tea/coffee making facilities and night storage heaters; bathroom/toilet, shower room/toilet; sitting room/dining room. Children welcome at reduced rates. Sorry, no pets. Open from April to October. A car is essential for touring the area, ample parking. There is much to see and do here - horse riding four miles, golf seven. The sea is only five miles away and there is shark fishing at Looe. Bed and Breakfast from £17. Cleanliness guaranteed. Brochure available on request.

LOOE. Mrs Carolyn Talling, Lansallos Barton Farm, Lansallos, Looe PL13 2PU (Tel & Fax: 01503 272192). Working farm.

Lansallos Barton is a National Trust coastal farm, with spectacular sea views. It is a beef and sheep farm with fields reaching Lansallos Cove (safe bathing) which is approximately 15 minutes walk. Ideal for coastal walking to the villages of Polperro and Polruan Fowey. We are just two miles from Polperro, with a good choice of pubs and restaurants. Looe and Fowey within easy reach. The farmhouse is 380 years old, with one double room and one family room with washbasins, tea/coffee facilities; bathroom with shower, TV lounge. Cream teas served during summer months. Ample parking. Bed and Breakfast from £15.

LOOE. Mrs Angela Eastley, Little Larnick Farm, Pelynt, Looe PL13 2NB (01503 262837). ETC

◆◆◆◆ Little Larnick is situated in a sheltered part of the West Looe river valley. Walk to Looe from our working dairy farm and along the coastal path to picturesque Polperro. The character farmhouse and barn offers twin, double and family en suite rooms. The bedrooms are superbly decorated to a high standard. The family room is in a downstairs annexe overlooking the garden. Our newly renovated barn offers three self-contained bedrooms with their own lounge areas. Cycling shed, drying room and ample parking. No pets, no smoking. Bed and Breakfast from £20 to £23. Open all year.

Mount View House

Mount View House is a Victorian former farmhouse standing in half-an-acre of gardens overlooking St. Michael's Mount. The house is furnished in traditional style and offers one room with sea views and another with rural views. Rooms have washbasins, central heating and tea/coffee making facilities. Guests' WC and shower room; sitting/dining room with open fire. Children welcome, cot available. Situated approximately three miles from Penzance and five miles from St. Ives. We are the ideal touring stopover. Our close proximity to the heliport (one mile) makes an ideal break en route to the Scilly Isles. Bed and Breakfast from £15 per person per night. Four night low season breaks £100 for two people sharing. Self-catering accommodation also available.

Jenny Birchall, Mount View House, Varfell, Ludgvan, Penzance TR20 8AW
Tel: 01736 710179

MEVAGISSEY. Mrs Dawn Rundle, Lancallan Farm, Mevagissey, St. Austell PL26 6EW (01726 842284).

Lancallan is a large 17th century farmhouse on a working 200 acre dairy and beef farm in a beautiful rural setting, one mile from Mevagissey. We are close to Heligan Gardens, lovely coastal walks and sandy beaches, and are well situated for day trips throughout Cornwall. Enjoy a traditional farmhouse breakfast in a warm and friendly atmosphere. Accommodation comprises one twin room and two double en suite rooms (all with colour TV and tea/coffee facilities); bathroom, lounge and diningroom. Terms and brochure available on request. SAE please.

MULLION. Ridgeback Lodge Hotel and Restaurant, Nansmellyon Road, Mullion TR12 7DH (01326 241300; Fax: 01326 241330).

Set between three beautiful coves and adjacent to the South West coastal path we have been the resting stop for walkers for 150 years. We boast traditional and exotic dishes, home cooked food and a strong local sea-food bias. We have a full bar. Why not use us as a base for walking on the Lizard Peninsula and start refreshed with our traditional breakfasts? We can arrange many other activities. Rooms have tea/coffee making facilities and TV.
e-mail: ridgebacklodge@compuserve.com

MULLION. Mrs Joan Hyde, Campden House, The Commons, Mullion TR12 7HZ (01326 240365). Campden House offers comfortable accommodation in a peaceful setting with large gardens and a beautiful sea view. It is within easy reach of Mullion, Polurian and Poldhu Coves, and is ideally situated for exploring the beautiful coast and countryside of the Lizard. Mullion golf course is less than one mile away. All eight bedrooms have handbasins with hot and cold water and comfortable beds; some rooms have en suite showers. There is a large sun lounge, TV lounge with colour TV and a large dining room and bar. Guests have access to the lounges, bedrooms and gardens at all times. Children and pets welcome. Bed and Breakfast £15.

NEWQUAY. Mrs B.L. Oakes, Shepherds Farm, Fiddlers Green, St. Newlyn East, Newquay TR8 5NW (01872 540502).

HIGHLY COMMENDED. Working farm. A warm welcome awaits you on our family-run 600 acre mixed working farm. Come and share our warm and friendly atmosphere with first class service in affordable quality accommodation. Cleanliness guaranteed. All rooms en suite and have colour TV and tea making facilities. Large garden. Central location, ideal for touring. The farm is set in rural, small hamlet of Fiddlers Green three miles from beautiful Cornish coastline, five miles from Newquay; 20 minutes from south coast. Glorious sandy beaches, ideal for surfing, little rivers for the very young. Beautiful breathtaking views and walks along scenic clifftops. One-and-a-half miles from National Trust property of Trerice. Good pub food close by. Come and join us! Bed and Breakfast from £16 to £19. Free horse riding seasonal.

See colour advertisment on page 4.

THE HOTEL BRISTOL

NARROWCLIFF • NEWQUAY • CORNWALL TR7 2PQ

Owned and managed since 1927 by four generations of the Young family, The Bristol continues to be one of Newquay's leading hotels. Enjoy traditional hospitality and dine in our sea view restaurant. We are the ideal centre from which to discover the many places of interest in Cornwall.

www.cornwall-online.co.uk/hotelbristol

TEL: 01637 875181 ☆☆☆ Best Western

NEWQUAY. Mike and Alison Limer, Alicia, 136 Henver Road, Newquay TR7 3EQ (Tel & Fax: 01637 874328).

Mike and Alison welcome you to relax on the Cornish Peninsula in their friendly home-from home-guest house. Look forward to the amazing panoramic views and traditional home cooking we offer you. The facilities include a beautiful lounge and dining room, you can relax and unwind in the sun lounge or see the last of the sun's rays from the porch. All bedrooms are furnished to a high standard with tea/coffee facilities and central heating. Some rooms are en suite. Large car park. We are ideally situated on the outskirts of Newquay close to Porth and Lusty Glaze beaches with easy access to other parts of Cornwall. Bed and Breakfast from £15 per person daily. Open all year. Please telephone or write for brochure.

NEWQUAY near. Cy and Barbara Moore, The Ranch House, Trencreek, Newquay TR8 4NN (01637 875419).

A detached bungalow one-and-a-half miles from Newquay town centre, with panoramic views of countryside, Newquay and the sea beyond. Half-acre of lovely gardens open April to October. En suite rooms. Ample parking. Pets welcome by arrangement. Bed and Breakfast £16 to £20 per day. No smoking. Please phone for brochure. Also two bedroomed self-catering chalet. Fully equipped. £225 to £350 per week. Details on request.

PADSTOW. Mrs Sandra May, Trewithen Farm, St Merryn, Near Padstow PL28 8JZ (01841 520420).

Trewithen farmhouse is a newly renovated Cornish Roundhouse, set in a large garden and situated on a working farm enjoying country and coastal views. The picturesque town of Padstow with its pretty harbour and narrow streets with famous fish restaurants is only three miles away. St Merryn Parish boasts seven beautiful sandy beaches and bays. Also coastal walks, golf, fishing and horse riding on neighbouring farm. Hire a bike or walk along the Camel Trail cycle and footpath - winding for 18 miles along the River Camel. The accommodation has been tastefully decorated to complement the exposed beams and original features. All bedrooms are en suite or have vanity units, with hot drink facilities. Parking. Full English breakfast. TV lounge. Bed and Breakfast from £22 per person per night. Weekly rates and Winter weekend breaks available.

Terms quoted in this publication may be subject to increase if rises in costs necessitate

PADSTOW. Andrew and Sue Hamilton, Trevone Bay Hotel, Trevone, Near Padstow PL28 8QS (01841 520243; Fax: 01841 521195). ◆◆◆◆. On arrival relax with a pot of tea, then stroll through the tranquil village to the beautiful sandy bay. Follow the coast path along the rocky bay, then back across the fields to your comfortable Hotel. Does this tempt you? How about an excellent home-cooked meal, coffee watching the sunset and an evening socialising in the bar. Our hotel is non-smoking throughout. All bedrooms en suite. Ideal for walking, touring, bird watching or relaxing on the beach. From £34 for Dinner, Bed and Breakfast. Open Easter to October. If this sounds like your sort of holiday, write or phone for brochure.

PAR. Mr and Mrs Rowe, Tregaminion Farm House, Menabilly, Par PL24 2TL. En suite and self contained family B&B throughout the year. Our farm nestles in the hollows of the South Cornish Coast set deep within the Du Maurier countryside. We can offer you a peaceful, relaxed and friendly holiday in our family-run farmhouse. We are within easy walking distance of Polkerris and Polridmouth Bays, both beautiful, small, safe beaches for you and your children to enjoy. The ancient port of Fowey is also within walking distance, approximately two to three miles. Stay with us for as little or as long as you like. For more information and prices please contact **Jill Rowe (01726 812442).**

PENZANCE. Mrs Penny Lally, Rose Farm, Chyanhal, Buryas Bridge, Penzance TR19 6AN (01736 731808). ♛♛ *COMMENDED.* Rose Farm is a small working farm in a little hamlet close to the picturesque fishing villages of Mousehole and Newlyn and seven miles from Land's End. The 200-year-old granite farmhouse is cosy with pretty, en suite rooms. One double, one family suite and a romantic 15th century four-poster room in barn annexe. We have all manner of animals, from pedigree cattle to pot-bellied pigs! Open all year (closed Christmas).

PENZANCE. Mrs Monica Olds, Mulfra Farm, Newmill, Penzance TR20 8XP (01736 363940). Superb accommodation on this hill farm high on the edge of the Penwith Moors. The 17th century stone-built beamed farmhouse has far reaching views, is attractively decorated and furnished offering two double en suite bedrooms with tea/coffee trays, TV, shaver points and heated towel rails. The comfortable lounge has an inglenook fireplace and Cornish stone oven. Dining room has separate tables; sun lounge. Car essential, ample parking. Warm friendly atmosphere, good food. Beautiful walking country and ideal centre for exploring West Cornwall. We have our own Iron Age village as well as cows, calves and horses. Bed and Breakfast from £16.50 per night. Evening meals £7. Weekly reductions. Further details with pleasure.

PENZANCE. Mrs Rosalind Wyatt, South Colenso Farm, Goldsithney, Penzance TR20 9JB (01736 762290). Working farm. South Colenso Farm is a 76 acre working arable farm. The spacious Georgian style farmhouse is set in beautiful unspoilt countryside, peaceful and secluded, yet not isolated. Ideally situated between Marazion and Praa Sands, a perfect location for touring both coasts of Cornwall, with sandy beaches and pretty coves nearby. The large en suite bedrooms (two double and one family room) have tea/coffee making facilities and a lovely country view. Relax in our comfortable lounge with colour television and log fire. Full English breakfast is served in our sunny diningroom with separate tables. Ample private parking. Non-smoking. Children over four years welcome, pets by arrangement only.

PENZANCE (near Porthcurno). Mrs P.M. Hall, Treen Farmhouse, Treen, St. Levan, Penzance TR19 6LF (01736 810253). Situated just off the South West coastal footpath, Treen Farm is a family-run dairy farm in the village of Treen, set in 80 acres of pastureland by the sea near Land's End (four miles). Visitors are welcome to use the gardens, walk around the farm and watch the milking. Pub, shop, cafe, campsite and beaches nearby. Ideal for walking and sightseeing. Comfortable farmhouse Bed and Breakfast accommodation, single, twin and double (en suite) rooms with tea/coffee making facilities, views of gardens, pastureland and sea, some with TV. Traditional English Breakfast served. Guests' lounge with open fire and television. Private parking. Pets welcome. Reductions for children. Sorry, no smoking. Bed and Breakfast £12.50 to £18.50. Self-catering also available for two people (plus cot) from £150.

PORT ISAAC. Chris and Liz Bolton, Trewetha Farm, Port Isaac PL29 3RU (01208 880256). 18th century traditional farmhouse in Betjeman country in an area designated as outstanding natural beauty. Spectacular views over the sea and surrounding countryside. Pet the miniature Shetland ponies, help feed the hens or watch the sheep graze. Ideal location for sandy beaches, walking, cycling and all water sports. The double and twin en suite rooms are tastefully decorated and centrally heated. Each has colour TV and tea/coffee making facilities. ENQUIRE ABOUT OUR COASTAL WALKING BREAKS: full English breakfast, packed lunch, three-course dinner and transport to the start of the walk. Self-catering cottages also available.

ROSELAND PENINSULA. Mrs Shirley E. Pascoe, Court Farm, Philleigh, Truro TR2 5NB (01872 580313). Working farm. Situated in the heart of the Roseland Peninsula at Philleigh, with its lovely Norman church and 17th century Roseland Inn, this spacious and attractive old farmhouse, set in over an acre of garden, offers Bed and Breakfast accommodation. There are double, single and family bedrooms with washbasins and tea making facilities; bathroom, separate toilet; large comfortable lounge with colour TV. Enjoy a full English breakfast in the traditional farmhouse kitchen. Children welcome, cot, high chair, babysitting available. Sorry, no pets indoors. Car essential – ample parking. The family livestock and arable farm includes 50 acres of woodlands which border the beautiful Fal Estuary providing superb walking, picnic areas and bird-watching opportunities, while the nearest beaches are just over two miles away. Please write or telephone for brochure and terms.

See also Colour Display Advertisement **ST. AGNES. Marion and Derek Falconer, Rosemundy House Hotel, St. Agnes TR5 0UF (01872 552101; Fax: 01872 554000).** ♛♛♛ COMMENDED. Rosemundy House Hotel occupies a most sheltered and secluded position in the village of St. Agnes and within a mile of Trevaunance Cove beach. Built around 1780, Rosemundy has been tastefully extended to provide a charming dining room and bedrooms with en-suite facilities. Our amenities include an attractive licensed bar, 45ft outdoor heated swimming pool and a large games room with table tennis, pool, snooker, darts, etc. The informal grounds comprise some four acres of gardens and woodland secluding the property and making Rosemundy ideal for a restful holiday. Badminton, croquet and putting may be enjoyed in the grounds. Our hotel boasts a warm and friendly atmosphere with good English home cooking. Dinner, Bed and Breakfast from £200 to £300 per week, Bed and Breakfast from £175 to £275 weekly (incl. VAT).

ST. AUSTELL. Mrs Liz Berryman, Polgreen Farm, London Apprentice, St. Austell PL26 7AP (01726 75151). ETB ♦♦♦ Polgreen is a family-run dairy farm nestling in the Pentewan Valley in an Area of Outstanding Natural Beauty. One mile from the coast and four miles from the picturesque fishing village of Mevagissey. A perfect location for a relaxing holiday in the glorious Cornish countryside. Centrally situated, Polgreen is ideally placed for touring all of Cornwall's many attractions. Pentewan Valley Leisure Trail adjoining, Lost Gardens of Heligan three miles. Bed and Breakfast accommodation includes en suite rooms, colour TV in bedrooms, tea/coffee facilities, guests' lounge. Children welcome. Terms from £17 per night

ST. IVES. Mrs C.E. Quick, Menwidden Farm, Ludgvan, Penzance TR20 8BN (01736 740415). ETC

◆◆◆. Menwidden Farm is centrally situated in West Cornwall, five miles from St. Ives (north coast) and three miles from Marazion (south coast). Within easy reach of Land's End and the Lizard Peninsula. Comfortable bedrooms and good home cooking including roast meats, pasties and Cornish cream. Three double (one en suite), one twin bedded and one single bedrooms all with tea/coffee making facilities; bathroom and shower room; sitting room and dining room. Children welcome and pets allowed. Open March to October. Car essential – parking. Fire Certificate and basic Hygiene Certificate held. Past winner of Farm Holiday Guide Diploma. Evening Meal, Bed and Breakfast from £140 per week, or from £16.50 per night.

ST. IVES. Mrs N.I. Mann, Trewey Farm, Zennor, St. Ives TR26 3DA (01736 796936). Working farm. On the main St Ives to Land's End road, this attractive granite-built farmhouse stands among gorse and heather-clad hills, half-a-mile from the sea and five miles from St Ives. The mixed farm covers 300 acres, with Guernsey cattle and fine views of the sea; lovely cliff and hill walks. Guests will be warmly welcomed and find a friendly atmosphere. Five double, one single and three family bedrooms (all with washbasins); bathroom, toilets; sittingroom, diningroom. Cot, high chair and babysitting available. Pets allowed. Car essential – parking. Open all year. Electric heating. Bed and Breakfast only. SAE for terms, please.

ST IVES. Mrs S. Britnell, Little Pengelly Farmhouse, Trenwheal, Leedstown, Hayle TR27 6BP (01736 850452).

17th century picturesque farmhouse just off B3302 midway between St. Ives and Helston. Spacious accommodation, washbasins all rooms plus excellent shower and bathroom facilities. Traditional English breakfast with home-baked bread served in conservatory/tea-room overlooking garden and fields. Guest TV lounge. Considerate pet owners welcome. Sorry no smoking and not suitable for young children. Open Easter to end October. Central for touring West Cornwall. Bed and Breakfast £17.00 pppn. Cream Teas plus hot and cold savouries served every day. Large two-person SELF CATERING barn conversion available. Patio and garden. Pets welcome. No smoking. Open all year. Three day off-peak breaks. Please write or phone for full details.
e-mail: little@pengelly.freeserve.co.uk

ST. IVES. Julie Fitzgerald, Horizon Guest House, 5 Carthew Terrace, St Ives TR26 1EB (01736 798069).

Do you want a holiday with first-class accommodation and to feel at home instantly? Beautiful sea view rooms overlooking Portmeor Surf beach; we are close to the coastal footpath to Zennor yet only five minutes from Tate Gallery, town centre and beaches and have some private parking. There is access to your rooms at any time, guests' lounge with colour TV, separate tables for dining and option of home cooked dinner. En suite available. Horizon is highly recommended for friendliness and hospitality. For brochure and colour postcard:

ST MAWES/TRURO. Mrs A. Palmer, Trenestrall Farm, Ruan High Lanes, Truro TR2 5LX (01872 501259). Working farm, join in.

A tastefully restored 200 year old barn, now a farmhouse offering comfortable accommodation on a 300 acre mixed farm. Situated on beautiful Roseland Peninsula, within easy reach of St. Mawes and Truro. Close to safe beaches and beautiful Fal estuary for sailing, bird watching etc. Accommodation consists of double or twin room with washbasins and tea/coffee facilities, own sittingroom with TV, bathroom and shower room. Amenities include private fishing lake and snooker room, table tennis and pony riding. Pride taken with presentation of food using home produce whenever possible. Children welcome, babysitting service. Pets accepted. Phone or write for details of Bed and Breakfast from £16 per person per night.

Polrode Mill Cottage
17th Century Country Guest House
Allen Valley, St. Tudy, Cornwall PL30 3NS
Tel: 01208 850203 Web: cornwall-online.co.uk/polrode-mill

David and Deborah would like to welcome you to their picturesque country cottage set in three acres of gardens and woodland in the beautifull Allen Valley. The cottage has been carefully restored to retain its character and charm, with inglenook fireplaces, beams and flagstone floors.

The five en suite bedrooms are tastefully furnished with period furniture and antique brass beds or carved oak four-posters. Each bedroom has its own luxuriously appointed bathroom featuring a roll top bath and/or separate shower. Breakfast is served at your individual table overlooking the garden. A candlelit evening meal is available, cooked to the highest standard using the best of fresh local produce and seafood. A comprehensive selection of wines is available to complement your meal.

SHEVIOCK. Carol and Tony Johnson, Sheviock Barton, Sheviock, Torpoint PL11 3EH (Tel & Fax: 01503 230793; mobile: 07775 688403). Sheviock Barton is situated in the centre of the small unspoiled village of Sheviock, directly opposite the 14th century church, in an Area of Outstanding Natural Beauty. The 300-year-old farmhouse has been beautifully restored, with full central heating, and offers a very large farmhouse kitchen with oak beams and four-oven Aga. Guests' own sitting room. En suite family room; en suite double; and double with adjoining private bathroom. All bedrooms with TV. Relaxing gardens, and large games room for children. One mile to pub/restaurant, beach, coastal path and golf course. Plymouth, Looe and Polperro only 20 minutes. £20 per person per night. Sorry, no smoking.
e-mail: thebarton@sheviock.freeserve.co.uk
website: www.connexions.co.uk/clift-house/index.htm.

TINTAGEL. The Penallick Hotel, Treknow, Tintagel PL34 0EJ (01840 770296). A small homely-run licensed hotel. Magnificent cliff top position and walks. All double rooms en suite; ground floor, wheelchair friendly rooms available. All rooms with TV and tea/coffee making facilities. Most rooms with sea and coastal views. Restaurant overlooks outstanding coastal and sea views where sunsets are spectacular. Good home cooking - Grills a speciality. Vegetarians catered for. Regret no children under 12 years old. Good weekly rates available. Excellent Bargain Breaks. Homely Christmas Breaks. Nice dogs very welcome at no extra charge.
e-mail: penallick@yahoo.com

TRURO. Mrs S. Hicks, Pengelly Farmhouse, Trispen, Truro TR4 9BG (Tel & Fax: 01872 510245).

Working farm, join in. Situated in the centre of the county, Pengelly Farm is the ideal base for seeing all of Cornwall. The north coast beaches, with magnificent cliffs and surf are only a 10 minute drive away, the more peaceful south coast beaches are an easy 20 minute drive and Lands End and other attractions are easily accessible within an hour. The farmhouse is centrally heated throughout and has four bedrooms to let, two en suite and two sharing a main bathroom. All have washbasins, colour TV, tea/coffee making facilities and hairdryers. A friendly personal service is assured. Bed and Breakfast from £16 to £20. Also available is our self-catering mobile home, sleeping six - terms from £125 to £150 per week. Please write or call for our brochure.

TRURO. Mrs Pamela Carbis, Trenona Farm, Ruan High Lanes,Truro TR2 5JS (01872 501339). Trenona

Farm is a working mixed farm of 210 acres situated on the unspoilt Roseland Peninsula. Safe, sandy beaches and coastal footpath nearby. Central for touring and close to Gardens at Heligan, Trelissick and Trewithen. The 19th century farmhouse has four guest bedrooms. All can accommodate two to four persons and have their own washbasins and tea making facilities. Two have en suite showers and toilets. Guest lounge with colour TV. Separate diningroom. Children welcome. Terms from £15 per night, £95 per week. Brochure available. Open April to October

See also Colour Display Advertisement

TRURO. Mrs V. Maltwood, Old Inn Cottage, Mount Hawke Truro TR4 8BX (01209 890545). 16th/17th century cottage in pretty hamlet near St Agnes. A short walk leads to National Trust valley to Chapel Porth beach. Old Inn Cottage has two double bedrooms each with four poster bed, one twin bedded room, all with washbasins; one single bedroom, bathroom, toilet, large cosy sitting room, TV, books, open fireplace, oak beams; dining room. (Self-catering available. Details on request). Off road parking. Regret not suitable for tiny children. No smokers or pets. Bed and Breakfast from £15.50 per person.

TRURO. Mrs M.A. Hutchings, Lands Vue, Three Burrows, Truro TR4 8JA (01872 560242). You will find

a warm welcome at our peaceful Country House, set in two acres of garden where you may relax or enjoy a game of croquet. There are three lovely bedrooms all with en suite facilities, TV and tea making facilities. There is a cosy lounge with log fire and large dining room with superb views over the Cornish countryside where we serve a delicious farmhouse breakfast. Being very central for all Cornwall's famous gardens and coastline, Lands Vue is an ideal base highly recommended by many of our guests who return year after year. AA QQQQ Selected.

TRURO. Mrs Diane Dymond, Great Hewas Farm, Grampound Road, Truro TR2 4EP (Tel & Fax: 01726

882218; mobile 07850 117572). ETC ◆◆◆ Great Hewas is ideally situated in central Cornwall, just two miles from the main A30. This spacious centrally heated farm guesthouse has extensive views from all bedrooms and is ideal for touring or relaxing. Personal attention and good home cooking assured. Double, twin, single and family rooms, en suite, with TV and tea/coffee facilities. Public WC. Comfortable lounge, dining room with separate tables. Fire Certificate/Food and Hygiene Certificate. Traditional breakfast or fresh fruit and yoghurt. Bed and Breakfast from £18.00 nightly. Evening Dinner available early and late season. Family room and weekly terms available on request. Open March to October. Car essential. No smoking. From A30 take exit to Grampound Road. Please telephone for brochure, without obligation.

WADEBRIDGE. Mrs E. Hodge, Pengelly Farm, Burlawn, Wadebridge PL27 7LA (01208 814217).

Working farm, join in. 🏅 *COMMENDED* A Listed Georgian farmhouse situated in a quiet location on a 150 acre mixed farm overlooking wooded valleys, approximately one-and-a-half miles from Wadebridge. Ideal location for country walks, with easy access to the start of the Camel Trail. Also close to the coast with a number of beaches and activities. Guests are welcome to roam the farm and see the variety of animals. Large garden where children can play. Prettily decorated bedrooms with own washbasins and tea/coffee making facilities. Guests' bath/shower room. Traditional English breakfast served, or special requests by prior arrangement. Lounge with colour TV. Children welcome - cot and highchair available, babysitting on request. Bed and Breakfast £16. Cornwall Registered Accommodation.

ZENNOR. Sue & John Wilson, Tregeraint House, Zennor, St. Ives TR26 3DB (Tel & Fax: 01736

797061). Traditional cottage in an acre of gardens overlooking the Atlantic coastline in one of the most beautiful parts of Cornwall. The house has been lovingly restored, providing a base from which to explore this fascinating area. Each bedroom (one twin, one double, one family) is comfortably furnished with a plumbed-in traditional pine washstand and central heating. Tea and coffee making facilities. Vegetarian and other diets can be catered for and there are nearby pubs where reasonable meals can be had while St. Ives and Penzance offer excellent eating, artistic and other facilities. Open all year except at Christmas. £19 per person (£2 single supplement).

CUMBRIA

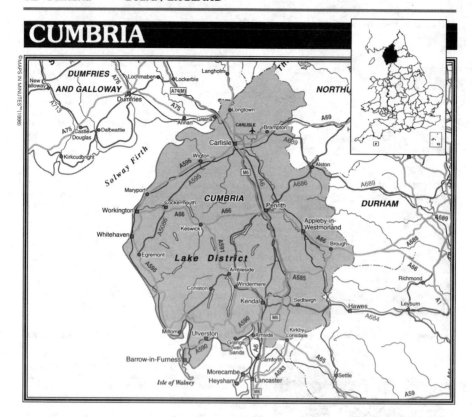

©MAPS IN MINUTES™ (1998)

AMBLESIDE. Peter and Anne Hart, Bracken Fell, Outgate, Ambleside LA22 0NH (015394 36289). ◆◆◆. A delightful country residence with 2 acres of gardens, situated in beautiful open countryside between Ambleside and Hawkshead in the picturesque hamlet of Outgate. This comfortable home with its lovely accommodation and friendly service is ideally located for exploring the Lake District. Each bedroom has its own private facilities, colour TV, hairdryer, complimentary tea and coffee and a super view. There is a comfortable lounge, dining room and ample private parking. Two country inns are within walking distance where evening meals are available. Bed and Breakfast from £21.50. No pets or children under 12 years. Non smoking. Self-catering accommodation also available. Write or phone for brochure.
e-mail: hart.brackenfell@virgin.net.

Bracken Fell

AMBLESIDE. Mrs S. Briggs, High Wray Farm, High Wray, Near Ambleside LA22 0JE (015394 32280). ◆◆◆◆. **Working farm**. Charming 17th century olde worlde farmhouse with Beatrix Potter connections. Original oak beams, cosy lounge with log burning fire, pretty colour co-ordinated bedrooms, all with en suite facilities. Heating and tea/coffee trays are in all rooms. Situated in a quiet unspoilt location, panoramic views and lake shore walks close by. A warm welcome awaits all who visit us, where comfort, cleanliness and personal attention are assured. Follow the B5286 from Ambleside towards Hawkshead turn left for Wray. Follow road to High Wray, the farm is on the right. Families welcome. Terms from £18. FHG Diploma Winner.

High Wray Farm

AMBLESIDE. Colin and Rosemary Haskell, Borwick Lodge, Outgate, Hawkshead, Ambleside LA22 0PU Telephone: Hawkshead 015394 36332.

A leafy driveway entices you to the most enchantingly situated house in the Lake District, a very special 17th century country lodge with magnificent panoramic lake and mountain views, quietly secluded in beautiful gardens. Ideally placed in the heart of the Lakes and close to Hawkshead village with its good choice of restaurants and inns. Beautiful en suite bedrooms with colour television and tea/coffee facilities, including "Special Occasions" and "Romantic Breaks", two king-size four-poster rooms. Tourist Board ◆◆◆◆ and SILVER AWARD. 4 times winner of FHG Diploma for Accommodation and Service. Colin and Rosemary welcome you to their "haven of peace and tranquillity" in this most beautiful corner of England. Ample parking. NON SMOKING. Bed and Breakfast from £25. May we send our brochure?

AMBLESIDE. Liz, Mary and Craig, Wanslea Guest House, Lake Road, Ambleside LA22 0DB (015394 33884). ◆◆◆◆.

Wanslea is a spacious family-run Victorian non-smoking guest house with fine views, situated just a stroll from the village and Lake shore with walks beginning at the door. We offer a friendly welcome and comfortable rooms, all of which have colour TV and tea/coffee tray; most rooms are en suite. A good breakfast will start your day before enjoying a fell walk or maybe a more leisurely stroll by the lake. Relax in our licensed residents' lounge with a real fire on winter evenings. Children are welcome and pets accepted by arrangement. Bed and Breakfast from £17.50 per person. Evening Meal also available to party bookings. Autumn, Winter, Spring Breaks at reduced rates. Brochure on request.
e-mail:wanslea.guesthouse@virgin.net

AMBLESIDE. Mrs P. Benson, Tock How Farm, High Wray, Ambleside (015394 36481). A beautiful

Lakeland farm giving the visitor an opportunity to sample the peaceful life of a Lake District farmer. It is set in idyllic surroundings overlooking Blelham Tarn with magnificent panoramic views of the Langdale Pikes, Coniston Old Man, the Troutbeck Fells and Lake Windermere. High Wray is a quiet unspoilt hamlet set between Ambleside and Hawkshead making this an ideal base for walking or touring. Visitors can expect to taste at breakfast the culinary delights of a working farmhouse kitchen. Sky TV and tea/coffee making facilities are provided in all rooms, together with washbasin and towels. Please write or phone for terms and further details.

AMBLESIDE. Rothay House, Rothay Road, Ambleside LA22 0EE (015394 32434). Rothay House is an

attractive modern detached guest house set in pleasant gardens with views of the surrounding fells. All bedrooms are comfortable and well furnished with en suite facilities, colour TV, tea and coffee trays. Our visitors are assured of warm and friendly service in attractive surroundings. The house is within easy walking distance of the village centre. Ambleside has a variety of interesting shops and restaurants and makes an ideal base for walking, touring or enjoying sailing, watersports and angling on Lake Windermere. Car not essential, but ample parking. Open all year. Children welcome; sorry, no pets. Bed and Breakfast from £20 to £25; Winter Weekend Breaks available.

AMBLESIDE. Helen and Chris Green, Lyndhurst Hotel, Wansfell Road, Ambleside LA22 0EG (015394 32421). 👑👑 COMMENDED. RAC Acclaimed, AA Listed. Attractive small Victorian hotel quietly situated in its own garden with private car park. Only two minutes from Ambleside centre. Lovely bedrooms, all en suite. Four poster bedroom or luxury bedroom for that special occasion. Scrumptious food, friendly service. Full central heating for all-year comfort. Cosy bar. Winter and Summer Breaks. A delightful base from which to explore the Lakes either by car or as a walker. Bed and Breakfast from £20. Phone or write for colour brochure, please.

AMBLESIDE. Anthony Marsden, Betty Fold, Hawkshead Hill, Ambleside LA22 OPS (015394 36611). ❦❦ *HIGHLY COMMENDED.* Betty Fold is a large country house in its own spacious grounds, rich in fauna and flora, with magnificent views and set in the heart of the Lake District National Park. Hawkshead, Coniston and Ambleside are all within easy reach and the beauty spot Tarn How is 20 minutes' walk away. This privately licensed guest house, run by the resident owner, offers Bed, Breakfast, Evening Meals and Packed Lunches. All bedrooms are en suite. Parties are particularly welcome from November to Easter. We regret, no pets in the guest house. Open all year. Terms approximately £38 per night for Bed, Breakfast and Evening Dinner. See also advertisement in SELF-CATERING section of the guide.

AMBLESIDE. Mr O'Brian, Ferndale Hotel, Lake Road, Ambleside LA22 0DB (015394 32207). ❦❦ *COMMENDED.* The Ferndale Hotel is a small, family run Hotel where you will find a warm, friendly welcome and personal attention at all times. Offering excellent accommodation with good home cooked English or Vegetarian breakfast. Our nine attractive bedrooms have all been individually decorated and furnished, each with full en suite facilities, colour television and tea/coffee making tray. Full central heating throughout, several rooms having views of the fells, and including ground floor bedrooms. The Ferndale is open all year round with a car park, is licensed, offers packed lunches, hair dryer, clothes/boot drying and ironing facilities. A wide choice of places to dine, within minutes' walking distance, ranging from excellent pub food to superb restaurants of many varied cuisines will complete your day.

AMBLESIDE. Mr D. Woodhouse, Glenside, Old Lake Road, Ambleside LA22 0DP (015394 32635). ETC

◆◆◆. Janice and David welcome you to their non-smoking three-bedroomed old farm cottage dating back to the 18th century and offering a high standard of accommodation. All bedrooms have the original beamed ceilings, cottage-style furnishings, washbasins and tea and coffee making facilities. They all share two well-appointed shower/bathrooms, cosy TV lounge and quaint diningroom serving a traditional English breakfast. The house is situated midway between the village and Lake Windermere and lovely walks start from the door. Private parking. Bed and Breakfast from £16 to £17 per person.

AMBLESIDE. Mrs Elizabeth Culbert, Kingswood, Old Lake Road, Ambleside LA22 0AE (015394 34081). ❦ *COMMENDED.* Kingswood is ideally situated near the town centre, yet off the main road. Ample car parking. Well-equipped and comfortable bedrooms with hot and cold water, and tea/coffee making facilities. Colour TV. Central heating. Single, double, twin and family rooms. Pets welcome. Open most of the year, with special bargain breaks off season. No smoking. Write or phone for rates and details.

APPLEBY. The Gate Hotel, Bongate, Appleby CA16 6LH (017683 52688; Fax: 017683 53858). An attractive family-run business on the outskirts of Appleby in easy reach of the town centre with its shops, castle and swimming pool and approximately one mile from the golf course. It is tastefully decorated with panelling from the steam ship 'Berengaria'. A traditional log fire enhances the warm and friendly service offered all year round. Our rooms are en suite and well furnished with colour TV and tea/coffee trays. There is ample parking, a pleasant enclosed garden and play area. Pets welcome by arrangement. Specialising in Thai food we also offer conventional English food. Licensed. Bed and Breakfast from £17.50 to £27.50 per person; Evening Meal from £4.95 to £10.95.

APPLEBY-IN-WESTMORLAND. Mrs Dorothy Hayton, Asby Grange, Great Asby, Appleby CA16 6HF (01768 352881). ❦ *COMMENDED.* A comfortable

farm house in peaceful surroundings situated in the Eden Valley. Start the day with a hearty English breakfast before visiting nearby Appleby-in-Westmorland, Lakes and Yorkshire Dales. In excellent walking country close to coast and the Westmorland Way. Two double rooms, both with fitted hand basins and tea/coffee making facilities. Diningroom/lounge with colour TV. A good overnight stop, or weekly stays welcome. Within easy reach of Junction 38 of the M6 motorway. Bed and Breakfast from £16 per person.

APPLEBY-IN-WESTMORLAND. Mrs Sylvia Harland, Old Hall Farmhouse, Bongate, Appleby CA16 6HW (017683 51773). Situated on the outskirts of the town, this

17th Century house is no longer a working farm. Excellent position for touring the Yorkshire Dales and the Lakes. We are one mile from a golf course and there is an indoor swimming pool in the town. You will find a very warm welcome awaits you. There are three double/twin bedrooms with TVs, mini-ironing room, tea/coffee. We have beautiful panelling with log fires both in the lounge and dining room. Bed and Breakfast £17.00, en suite £20.00 per person.

APPLEBY-IN-WESTMORLAND. Barbara and Derick Cotton, Glebe House, Bolton, Appleby-in-Westmorland CA16 6AW (017683 61125); Our 17th century

former farmhouse is ideally located for exploring the Eden Valley, an area waiting to be discovered by those who seek tranquillity in an area of outstanding natural beauty. Very quiet location with outstanding views of the Pennines. Approximately one mile from the A66 and four miles west of Appleby, and very convenient for visits to the Lake District, Yorkshire Dales and Scottish Borders. Centrally heated accommodation includes two doubles (one en suite) and one twin room, all with tea-making facilities. Hearty breakfasts are served, with special diets catered for. Children welcome. No smoking. Bed and Breakfast £15 to £18. Please send SAE for brochure.
E-mail: derick.cotton@btinternet.com

APPLEBY/PENRITH. Mrs Hardre Jackson, Mill Beck, Water Street, Morland CA10 3AY (Tel and Fax: 01931 714567). Riverside character cottage overlooking fields

in quiet picturesque, unspoilt Eden Valley village on border of the Lake District National Park and at the foot of the Pennines. M6/A66 ten minutes. Easy reach of the Yorkshire Dales (40 minutes). Beautifully furnished rooms, comfy beds and good reading lamps, all facilities, TV, private bathroom and morning sun. Terms from £18 per person per night. Excellent Aga food, evening meals, packed lunches by arrangement in advance. Trains met (direct London/Glasgow/Edinburgh/West Country service); walkers collected. Good village pubs. Map S91/599224.

BASSENTHWAITE. Mr S. Semple, Lakeside Guest House, Dubwath, Bassenthwaite Lake, Bassenthwaite CA13 9YD (Tel & Fax 017687 76358)

👑👑👑. Lakeside is an elegant country house offering friendly and relaxing hospitality, set in peaceful surroundings near the shore of Bassenthwaite Lake. There are magnificent views of the Lake of Buttermere and Crummock Water, with the Solway Coast and the city of Carlisle within easy reach. The house has a panelled hall and oak floors with the comfortably furnished eight bedrooms (seven en suite) offering colour TV, radio/alarm, hairdryer, shoe-cleaner and tea/coffee making facilities. Two of the rooms have lake views. The smaller eighth bedroom also with lake view, has its own private bathroom. Delicious home cooking is a speciality, using fresh and local ingredients. The evening meal is a set menu served at 7pm and consists of four courses plus coffee and mints, complemented by a small selection of wines. Guests have access at all times to their own bedrooms and the pleasant lounge which overlooks the lake. Around the lake there is a bird reserve, nature trails, fishing, golf, sailing and riding. Residential licence. No-smoking. No pets. Self-catering also available.

FHG Please mention *The Farm Holiday Guide* when enquiring about accommodation featured in these pages.

BOOTLE. Jennifer and Rodney Light, The Stables, Bootle, Near Millom LA19 5TJ (01229 718644).

Set on the western edge of the Lake District National Park within two miles of the sea, we offer comfortable accommodation in a pleasing modern stable conversion set in gardens with two rivers, in a tranquil setting off the beaten tourist track but within an hour's drive of most of the Lake District's major attractions. We have three lovely bedrooms, some en suite, one for families, with guest lounge and dining room. All rooms have TV and tea/coffee trays. Bed and Breakfast from £16 per person. Evening meals available by request (normally all fresh ingredients – some from our garden).

BORROWDALE. Sarah Edmondson, Seathwaite Farm, Borrowdale, Near Keswick CA12 5XT (017687 77394). A warm welcome is assured at Seathwaite, a working fell farm set amidst magnificent scenery at the head of the Borrowdale Valley. An ideal base for walkers and climbers, we are at the foot of the Scafell and Gables routes. Big breakfasts, en suite rooms with hot drinks making facilities, open fires and central heating will all make your stay comfortable. Well behaved dogs accepted. Non-smoking. Bed and Breakfast from £16 to £20 per person per night; discounts for return visitors and children.

BRAMPTON. Margaret Mounsey, Walton High Rigg, Walton, Brampton CA8 2AZ (016977 2117).
👑 *COMMENDED.* Guests are assured of warm hospitality at this Georgian Listed farmhouse on a working sheep and dairy farm with spectacuIiar views of Lake District and Pennines.has very comfortable spacious rooms,   Colour TV and washbasin in bedroom, including tea/coffee facilities. Excellent site to explore Scotland, Hadrians Wall country or the Pennines. Fishing, Riding and Golf available locally.

BRAMPTON. Mrs Una Armstrong, Town Head Farm, Walton, Brampton CA8 2DJ (016977 2730).
◆◆◆ Town Head offers comfortable and pleasant accommodation. Our 100 acre beef/sheep farm is situated in the peaceful village of Walton overlooking the village green and commanding scenic views of the Pennines and Lakeland hills. An ideal base for touring the Lakes, Hadrian's Wall and Scottish Borders; three miles from Brampton, 10 miles from Carlisle – leave the M6 at Junction 43. One dounle, one twin or family bedrooms with tea making facilities and TV; lounge/dining room. Children welcome. Open all year except Christmas and New Year. Bed and Breakfast from £15. Reduced rate for children and Short Breaks.

BRAMPTON. Marjorie Stobart, Cracrop Farm, Kirkcambeck, Brampton CA8 2BW (016977 48245; Fax: 016977 48333). 👑👑 *HIGHLY COMMENDED.*
If you are looking for somewhere special, then try our superbly appointed large 1847 farmhouse set in peaceful countryside with superb views. Excellent for bird-watching and walking. Spacious en suite bedrooms, hostess tray, colour TV and fresh flowers. Relax in spa bath or sauna. Games room. Near Roman Wall and Borders. Excellent pubs nearby. AA Selected QQQQ. Terms on request.

Swaledale Watch

Ours is a mixed farm of 300 acres situated in beautiful countryside within the Lake District National Park. Central for Scottish Borders, Roman Wall, Eden Valley and Lakes. Primarily a sheep farm (everyone loves lambing time). Visitors are welcome to see farm animals and activities. Many interesting walks nearby or roam the peaceful northern fells. Enjoyed by many Cumbrian Way walkers. Very comfortable accommodation with excellent home cooking. All rooms have private facilities. Central heating. Tea making facilities. 💛💛 Highly Commended. AA ◆◆◆.

We are a friendly Cumbrian farming family and make you very welcome.

Bed and Breakfast from £18 to £22; Evening Meal £11.

Mr and Mrs A. Savage, Swaledale Watch, Whelpo, Caldbeck CA7 8HQ

Tel & Fax: 016974 78409   e-mail: nan.savage@talk21.com

CARLISLE. Mrs Elizabeth Woodmass, Howard House Farm, Gilsland, Carlisle CA6 7AJ (016977 47285). 💛💛 *HIGHLY COMMENDED.* **Working farm, join in.**

A 250 acre mixed farm with a 19th century stone-built farmhouse situated in a rural area overlooking the Irthing Valley on the Cumbria/Northumbria border. Half-a-mile from Gilsland village and Roman Wall; Haltwhistle five miles and the M6 at Carlisle, 18 miles. Good base for touring – Roman Wall, Lakes and Scottish Borders. Trout fishing on farm. Guests' lounge with colour TV where you can relax anytime in comfort. Diningroom. One double room en suite, one twin and one family room with washbasins, bath or shower. All bedrooms have tea/coffee making facilities. Bathroom with shower, toilet. Children welcome at reduced rates. Sorry, no pets. Car essential - parking. Open January to December for Bed and Breakfast from £19 to £21; Evening Meal optional. Weekly terms available. SAE or telephone for brochure.

CARLISLE. Mrs Dorothy Nicholson, Gill Farm, Blackford, Carlisle CA6 4EL (01228 675326). 💛

In a delightful setting on a beef and sheep farm, this Georgian style farmhouse dated 1740 offers a friendly welcome to all guests breaking journeys to or from Scotland or having a holiday in our beautiful countryside. Near Hadrian's Wall, Gretna Green and Lake District. Golf, fishing, swimming and large agricultural auction markets all nearby; also cycle path passes our entrance. Accommodation is in one double, one family and one twin/single bedrooms, all with washbasins, shaver points and tea/coffee making facilities; two bathrooms, shower; lounge with colour TV; separate diningroom. Open all year. Reductions for children; cot provided. Central heating. Car essential, good parking. Pets permitted. Telephone for further details or directions.

CARLISLE. Mrs M. Sisson, Bessiestown Farm Country Guest House, Catlowdy, Near Longtown, Carlisle CA6 5QP (Tel & Fax: 01228 577219). ETC

◆◆◆◆ *SILVER AWARD* CUMBRIA and ENGLAND BEST BED AND BREAKFAST AWARD WINNER. Guests return year after year to enjoy the warm welcome, peace and quiet, pretty en suite bedrooms, delightful public rooms and simply delicious home cooking. Indoor heated pool. Courtyard cottages and new honeymoon suite. Bed and Breakfast from £24.50, Evening Meal £12.50. Exit 44 M6 – Longtown and follow signs to Catlowdy.

Terms quoted in this publication may be subject to increase
if rises in costs necessitate

CARLISLE. Mrs Georgina Elwen, New Pallyards, Hethersgill, Carlisle CA6 6HZ (01228 577308).

◆◆◆. **Working farm, join in.** GOLD AWARD WINNER. Farmhouse filmed for BBC TV. Relax and see beautiful North Cumbria and the Borders. A warm welcome awaits you in our country farmhouse tucked away in the Cumbrian countryside, yet easily accessible from M6 Junction 44. In addition to the surrounding attractions there is plenty to enjoy, including hill walking, peaceful forests and sea trout/salmon fishing or just nestle down and relax with nature. Two double en suite, two family en suite rooms and one twin/single bedroom, all with tea/coffee making equipment. Bed and Breakfast from £20 per person, Dinner £13; Dinner, Bed and Breakfast weekly rates from £160 to £170. Menu choice. Self-catering offered. Disabled facilities. We are proud to have won a National Salon Culinaire Award for the "Best Breakfast in Britain".
website: newpallyards.freeserve.co.uk
e-mail: info@newpallyards.freeserve.co.uk

COCKERMOUTH. Mrs B. Woodward, Toddell Farm, Brandlingill, Cockermouth CA13 0RB (01900 828423).

Beautifully restored 17th century barn with open beams, self-contained lounge with TV and tea/coffee making facilities. One double bed and a slumber loft above with two singles, also a bed setttee for extras! Private entrance leads to this very spacious suite with its own private bathroom. Situated three miles from Cockermouth, yet within the National Park, Toddell Farm is set in seven acres. With splendid views from the house, the fells provide some very good walks from the property. Dogs welcome. Bed and Breakfast from £22.

CONISTON near. Mrs Helen Dugdale, Browside Guest House, Little Arrow, Near Coniston LA21 8AU (015394 41162).

AA QQQQ. Situated two miles from Coniston village with excellent views across Coniston Water to Brantwood and Grizedale forest. Overlooking a traditional hill sheep farm, Browside offers a peaceful base to enjoy the Lake District. Many nice walks from our door, lake shore or fell walking. Spacious en suite accommodation, with power shower, TV, tea tray, own keys. Large breakfast of your choice including our own free-range eggs and home-made bread. Private parking. Non-smoking. Reduced rates for children. Tariff £17 to £22.

See also Colour Display Advertisement **GRASMERE. Mr and Mrs J.D. Clement, Redmayne, Grasmere LA22 9QY (015394 35635). ETC ◆◆◆◆.** In a superb elevated private situation, Redmayne enjoys beathtaking views of the lake and mountains, only five minutes' walk from Grasmere village amenities. Spacious luxury en suite double bedrooms have colour television, hospitality tray and many thoughful extras. Bed and Breakfast from £22 to £26. Regret no children or pets. Exclusively for non smokers. Private enclosed parking.

HAWKSHEAD. Peter and Anne Hart, Bracken Fell, Outgate, Ambleside LA22 0NH (015394 36289). ◆◆◆. A delightful country residence with 2 acres of gardens, situated in beautiful open countryside between Ambleside and Hawkshead in the picturesque hamlet of Outgate. This comfortable home with its lovely accommodation and friendly service is ideally located for exploring the Lake District. Each bedroom has its own private facilities, colour TV, hairdryer, complimentary tea and coffee and a super view. There is a comfortable lounge, dining room and ample private parking. Two country inns are within walking distance where evening meals are available. Bed and Breakfast from £21.50. No pets or children under 12 years. Non smoking. Self-catering accommodation also available. Write or phone for brochure.
e-mail: hart.brackenfell@virgin.net.

Bracken Fell

HAWKSHEAD. Edward and Judith Ireton, Holmeshead Farm, Skelwith Fold, Ambleside, Hawkshead LA22 0HU (015394 33048). Working farm. A warm, comfortable 17th century farmhouse nestling between Ambleside and Hawkshead, just outside the hamlet of Skelwith Fold. The Drunken Duck Inn is within easy walking distance (one mile). Family, twin and double en suite rooms, all with washbasin, colour TV and tea/coffee making facilities. Cosy lounge/dining room. Central heating, log fire in winter. Full breakfast, traditional and vegetarian. Home-made Evening Meals. Bed and Breakfast. Terms on request. Open all year. An ideal base for all outdoor activities. Walkers' paradise. Pets welcome by arrangement.

See also Colour Display Advertisement

HAWKSHEAD. Colin and Rosemary Haskell, Borwick Lodge, Outgate, Hawkshead, Ambleside LA22 0PU (015394 36332). ETC ◆◆◆◆. A leafy driveway entices you to the most enchantingly situated house in the Lake District, a very special 17th century country lodge with magnificent panoramic lake and mountain views, quietly secluded in beautiful gardens. Ideally placed in the heart of the Lakes and close to Hawkshead village with its good choice of restaurants and inns. Beautiful en suite bedrooms with colour TV and tea/coffee facilities including "Special Occasions" and "Romantic Breaks" two king-size four-poster rooms. Colin and Rosemary welcome you to their "haven of peace and tranquillity" in this most beautiful corner of England. Ample parking. NON-SMOKING. Bed and Breakfast from £25. May we send our brochure?.

HAWKSHEAD. Mrs L. Woodhouse, Howe Farm, Hawkshead, Ambleside LA22 0QB (015394 36345). Working farm. ETC ◆◆ *SILVER AWARD.* Built in 1695, Howe Farm is a traditional working Lakeland farm. The house holds many original features and the rooms are well appointed with private bathrooms and a high standard of furnishings. All rooms overlook Esthwaite Water. Bed and full English Breakfast from £17 to £18 per person.

HAWKSHEAD (Near Ambleside). Gitte and David Leete, High Grassings, Sunny Brow, Outgate, Hawkshead LA22 0PU (015394 36484). High Grassings is situated only five minutes from the quaint village of Hawkshead, two minutes from the famous Drunken Duck Pub and less than five minutes from the beautiful Tarn Hows. High Grassings stands in an elevated position in seven acres of wooded fellside with breathtaking mountain views. Our extensive grounds are inhabited by a variety of wildlife and has ponds and streams which make this one of the most tranquil settings in the heart of the Lakes. All our rooms are en suite with tea/coffee making facilities, offering a high standard of comfort with outstanding views. Ample parking. Bed and Breakfast from £25 per person.

KENDAL. **Mrs D. M. Swindlehurst, Tranthwaite Hall, Underbarrow, Near Kendal LA8 8HG (015395 68285).** 👑👑 **Working farm.** Highly Commended with the

English Tourist Board for excellent standards of comfort and quality. Tranthwaite Hall is said to date back to 1186. A charming olde world farmhouse with beautiful oak beams, doors and rare black iron fire range. This working dairy/sheep farm has an idyllic setting half-a-mile up an unspoilt country lane where deer can be seen, herons fishing in the stream and lots of wild flowers. This is a very peaceful and quiet retreat yet only minutes from all Lakes and local attractions. Attractive bedrooms, all are en suite and have tea/coffee making facilities, hair dryer, radio and full central heating. Lounge with colour TV. Full English breakfast is served with eggs from our farm and home-made jam and marmalade. We like guests to enjoy our home and garden as much as we do. Walking, pony trekking, golf and many good country pubs and inns nearby. Bed and Breakfast £21 to £25.

KENDAL. **Mrs Sylvia Beaty, Garnett House Farm, Burneside, Kendal LA9 5SF (01539 724542).** ♦♦♦ **Working farm.** This is an AA/RAC Acclaimed 15th

century farmhouse on large dairy/sheep farm situated half a mile from A591 Kendal/Windermere road. Accommodation comprises double, twin and family rooms, (most en suite), all with washbasins, colour TV, clock/radio and tea making facilities. Lovely oak panelling, beams, door and spice cupboard. Full English breakfast served at separate tables. Children welcome at reduced rates if sharing with adults. Good private parking. Near village and public transport.; 10 minutes from Windermere. Special offer November to March - three nights Bed and Breakfast £45, en suite £54.

KENDAL. **Glynis Byrne, Marwin House, Duke Street, Holme, Near Carnforth LA6 1PY (01524 781144). Tourist Board Listed** *COMMENDED*. Marwin House

is a delightful country cottage situated in the small unspoilt village of Holme, gateway to the Lake District and Yorkshire Dales, yet only five minutes from M6 Junction 36. We are an ideal base for walking. Bedrooms are comfortable and tastefully decorated with colour TV, tea/coffee making facilities and central heating. Private lounge with colour TV/video. Children are most welcome. Off road parking. Breakfast a speciality served in a warm friendly atmosphere. Bed and Breakfast from £15 to £17. Open all year.

KENDAL. **Mrs Jean Bindloss, Grayrigg Hall Farm, Grayrigg, Near Kendal LA8 9BU (01539 824689). Tourist Board Listed** *COMMENDED*. **Working farm.**

Comfortable, peaceful 18th century farmhouse set in a beautiful country location, ideal for touring the Lakes and famous Yorkshire Dales. We run a beef and sheep farm only four-and-a-half miles from Kendal and with easy access to the M6 motorway, Junction 38. Guests are assured of the finest accommodation and a friendly welcome. One spacious family room and one double bedroom, tasteful lounge/dining room with colour TV; bathroom. Children most welcome, cot, babysitting if required. Open March to November. Bed and Breakfast from £16 per person; Evening Meal £9. Further information gladly supplied.

KENDAL. Mrs Anne Knowles, Myers Farm, Docker, Grayrigg, Kendal LA8 0DF (01539 824610). ETC

◆◆ A mixed farm of 220 acres with sheep and dairy cows. Children are welcome to see the working of the farm. The house is over 250 years old with oak beams and a beautiful partition in the lounge/dining room, where a log fire burns. Two double rooms and one twin room; bathroom, shower and toilet, all providing homely and friendly accommodation. Peaceful, scenic countryside, beautiful area for walking locally and further afield, yet close to Kendal amenities. Two-and-a-half miles from Junction 37 of the M6, good halfway stop en route to Scotland and within easy reach of the Lake District, Dales National Park and the coast. Central heating. Reduced rates for children under 11 years, with high chair and babysitting available. Open from March to November for Bed and Breakfast from £17.50. Car essential. Parking. SAE, please.

KENDAL near. Mrs. Betty Fishwick, Stock Bridge Farm, Staveley, Kendal LA8 9LP (01539 821580).

A comfortable, well appointed 17th century farmhouse on edge of By-passed village, just off A591 Kendal-Windermere Road. Situated at the foot of the Kentmere Valley. Ideal for walking. All bedrooms have fitted washbasins with shaver points. Bathroom with shower and toilet, plus separate toilet. Cosy lounge/diningroom with open fire, colour TV. Fire certificate. Full central heating. Full English Breakfast served at separate tables; friendly personal service. Good off-road parking facilities. Three good village pubs within walking distance of the farm. Excellent stop-off for England-Scotland routed through beautiful English Lakeland.

KESWICK. Ken and Heather Armstrong, Kiln Hill Barn, Bassenthwaite, Keswick CA12 4RG (017687 76454). Kiln Hill Farm is set in open countryside with beautiful views. It offers single, twin and family bedrooms. TV. Lounge with a log fire for cooler evenings and central heating throughout. Coffee and tea making facilities in each room. En suite available. Evening meals and packed lunches on request. Meals served in the Barn Dining Room adjacent to the farmhouse. Terms and further details available on reques

KESWICK. Mrs M.A. Illman, Beckstones Farm, Thornthwaite, Keswick CA12 5SQ (017687 78510). ETC ◆◆◆. Beneath the forest and looking over fields to the magnificent mountain scenery of Skiddaw and the Helvellyn Ranges, Beckstones is peacefully situated off the beaten track and within a short stroll of the southern shores of Bassenthwaite Lake. Built in 1726, the Georgian Farmhouse has been extended into the barn, providing quality, centrally heated en suite bedrooms with hospitality trays. Beckstones has a cosy oak beamed diningroom, TV lounge, ample parking, a large garden and a cycle store. Dogs by arrangement. Bar meals three minutes' walk away, Keswick 10 minutes' drive. Excellent touring and walking base. B&B from £21.50. Brochure available.

Beckstones Farm
Thornthwaite, Keswick, Cumbria.

KESWICK. Mrs E. M. Richardson, Fold Head Farm, Watendlath, Borrowdale, Keswick CA12 5UW (017687 77255). Working farm. Fold Head Farmhouse is a white Lakeland farmhouse situated on the banks of Watendlath Tarn in this picturesque hamlet. It is a 3000 acre sheep farm and an ideal centre for touring, climbing, fell walking and fishing. Fly-fishing for rainbow trout at Watendlath Tarn; permits available. Guests are accommodated in two double bedrooms and one twin bedroom, with washbasins; bathroom, two toilets; sittingroom; diningroom. Full central heating; separate TV lounge. Pets are allowed free. Open from February to December. Car essential; parking. Sir Hugh Walpole used this farmhouse in his book "Judith Paris" as the home of Judith Paris. Evening Dinner, Bed and Breakfast or Bed and Breakfast. Terms on request.

KESWICK. Mrs M. M. Beaty, Birkrigg Farm, Newlands, Keswick CA12 5TS (017687 78278). Tourist

Board Listed *APPROVED.* **Working farm**. Birkrigg is a working dairy and sheep farm, very pleasantly and peacefully situated, with an excellent outlook in the lovely Newlands Valley. Five miles from Keswick between Braithwaite and Buttermere. Being in a beautiful mountainous area makes this an ideal place to stay especially for those wishing to walk or climb. Centrally located for touring the many beauty spots in the Lake District. Clean, comfortable accommodation awaits you. A good breakfast is offered at 8.30am, evening tea at 9.30pm. Packed lunches available. Sorry, no evening meals. Local inns all provide good food, two to four miles away. Open March to November.

KESWICK. "Cragside" Guest House, 39 Blencathra Street, Keswick CA12 4HX (017687 73344)

AA QQQ. David and Katie extend a warm welcome to non-smoking visitors to stay at Cragside, their quiet, comfortable guest house which has beautiful views of the surrounding fells and yet is close to the town centre of Keswick. All rooms are tastefully decorated, centrally heated and have clock radio, colour TV and tea/coffee making facilities. En suite rooms available. Rest assured you will have a comfortable and relaxed stay with us. Bed and Breakfast from £16 to £18. 50. Children from three years welcome. Pets welcome.

KESWICK. Colin and Lesley Smith, Mosedale House, Mosedale, Mungrisdale CA11 0XQ (017687

79371). ♕♕♕ *COMMENDED.* Traditional 1862 built, Lakeland farmhouse. Listed building. A smallholding with sheep, donkeys, ducks, hens and pet pig, it enjoys a magnificent position, nestling at the foot of Carrock Fell, overlooking open fields, only three and a half miles to the A66 Keswick to Penrith road. Vegetarians welcome. Home baked bread and our own free-range eggs. packed lunches. Non-smoking establishment. Central heating. Open all year. Most bedrooms have en suite facilities. Visitors' diningroom and lounge. Excellent facilities for disabled guests - ground floor twin bedded room with en suite bathroom; no steps throughout. Bed and Breakfast from £23 per person. Also self-catering cottage in adjacent barn.

See also Colour Display Advertisement

KESWICK. Mrs M.A. Relph, Littletown Farm, Newlands, Keswick CA12 5TU (017687 78353; Fax: 017687 78437). Working farm. Littletown Farm, situated in a peaceful part of the beautiful Newlands Valley has all the facilities of a small hotel. Although fully modernised, the farmhouse retains a traditional character with comfortable lounge, diningroom and licensed bar. Most bedrooms are en suite with tea-making facilities, heating and washbasins. Traditional four-course dinner served six nights a week. Excellent walking and climbing nearby. The market towns of Keswick and Cockermouth and the Lakes are all within easy distance. Ample parking. Dinner Bed & Breakfast from £38 to £42 per person. Bed and Breakfast from £26 to £30 per person. SAE please.

KESWICK. Mr & Mrs Bradley, Rickerby Grange Country House Hotel, Portinscale, Keswick, Cumbria CA12 5RH (017687 72344). ◆◆◆ Set within its own garden with private car parking, in the picturesque village of Portinscale near the shores of Lake Derwentwater within walking distance of the market town of Keswick, ideally situated for exploring all parts of the Lakes. Offering comfort, friendly service, these being the essential qualities provided by the resident proprietor. A well stocked bar, comfortable lounge and elegant dining room where a four course dinner can be enjoyed, with a varied selection of fine wines. Three ground floor bedrooms, all rooms en suite with tea and coffee making facilities, colour TV, direct dial telephone. B&B from £28, DB&B from £41, Winter Rates Available (Special Breaks) Open all Year, including Christmas and New Year. Brochure sent on request.

KESWICK. Mrs Deborah Mawson, Dalton Cottage, Bassenthwaite CA12 4QG (017687 76952). Dalton

Cottage is a traditional Lakeland farm cottage nestling at the foot of Skiddaw. Its situation is idyllic, with spectacular views over Bassenthwaite Lake to the front, Ullock Pike and Skiddaw to the rear, making it an ideal base for walking and touring the Lakes. Both bedrooms are tastefully decorated and are en suite with tea/coffee making facilities. We serve hearty English breakfasts and local inns provide good food nearby in the evenings. Dalton Cottage is typical of the period, with beams, open log fires and antiques. It is the perfect place to relax and unwind and is ideal for families – cot and high chair available. Open all year. Bed and Breakfast from £22, £140 weekly. Friday/Saturday/Sunday Special Breaks £62. Deborah and Martyn look forward to meeting you.

KESWICK. Mrs S. Park, Langdale, 14 Leonard Street, Keswick CA12 4EL (017687 73977).

Victorian town house, quietly situated, yet close to town, park, lake and fells. Comfort and cleanliness our top priority. All rooms are en suite, are tastefully decorated and centrally heated with colour TV, and tea making facilities. We also have a comfortable residents' lounge with colour TV and video.. Enjoy a good home cooked English breakfast or our very popular extensive Continental-style breakfast. We have a non-smoking policy throughout the house. Bed and Breakfast from £19 per person.

KESWICK. Lyndhurst Guest House, 22 Southerby Street, Keswick CA12 4EF (017687 72303). Well established Bed and Breakfast for non-smokers, two minutes' walk from town centre and ideally situated for local walks. All rooms are fully en suite and have colour TV, central heating and tea/coffee making facilities. Family, twin and double rooms available. Children and groups welcome; child discount applies. Cyclists welcome and cycle storage available. Packed lunches available. Bed and full English Breakfast £19 per person.

KESWICK (Newlands). Mrs Christine Simpson, Uzzicar Farm, Newlands, Keswick CA12 5TS (017687

78367). A warm welcome awaits you at Uzzicar Farm situated in the peaceful Newlands Valley, only three miles from Keswick with magnificent views of the surrounding fells. Being within 30 minutes of the M6 Junction 40 makes this the ideal place for a holiday in the Lake District or a break in your journey when travelling north or south. Well located for touring by car and the comfortable farmhouse makes a particularly good base for fell walking and sailing. Fishing, swimming, golf and pony trekking are all relatively close. All bedrooms have washbasins, central heating, tea/coffee making facilities and shaver points. There is a separate sittingroom and dining room, toilet and bathroom with toilet. Sorry no smoking. Open all year except Christmas. Ample parking. Bed and Breakfast £16 to £18 per person. Please write or phone for further details.

KIRKBY STEPHEN. Pauline and Colin Dean, Sower Pow, Victoria Square, Kirkby Stephen CA17 4QA (017683 71030). Family-run Bed and Breakfast accommodation available at Kirkby Stephen in the Upper Eden Valley. This is a beautiful part of Cumbria, situated on the Coast to Coast Path and Settle to Carlisle railway line, also an ideal location for the Lakes and Dales. Separate guest lounge; en suite available with tea and coffee facilities. Bed and Breakfast from £16 per person. People with learning difficulties most welcome. For further information please telephone.

PLEASE MENTION THIS GUIDE WHEN YOU WRITE

OR PHONE TO ENQUIRE ABOUT ACCOMMODATION.

IF YOU ARE WRITING, A STAMPED,

ADDRESSED ENVELOPE IS ALWAYS APPRECIATED.

LAKE DISTRICT/HAWKSHEAD. Grizedale Lodge, Hawkshead, Ambleside LA22 0QL (015394 36532; Fax: 015394 36572}. Set in the heart of the South Lakeland National Park, Grizedale Lodge is one of the most beautiful bed and breakfast locations. Within easy reach are the famous sculpture trails, sailing on Windermere or Coniston, Brantwood, Beatrix Potter country, trout fishing,and other attractions; Hawkshead five minutes. All rooms are en suite, centrally heated, and have colour TV,. tea and coffee making facilities and hair dryers. Some have the added luxury of four-poster beds. Ample parking, a winter log fire, TV lounge and sun terrace. Residential licence. Open all year, rates start from £25 per person per night.
email: enquiries@grizedale-lodge.com
website: www.grizedale-lodge.com

LOWICK (near Coniston).Mrs J. Wickens, Garth Row, Lowick Green, Ulverston LA12 8EB (01229 885633). ETC ◆◆◆. Traditional, beamed Lakeland house

only three miles from Coniston Water in this beautiful and peaceful corner of the National Park. The house stands alone amidst farmland and common with lovely valley and mountain views. We offer quality accommodation with two attractive rooms for guests. Our super family room with its gallery (children love it!) can also serve as a double or twin. Comfortable lounge with books, TV and a real fire on cold nights. Good food, tea/coffee in rooms, dogs welcome, wonderful walking, drying room, no smoking. Super quiet holiday spot or overnight stay. Bed and Breakfast from £18, £100 per week. Brochure.

NEAR SAWREY. Miss Gillian Fletcher, High Green Gate Guest House, Near Sawrey, Ambleside LA22 0LF (015394 36296). ♨♨ The Guest House is a converted

18th-century farmhouse in the quiet hamlet where Beatrix Potter lived and wrote. Her house, owned by the National Trust, is close by and open to the public. The area abounds with pleasant easy walks and is a good centre for the Southern Lakes. Open from March to October. Good food and service under the personal attention of the owner. Spacious diningroom, lounge and separate TV lounge. All bedrooms have hot and cold water and individual heating in addition to central heating. Rooms with private facilities available. Reduced rates for children sharing with parents. Cot and highchair are available and babysitting can be arranged. Dogs welcome. A car is desirable and there is parking for seven cars. AA QQ, RAC Acclaimed. Bed and Breakfast from £23 per night; Bed, Breakfast and Evening Meal from £33 per night (£209 weekly).

NEAR SAWREY. Mrs Elizabeth Mallett, Esthwaite How Farmhouse, Near Sawrey, Ambleside LA22 0LB (015394 36450). A warm and friendly welcome awaits you at Esthwaite How Farmhouse, situated in this lovely village where Beatrix Potter wrote her books. Beautiful views of the countryside and the lake (where part of the television film about her life was made) can be seen from bedrooms and the diningroom. Ideal for walking, fishing and touring. Accommodation comprises one double and one family bedrooms with washbasins; bathroom with shower; dining/sitting room with open log fire, central heating. Children welcome; babysitting can be arranged. Open all year. Car essential, parking for two cars. Bed and Breakfast from £15; Bed, Breakfast and Evening Meal from £23. Half rates for children sharing room.

NEWBIGGIN ON LUNE. Mrs Brenda Boustead, Tranna Hill, Newbiggin-on-Lune, Kirkby Stephen CA17 4NY (015396 23227 or 07961 189569). ETC ◆◆◆. Tranna Hill offers a relaxing and friendly atmosphere in

a non-smoking environment. Five miles from M6 Junction 38, beautifully situated on the fringe of a small village, ideal base for country lovers and walkers, with the nature reserve and Howgill Fells nearby. Well placed for touring the Lakes and Dales and for breaking your journey. Relax in guests' lounge and then have a good night's sleep in en suite rooms with TV, refreshment facilities, central heating and beautiful views, followed by a delicious breakfast. Bed and Breakfast from £18.

PENRITH. Mrs Mary Teasdale, Lisco Farm, Troutbeck, Penrith CA11 0SY (017687 79645). Lisco has beautiful views of Saddleback and the Fells. Three miles from Keswick Golf Club, six miles from Derwentwater and five from Ullswater. A good base for touring lovely Lakeland. Comfortable accommodation offered in one double and two en suite family rooms, all with tea/coffee making facilities and washbasins. Bathroom with shower. Lounge and separate dining room. Bed and Breakfast, optional Evening Meal. Good home cooking. Colour TV. Children welcome. Outside accommodation available for dogs if required. Large dogs also welcome. SAE or phone for further information.

PENRITH. Mrs Yvonne Dent, Bridge End Farm, Kirkby Thore, Penrith CA10 1UZ (01768 361362). ◆◆◆◆◆ Relax in our 18th century farmhouse on a dairy farm in the Eden Valley. Lovely spacious en suite bedrooms, tastefully furnished with antiques, featuring beautiful handmade patchwork quilts and craft work. All rooms have coffee/tea making facilities, hair dryer, clock radio and TV. Enjoy delicious home made breakfast and dinner served in the dining room. All the food is freshly prepared and you will never forget Yvonne's sticky toffee pudding. Finish the evening in front of the fire in the delightfully furnished guest lounge or take a stroll along the banks of the River Eden. Private fishing available.

PENRITH. Mrs Margaret Taylor, Tymparon Hall, Newbiggin, Stainton, Penrith CA11 0HS (Tel and Fax: 017684 83236). Working farm. AA, RAC, ETB INSPECTED, Farm Holiday Bureau Member. Enjoy a relaxing break on the beautiful North Lakes and explore the Eden Valley. A delightful 18th century Manor House and colourful summer garden situated on a 150 acre sheep farm in a peaceful rural area close to Lake Ullswater. Enjoy old-fashioned hospitality, home cooked farmhouse breakfasts and three-course dinners. Guests' bedrooms, en suite or standard, offer space and tranquillity with every facility for a memorable time. Evening Dinner, Bed and Breakfast. Brochure on request with SAE.

PENRITH. Mrs Mary Harris, Whitbarrow Farm, Penrith CA11 0XB (017684 83366). 👑👑 *COMMENDED* **Working farm.** A warm friendly welcome is extended to guests on our 255 acre dairy farm set in an attractive hilltop position with superb views of the Lakeland hills and overlooks the Eden Valley. The accommodation consists of double/twin en suite rooms and a standard family room, all tastefully decorated to a high standard and with tea/coffee facilities and TV. Full central heating. Penrith and M6 seven miles, Ullswater five miles making the farm an ideal centre for touring the Lake District and Scottish Borders. Tariffs from £21.50 per person per day Bed and Breakfast. Mid week bookings accepted. SAE for brochure.

PENRITH. Mrs C. Jackson, Wickereslack Farm, Crosby Ravensworth, Penrith CA10 3LN (01931 715236) 👑👑 *COMMENDED*. A very warm welcome awaits you on our family run working farm. Peaceful rural setting with superb views, ideal base for walking and touring holidays or just to relax. Beautifully decorated, spacious accommodation with three rooms, one en suite. Guest's lounge with TV and log fire which is accessible all day. Light suppers available. For bookings or further details contact: Christine Jackson.

PENRITH. Mrs Brenda Preston, Pallet Hill Farm, Penrith CA11 0BY (017684 83247). Pallet Hill Farm is pleasantly situated two miles from Penrith on the Penrith-Greystoke-Keswick road (B5288). It is four miles from Ullswater and has easy access to the Lake District, Scottish Borders and Yorkshire Dales. There are several sports facilities in the area - golf club, swimming pool, pony trekking; places to visit such as Lowther Leisure Park and the Miniature Railway at Ravenglass. Good farmhouse food and hospitality with personal attention. Double, single, family rooms; diningroom and sittingroom. Children welcome - cot, high chair available. Sorry, no pets. Car essential, parking. Open Easter to November. Bed and Breakfast from £10.50 (reduced rates for children and weekly stays).

PENRITH. Mrs P Bonnick, Scalehouse Farm, Scalehouses, Renwick, Penrith CA10 1JY (Tel & Fax: 01768 896493). A traditional Cumbrian farmhouse in a tiny hamlet overlooking the unspoilt Eden Valley. The North Pennines is an area of outstanding natural beauty, known as 'England's Last Wilderness'. Wildlife, rare elsewhere, is common here with hares, skylarks, lapwings, curlews, snipe, etc. There are lots of interesting places to visit - Carlisle Castle, Hadrian's Wall and Ullswater are just 25 minutes drive away, and so much more. All rooms have period furniture, books, paintings and central heating. The cosy drawingroom has a log fire, TV and games. Home made evening meals are available, with produce from our garden in season. Two double bedrooms and one twin room available. Children welcome. Bed & Breakfast from £14 per person. We are a non-smoking house.

SHAP. Mr and Mrs D. L. and M. Brunskill, Brookfield, Shap, Penrith CA10 3PZ (01931 716 397). ◆◆◆◆. Situated one mile from M6 motorway (turn off at Shap interchange No. 39), first accommodation off motorway. Excellent position for touring Lakeland, or overnight accommodation for travelling north or south. Central heating throughout, renowned for good food, comfort and personal attention. All bedrooms are well-appointed and have remote-control colour TV, hospitality tray and hairdryer; en suite available. Diningroom where delicious home cooking is a speciality. Well-stocked bar. Residents' lounge. Sorry, no pets. Open from January to December. Terms sent on request. Car essential, ample parking. Fire Certificate granted.

TROUTBECK. Gwen and Peter Parfitt, Hill Crest, Troutbeck, Penrith CA11 0SH (017684 83935). Gwen and Peter assure you of a warm and friendly welcome at Hill Crest, their unique Lakeland home which offers two en suite double/family rooms, one twin room. Home cooking, choice of menu including vegetarian; lounge/dining room, early morning tea, bedtime drinks; packed lunches. Panoramic mountain views. Aira Force waterfalls, Ullswater 10 minutes, Keswick 15 minutes, a good base for walking, boating, touring, Lakes, Hadrian's Wall and the Borders. Books, maps and hints from Gwen on what to see. Walkers, children and dogs welcome. Bed and Breakfast £14 per person twin room, £16 per person en suite rooms. Children half price sharing. Dinner from £5 (optional). Weekly rates. 10 minutes Junction 40 M6. At Hill Crest we aim to create a relaxed and informal atmosphere where guests are treated as part of the family. Highly recommended by previous guests. Non smoking establishment.

TROUTBECK. Mrs Maureen Dix, Greenah Crag, Troutbeck, Penrith CA11 0SQ (017684 83233). Enjoy a relaxing break at Greenah Crag, a 17th century former farmhouse peacefully located in the Lake District National Park, just 10 miles from Keswick and only eight miles from the M6 motorway. Ideal for exploring Northern Lakes, Eden Valley, Carlisle, Hadrian's Wall and the Western Pennines. Accommodation is in two double bedrooms with bathroom en suite, and one twin-bedded room with washbasin, all with tea/coffee making facilities. The guests' sittingroom with TV and woodburning stove is a cosy place on the coldest days! A full breakfast is served in the oak-beamed diningroom. Pub/ restaurant three-quarters-of-a-mile. Regret no pets or smoking in the house. Bed and Breakfast from £16.50 per person. Please telephone for brochure.

See also Colour Display Advertisement

WINDERMERE. Irene and George Eastwood, Sandown, Lake Road, Windermere LA23 2JF (015394 45275). Superb Bed and Breakfast accommodation. All rooms en suite with colour TV and tea/coffee making facilities. Situated two minutes from Lake Windermere, shops and cafes. Many lovely walks. Open all year. Special out of season rates, also Saturday/Sunday Breaks, two days, £30 per person. Well-behaved dogs welcome. Each room has own safe private car parking. SAE or telephone for further details.

FOR THE MUTUAL GUIDANCE OF GUEST AND HOST

Every year literally thousands of holidays, short breaks and overnight stops are arranged through our guides, the vast majority without any problems at all. In a handful of cases, however, difficulties do arise about bookings, which often could have been prevented from the outset.

It is important to remember that when accommodation has been booked, both parties – guests and hosts – have entered into a form of contract. We hope that the following points will provide helpful guidance.

GUESTS: When enquiring about accommodation, be as precise as possible. Give exact dates, numbers in your party and the ages of any children. State the number and type of rooms wanted and also what catering you require – bed and breakfast, full board etc. Make sure that the position about evening meals is clear – and about pets, reductions for children or any other special points.

Read our reviews carefully to ensure that the proprietors you are going to contact can supply what you want. Ask for a letter confirming all arrangements, if possible.

If you have to cancel, do so as soon as possible. Proprietors do have the right to retain deposits and under certain circumstances to charge for cancelled holidays if adequate notice is not given and they cannot re-let the accommodation.

HOSTS: Give details about your facilities and about any special conditions. Explain your deposit system clearly and arrangements for cancellations, charges etc. and whether or not your terms include VAT.

If for any reason you are unable to fulfil an agreed booking without adequate notice, you may be under an obligation to arrange suitable alternative accommodation or to make some form of compensation.

While every effort is made to ensure accuracy, we regret that FHG Publications cannot accept responsibility for errors, omissions or misrepresentations in our entries or any consequences thereof.
Prices in particular should be checked because we go to press early. We will follow up complaints but cannot act as arbiters or agents for either party.

DERBYSHIRE

AMBERGATE. Mrs Carol Oulton, Lawn Farm, Whitewells Lane (off Holly Lane), Ambergate DE56 2DN (01773 852352). Working farm, join in. Enjoy comfortable Bed and Breakfast accommodation on a working beef and sheep farm, one mile from the A6 at Ambergate. Ambergate has many woodland walks and a picturesque canal which leads to nearby Cromford, home of the Arkwright Mill. Matlock Bath is 10 miles away and offers many attractions including cable cars. Within easy travelling distance of Haddon Hall, Chatsworth House and Gardens, The Peak District National Park and The National Tramway Museum at Crich. Accommodation comprises double en suite room and family room with handbasin. Children welcome at reduced rates. Pets welcome by arrangement. Terms on request from £17.50 per night. Non-smokers preferred.

ASHBOURNE. Alan and Liz Kingston, Old Boothby Farm, The Green, Ashbourne DE6 1EE (01335 342044). The converted Hayloft and Stables of our 17th century farmhouse are an idyllic location for your stay in the "Gateway to the Peak District". Just a five minute level walk to the centre of Ashbourne with its historic pubs and wide variety of restaurants. Handy for visiting Alton Towers, Dovedale, Buxton, Matlock and numerous stately homes. Excellent walking country. The Hayloft with its verandah, exposed beams, log fire, fully equipped kitchen, lounge with colour TV, two double bedrooms and one twin bunk bedroom is ideal for party or family bookings; cot and high chair available. The Stables studio flat with en suite facilities, king-size bed, colour TV and kitchen is the perfect setting for that romantic break away from it all. Bed and full English, or alternative, Breakfast available. Also let as self-catering accommodation.

ASHBOURNE. Mrs E.M. Smail, New House Farm, Kniveton, Ashbourne DE6 1JL (01335 342429). Working farm. Organically managed, this traditional family farm is in the South Peak District. Carsington Water is two miles, Ashbourne three miles and Dovedale a lovely five mile walk; Alton Towers 10 miles. There are pets, free-range livestock, archaeological features and farm shop. Guided farm walks. We serve organic, free-range and fair-traded foods. Vegetarians and other diets welcome. Children's teas, light suppers, babysitting and play area available. Pets welcome. Tea/coffee facilities, central heating, TV and radio in rooms. We also arrange FREE WORKING HOLIDAYS, individual/group camping and a venue for courses. Bed and Breakfast from £8 to £15.

ASHBOURNE. Michael and Linda Adams, Park View Farm, Weston Underwood, Ashbourne DE6 4PA

(Tel & Fax: 01335 360352). AA ◆◆◆◆◆. Enjoy country house hospitality in our elegant farmhouse set in large gardens with lovely views overlooking the National Trust's magnificent Kedleston Park, hence the farm's name. Double en suite rooms with romantic antique four-poster beds and drinks facilities. Guests own sitting room. Delicious breakfasts served in the delightful dining room. Country pubs and restaurants close by. Bed and Breakfast from £27.50 per person. Three double en suite rooms available. No smoking or pets. Children over 12 years. Open all year except Christmas.

ASHBOURNE near. Mrs Mary Hollingsworth, Collycroft Farm, Near Ashbourne DE6 2GN (01335

342187). Working farm. AA QQQQ Selected. This is a 260 acre mixed farm located two miles south of Ashbourne on the A515, within easy reach of Alton Towers, Peak District and Carsington Water. Accommodation includes double room en suite, twin-bedded room and a family room; colour TV, tea/coffee making facilities and full central heating. All rooms overlook beautiful country views. A warm welcome awaits you at Collycroft Farm which is open all the year round for Bed and Breakfast £20 per person including bedtime drink. Reductions for children.

ASHFORD. Mrs Ann Lindsay, Gritstone House, Greaves Lane, Ashford in the Water, Bakewell DE45 1QH (Tel & Fax: 01629 813563). 👑👑 *HIGHLY COMMENDED*. Be assured of a warm welcome at this charming Georgian house located in Peak District National Park on B6465 leading to Monsal Dale and set in picturesque village on the Wye, one-and-a-half miles north-west of Bakewell off A6. Lounge with TV; one twin-bedded room en suite, two double bedrooms with washbasins, all with TV, tea/coffee facilities. Luxury bathroom with bath, shower, etc; extra toilet. Full central heating. A perfect location for visiting the Stately Homes and Dales of Derbyshire. Bed and Breakfast from £20 to £28; reduced for weekly stays. Sorry, no pets.

BAKEWELL. Mrs Alison Yates, Smerrill Grange, Middleton, By Youlgrave, Bakewell DE45 1LQ (01629 636232). Working farm. Traditional bed and breakfast on working farm. Beautiful setting in heart of Peak district. Old farmhouse dating back to medieval times. Many tourist attractions within short driving distance, e.g. Chatsworth House and Haddon Hall. Bakewell and Matlock six miles. Glorious walks in Derbyshire Dales. Double en suite, double and twin bed rooms with private bathroom. Private guests' sittingroom with tea/coffee making facilities. Colour TV. Children welcome. Bed and Breakfast from £16.

BASLOW. Mrs S. Mills, Bubnell Cliff Farm, Wheatlands Lane, Baslow, Bakewell DE45 1RH (01246 582454). Working farm. A 300 acre working farm situated half-a-mile from the village of Baslow in the beautiful Derbyshire Peak District. Guests can enjoy, from their bedroom window, breathtaking views of Chatsworth Park and surrounding area. Chatsworth House, the majestic home of the Duke of Devonshire, medieval Haddon Hall and the traditional market town of Bakewell (famous for its puddings), are all close by. Accommodation comprises one double and one family room, guests' lounge/dining room with TV and log fires in the winter. NON-SMOKERS ONLY. Bed and Breakfast from £17 per person. Reductions for children. Varied breakfast menu.

BUXTON. The Old Bake and Brewhouse, Blackwell Hall, Blackwell-in-the-Peak, Taddington, Near

Buxton SK17 9TQ (01298 85271). ETC ◆◆◆. Visitors remark on the peace and quiet they enjoy whilst staying in our 18th century much loved farmhouse home. Walks in beautiful Chee Dale, Millers Dale and Monsal Dale all within one mile of the door. A dairy, sheep and cereal farm that also has conservation areas and archaeological/historical interest. Hearty delicious Derbyshire breakfasts add to enjoyable, memorable days. Guests' private lounge with colour TV and woodburner. Breakfast and relax in our new conservatory. Twin with en suite facilities, double with private facilities. Both rooms have colour TV, etc. Guests' car park in lovely mature garden. Central for all Dales, superb Chatsworth, romantic, heavenly Haddon, Bakewell, Buxton and beautiful villages too numerous to mention.

Shallow Grange

Located between the towns of Buxton and Bakewell, this is an ideal hideaway for your break – whatever the time of year. As part of a traditional working dairy farm, this striking 18th century farmhouse is an ideal base to enjoy peace and quiet whilst experiencing the joys of green meadows roped in woodland.Shallow Grange is set away from the main road and a stone's throw from your door there are a variety of unspoilt walks where you can venture out on nature trails. Take your choice of cycling by heather-covered moors, walking through rocky valleys or picturesque villages nearby.

Your comfort is our business and we have made sure that you will be well looked after at Shallow Grange, which is centrally heated, double-glazed and all bedrooms are oak-beamed and have en suite bathroom, colour television and tea and coffee making facilities. Down on the farm you can experience the atmosphere of the countryside. Throughout the year there is plenty of farm activity with calving, lambing and haymaking.
PROPRIETOR: CHRISTINE HOLLAND   SEE ALSO COLOUR ADVERTISEMENT.

Shallow Grange, Chelmorton, Near Buxton, Derbyshire SK17 9SG
Telephone: (01298) 23578   Fax: (01298) 78242   Mobile: 07836 535353

CASTLETON. Mrs G. Cundy, Myrtle Cottage, Market Place, Castleton, Hope Valley S33 8WQ (01433 620787). Myrtle Cottage is pleasantly situated near the village green, in the picturesque village of Castleton, famous for its castle, caverns and 'Blue John'. It is an ideal base for walking, caving, cycling, or touring the Peak District and Derbyshire Dales. Buxton, Bakewell, Chatsworth House and the plague village of Eyam are within 20 minutes' drive. The guest accommodation comprises family, triple and double bedrooms all with private shower/bath, toilet, colour TV and tea/coffee making facilities; pleasant diningroom, all rooms centrally heated. Fire certificate held. Regret no smoking or pets. Parking. Open all year (except Christmas). For Bed and Breakfast only (Breakfast being a feast!).

CHINLEY, Near Buxton. Mrs Barbara Goddard, Mossley House Farm, Maynestone Road, Chinley, High Peak SK23 6AH (Tel & Fax: 01663 750240). ETC ♦♦♦. **Working farm.** Enjoy a stay at our 150 acre hill farm situated in a Special Landscaped Area in the lovely Peak District. A traditional spacious farmhouse offering a high standard of comfort and hospitality. One family room en suite, one double room with private bathroom. Colour TV. Central heating. Children welcome. Village half a mile away. Ideal spot for a holiday. Open all year. Bed and Breakfast from £18.

DOVEDALE, Near Ashbourne. Liz Round, St. Leonard's Cottage, Thorpe, Ashbourne DE6

2AW (01335 350224/465). One of the oldest cottages in the village, St. Leonard's stands in its own grounds of one third of an acre, overlooking the village green, near to the entrance to Dovedale. Thorpe Cloud rises in the background. The village of Thorpe is ideally situated for touring in the Peak District with many historic houses closely reached. For walkers the Manifold Valley and Tissington Trail are close by, along with Carsington Water for fishing and sailing. The cottage is fully modernised but retains the original oak beams. Three bedrooms all en suite with tea/coffee facilities. Centrally heated throughout. Dining room and sitting room with colour TV. The cottage is open all day for guests. Sorry no pets and no smoking. Ample parking. Full Fire Certificate held. Bed and Breakfast £20.

GLOSSOP. Margaret Child, Rock Farm, Monks Road, Glossop SK13 6JZ (01457 861086). Tourist Board

Listed *COMMENDED*. Delightful secluded farmhouse, with panoramic views all round, set in the beautiful scenery of the Dark Peak, yet only 40 minutes from Manchester. Warm, friendly, atmosphere makes for a very relaxing stay. Plenty of good walks from the doorstep, with many local pubs nearby offering excellent, good-value meals. Tastefully decorated bedrooms each have beamed ceilings, colour TV, radio and tea/coffee making trays. South-facing guest lounge can be used throughout the day if the weather lets you down. Centrally heated throughout, with drying facilities. Please send for colour leaflet.

GLOSSOP. Graham and Julie Caesar, Windy Harbour Farm Hotel, Woodhead Road, Glossop SK13 7QE

(01457 853107). Situated in the heart of the Peak District on the B6105, approximately one mile from Glossop town centre and adjacent to the Pennine Way. Our 10-bedroom hotel with outstanding views of Woodhead and Snake Passes and the Longdendale Valley is an ideal location for all outdoor activities. A warm welcome awaits you in our licensed bar and restaurant serving a wide range of excellent home-made food. Bed and Breakfast from £18 per night singles to £40 per night family.

KIRK LANGLEY. Ms. Diane Buxton, New Park Farm, Lodge Lane, Kirk Langley DE6 4NV (01332

824262). Working farm. An early 19th century farmhouse situated seven miles from Ashbourne and four miles from Derby, within easy reach of Alton Towers and The American Adventure Park, Dovedale, Carsington Water, two miles from Kedleston Hall. Hotels and pubs are only a few miles away where good food is served. Accommodation consists of one double bedroom, one family bedroom and one twin bedroom, all with TV and tea/coffee making facilities. Parking is off road, close by the house. Situated in peaceful surroundings overlooking Kirk Langley Village and countryside. Bed and Breakfast from £14 per person. Reductions for children. Self-catering flat also available. Open all year. Write or telephone for details.

MATLOCK. Mrs Linda Lomas, Middlehills Farm Bed and Breakfast, Grange Mill, Matlock DE4 4HY

(01629 650368). We know the secret of contentment - we live in the most picturesque part of England. Share our good fortune, breathe the fresh air, absorb the peace, feast your eyes on the beautiful scenery that surrounds our small working farm, with our pot bellied pig who just loves to have her ears scratched, and Bess and Ruby who are ideal playmates for children of all ages. Retire with the scent of honeysuckle and waken to the aroma of freshly baked bread and sizzling bacon then sample the delights of the Peak District and Derbyshire Dales such as Dovedale, Chatsworth and Haddon Hall.

MATLOCK. Mrs D. Wootton, Old School Farm, Uppertown Lane, Uppertown, Ashover, Near Chesterfield S45 0JF (01246 590813). 👑👑 COMMENDED. Working farm, join in. This working farm in a small hamlet on the edge of the Peak District enjoys unspoilt views. Ashover is three miles away and mentioned in the Domesday Book; Chatsworth House, Haddon Hall, Hardwick Hall, Matlock Bath and Bakewell all within seven miles. Accommodation comprises two family rooms with en suite facilities, one double, one single rooms. Guests have their own bathroom; washbasins in three of the large rooms. Plenty of hot water; fitted carpets; large livingroom/diningroom with colour TV. Non-smoking accommodation available. Car essential. NO PETS. Disabled guests welcome. Children welcome. Open from April to October. Bed and Breakfast from £22 per person per night; Bed, Breakfast and Evening Meal £30 per person per night. Evening meal minimum two persons. Reductions for children. Take the B5057 Darley Dale Road off the A632 Chesterfield to Matlock main road. Take second left. Keep on this road for approximately one mile. Old School Farm is on left opposite the stone water trough. RAC Listed.

MELBOURNE near. Mrs Mary Kidd, Ivy House Farm, Stanton-by-Bridge, Near Melbourne DE73 1HT

(Tel & Fax: 01332 863152). Tourist Board Listed *COMMENDED.* **Working farm, join in.** Ivy House Farm is a 400-acre arable farm with horses at livery. The farmhouse was built in the 17th century and has been 'open house' for bed and breakfast guests since 1992. We have now converted some cowsheds into chalets, all of which are en suite with tea/coffee making and TV. Each chalet has a theme – Cowshed, Sheep Pen, Stable and Pigsty. The area has lots to do and see, such as Calke Abbey, ski slopes, Alton Towers, motor racing at Donington Park. There are also lots of places to eat. Children and pets are welcome, but we are strictly no smoking. Ample off-road parking. Bed and Breakfast from £20.

WHATSTANDWELL. Mrs J. Johnson, Meerbrook Farm, Wirksworth Road, Whatstandwell, Matlock

DE4 5HU (01629 824180; Mobile: 0771 3769074). ETC ◆◆◆ Peaceful setting on a working family dairy farm in a beautiful scenic area overlooking the Derwent Valley. Situated just one-and-a-half miles from the A6 at Whatstandwell on the Wirksworth Road, B5035. Enjoy a warm welcome and hearty breakfast in our lovely old stone farmhouse with oak beams and Aga cooker. Bedrooms have heating, colour TV and tea/coffee facilities. One room has king-size double bed and bunk beds, the second has comfortable 3 ft. twin beds. Large shared bathroom with shower cubicle. Children welcome. Regret, no pets. Convenient for Matlock, Cromford, Carsington Water, Mid Shires Path, High Peak Trail, Derbyshire Dales. Non-smoking. Bed and Breakfast from £18.50.

Key to Tourist Board Ratings

👑   **The Crown Scheme**

The **English Tourism Council** (formerly the English Tourist Board) has joined with the AA and RAC to create a new, easily understood quality rating for serviced accommodation. **Hotels** will receive a grading ranging from **one to five STARS**. Other serviced accommodation such as **guest houses** and **B&B establishments** will be graded from **one to five DIAMONDS**. These ratings represent Quality, Service and Hospitality not just facilities.

NB.Some properties had not been assessed at the time of going to press and in these cases the publishers have included the old CROWN gradings.

   The Key Scheme

The Key Scheme covering self-catering in cottages, bungalows, flats, houseboats, houses, chalets, etc remains unchanged. The classification from **One to Five KEYS** indicates the range of facilities and equipment. Higher quality standards are indicated by the terms APPROVED, COMMENDED, HIGHLY COMMENDED AND DE LUXE.

DEVON

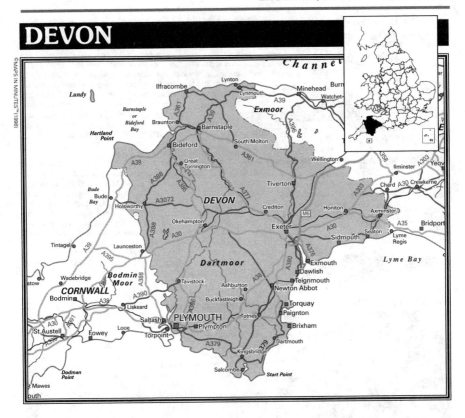

ASHBURTON. Mrs Mary Lloyd-Williams, Hooks Cottage, Bickington, Near Ashburton TQ12 6JS (01626 821312). Situated in 12 acres of woods and fields in a very quiet and picturesque setting at the end of a long farm lane with lovely walks on the doorstep. Relax by the swimming pool or enjoy the river that runs through the property. Central for the areas many attractions, and the beaches and moors. Family suite for guests comprising double room and twin-bedded room with connecting bathroom, dining room, lounge, colour TV, tea making facilities. Excellent meals with fresh produce a speciality. Bed and Breakfast with optional Evening Meal. Children very welcome. Regret no dogs. Please ring for brochure.

BAMPTON. Mrs Lindy Head, Harton Farm, Oakford, Tiverton EX16 9HH (01398 351209). ☙ Working farm, join in. Real farm holidays for country lovers. A unique rural experience for children and the chance to meet the animals on our traditional non-intensive farm near Exmoor. Tranquil 17th century stone farmhouse, secluded but accessible, ideal touring centre. Comfortable accommodation in three double bedrooms with washbasins and tea-making facilities; luxury bathroom with a view; dining room serving real country cooking with farm-produced additive-free meat and organic vegetables; home baking a speciality; guests' lounge with colour TV. Home spun wool. Garden. Children over four welcome. Pets accepted. Car essential - parking. Open for Evening Meal, Bed and Breakfast from £24; Bed and Breakfast from £16. Reductions for children. Farm walks. Fishing, shooting, riding can be arranged. Vegetarian meals available on request.

BAMPTON. Elaine Goodwin, Lodfin Farm, Morebath, Bampton EX16 9DD (Tel & Fax: 01398 331400)

ETC ◆◆. The calming ambience of this beautiful 17th century Devon farmhouse offers everything to relax and unwind. Lodfin Farm is situated on the edge of Exmoor National Park, one mile north of the historic floral town of Bampton and nestles in a secluded valley, of which five acres is a natural woodland habitat with a stream and lake, for our guests to enjoy. Accommodation is spacious, comfortable and inviting with log fires and interesting artefacts. Three pretty bedrooms, one en suite, with tea making facilities and TV. Hearty Aga cooked breakfast served in the inglenook diningroom. Sorry no smoking. Children and pets welcome. Bed and Breakfast from £18.50 per person.

BAMPTON. Mrs Anne Boldry, Newhouse Farm, Oakford, Tiverton EX16 9JE (01398 351347).

AA ◆◆◆◆. Home-baked bread, delicious puddings, home-made pies, pates and preserves... the best of country cooking - winner of "West Country Cooking Best Farmhouse B&B" Award 1999. Newhouse is a 17th century farmhouse tucked down our own stone lane in a peaceful valley. We have prettily and comfortably furnished twin and double rooms, all en suite and with tea trays. We specialise in relaxed, friendly holidays with many guests returning. Newhouse Farm is a perfect base for touring and exploring Exmoor and Devon. Sorry, but we do not take children under 10 years or pets. Bed and Breakfast from £18 to £21; Dinner £12.50. Weekly Bed and Breakfast £135.

BARNSTAPLE. Mrs Sheelagh Darling, Lee House, Marwood, Barnstaple EX31 4DZ (01271 374345).

Stone-built Elizabethan Manor House dating back to 1256, standing in its own secluded gardens and grounds with magnificent views over rolling Devon countryside. James II ceilings, an Adam fireplace, antiques and the work of resident artist add interest. Easy access to coast and moor. Family-run, friendly and relaxing atmosphere. Walking distance to local pub with excellent food. Open April to October. One double, one twin room and one four-poster room, all en suite with colour TV and tea/coffee making facilities. No children under 12 years. Bed and Breakfast from £20.

BARNSTAPLE. Mrs Hazel Kingdon, Waytown Farm, Shirwell, Barnstaple EX31 4JN (01271 850396).

Discover peace and tranquillity at our 17th century farmhouse set in the beautiful rolling countryside of North Devon. we have a family-run beef and sheep farm easily found just three miles north of Barnstaple. Ideal for touring Exmoor or just relaxing on the sandy beaches of Woolacombe and Saunton. Our comfortable, well appointed bedrooms have superb views, three of which are en suite and a single room with washbasin. All rooms have hospitality trays, colour TV, heating and hairdryer. A lounge to relax in is available at any time, with a separate dining room. Reductions for weekly bookings. Open all year except Christmas. Please send for our colour brochure.
e-mail: hazel@waytown.enterprise_plc.com

BARNSTAPLE. Mr and Mrs D. Woodman, The Old Rectory, Challacombe, Barnstaple EX31 4TS (01598 763342).

Within the Exmoor National Park, easily accessible on a good road, The Old Rectory is tucked away peacefully on the edge of Challacombe. A glance at the map of North Devon will show how excellently the house is placed, either for touring the spectacular coastline or for walking on Exmoor. Superbly furnished bedrooms, with tea/coffee making equipment, washbasins and heating. Ample bathroom, toilet, shower facilities. Comfortable dining room, lounge with colour TV. Bed and Beakfast from £18 per night, from £120 per week. No VAT charge. Further particulars on request.

Springfield Garden, Atherington, Umberleigh, North Devon EX37 9JA
Seven miles south of Barnstaple. Gillian and Robert Swann
Tel & Fax: 01769 560034

A substantial traditional English house on its own in a quiet countryside setting with panoramic views across the Taw Valley. Pretty garden of half-an-acre with many unusual plants. We offer homely, clean, comfortable and really friendly en suite B&B with good quality beds and furnished with our personal collection of antiques. Relaxing lounge with easy chairs, writing desk. Traditional English home cooking. Two en suite rooms. B&B £18–£25 pppn. Tea facility, hair dryer, colour TV, radio. Fresh Milk. Supper £5, Dinner £15. Fridge for your own use. Perfect North Devon touring base, approx. seven miles from Rosemoor, 30 minutes from North Devon Coast, Woolacombe, Lynmouth, Exmoor and Clovelly. Sorry no children. Totally non-smoking house. Sorry no pets in the house. Parking. Open all year. Easy to find!
E-mail: broadgdn@eurobell.co.uk   Website: broadgdn.eurobell.co.uk

BIDEFORD. Mrs S. Wade, Collaberie Farm, Welcombe, Bideford EX39 6HF (01288 331391). Situated on Devon/Cornwall border. Modern farmhouse on 90 acre dairy and beef farm overlooking wooded valley to Atlantic Ocean. Just one-and-a-half miles from Welcombe Mouth, voted cleanest beach in Britain in 1993. Clovelly, Hartland Quay, Bideford, Westward Ho! and Bude all within easy reach. Two bedrooms (one family, one double) both with washbasins and tea/coffee making facilities; bathroom, toilet; lounge with colour TV, video; dining room. Children welcome - high chair, cot; babysitting usually available. Open all year except Christmas. Fire Certificate held. Bed and Breakfast from £16. Evening meal optional. Reductions for children

BIDEFORD. Mrs C. Colwill, Welsford Farm, Hartland EX39 6EQ (01237 441296). Working farm, join in. Relax and enjoy the peace and tranquillity of the countryside, yet be within easy reach of picturesque beaches with miles of scenic cliff walks. Our 400 acre dairy farm is situated two miles from Hartland, four miles Clovelly and the magnificent rugged coastline of Hartland Quay. The farmhouse is comfortably furnished with colour TV/video in lounge. Bedrooms (one with sea view) have washbasins, radio alarm clocks, shaver points and tea/coffee facilities. Two bathrooms and toilets, games room with pool, table tennis, darts etc. Wander around the farm and unwind. Children welcome and babysitting available. Plenty of traditional wholesome farmhouse cooking. Bed, full English Breakfast £16 per person, four-course Evening Meal £9 per person. £150 per week Half Board. Reduced rates for children.

BIDEFORD near. Mrs Yvonne Heard, West Titchberry Farm, Hartland, Near Bideford EX39 6AU (01237 441 287). Working farm, join in. Spacious, completely renovated 17th century farmhouse, carpeted and well appointed throughout. One family room with washbasin, one double room with washbasin and one twin room; all with tea/coffee facilities and radio. Bathroom and toilet, seperate shower room. Downstairs lounge with colour TV; diningroom where excellent home cooking is served using fresh produce whenever possible. A games room and sheltered walled garden are available for guests' use. The easily accessible coastal footpath winds its way around this 150 acre mixed farm situated between Hartland Lighthouse and the National Trust beauty spot of Shipload Bay. Hartland three miles, Clovelly six miles, Bideford and Westward Ho! 15 miles, Bude 18 miles. Children welcome at

reduced rates; cot, high chair and babysitting available. Open all year except Christmas. Sorry no pets. Bed and Breakfast from £16.00 per person per night; Evening Meal (optional) £8.00. Reduced weekly terms available. Also self-catering cottage available (3 Keys COMMENDED).

BIDEFORD near. Mr and Mrs J. Ridd, Bakers Farm, Torrington EX38 7ES (01805 623260). 16th

century farmhouse on just over 100 acre farm offering a warm welcome to all visitors. The food and accommodation are both highly recommended and you are assured of delicious meals. Accommodation comprises one family and two double rooms; two toilets, one shower room, one bathroom. Comfortable lounge with colour TV. Full Fire Certificate. Indoor swimming pool, golf, tennis and fishing nearby (coarse fishing available within the farm). and we are within easy reach of Dartington Glass Factory, the coast, Exmoor, Dartmoor and many other places of interest, including Tarka Trail for cycling or walking. Evening Meal, Bed and Breakfast from £18 or Bed and Breakfast only. Reductions for children. Please send SAE for full particulars.

BRAUNTON. Mrs Roselyn Bradford, "St. Merryn", Higher Park Road, Braunton EX33 2LG (01271

813805). Set in beautiful, sheltered garden of approximately one acre, with many peaceful sun traps. Ros extends a warm welcome to her guests. Rooms (£20 per person) include single, double and family rooms, with washbasins, central heating, colour TV and tea/coffee making facilities. All rooms either en suite or with private bathrooms. Evening meal (£12) may be served indoors or out. Guests may bring own wine. Guest lounge with colour TV, patio door access to garden. Swimming pool, fish ponds, hens and thatched summerhouse plus excellent parking. Self Catering flat also available. Please send for brochure.

BRAUNTON. Audrey Isaac, Crowborough, Georgeham, Braunton EX33 1JZ (01271 891005). Sleeps

2-6. Open all year. Peaceful, secluded Georgian farmhouse situated in a valley outside the village of Georgeham. An ideal place from which to explore coastline and countryside. Coastal path and sandy beaches two miles. Exmoor National Park 45 minutes' drive, Saunton Championship Golf Course four miles. Many beautiful walks. Local pub with good food five minutes' walk. Crowborough offers accommodation to one booking of up to five people in three comfortable bedrooms sharing private bathroom and breakfast/sitting room with TV and beverage tray. Wood burner in winter. Unsuitable for young children. No smoking. B&B from £20 per person per night. Please write, phone or e-mail for more information.
e-mail: amisaac@aol.com

BRIXHAM. Allen and Judy Hoskins, Raddicombe Lodge, 102 Kingswear Road, Brixham TQ5 0EX

(01803 882125). ☜☜ *COMMENDED.* The Lodge lies midway between the picturesque coastal harbour towns of Brixham and Dartmouth, overlooking sea and country, with National Trust land between us and the sea. The Lodge is reached by a short drive off the B3205, in a quarter acre garden with the charm and character of pitched ceilings, lattice windows and cosy open fires for the winter months. Scrumptious traditional English breakfast with locally baked crusty bread or Continental Breakfast with croissants; light/vegetarian breakfast also available. All bedrooms are en suite and have colour TV and tea/coffee making facilities. Come and go as you please, make the Lodge your home from home. Smoking restricted to the lounge area only. Ample parking. Open all year. Children welcome. Sorry no pets. Offering room
and breakfast only from £21 per night each. Popular carvery restaurant just 400 yards away. MasterCard/Access/Visa cards accepted.

BUCKFASTLEIGH. Mrs O. Causey, The Lawns Farm, Buckfastleigh TQ11 0ND (01364 643650).

Working farm, join in. A friendly, mixed, working hilltop farm with breathtaking views of the South Hams and Dartmoor. Three minutes from the Devon Expressway yet very peaceful and secluded. Exeter and Plymouth only 20 minutes away with Torbay, the sea and Dartmoor even closer. Large rooms with tea/coffee facilities, vast guests' TV lounge and lots of traditional farmhouse Aga cooking. Bed and Breakfast from £15; Evening Meal by arrangement. Hundreds of local top quality attractions.

CALVERLEIGH (near Tiverton). Mrs Anne Nettley, New Inn Farm, Rackenford Road, Claverleigh, Tiverton EX16 8BE (01884 258851). A warm welcome awaits

at this 15th/17th century former Coaching Inn situated within easy reach of the A361, Junction 27 of M5. It has a wealth of oak beams and inglenook fireplaces. Comfortable Bed and Breakfast accommodation with private bath/shower. Residents' TV lounge. Off road parking. Full English breakfast. Charming village pub/restaurant within easy walking distance. Not suitable for children under 12 years. Small to medium dogs by arrangement. Open all year except Christmas and New Year. Bed and Breakfast from £18 per person, discount available for four nights or more.

CHALLACOMBE. Mrs Christine Johnson, Shorland Old Farm, Challacombe, Bratton Fleming EX31 4TX (01598 763505). Our 16th century farmhouse is beautifully

situated in 14 acres overlooking Exmoor, nine miles from the sea. The comfortable farmhouse is centrally heated, and all bedrooms are en suite and have drink-making facilities. There are two guests' lounges each with TV and wood burner. Our visitors can be sure of a homely welcome and enjoy good fresh food. Bed and Breakfast from £17; optional four course Evening Meal. Three night short break – including bed, breakfast and evening meals £84. Sorry, no smoking or pets.

CHERITON BISHOP. Mrs N.M. Stephens, Horselake Farm, Cheriton Bishop, Exeter EX6 6HD (Tel & Fax: 01647 24220). Horselake Farm offers unique accommodation

in a lovely 16th century Grade II Listed Tudor farmhouse. Set in beautiful gardens with outside heated swimming pool. Owner runs an Arabian horse stud and fruit farm. The accommodation comprises three rooms – one four-poster, one en suite and a twin room; all have washbasin, TV and tea/coffee making facilities. Central heating, log fires in winter. Children welcome. Bed and Breakfast from £18 to £22 per person.

CLOVELLY. Mrs Joanne Wade, Holloford Farm, Higher Clovelly, Bideford EX39 5SD (01237 441275).

ETC ◆◆◆◆. We invite you to stay on our 300 acre dairy farm, the farmhouse dates back to 16th century, with oak beams, open fireplace and pretty bedrooms, all set in peaceful, unspoilt surroundings. Two bedrooms, one twin and one double with single bed. Both have washbasins and drinks trays. Lovely bathroom, sitting room and dining room all beautifully decorated and for guests sole use. Outside enjoy our sheltered garden or take a quiet walk. Come to Holloford to sample a real Devonshire Farmhouse Breakfast and very warm welcome. Two miles from Clovelly and coast. Children welcome. Bed and Breakfast from £20.

COLYTON. Mrs Norma Rich, Sunnyacre, Northleigh, Colyton EX24 6DA (01404 871422). Working

farm, join in. Have a relaxing holiday in Bed and Breakfast and Evening Meal accommodation set in an area of outstanding natural beauty with plenty of things to do and see. Accommodation is in a bungalow on a working dairy farm. Join in with farm activities, feeding all the animals, watch cows being milked. Enjoy excellent and varied meals, all home cooked using fresh produce. Full English Breakfast, early morning tea, evening drinks. Three bedrooms with washbasins, separate WC; TV in lounge, games room. Children welcome, cot, high chair and babysitting available. Reasonable rates.

COLYTON. Mrs Maggie Todd, Smallicombe Farm, Northleigh, Colyton, EX24 6BU (01404 831340).

ETC ◆◆◆◆. Featured in 1998 'Guide to Good Food in the West Country'. Come and escape the stress to an idyllic rural setting, little changed since chronicled in the Domesday Book. Meet our friendly farm animals. Taste real pork from rare breed pigs. Explore this unspoilt corner of Devon with an abundance of wildlife, yet be close to the coast. Watch the buzzards soar overhead and try to spot the shy roe deer and badgers emerging from the wood. All rooms en suite, one ground floor. From £18.50 per night Bed and Breakfast. Reductions for children and weekly. Evening meals available. Open all year.
website: www.smoothhound.co.uk/hotels/smallico.html

COLYTON. Mrs Ruth Gould, Bonehayne Farm, Colyton EX13 6SG (01404 871396). Working farm.

Bonehayne Farm, situated in beautiful Coly Valley, set amidst 250 acres dairy farmland on banks of the River Coly, where daffodils are a feature in springtime, and Mallard duck and Kingfishers are a common sight. Trout fishing freely available. Woodlands to explore. Visitors welcome to participate in some farm activities and make friends with the animals. One family, one double bedrooms, with washbasins; bathroom, toilet. Spacious, homely lounge with inglenook fireplace, TV. A good English breakfast. Lawn and play area for children with extended large lawn overlooking surrounding countryside. Reduced rates, cot, high chair, babysitting for children. Small pets accepted. Parking. Farway Country Park, two riding schools, Honiton Golf Course, weekly cattle market, coastal area, all within four and a half miles. Open April to October. Bed and Breakfast; Evening Meal. Terms on request.

CREDITON. Mrs Janet Bradford, Oaklands, Black Dog, Crediton EX17 4QJ (01884 860645). Janet and

Ivor warmly welcome you to enjoy a relaxing stay, long or short, in peaceful surroundings with lovely views and countryside walks. Large comfortable bedrooms with en suite, tea/coffee facilities, colour TV and central heating. Large guest lounge with Sky TV and open fire in winter. Large garden with surrounding 20 acres of farmland where guests are free to wander. Walking distance of the 17th century Black Dog Inn pub/restaurant. Oaklands is situated between Dartmoor and Exmoor, ideal for touring all parts of Devon. Bed and Breakfast from £16. Reductions for children. Open all year.

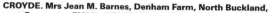

See also Colour Display Advertisement

CROYDE. Mrs Jean M. Barnes, Denham Farm, North Buckland, Braunton EX33 1HY (Tel and Fax: 01271 890297).

👑👑👑 *COMMENDED.* 10 beautiful en suite rooms, country views and pretty decor. Here you can relax with the satisfaction of knowing you will be well looked after. Situated in a quiet unspoilt hamlet only two-and-a-half miles from the golden sands of Woolacombe and Croyde. Nowhere is far away. Enjoy the natural beauty that North Devon offers and return to the comfort and charm of Denham. A children's paradise with play area, games room and pets' corner. This licensed farmhouse ensures you a friendly holiday, making Denham a place to return to. Farm Holiday Bureau Member, West Country Tourist Board Member, AA, RAC Acclaimed.

CULLOMPTON. Mrs Margaret Chumbley, Oburnford Farm, Cullompton EX15 1LZ (01884 32292). Working farm, join in. 👑👑👑 *COMMENDED*. Treat yourself to a "special break" and enjoy our welcoming friendly family atmosphere. Mentioned in the Domesday Book, Oburnford is a dairy farm where guests may watch the milking and the making of clotted cream. The Listed Georgian farmhouse is set in large gardens, and is ideally situated for the coasts, Exmoor, Dartmoor, coarse fishing and several National Trust properties. Cullompton (M5 J28) two-and-a-half miles. The spacious en suite bedrooms all have tea/coffee facilities; the guest lounge has a colour television and video; separate dining room. Generous farmhouse hospitality, licensed, full menu, four-course evening meals and fresh clotted cream all make for a perfect relaxing break at anytime of the year. Special diets welcome. Bed and Breakfast £17. Bed, Breakfast and Evening Meal £170 per week. Phone now "free wine", "free child". Open all year.

CULLOMPTON. Mrs Sylvia Baker, Wishay Farm, Trinity, Cullompton EX15 1PE (01884 33223). 👑👑 *COMMENDED*. **Working farm.** Wishay Farm is a 200 acre working farm with a recently modernised Grade II Listed farmhouse with some interesting features. It is situated in a quiet and peaceful area with scenic views, yet is central for touring the many attractions Devon has to offer. Comfortable and spacious accommodation in family room with en suite bathroom, double room with washbasin and private bathroom, both with colour TV, fridge, tea/coffee making facilities. Central heating, log fire when cold. Children welcome, cot and high chair available. Bed and Breakfast from £16. Reduced rates for children.

See also Colour Display Advertisement

CULLOMPTON. Fay Down, Upton House, Cullompton EX15 1RA (Tel & Fax: 01884 33097). We will welcome you to this beautiful 300-year-old farmhouse, charmingly furnished with oak panelled walls and lovely inglenook fireplaces, set in tranquil parkland. Lovely garden with superb views. All bedrooms are spacious and tastefully decorated, en suite with all facilities. We have a picturesque coarse fishing lake on this 120-acre organic farm. We are ideally placed for exploring Devon, National Trust properties and the north and south coasts. Just one-and-a-half miles off Junction 28, M5. Please ring for brochure. No smoking please in the house.

DARTMOUTH. Mrs Sue Hutchinson, Sloutts Farmhouse, Slapton, Kingsbridge TQ7 2PR (Tel & Fax: 01548 580872). Choose Sloutts Farmhouse for a relaxing holiday in the country by the sea; a delightful Georgian house tucked down a narrow lane in picturesque Slapton village. Just over half-a-mile from beach, coastal footpath and Slapton Ley Nature Reserve, midway between Dartmouth and Kingsbridge. En suite bedrooms have lovely open views of village and surrounding South Devon countryside. Wholesome meals prepared with fresh local produce. Log fires, central heating, garden and parking. Open early Spring until late Autumn. Sorry, no smoking or pets in the house. Brochure and tariff on request.

See also Colour Display Advertisement

DAWLISH. Radfords Country Hotel, Dawlish EX7 0QN (01626 863322). 👑👑👑 *COMMENDED*. Enjoy a family holiday in the beautiful setting of our 18th century hotel, enveloped by six acres of glorious gardens. We are situated in beautiful countryside within easy reach of the town and the beach. Excellent family en suite accommodation in family or two bedroom suites all with tea/coffee facilities, colour TV and baby listening intercoms. Three heated swimming pools, toddlers' playroom and soft play area, supervised play evenings, playgroup three mornings a week and varied entertainment programme. Flexible mealtimes. Our aim is to give you and your children a totally stress free stay. Please contact Janet and Terry Crump for further information.
website: www.eclipse.co.uk/radfords

EAST PRAWLE. Mrs Linda Tucker, Welle House, East Prawle, Kingsbridge, Devon TQ7 2BU (01548

511531). Working farm. Welle House is part of a working mixed farm situated in the most southerly point of Devon's beautiful, unspoilt coastline. The house is in a quiet location with ample safe parking, a large garden with plenty of grass for games and views towards the village of East Prawle and the sea. All rooms (two double, one twin and one family) have en suite facilities and central heating. Access at all times and guests' lounge with colour TV and log fire. Help yourself to tea and coffee at any time. Flexible meal times. Children most welcome. Regret, no pets. Good pubs within easy walking distance. Bed and Breakfast from £15.

EAST PRAWLE. Mrs Helen Tucker, Honey Lane House, East Prawle, Kingsbridge TQ7 2BU (01548

511531). Working farm. Welcoming spacious farmhouse Bed and Breakfast. Convenient for secluded beaches, coastal walks, fishing and bird-watching (Cirl Bunting country). The beautiful towns of Kingsbridge and Salcombe are only twenty minutes away (the latter by foot-ferry) with Plymouth and Exeter only an hour away. All rooms are en suite. There is a large comfortable livingroom with colour TV and tea/coffee making facilities and extensive garden with large grassy area for children to play. We are just five minutes from the village of East Prawle (Devon's most southerly point) with its two pubs (where children are welcome), seasonal shops and cafe. Children welcome, regret no pets. Bed and Breakfast from £15 to £20.

EXETER. Joyce Dicker, Moor Farm, Dunsford, Exeter EX6 7DP (01647 24292). Working farm.

Listed *COMMENDED.* Devon longhouse with beautiful view of rolling hills in the heart of the countryside, set on a traditional working farm. Guests have their own view of the farmhouse in a quiet location, although the farm is only two-and-a-half miles from the A30. Ideal for touring Dartmoor or seaside resorts. A good hearty breakfast is served, using home made produce. One family and one double room are available each with tea/coffee making facilities. Bed and Breakfast from £14. Non-smoking. Open March to October.

EXETER. Mrs Sally Glanvill, Rydon Farm, Woodbury, Exeter EX5 1LB (01395 232341). 👑👑 *HIGHLY*

COMMENDED. Working farm. Come, relax and enjoy yourself in our lovely 16th century Devon longhouse. We offer a warm and friendly family welcome at this peaceful dairy farm. Three miles from M5 Junction 30 on B3179. Ideally situated for exploring the coast, moors and the historic city of Exeter. Only 10 minutes' drive from the coast. Inglenook fireplace and oak beams. All bedrooms have central heating, private or en suite bathrooms, hair dryers and tea/coffee making facilities. One room with romantic four-poster. A traditional farmhouse breakfast is served with our own free range eggs and there are several excellent pubs and restaurants close by. Pets by arrangement. Farm Holiday Bureau member, AA QQQQ Selected. Open all year. Colour brochure available. Bed and Breakfast from £22 to £27.

See also Colour Display Advertisement

EXETER. Great Leigh Farm & Guest House, Doddiscombsleigh, Exeter EX6 7RF (01647 252058; Fax: 01647 253008). Situated in the beautiful picturesque Teign Valley, where peace and solitude rule, but only a few miles from Exeter and Dartmoor. The farm owns 170 acres of land completely surrounding it. Rough shooting and fishing; golf nearby. The spacious rooms, all with en suite facilities are beautifully converted in an old stone barn retaining much of the 'old world' charm. There is a games room with a full size snooker table. Pets allowed. Two double/two twin-bedded rooms. All en suite with TV and tea-making facilities, hairdryers and shoe cleaning kits. £25/£30 per person for a double room Single £35/£40 per person. Open all the year round. There are also three self contained cottages with open fires and magnificent views.

EXETER. Mrs Jackie Bolt, Wood Barton, Farringdon, Exeter EX5 2HY (01395 233407; Fax: 01395

227226). Wood Barton is an attractive 17th century farmhouse set in quiet countryside with beautiful rural views. Spacious en suite bedrooms with colour TV, central heating, radio, hairdryer and tea/coffee facilities. Farmhouse breakfast cooked on the Aga. Good local eating places. Approximately six miles from the city of Exeter, sandy beaches, National Trust properties, bird reserve, carp fishing lake, golf course and children's play area. Three miles from M5 Junction 30. Open all year. Parking, easy access. Sorry no smoking or pets. Also available self-catering cottages. Bed and Breakfast from £21 per person.

EXETER. Karen Williams, Stile Farm, Starcross, Exeter EX6 8PD (Tel & Fax: 01626 890268). Enjoy a

peaceful break in beautiful countryside. Close to the Exe Estuary and only two miles to the nearest sandy beach. Take a stroll to the village (only half a mile) to discover many eating places, or a little further to some specially recommended ones. Birdwatching, golf, fishing, racing, etc. all nearby, and centrally situated for exploring all the lovely countryside and coastline in the area. Good shopping in Exeter. Comfortable rooms, guests' lounge, English breakfast. Nice garden. Plenty of parking. NON-SMOKING. Personal service and a 'home from home' atmosphere guaranteed.

EXETER near (Doddiscombsleigh). Mrs B. Lacey, Whitemoor Farm, Doddiscombsleigh, Near Exeter

EX6 7PU (01647 252423). Working farm. 👑 *APPROVED.* Listed 16th century thatched farmhouse, set in seclusion of its own garden and farmland within easy reach of Exeter, coast, Dartmoor and forest walks. The Cobb House has exposed beams, log fires. Home made preserves. Good meals at local inn. Evening meal on request. Children and pets welcome. Swimming pool available. Open all year. Bed and Breakfast from £17.50; Evening Meal from £8. Non-smoking. Camp site also available.

EXMOOR. Mr and Mrs P. Carr, Greenhills Farm, Yeo Mill, West Anstey, South Molton EX36 3NU (01398

341300; mobile: 07974 806099).◆◆◆◆ *SILVER AWARD.* A warm friendly atmosphere awaits you at Greenhills. Our charming farmhouse on a working farm, situated in the southern foothills of Exmoor, offers an exceptionally high standard of accommodation. Delicious food using home-grown and local produce. Warm, comfortable private suite of rooms, one twin and one double en suite. Separate dining room and lounge, both with beams, inglenooks and log fires. On the Two Moors Way, it's a country-lovers paradise. Bed and Breakfast from £18 to £22. Evening Meal £10.

EXMOOR NATIONAL PARK. Mrs Renee Dover, Rockley Farmhouse, Near Brayford, Barnstaple EX32 7QR (Tel & Fax: 01598 710429). ◆◆◆◆ *SILVER AWARD*

Red Deer can be seen grazing around our farmhouse situated in EXMOOR NATIONAL PARK and surrounded by spectacular views. We are not a working farm, but we do have farmyard friends. Rockley is an ideal base for coastal and moorland walks, riding or exploring the Moor. There is a stream bordered garden for you to relax in and for children, a tree house. All bedrooms have central heating and tea/coffee making facilities. You can choose between a room with a cast iron bed or pine furnishings. En suite or beautiful bathroom. There is a residents' lounge with a log fire. Bed and Breakfast from £20 to £23. Self-catering two bedroom cottage (sleeping 2-4) also available.
e-mail: rockley@hicon.co.uk

EXMOUTH. Mrs J. Hallett, Gulliford Farm, Lympstone, Near Exmouth EX8 5AQ (01392 873067).

Working farm. You are assured of a warm welcome to our 16th century farmhouse with its spacious rooms and beautiful garden with sun terrace, lawns, tennis court and swimming pool. This working farm stands in the beautiful Exe Valley only a short distance from the many beaches. One family suite, two double or family rooms, one single room, most with washbasin and tea-making facilities. Lounge with colour TV and inglenook fireplace, diningroom with separate tables. Ample parking. There is access to rooms at all times. A full English breakfast is served and there are many delightful inns and restaurants to provide your evening meal. Terms for Bed and Breakfast are from £20 per person per night. We also have TWO comfortable SELF-CATERING COTTAGES from £350 plus VAT.

HIGHAMPTON. Mrs Gillian M. Bowden, Higher Odham, Highampton, Beaworthy EX21 5LX (01409 231324).

A dairy/beef 150 acres working farm, stream and open moorland. Watch milking, go for walks. Red brick farmhouse situated down a quiet country road off the A3072 between Holsworthy and Hatherleigh market towns. One mile to village shop, Post Office and village pub serving good food. Ideally situated for touring coast, Dartmoor and Exmoor. Fishing in many local ponds, near Tarka Trail for walking, cycling. Diningroom, lounge with open log fireplace, colour TV. Good views of Dartmoor. Large lawns with two ornamental ponds. Sorry no smoking or pets. One double en suite, one family with shower and washbasin, one twin with adjacent bathroom, separate WC. All with tea/coffee facilities. Bed and Full English Breakfast £18.

HOLSWORTHY. Mrs L.D. Marshall, School Lane Farm, Chilsworthy, Holsworthy EX22 7BQ (01409 253389).

This family-run sheep and beef farm is set in the quiet countryside, two miles from the market town of Holsworthy, nine miles from the coast with its sandy beaches. This 17th century farmhouse offers comfortable accommodation with central heating. Guests breakfast in the conservatory. Lounge with colour television for guests' use only. One family room with en suite facilities and one double room. Both rooms have tea/coffee making facilities. Children welcome, cot available. Bed and Breakfast £17, reductions for children. A warm welcome awaits throughout the year.

HOLSWORTHY near. Mrs S. Plummer, Long Cross House, Black Torrington EX21 5QG (01409 231219).

Quiet country house situated at the edge of the delightful village of Black Torrington in rural north west Devon, providing an ideal base from which to explore the area. North Dartmoor and the beautiful coastline from the sandy beaches at Bude to rugged Hartland Point and quaint Clovelly, are all within easy reach. The centrally heated rooms are en suite, with television and tea/coffee making facilities. Children welcome, lounge available. Bed and Breakfast from £17.50 with evening meal by arrangement. Reductions for more than four nights.

HONITON. Pamela Boyland, Barn Park Farm, Near Cotleigh, Stockland Hill, Honiton EX14 9JA (Tel: 01404 861297; Freephone: 0800 328 2605). 🏠 *COMMENDED.* Barn Park Farm is a working dairy farm situated one-and-a-half miles off A30/A303 Junction, Road sign marked Axminster/Stockland. Within reach of many beauty spots. coast nine miles. Traditional farmhouse breakfasts using eggs from our free-range hens. Barn Park farm has en suite/private bathrooms. All bedrooms having beverage trays (TV on request). The farmhouse is brimming with character with a homely atmosphere. We are open all year except Christmas Day. TV Lounge, quiet sittingroom. Ground floor bedroom by arrangement. Bed and Breakfast from £16. Evening meal if required, £9. No smoking in the house please.

HONITON. Mrs Elizabeth Tucker, Lower Luxton Farm, Upottery, Honiton EX14 9PB (01823 601269). Working farm. If you are looking for a quiet, peaceful and relaxing holiday, come to Lower Luxton Farm, where a warm and friendly welcome awaits you. Situated in an area of outstanding natural beauty in the centre of the Blackdown Hills, overlooking the Otter Valley. Ideal centre for touring. Carp and tench fishing in our farm pond. Olde worlde farmhouse with inglenook and beams, fully modernised and offering family, double or twin rooms with tea/coffee making facilities, TV, washbasins, etc; separate bathroom and shower room, both with toilets. Good home cooking assured and plenty of it! Bed and Breakfast from £15 per night. Weekly Bed and Breakfast with six Evening Dinners from £130 per week. Children and pets welcome. Open all year. SAE, or telephone, for our brochure.

HONITON. Mrs June Tucker, Yard Farm, Upottery, Honiton EX14 9QP (01404 861680). A most attractively situated working farm. The house is a very old traditional Devon farmhouse located just three miles east of Honiton and enjoying a superb outlook across the Otter Valley. Enjoy a stroll down by the River Otter which runs through the farmland. Try a spot of trout fishing. Children will love to make friends with our two horses. Lovely seaside resorts 12 miles, swimming pool three miles. Traditional English breakfast, colour TV, washbasin, heating, tea/coffee facilities in all rooms. Bed and Breakfast £16. Reductions for children.

ILFRACOMBE. Michael and Lynda Hunt, Sunnymeade Country Hotel, Dean Cross, West Down, Ilfracombe EX34 8NT (01271 863668).◆◆◆ Small, friendly comfortable country hotel with our own enclosed garden set in beautiful countryside. A few minutes away from Woolacombe beach, Ilfracombe and Exmoor. Award-winning home-cooked traditional English food, using fresh local produce. Special diets can be accommodated. Licensed bar. Eight en suite rooms, two on the ground floor. Open all year including Christmas. Polite dogs welcome. website: www.btinternet.com/~sunnymeade

ILFRACOMBE. Wentworth House Hotel, 2 Belmont Road, Ilfracombe EX34 8DR (01271 863048). Wentworth House, a family-run hotel, was built originally as a residence for a gentleman of Ilfracombe in 1857 and stands quietly in lovely gardens only a stone's throw from the town and minutes from the sea, harbour and famous Torrs Walks. En suite rooms with colour TV. Family rooms sleeping up to four persons. Home cooked food and spacious licensed bar/lounge. Rooms have tea/coffee facilities. Parking in grounds. Open all year. Bed and Breakfast from £16; Bed, Breakfast and Evening Meal from £21.50. Stay a few days or weeks, we will make your visit a pleasant one.

IVYBRIDGE. Pat Stephens, Venn Farm, Ugborough, Ivybridge PL21 0PE (01364 73240). 👑👑

COMMENDED. Venn Farm is situated in a peaceful position in the South Hams. All our visitors appreciate the quietness, bird lovers remark on variety of birds and constant song. We are near Dartmoor and many sandy beaches. Carve your own roast is a favourite here and many come back for more! Gardens are expansive, we are bordered by streams and a wild garden has been added recently. Two family rooms en suite and a two-bedroomed garden cottage also en suite available. Send for brochure for more details.

IVYBRIDGE near. Mrs Susan Winzer, "The Bungalow", Higher Coarsewell Farm, Ugborough, Near Ivybridge PL21 0HP (01548 821560). Working farm. Higher

Coarsewell Farm is a traditional family-run dairy farm situated in the heart of the peaceful South Hams countryside, near Dartmoor and local unspoilt sandy beaches. It is a very spacious bungalow with beautiful garden and meadow views. One double room with bathroom en suite and one en suite family room. Guest lounge/dining room. Good home cooked food, full English breakfast served. Children welcome - cot, high chair and babysitting available. Bed and Breakfast from £16 daily; optional Evening Meal extra. Open all year. A379 turnoff from the main A38 Exeter to Plymouth road.

KINGSBRIDGE. Anne Rossiter, Burton Farm, Galmpton, Kingsbridge TQ7 3EY (01548 561210).

👑👑 *HIGHLY COMMENDED.* **Working farm, join in.** Working farm in South Huish Valley, one mile from the fishing village of Hope Cove, three miles from famous sailing haunt of Salcombe. Walking, beaches, sailing, windsurfing, bathing, diving, fishing, horse-riding - facilities for all in this area. We have a dairy herd and two flocks of pedigree sheep. Guests are welcome to take part in farm activities when appropriate. Traditional farmhouse cooking and home produce. Four-course Dinner, Bed and Breakfast. Access to rooms at all times. Tea/coffee making and TV in rooms, all of which are en-suite. Games room. No smoking. Open all year, except Christmas. Warm welcome assured. Functions catered for. Self-catering cottages also available. Dogs by arrangement. Details and terms on request.

KINGSBRIDGE near. Mrs Ann Mulligan, Heath Farm, Loddiswell TQ7 4EE (Tel & Fax: 01548 550565).

Please try and find us at the end of a country lane where a warm welcome and "cuppa" will greet you at Heath Farm. A large house, surrounded by shrubs and flowers, with well proportioned rooms offers guests peace in the heart of unspoiled countryside. Enjoy large, tasty Aga cooked breakfasts using local produce along with home-baked muffins to start your day. Double room with private bathroom, twin room with private shower, single room for an additional family member. All rooms have vanity units, TV, tea/coffee making facilities and are newly carpeted and decorated. Regret no children under 12 years. Sorry no pets. Bed and Breakfast from £18. Open from Whitsun to September. Non-smoking.

KINGSBRIDGE. Mrs M. Darke, Coleridge Farm, Chillington, Kingsbridge TQ7 2JG (01548 580274).

Coleridge Farm is a 600 acre working farm situated half-a-mile from Chillington village, midway between Kingsbridge and Dartmouth. Many safe and beautiful beaches are within easy reach, the nearest being Slapton Sands and Slapton Ley just two miles away. Plymouth, Torquay and the Dartmoor National Park are only an hour's drive. Visitors are assured of comfortable accommodation in a choice of one double and one twin-bedded rooms; private shower; toilet; shaver points and tea/coffee making facilities. Spacious lounge with TV. A variety of eating establishments in the locality will ensure a good value evening meal. Children welcome. Small dogs by arrangement. Terms on request.

BLACKWELL PARK

Loddiswell, Kingsbridge Tel: 01548 821230   ETC ◆◆

Blackwell Park is a 17th century farmhouse situated five miles from Kingsbridge and two miles from Loddiswell. Many beaches within easy reach, also Dartmoor, Plymouth, Torbay and Dartmouth. Seven bedrooms for guests; all with washbasins and tea-making facilities, some en suite. Separate tables in diningroom; lounge with colour TV. Large games room with darts, snooker, skittles etc. Garden with plenty of grass for games adjoining 54 acres of woodland/nature reserve. Large car parking area. Ample food with choice of menu. Help yourself to tea and coffee at any time. Fire Certificate. CHILDREN AND PETS ESPECIALLY WELCOME. Babysitting. Open all year round for Bed, Breakfast and Evening Meal. Reduced rates out of season.

KINGSBRIDGE. Mrs Angela Foale, Higher Kellaton Farm, Kellaton, Kingsbridge TQ7 2ES (Tel & Fax 01548 511514).👑👑 *COMMENDED*. **Working farm.** Smell the fresh sea air, delicious Aga-cooked breakfast in the comfort of this lovely old farmhouse. Nestled in a valley, our farm with friendly animals welcomes you. Spacious, well-furnished rooms, en suite, colour TVs, tea/coffee making facilities, own lounge, central heating and log fires. Flexible meal times. Attractive walled garden. Safe car parking. Situated between Kingsbridge and Dartmouth. Visit Salcombe by ferry. One-and-a-half miles to the lost village of Hallsands and Lanacombe Beach. Beautiful, peaceful, unspoilt coastline with many sandy beaches, paths, wild flowers and wildlife. Ramblers' haven. Good pubs and wet-weather family attractions. Open Easter to October. Non-smoking. B & B from £16.50.

See also Colour Display Advertisement

KINGSBRIDGE. Sally and Peter Barber, Maelcombe House, East Prawle, Near Kingsbridge, Devon TQ7 2DE (01548 511521; Fax: 01548 511501). Idyllically situated in a classified Area of Outstanding Natural Beauty. Nestled in a private bay beneath wooded cliffs, well away from the bustle of busy tourist spots. Spectacular walking, climbing, sailing, golfing and riding in the area. We also have a fine all weather tennis court. All set in extensive tropical gardens overlooking the sea, one minute from the beach. Three luxury self-contained and well-equipped apartments, each sleeping up to six. East Prawle is one mile distant, Kingsbridge and Salcombe are nearby with excellent facilities. Camping and B&B also available. Please ring for full colour brochure.

KINGSBRIDGE near. Mrs Reeves, Home Farm, Churchstow, Near Kingsbridge TQ7 3QR (01548 853469). Working farm. Churchstow is situated one-and-a-half miles north west of Kingsbridge on the A379, 16 miles from Plymouth. Home Farm is a traditionally-run familybusiness with a dairy herd and calves, and poultry in the yard. We have two family rooms, one being en suite; each comprises one double and two single beds with a tray for tea or coffee, and a cot is available on request. A self-catering bungalow is also available, this sleeps four people. All this is just a few minutes from lovely sandy beaches and Dartmoor by car. Details and prices on request.

Terms quoted in this publication may be subject to increase
if rises in costs necessitate

KINGSBRIDGE near. Mrs M. Newsham, Marsh Mills, Aveton Gifford, Kingsbridge TQ7 4JW (Tel & Fax: 01548 550549). Georgian Mill House, overlooking the River Avon, with mill pond, mill leat and duck pond. Small farm with friendly animals. Peaceful and secluded, just off A379, Kingsbridge four miles, Plymouth 17 miles. Bigbury and Bantham with their beautiful sandy beaches nearby, or enjoy a walk along our unspoilt river estuary, or the miles of beautiful South Devon Coastal Paths. We are only eight miles from Dartmoor. One double and one double/twin room, both en suite with colour TV; other rooms have washbasins, and there is a guest bathroom with additional separate WC. All bedrooms have tea/coffee making facilities and room heaters. Guests have their own lounge/dining room with colour TV. Beautiful gardens, ample car parking. Bed and Breakfast from £17 per night. Phone, fax or SAE for brochure or enquiries.

LYNMOUTH. Tricia and Alan Francis, Glenville House, 2 Tors Road, Lynmouth EX35 6ET (01598 752202). AA ◆◆◆ Charming licensed Victorian house built in local stone, overlooking East Lyn River at the entrance to the famous Watersmeet Valley. Picturesque village, harbour and unique cliff railway nestled amidst wooded valleys. This beautiful part of Exmoor with its breathtaking scenery, tumbling rivers and spectacular coastline is a haven of peace and tranquillity for walkers and country lovers – a special place to which guests return time and again. Delightfully decorated bedrooms, pretty en suite bathrooms. Tea/coffee facilities. Attractive dining room offering a four-course breakfast to start your day. Non-smoking. An idyllic setting for a relaxing holiday. Bed and Breakfast from £20 to £25 per person per night. Open from March to November.

MORETONHAMPSTEAD. Mrs T.M. Merchant, Great Sloncombe Farm, Moretonhampstead TQ13 8QF (01647 440595). 👑👑👑 *HIGHLY COMMENDED.* **Working farm.** Share the magic of Dartmoor all year round while staying in our lovely 13th century farmhouse full of interesting historical features. A working dairy farm set amongst peaceful meadows and woodland abundant in wild flowers and animals, including badgers, foxes, deer and buzzards. A welcoming and informal place to relax and explore the moors and Devon countryside. Comfortable double and twin rooms with en suite facilities, TV, central heating and coffee/tea making facilities. Delicious Devonshire suppers and breakfasts with new baked bread. Open all year. No smoking. Farm Holiday Bureau member. AA QQQQ Selected.

See also Colour Display Advertisement

NEWTON ABBOT. Mrs L. Westcott, Chipley Farm, Bickington, Newton Abbot TQ12 6JW (01626 821947; Tel & Fax: 01626 821486). Working farm. Near sandy beaches and rugged moor our delightful modern farmhouse nestles into the southern slope of a beautiful Devon valley. Double, twin and en suite family room (with a four-poster bed, comfy armchairs, an overflowing bookcase and patio doors onto gardens where you can sit under a wisteria-covered pergola and enjoy our wonderful views). As well as delicious breakfasts, our farmhouse suppers cooked on an Aga are a speciality. Relaxed family atmosphere and a warm welcome with the help of Spring and Badger, our Golden Retriever and Border Collie. Twin and double rooms £40.00, family room £50.00. For each child sleeping in parents' room please add £10.00. No smoking please. Brochure available. e-mail: louisachipleyfarm@callnetuk.com).

FHG PUBLICATIONS LIMITED
publish a large range of well-known accommodation guides. We will be happy to send you details or you can use the order form at the back of this book.

NORTH TAWTON. Lower Nichols Nymet Farm, Lower Nichols Nymet, North Tawton, Devon EX20 2BW (Tel & Fax: 01363 82510). ♛♛ *HIGHLY COMMENDED.* Jane

and David Pyle welcome you to their home. We offer a haven of comfort and rest on our 160 acre farm. It is set in rolling countryside in the centre of Devon, just north of Dartmoor. On holiday food becomes important, we serve hearty and healthy breakfasts and candle-lit dinners using local produce. Our elegantly furnished en suite bedrooms have glorious views. There are many National Trust properties and other attractions to visit. this is a perfect base for exploring the beauties of the South West. A non-smoking establishment. Brochure available. Bed and Breakfast from £20. Open Easter to October inclusive.

OKEHAMPTON. Mrs Rosemary Ward, Parsonage Farm, Iddesleigh EX19 8SN (01837 810318). ♛♛

HIGHLY COMMENDED. A warm welcome awaits you in our period farmhouse, home of the famous Parson Jack Russell, situated approximately one mile from the picturesque village of Iddesleigh and three miles from the market town of Hatherleigh. The Tarka Trail passes through our farmyard, with fishing available on the farm boundary. An ideal base from which to explore Dartmoor, Exmoor and coastlines. Accommodation consists of one family room and one double room, both en suite with tea/coffee making facilities and colour TV. Bed and Breakfast from £18 per person per night. Open Easter to October. No smoking or pets. Reductions for children.

OKEHAMPTON. Mrs Jenny King, Higher Cadham Farm, Jacobstowe, Okehampton EX20 3RB (01837 851647). ♦♦♦♦ **Working farm.** 139 acre beef and sheep farm

just off the A3072, five miles from Dartmoor. 16th century farmhouse with barn conversions offering a total of nine rooms - five en suite, the rest have washbasins, shaver points, etc., with bathroom and toilets close by. Two of the four lounges are non-smoking as is the dining room. The accommodation is of the highest standard with plenty of hearty Devonshire food, a residential licence and a warm welcome. Babies and dogs are accepted by arrangement only but older children are very welcome. We have farm walks, ducks on the ponds and other animals to amuse all the family. Walkers on the Tarka Trail are fully catered for with drying room, packed lunches, etc. AA QQQQ Selected and DATI Warmest Welcome Award 1992 has helped make Higher Cadham Farm the "place to stay" when in West Devon. Bed and Breakfast from £18.50; Dinner £10. Weekly from £190; supplement for en suite rooms. Member of Farm Holiday Bureau. AA Landlady of the Year Top 20 Finalist, 1998.

OKEHAMPTON. Little Bidlake Farm, Bridestowe, Okehampton EX20 4NS (Tel & Fax: 01837 861233).

ETC ♦♦♦. Farm Bureau Member. Farmhouse B&B, four self-catering units; Dartmoor horse trails. A warm welcome awaits you at Little Bidlake on the edge of Dartmoor. Relax and enjoy traditional farmhouse fare or stay in one of our tastefully converted self-catering barns (one of which is on the ground floor). Meals are available as are packed lunches. Plenty of fishing, cycling, walking and golf nearby or bring your own horse on holiday with you and try our Dartmoor Horse Trails .Ranging from ten to 25 miles, they are suitable for any age and experience. These trails take the rider on a magical tour through Dartmoor's past. Guided riding can be arranged. Please telephone for brochure.
e-mail: bidlakefrm@aol.com

PAIGNTON (Torbay). Mrs Mandy Tooze, Elberry Farm, Broadsands, Paignton TQ4 6HJ (01803 842939). Working farm. Elberry Farm is a working farm uniquely situated close to Broadsands Beach, Elberry Cove and a pitch and putt golf course. Close to many of Torbay's tourist attractions. Warm welcome and good hearty meals (using local and home grown produce) are guaranteed. The comfortable rooms (one double, two family and one twin) all have tea/coffee making facilities. Baby listening, cot and high chair available. Pets by arrangement. Restricted smoking. Open January to November. Bed and Breakfast from £13.50 per person; Evening Meals £6.95. Reductions for children.

PLYMOUTH. Mrs Margaret MacBean, Gabber Farm, Down Thomas, Plymouth PL9 0AW (01752 862269). 👙👙 *COMMENDED*. **Working farm, join in.** Come and join us on this 120 acre working farm in an area of outstanding natural beauty with lovely walks on the farm and coastline. It is ideally situated for touring and near the historic city of Plymouth. Good food and a warm welcome are assured with Bed and Breakfast or Bed, Breakfast and Evening Meal available. One double and one family room en suite, two twins and family room with washbasins. All have tea/coffee making facilities and clock radios. Iron, ironing board, hair dryer available. TV lounge, dining room. Fire Certificate. Bed and Breakfast from £16.50. Special rates for Senior Citizens and children. Brochure available on request.

SEATON. Mrs Jenny Webber, Axe Farm, Axmouth, Seaton EX12 4BG (01297 24707). Working farm. 12th century farmhouse situated one mile from Seaton and beach. Accommodation comprises one double and one family room with TV and tea/coffee making facilities; both en suite; lounge for guests' use. Central heating. Ample car parking. Children and pets welcome. Lovely walks and bird watching on Axe Estuary. Bed and breakfast from £18. Excellent evening meals available at local inns.

SEATON. Three Horseshoes Inn, Branscombe, Seaton EX12 3BR (01297 680251). 👙👙 Beautiful 16th century coaching house with log fires and brasses. Jan and John Moore will give you the warmest of welcomes and help plan your days if you wish. Set in an area of outstanding natural beauty. Central for sea or country. Footpaths lead through woodland. Cliff walks. Wonderful wildlife. Honiton's antique shops and lace, historic Exeter, all at hand; Sidmouth is just 10 minutes away. All bedrooms are centrally heated and have tea/coffee making facilities. Traditional jazz every Saturday night in the function room, so if you want a quiet drink in the lounge bar you are not disturbed. Real ales served. Bed and Breakfast from £14.

SIDMOUTH. Mrs Betty S. Sage, Pinn Barton, Peak Hill, Sidmouth EX10 0NN (Tel & Fax: 01395 514004). ETC ◆◆◆ A 330-acre farm set peacefully just off the coastal road, two miles from Sidmouth and close to the village of Otterton. Safe beaches and lovely cliff walks. Pinn Barton has been highly recommended, and offers a warm welcome in comfortable surroundings with good farmhouse breakfast. All bedrooms have bathrooms en-suite; colour TV; central heating; free hot drinks facilities; electric blankets. Children very welcome. Reductions for children sharing parents' room. Open all year. Bed and Breakfast including bedtime drink from £20 to £22. Own keys provided for access at all times.

SIDMOUTH. Mrs Elizabeth Tancock, Lower Pinn Farm, Peak Hill, Sidmouth EX10 0NN (01395 513733). ETC ◆◆◆. **Working farm**. Lower Pinn is in an area of outstanding natural beauty, two miles west of the unspoilt coastal resort of Sidmouth and one mile to the east of the pretty village of Otterton. Comfortable, spacious en suite rooms with colour TV, hot drink facilities, electric blankets and central heating. Guests have their own keys and may return at all times throughout the day. Ample parking. Substantial breakfast served in dining room. Local inns and restaurants nearby provide excellent evening meals. Children and pets welcome. Open most of the year. Bed and Breakfast from £19 to £22. Full details on request.

SIDMOUTH. Mrs B.I. Tucker, Goosemoor Farm, Newton Poppleford, Sidmouth EX10 0BL (01395

568279). Goosemoor Farmhouse is an old Devon Long House with a bread oven in the dining room. The 25-acre mixed farm is on the Exeter - Lyme Regis bus route, about four miles from the sea, and has streams running through its meadows. There are many delightful walks in country lanes, or over Woodberry and Alsbeare Commons. Guests may wander freely on the farmland. Coarse fishing available also. There are two double and one family rooms, all with washbasins; two bathrooms, three toilets; sitting room; dining room. Open all year with log fires. Central heating throughout. Car not essential, but there is parking. Also self-catering available- two bedrooms, sleeps five. Own entrance. Bed and Breakfast from £15. Cream teas also available.

See also Colour Display Advertisement

SOUTH DEVON. Mrs Amelia Wood, Higher Barton, Moreleigh, Totnes TQ9 7JN (01548 821475 or 07721 068181). Higher Barton is part of an arable farm. The house, being on its own, is in a very peaceful position with a large garden and private parking. The bedrooms have wonderful views over open countryside and out towards the coast. They are beautifully furnished and have colour TV and tea/coffee making facilities. A full English breakfast is served along with a selection of fresh fruit and cereals. Ideally situated for the lovely beaches and coastal walks of South Devon and also, for the keen walker, Dartmoor is close by. Please telephone for further information.

SOUTH MOLTON. Mr Watson, Bremley, Molland, South Molton EX36 3NH (Tel & Fax: 01398 341347).

The old timers certainly knew a thing or two when they sited their farm houses years ago. Bremley is a classic Grade II Listed Devon farmhouse near Molland with one double, one twin and one family room. Molland is the perfect base to discover southern Exmoor. A paradise for walkers and riders or anyone who wants to explore this truly rural area, with several good country pubs close at hand. Bremley is very easy to find, being ten minutes drive from the A361 North Devon Link Road, midway between Dulverton and South Molton. Bed and Breakfast from £20 per night.

SOUTH MOLTON near. Messrs H.J. Milton, Partridge Arms Farm, Yeo Mill, West Anstey, Near South Molton EX36 3NU (01398 341217; Fax: 01398 341569).

👑👑 COMMENDED. Now a working farm of over 200 acres, four miles west of Dulverton, "Partridge Arms Farm" was once a coaching inn and has been in the same family since 1906. Genuine hospitality and traditional farmhouse fare await you. Comfortable accommodation in double, twin and single rooms, some of which have en suite facilities. There is also an original four-poster bedroom. Children welcome. Animals by arrangement. Residential licence. Open all year. Fishing and riding available nearby. Farm Holiday Guide Diploma Winner. Dinner, Bed and Breakfast from £30.50 per person; Bed and Breakfast from £20.50

TEIGN VALLEY. S. and G. Harrison-Crawford, Silver Birches, Teign Valley, Trusham, Newton Abbot TQ13 0NJ (01626 852172). A warm welcome awaits you at

Silver Birches, a comfortable bungalow at the edge of Dartmoor. A secluded, relaxing spot with two acre garden running down to river. Only two miles from A38 on B3193. Exeter 14 miles, sea 12 miles. Car advisable. Ample parking. Excellent pubs and restaurants nearby. Good centre for fishing, bird watching, forest walks, golf, riding; 70 yards salmon/trout fishing free to residents. Centrally heated guest accommodation with separate entrance. Two double bedded rooms, one twin bedded room, all with own bath/shower, toilet. Guest lounge with colour TV. Diningroom, sun lounge overlooking river. Sorry, no children under eight. Terms including tea on arrival - Bed and full English Breakfast from £24 nightly, £168 weekly. Evening Meal optional. Open all year. Self catering caravans also available.

TIVERTON. Mrs Sylvia Hann, Great Bradley Farm, Withleigh, Tiverton, Devon EX16 8JL (Tel & Fax: 01884 256946). ETC ◆◆◆◆. Lovely historic farmhouse

with original oak panelling, just twenty minutes from the M5/J27 in glorious countryside. Leafy lanes and peaceful hills, wide open spaces and friendly people. Welcoming, bright comfortable rooms with private bathrooms. Delicious West Country breakfasts using local bacon and our own free-range eggs, freshly cooked and with plenty of choice. Gardens to visit and local Antique/Art and Craft Markets for browsers! Beaches and moors easily reached. Walkers welcomed. Safe parking. No smoking please. Bed and Breakfast from £19 to £22. Weekly reductions.

TIVERTON. Mr & Mrs B. Reader, Lodgehill Farm Hotel, Tiverton EX16 5PA (01884 252907; Fax: 01884 242090). In a peaceful setting off the A396, just one mile south of Tiverton, overlooking the beautiful Exe valley. Each en suite bedroom is individually furnished with TV, radio and telephone, and is non-smoking. The bar is well stocked and equipped with ash trays! For evening meals, we have a modest wine list and a comfortable diningroom. Dinner is informal and local produce is the main ingredient. Easy access from Tiverton–Bickleigh road, 400 metres up a private drive. Lodge Hill Farm is no longer a working farm but is still shown on OS maps. It enjoys the solitude of an old farmhouse with the convenience of a hotel. Why not relax with the Readers!

e-mail: lodgehill@dial.pipex.com
website: www.lodgehill.co.uk

TORQUAY. Carysfort Guest House, 13 Warren Road, Torquay TQ2 5TQ. The Carysfort Guest House is ideally situated for the harbour, town centre, beaches and Torquay's night life, all being only a short walk away. Most rooms are en suite with own showers, WC, TV, hairdryer, fridge etc. Bed and Breakfast from £18.00 to £21.00. Open all year. For further information please contact: **Mr and Mrs Tanner (01803 294160).**
e mail: etanner@talk21.com
website: www.torbay.gov.uk/tourism/t-hotels/carysfort.htm

TORQUAY. Peter and Carol White, Braddon Hall Hotel, Braddons Hill Road East, Torquay TQ1 1HF (01803 293908). ETC/AA ◆◆◆. This delightful personally

run hotel is situated in a peaceful yet convenient position, only a few minutes from the harbour, shopping centre and entertainments. All en suite rooms are individual in character and tastefully decorated and have remote control colour TVs and tea/coffee making facilities. Romantic four-poster bed available for that special occasion. Full central heating for those early and late breaks. Parking. Bed and Breakfast from £16 to £20 per person per night.

TOTNES. Mrs J. Allnutt, The Old Forge at Totnes, Seymour Place, Totnes TQ9 5AY (01803 862174).👑👑 *HIGHLY COMMENDED.* A charming 600-year-old stone building, delightfully converted from blacksmith and wheelwright workshops and coach houses. Traditional forge, complete with blacksmith's prison cell. We have our own bit of "rural England" close to the town centre. Very close to the River Dart steamer quay, shops and station (also steam train rides). Ideally situated for touring most of Devon - including Dartmoor and Torbay coasts. A day trip from Exeter, Plymouth and Cornwall. Elizabethan costume markets on Tuesdays in Summer (May to September). Double, twin and family rooms, all en suite. Ground

As seen on BBC TV's
Holiday Programme

floor rooms suitable for most disabled guests. All rooms have colour TV, telephones, beverage trays (fresh milk), colour co-ordinated Continental bedding, central heating. Licensed lounge and patio. Conservatory style leisure lounge with whirlpool spa. No smoking indoors. Parking, walled gardens. Excellent choice of breakfast menu including vegetarian and special diets. Children welcome but sorry, no pets. Bed and Breakfast from £26 to £36 per person. (en suite). Cottage suite for two to six persons, suitable for disabled visitors. AA Selected (QQQQ) Award.

WOOLACOMBE. Mr & Mrs R. Pearson, Blue Bay Guest House, Mortehoe, Woolacombe EX34 7EA (01271 870385). Small friendly guest house situated in a quiet spot close to the beach with breathtaking sea views and surrounded by beautiful National Trust land. Ideal for beach and walking holidays and for exploring the North Devon Coast and Exmoor. All rooms are on the ground floor and there are no steps up to the house. Ample private car parking. Excellent cuisine. Bed, Breakfast and Evening Meal from £140 per week. Open Easter to October with Spring holidays recommended. Please ask for brochure. Non smokers only.

WOOLACOMBE. Dave and Chris Ellis, Crossways Hotel, The Seafront, Woolacombe

EX34 7DJ (Tel & Fax: 01271 870395). ETC ★ *SILVER AWARD*. Cosy, family-run, licensed hotel, situated in one of the finest sea front positions in Woolacombe, overlooking the pretty Combesgate beach and Lundy Island and being surrounded by National Trust land. Bathing and surfing from hotel and ideally situated for golf, horse riding and beautiful walks. Menu choice for breakfast and evening dinner, and children's menu. Varied bar snacks available at lunchtime. All bedrooms individually refurbished to a high standard, many en suite and with fabulous sea views. Colour TV and tea/coffee making facilities in all rooms. Children half price or Free. Pets welcome. Free on-site parking. AA/RAC one star, RAC Merit Awards for Hospitality, Service and Comfort. Why not find out why many of our guests return year after year?.

YELVERTON. Mrs Colton, Peek Hill Farm, Dousland, Yelverton PL20 6PD (Tel & Fax: 01822 854808).

Sizzling sausages, new laid eggs. Comfy beds to rest your legs. Dartmoor to Bodmin quite a view. TV, kettle too. Take a hike, hire a bike, the choice is yours to view the moors. Yummy cream teas - have one on us! Need a picnic, it's no fuss. Pack a bag, come away, promise of a pleasant stay. Open all year except Christmas.

DORSET

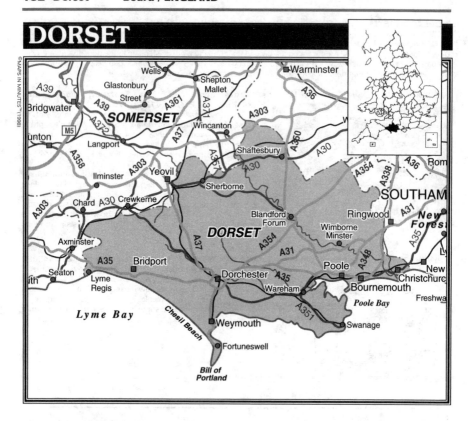

©MAPS IN MINUTES™ (1998)

BLANDFORD FORUM. Mrs C.M. Old, Manor House Farm, Ibberton, Blandford Forum DT11 0EN

(01258 817349). Working farm, dairy and sheep. Situated nine miles west of Blandford Forum. Small 16th century manor house, now a farmhouse, surrounded by large colourful garden in a quiet unspoilt village which at one time was given to Katherine Howard by Henry VIII. The oak beams and nail studded doors confirm its centuries-old past. One double bedroom, one double or twin (both en suite), and one twin bedroom (separate bathroom); all with tea-making facilities. Bathroom and toilet; lounge with TV, dining room with separate tables. Children welcome, cot and high chair provided. Bed and Breakfast from £13.50 to £17. Open all year. No evening meal. Good food at Crown Inn nearby. Self catering accommodation also available.

BRIDPORT. Jane Greening, New House Farm, Mangerton Lane, Bradpole, Bridport DT6 3SF (Tel & Fax:

01308 422884). 👑👑 *COMMENDED.* Stay in a modern, comfortable farmhouse on a small working farm set in the rural Dorset hills and become one of the family. A large wild garden where you are welcome to sit or stroll round. Two large rooms available, both en suite, both with lovely views over the surrounding countryside, both with television and tea/coffee making facilities. There is also a large sittingroom where you can relax. We are near to Bridport and the seaside, golf courses, fossil hunting, beautiful gardens, wonderful walking, coarse fishing lake - lots to do. Simple traditional farmhouse evening meals can be provided, subject to booking. Bed and Breakfast from £18.

BRIDPORT. Mrs Sue Diment, Rudge Farm, Chilcombe, Bridport DT6 4NF (01308 482630). 👑👑

HIGHLY COMMENDED. Peacefully situated in the beautiful Bride Valley, just two and a half miles from the sea. Double, twin and family en suite rooms are available, either in the Farm House or in the adjacent converted barn, all with far reaching views. On chilly afternoons, a log fire burns in the cosy, book-lined sitting room. While in summer, the French windows open onto a tranquil walled garden filled with the scent of roses, honeysuckle and jasmine. £24 to £26 per person per night. Children half price. Non-smoking. Open all year.
website: www.rudge-farm.co.uk

BRIDPORT. Mrs D.P. Read, The Old Station, Powerstock, Bridport DT6 3ST (01308 485301). Peacefully

situated deep in the glorious Dorset countryside, one mile south east of Powerstock, in two-and-a-half acres of garden, this former railway station enjoys beautiful views. Conveniently situated for drives into neighbouring counties; many rural walks; can be reached by public transport. Two double bedrooms, one single, all with washbasins and tea-making facilities; bathroom, three toilets; central heating. Daytime access. Off road parking; tennis, fun golf. Hearty English breakfast prettily served (vegetarian breakfast by previous arrangement). Open March through October, from £16. Badger watching possible most evenings from house. SAE, please, for details. Sorry no children or pets. No smoking.

BRIDPORT. Britmead House Hotel, West Bay Road, Bridport DT6 4EG (Tel: 01308 422941; Fax:

01308 422516). ETC/AA ◆◆◆ Guestaccom Good Room Award 1998/9. Personal service and putting guests' comfort first means visitors return time after time. Situated between Bridport and West Bay Harbour with its Beaches, Golf Course, Chesil Beach and the Dorset Coastal Path. Full en suite rooms (one ground floor), all with colour TV, tea-making facilities, hairdryer and mini-bar. South-facing lounge and diningroom overlooking the garden. Licensed. Private parking. Optional Dinner £14.00. B&B from £40 to £54 for 2 nights; £60 to £75 for 3 nights. Rates for longer stays on request.

BRIDPORT near. Mrs Sue Norman, Frogmore Farm, Chideock, Bridport DT6 6HT (01308 456159).

Working farm. Set in the rolling hills of West Dorset, enjoying splendid sea views, our delightful 17th century farmhouse offers comfortable, friendly and relaxing accommodation. An ideal base from which to ramble the many coastal and country footpaths of the area (nearest beach Seatown one-and-a-half miles) or tour by car the interesting places of Dorset and Devon. Bedrooms with en suite shower rooms, TV and tea making facilities. Guests' dining room and cosy lounge with woodburner. Well behaved dogs welcome. Open all year; car essential. Bed and Breakfast from £16 (evening meal optional). Brochure and terms free on request.

BURTON BRADSTOCK. Mrs Andrea Gisborne, Burton Lodge, Burton Bradstock, Bridport DT6 4PU

(01308 897378; Fax: 01308 898008). Country House set in the rolling hills of West Dorset and enjoying splendid views over National Trust land to the coast. All principal rooms and bedrooms have sea views. The golf course at West Bay which is open to visitors can also be viewed from the house and garden. The area abounds in wildlife and there are several popular beaches in the locality. Enjoy bed and breakfast in our friendly family home. Traditional breakfast and tea/coffee available (no extra charge) at all times. Children and pets welcome. Bed and Breakfast from £17 to £20 per person per night.

CERNE ABBAS. Mrs T. Barraclough, Magiston Farm, Sydling St. Nicholas, Dorchester DT2 9NR (01300 320295). Working farm. Listed *APPROVED*. Magiston is a 400 acre working farm with a comfortable 17th century cob and brick farmhouse set deep in the heart of Dorset. Large garden with river. Situated in an ideal touring centre and just half an hour's drive from coast and five miles north of Dorchester. The farmhouse comprises double, twin and single bedrooms. Delicious evening meals served. Children over 10 years and pets welcome. Central heating. Open January to December. Bed and Breakfast from £18.50 per person per night. Please write or telephone for further details.

See also Colour Display Advertisement

CHARMOUTH. Mrs S. M. Johnson, Cardsmill Farm, Whitchurch, Canonicorum, Charmouth, Bridport DT6 6RP (Tel & Fax: 01297 489375). ETC ◆◆◆ Working farm, join in. A Grade II Listed comfortable quiet farmhouse in the picturesque Marshwood Vale, three miles from Charmouth. Ideal location for touring, safe beaches, fossil hunting, golf and walking the coastal path. See the farm animals, pets and crops. Family and double en suite rooms available, each with CTV, shaver points, tea/coffee trays. Cot available. Full central heating and double glazed windows throughout. Lounge with Inglenook fireplace, woodburning stove, oak beams, colour TV, games and books. Dining area with separate tables. English and varied breakfasts. Access at all times. Children and well behaved pets welcome. Large garden with patio, picnic table and seats. Bed and Breakfast from £18 - £22 per person per night. Open Febuary till end of November. Please phone or write for a brochure. Also two self-catering farmhouses (ETC ♔♔♔♔ Approved) each to sleep 11-12 plus cot, for long or short stays all year. e-mail: cardsmill@aol.com

CHARMOUTH. Marshwood Manor, Near Bridport, Near Charmouth DT6 5NS (01308 868442). ♛♛♛ *COMMENDED*. Five tastefully furnished en suite rooms. Close to Charmouth and Lyme Regis. Bed & Breakfast with Evening Meal on request. Speciality Home Cooking. Outdoor heated swimming pool. Weekly or Short Breaks available. Brochure on request. AA Listed

CHARMOUTH. Ann and Andy Gorfin, Kingfishers, Newlands Bridge, Charmouth DT6 6QZ (01297 560232). Come to Kingfishers and relax on your large sunny balcony overlooking the river and garden. Set in beautiful surroundings on the banks of the River Char, Kingfishers offers a secluded setting yet it is only a short stroll to the beach and village amenities. Ann and Andy can assure you of a warm welcome, great food and a friendly atmosphere. From £19 per night we offer a full selection of breakfasts including vegetarian. All rooms are en suite or with private bathroom, balcony, drink making facilities, colour TV and central heating. Home-baked food and clotted cream teas available throughout the day in our lovely Garden Room or outside in the garden. Free access and ample parking. Children and pets welcome.

Unusual Colonial bungalow. En-suite rooms overlooking an acre of beautiful Gardens; Each room with C/H, colour T.V, radio, easy chairs, tea/coffee facilities, fridge for your use, fresh milk, electric fan, hairdryer, Furnished with our personal collection of antiques. Achieving top quality awards for friendliness and cleanliness. Guests comments: "What a lovely home and a beautiful garden! You have thought of everything!" Perfect base for garden lovers, antique enthusiasts, N/T houses, moors, quaint old villages, 20 mins from Dorset coast. Open all year.

BROADVIEW GARDENS   Crewkerne, Somerset TA18 7AG   Tel/Fax 01460-73424

A no-smoking house. Secure parking behind electrically operated entrance gate.
e-mail: broadgdn@eurobell.co.uk   website: www.broadgdn.eurobell.co.uk

DORCHESTER. Mrs Jane Bootham, The Old Post Office, Martinstown, Dorchester DT2 9LF (01305 889254). Listed *APPROVED.* Situated in the Winterbourne Valley, The Old Post Office is a stone and slate Georgian cottage used as the village post office until 1950. It is part of a row of cottages that are all listed buildings. Winterbourne St Martin (Martinstown) is in the heart of Hardy country, two miles from the Neolithic Hill Fort of Maiden Castle, Hardy's monument and the town of Dorchester. The coast and beach are five miles away and it is an ideal walking and touring base. The bedrooms all have washbasins, tea/coffee making facilities and some have TV. Pets and children welcome. Bed and Breakfast from £15 to £20.

DORCHESTER. Michael and Jane Deller, Churchview Guest House, Winterbourne Abbas, Near Dorchester DT2 9LS (01305 889296). ETC/AA ◆◆◆. Our 17th century Guest House, noted for warm hospitality and delicious breakfasts and evening meals, makes an ideal base for touring beautiful West Dorset. Our character bedrooms are all comfortable and well appointed. Meals, served in our beautiful diningroom, feature local produce, with relaxation provided by two attractive lounges and licensed bar. Your hosts Jane and Michael Deller are pleased to give every assistance with local information to ensure a memorable stay. NON SMOKING. Terms: Dinner, Bed and Breakfast £35 to £42; Bed and Breakfast £21 to £28. Please call for further details.

DORCHESTER. Mrs Rita Bown, Lamperts Farmhouse, 11 Dorchester Road, Sydling St. Nicholas, Dorchester DT2 9NU (01300 341790). 👑👑 17th century thatched Listed farmhouse nestling in the Sydling valley. Choose either Bed and Breakfast in tastefully decorated en suite bedrooms with Victorian brass beds and antique pine furniture or self catering in our fully restored well-equipped one bedroom farm cottage (3 KEYS). Guests' own sitting room with inglenook fireplace and colour TV. Sheltered garden. Home-cooked evening meal optional. Bed and Breakfast from £20; Self Catering £160 to £220. Farm Holiday Bureau member.

Lamperts Farmhouse and Cottage

FURZEHILL. Mrs King, Stocks Farm, Furzehill, Wimborne BH21 4HT (Tel & Fax: 01202 888697). Stocks Farm is a family-run farm and nursery situated in peaceful countryside just one-and-half miles from the lovely country town of Wimborne Minster, off the B3078. Surrounded by lovely Dorset countryside and pretty villages; coastline, beaches and New Forest within easy reach. Bed and Breakfast accommodation consists of one double en suite bedroom and one twin bedroom with private bathroom, both on ground level. Disabled guests are very welcome. Tea and coffee making facilities in both rooms. All accommodation is non-smoking. Situated in secluded garden with patio for guests to enjoy breakfast outside. Local pubs and restaurants offer varied menus. Bed and Breakfast from £19 to £20 per person per night.

KIMMERIDGE. Mrs Annette Hole, Kimmeridge Farmhouse, Kimmeridge, Wareham BH20 5PE (Tel: 01929 480990). ETC ◆◆◆◆ (pending). Relax and take a well earned break in our period 14th Century farmhouse with views of Kimmeridge Bay across 700 acres of farmland. There are many spectacular walks either along the coastal paths or inland over the Purbeck Hills surrounding the ruins of Corfe Castle. Spacious and attractively furnished en suite rooms with colour television, beverage tray and full central heating for those off-season breaks. A delicious home-cooked breakfast of your choice and a warm welcome assured. Bed and Breakfast from £21 per person. Open all year except Christmas Day. Evening Meal by arrangement (October to March). Further details on request.

POOLE. Mrs Stephenson, Holly Hedge Farm, Bulbury Lane, Lytchett Matravers, Poole BH16 6EP (01929 459688). Built in 1892, Holly Hedge Farm is situated next to Bulbury Woods Golf Course, set in 11 acres of wood and grassland adjacent to lake. We are just 15 minutes away from the Purbecks, the beach and the forest. The area is ideal for walking or cycling and Poole Quay and Harbour are also nearby. Accommodation comprises two double/family rooms, one twin and one single, all with en suite showers, colour TV, tea/coffee making facilities, radio alarms and central heating. Prices for a single room £25 to £30, double £40. Open all year round for summer or winter breaks. Full English or Continental breakfast served.

Buckland Farm

Situated in quiet and unspoilt surroundings with gardens and grounds of five acres which are ideal for guests to relax or stroll in; about three miles from the lovely coastal resorts of Lyme Regis and Charmouth. A warm welcome awaits you. Accommodation mainly on the ground floor. Two family bedrooms, one double en suite shower and one twin bedded room, all with TV, washbasin, tea/coffee making facilites. Bathroom, shower in bath, separate WC. Lounge with colour TV, video and log fire. Dining area with separate tables. A good English Farmhouse breakfast served, a real home from home plus our very friendly dog. Friendly pub within two minutes' walk for evening meals. Payphone. No smoking in bedrooms. Bed and Breakfast from £15. Send SAE for further details. Self-catering caravan and chalet Bungalow available. Sheila and David Taylor.

Raymonds Hill, Near Axminster EX13 5SZ
Tel/Fax: 01297 33222 or e-mail: bucklandfarm@fsnet.co.uk

SHAFTESBURY. Mrs G. Gosney, Kington Manor Farm, Church Hill, Kington Magna, Near Gillingham SP8 5EG (01747 838371). ETC ◆◆◆◆ Working farm. Attractive farmhouse situated in a quiet, pretty village, with splendid views over the picturesque Blackmore Vale. The village lies one mile off A30 between the historic towns of Shaftesbury and Sherborne; Stourhead National Trust house and gardens and stately home of Longleat and Safari Park nearby. Bath 45 minutes' drive. Spacious quality accommodation comprising one double en suite, one double/family room and one twin room. Tea/coffee making facilities. Visitors' diningroom and lounge with TV. Bed and hearty Breakfast £19 per person per night. Reductions for children. Excellent pub food nearby. Heated swimming pool.

FHG
Visit the FHG website
www.holidayguides.com
for details of the wide choice of accommodation
featured in the full range of FHG titles

SHERBORNE. Mrs J. Mayo, Almshouse Farm, Hermitage, Sherborne DT9 6HA (Tel and Fax: 01963

210296). ETC ◆◆◆◆. This charming old farmhouse was a monastery during the 16th century, restored in 1849 and is now a listed building. A family-run working dairy farm, it is surrounded by 140 acres overlooking the Blackmoor Vale, just one mile off the A352. Accommodation is in three comfortable en suite rooms with colour TV and tea/coffee making facilities. Diningroom with inglenook fireplace, lounge with colour TV, for guests' use at all times. Also garden and lawn. Plenty of reading material and local information provided for this ideal touring area. Bed and Breakfast from £20. Excellent evening meals in all local inns nearby. Situated six miles from Sherborne with its beautiful Abbey and Castle. SAE for further details.

SHILLINGSTONE. Mrs Rosie Watts, Pennhills Farm, Sandy Lane, off Larchards Lane, Shillingstone,

Blandford DT11 0TF (01258 860491). Pennhills Farmhouse, set in one-and-a-half acres, is situated half-a-mile from the village of Shillingstone in the heart of the Blackmore Vale, with woodland walks extending through unspoiled countryside with an abundance of wild life; an ideal peaceful retreat, or exciting drives for 4x4s. It offers spacious comfortable accommodation for all ages, with downstairs bedroom; all rooms have en suite, TV, tea/coffee making facilities, complemented by traditional English breakfast. From £18 per person. Children of all ages welcome. Pets by arrangement. Good meals available locally. Brochure available. A warm and friendly welcome assured by your host Rosie Watts. Also space for caravan and camping.

SWANAGE. Mrs Justine Pike, Downshay Farm, Haycrafts Lane, Harmans Cross, Swanage BH19 3EB

(01929 480316). Working dairy farm in the heart of beautiful Isle of Purbeck, midway between Corfe Castle and Swanage. This Victorian Purbeck stone farmhouse has one family and one double room with washbasins, tea-making facilities and TV. Shower and bathrooms close by. Sandy beaches, coastal path and steam railway are all within easy reach, as are excellent pubs and restaurants. Open Easter to end October for Bed and Breakfast from £18 to £20.

SWANAGE. Mrs Rosemary Dean, Quarr Farm, Valley Road, Swanage BH19 3DY (01929 480865). Quarr is a working family farm steeped in history dating back to the Domesday Book. Animals kept naturally - cows, calves, horses, poultry. Bring your children to feed ducks, chickens, peacocks and watch steam trains passing through our meadows. Accommodation in family room with en suite bathroom, own sitting room with colour TV, real log fire, tea making facilities. Old Dairy, low beamed ceilings, small windows, double room with en suite shower, sittingroom with colour TV, kitchen. Choice of Bed and Breakfast or Self Catering. Cot and Z-bed available. Easy reach high class restaurants, pubs; sea three miles. Studland, sandy beach just five miles away. Ideal for walking, cycling, coastal path, RSPB Reserves, golf courses, riding. Please write, or telephone, for further details and terms.

WINTERBORNE ZELSTON. Mrs Irene Kerley, Brook Farm, Winterborne Zelston, Blandford DT11 9EU

(01929 459267). ETC ◆◆◆. A warm welcome awaits you at Brook Farm, a friendly working farm situated in a pretty, peaceful hamlet overlooking the River Winterborne, between Wimborne and Dorchester. Central for visiting the many attractions of Dorset. Two large double/twin en suite rooms and one twin room with private facilities. Colour TV, beverage making facilities, hairdryers etc. in all rooms. Guests have own keys, plenty of parking space. Hearty English breakfasts are served with our free range eggs and home-made marmalade. Excellent food at the local country inns. Open all year except Christmas. Children over 10 years welcome, regret no pets or smoking. Terms from £20 to £22 per person per night, (extra for single occupancy) with reductions for three or more nights and favourable weekly terms.

DURHAM

CHESTER LE STREET. Mrs H. Johnson, Low Urpeth Farm, Ouston, Chester Le Street DH2 1BD (0191 4102901; Fax: 0191 4100081). ◆◆◆◆. Superb farmhouse

accommodation, spacious rooms, well furnished in a very traditional style. Beverage facilities, TV and comfortable chairs. Our large square stone farmhouse is within easy distance of county cricket at Chester-le-Street, Beamish Museum, Durham Cathedral (a World Heritage site), Durham Dales and Castles and coastline of Northumberland. Directions: leave A1M at Junction 63, follow A693, one-and-a-half miles turn right to Ouston, continue a further one-and-a-half miles, down hill, over roundabout, turning left at "Trees Please", sign into Low Urpeth. Bed and Breakfast from £20 to £25. Closed Christmas and New Year.

CORNFORTH. Mrs D. Slack, Ash House, 24 The Green, Cornforth DL17 9JH (01740 654654). Built mid

19th Century, Ash House is a beautifully appointed period home combining a delicate mixture of homeliness and Victorian flair. Elegant rooms, individually and tastefully decorated, combining antique furnishings, beautiful fabrics, carved four posters and modern fittings. Spacious and graceful, filled with character, Ash House offers a warm welcome to both the road-weary traveller and those wishing merely to unwind in the quiet elegance of this charming home on quiet village green. Private parking. 10 minutes Historic Durham City, and adjacent A1 (M) motorway. Well placed between York and Edinburgh. Excellent value.

DURHAM. Mrs J. Dartnall, Idsley House, 4 Green Lane, Spennymoor DL16 6HD (01388 814237). ♛♛

HIGHLY COMMENDED. A large Victorian detached house situated in a quiet residential area close to the A167/A688 junction just eight minutes from Durham City. Direct route to Beamish, Metro Centre and the Dales. All rooms are spacious and well furnished. Double, twin and family bedrooms are all en suite with have colour TV and welcome tray. Full English or vegetarian breakfast is served in a pleasant conservatory overlooking a mature garden. Large guest lounge to relax. Safe parking on premises. Prices for a twin or double room £45-£48. Evening Meal optional. Open all year except Christmas. AA QQQ. Visa, Mastercard, Switch, Delta cards all accepted.

STANLEY. Mrs P. Gibson, Bushblades Farm, Harperley, Stanley DH9 9UA (01207 232722). ◆◆◆.

Ideal stop-over when travelling north or south. Only 10 minutes from A1M Chester-le-Street. Durham City 20 minutes, Beamish Museum two miles, Metro Centre 15 minutes, Hadrian's Wall and Northumberland coast under an hour. Comfortable Georgian farmhouse set in large garden. Twin ground floor en suite room plus two first-floor bedrooms. All rooms have tea/coffee making, colour TV and easy chairs. Ample parking. Children welcome over 12 years. Sorry, no pets. Bed and Breakfast from £17 to £19.50 per person per night, single £20 to £25. Self-catering accommodation also available. Leave A1(M) at Chester-le-Street for Stanley on the A693, then Consett half-mile after Stanley. Follow signs for Harperley Farm on right, half-mile from Crossroads.

When making enquiries or bookings,
a stamped addressed envelope is always appreciated.

ESSEX

COLCHESTER. Mrs Jill Tod, Seven Arches Farm, Chitts Hill, Lexden, Colchester CO3 5SX (01206 574896). Working farm. Georgian farmhouse set in large garden close to the ancient town of Colchester. The farm extends to 100 acres and supports both arable crops and cattle. Private fishing rights on the River Colne, which runs past the farmhouse. This is a good location for visits to North Essex, Dedham and the Stour Valley which have been immortalised in the works of John Constable, the landscape painter. Children and pets welcome. Open all year. Bed and Breakfast from £25; Evening Meal from £5. Twin room £40; family room en suite. Static caravan on caravan site also available.

FHG DIPLOMA WINNERS 1999

*Each year we award a small number of diplomas to holiday proprietors
whose services have been specially commended by our readers.
The following were our FHG Diploma Winners for 1999.*

Mr & Mrs Haskell, Borwick Lodge, Outgate, Hawkshead, Cumbria, LA22 0PU (015394 36332)

Mrs Val Sunter, Higher House Farm, Oxenholme Lane, Natland, Kendal, Cumbria LA9 7QH (015395 61177)

Mrs Ellis, Efford Cottage Guest House, Milford Road, Everton, Lymington, Hampshire SO41 0JD (015906 42315)

Mrs Melanie Smith, Capernwray House, Capernwray, Via Carnforth, Lancashire LA6 1AE (01524 732363)

Mrs D. Cole, Hillcrest House, Barrasford, Hexham, Northumberland NE48 4BY (01434 681426)

Mrs J. Hartsilver, Perhams Farm, Templecombe, Somerset BA8 0NE (01963 371123)

SCOTLAND

Mr Ewan, Glen Lyon Lodge, Nairn, Nairnshire IV12 4RH (01667 452780)

Mr Sutton, Linnhe Caravan and Camping Park, Corpach, Fort William, Inverness-shire PH33 7NL (01397 772376)

WALES

Mrs Hazel Davies, Caebetran Farm, Felinfach, Brecon, Powys, LD3 0UL (01874 754460)

Mrs Bronwen Prosser, Upper Genffordd Guest House, Talgarth, Brecon, Powys LD3 0EN (01874 711360)

GLOUCESTERSHIRE

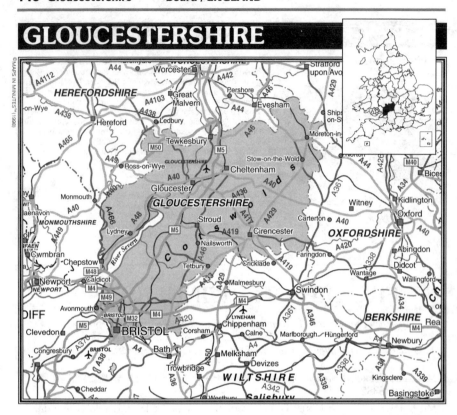

BATH near. Mrs Pam Wilmott, Pool Farm, Wick, Bristol BS30 5RL (0117 937 2284). **Working farm, join in.** Welcome to our 350 year old Grade II Listed farmhouse on a working dairy farm. On A420 between Bath and Bristol and a few miles from Exit 18 of M4. We are on the edge of the village, overlooking fields, but within easy reach of pub, shops and golf club. We offer traditional Bed and Breakast in one family and one twin room with tea/coffee facilities; TV lounge. Central heating. Ample parking. Open all year except Christmas. Terms £16 to £20

BOURTON-ON-THE-WATER. Mrs Julia Wright, Farncombe, Clapton, Bourton-on-the-Water, Cheltenham GL54 2LG (Tel & Fax: 01451 820120; Mobile: 0771 4703142). ETC ◆◆◆◆. Farncombe provides peace and tranquillity, with superb views of the Windrush Valley, in Clapton-on-the-Hill, two-and-a-half-miles from Bourton-on-the-Water in the centre of the Cotswolds. This comfortable non-smoking family Cotswold home is set in large gardens. Two double rooms with showers and basins, one en suite twin room, each with hairdryer and radio. Large diningroom with tea/coffee making facilities. Television lounge.

BREDON'S NORTON. Michael and Pippa Cluer, Lampitt House, Lampitt Lane, Bredon's Norton, Tewkesbury GL20 7HB (01684 772295). 👑👑

COMMENDED. Lampitt House is situated in a large informal garden on the edge of a quiet village at the foot of Bredon Hill. Splendid views across to the Malverns. Ideal for visiting the Cotswolds, Stratford, Worcester, Cheltenham, Gloucester and the Forest of Dean. All rooms are furnished to a high standard and have private bathrooms, central heating, colour TV and tea/coffee making facilities. Ground floor room available. Children are welcome. Ample parking. No smoking. Open all year. Hill and riverside walks. Arrangements can be made for windsurfing and riding. Double room from £45. Bed and Breakfast.

BRISTOL. Mrs Marilyn Collins, Box Hedge Farm, Coalpit Heath, Bristol BS36 2UW (01454 250786).

Box Hedge Farm is set in 200 acres of beautiful rural countryside on the edge of the Cotswolds. Local to M4/M5, central for Bristol and Bath and the many tourist attractions in this area. An ideal stopping point for the South West and Wales. We offer a warm, friendly atmosphere with traditional farmhouse cooking. All bedrooms have colour TV and tea/coffee making facilities. Bed and Breakfast from £17.50 single, from £30 double; Dinner from £7.50. Prices exclude VAT.

CHELTENHAM. Sandra and David Tompkins, Wishmoor House, 147 Hales Road, Cheltenham GL52 6TD (01242 238504; Fax: 01242 226090). ◆◆◆◆.

Wishmoor House is a late Victorian residence, tastefully refurbished to retain its original charm and character. Situated on the eastern side of Cheltenham town, just a walk from the shopping centre, the Racecourse and Pittville Park. Conveniently situated at the base of the Cotswold Hills making it an ideal location for touring the Wye Valley, Malvern Hills, the Royal Forest of Dean and the Cotswold villages. The scenic towns of Hereford, Stratford-on-Avon and Bath City are also conveniently situated for day visits. At Wishmoor you will find a warm and friendly welcome from your hosts who aim to provide a relaxed but efficient atmosphere so that you may enjoy your stay to the full. We have available eleven bedrooms, most en suite. All have colour TV, hospitality trays, central heating and lashings of hot water. Quiet guest lounge and private off road parking. Bed and Breakfast from £22.50 per person. Family rooms and evening meals available.

CHELTENHAM near. Mr and Mrs C. Rooke, Frogfurlong Cottage, Frogfurlong Lane, Down Hatherley, GL2 9QE (01452 730430).

At Frogfurlong Cottage we offer exclusive accommodation for a truly "get away from it all" break. The 18th century cottage surrounded by fields is situated on the green belt area within the triangle formed by Cheltenham, Gloucester and Tewkesbury. The accommodation, which is totally non-smoking and self-contained, consists of one double room with luxury en suite bathroom and jacuzzi. There is also an independent twin/double room with en suite with direct access to the 30' indoor heated swimming pool. Both rooms have colour TV and tea maker. Local attractions include the Cotswolds, Malverns, Forest of Dean, National Waterways Museum, National Falconry Centre, Three Choirs Vineyard, Slimbridge Wildfowl Trust, Nature in Art, Cheltenham Festivals. Sorry no pets. Bed and Breakfast from £20 per person per night; Evening Meals by arrangement.

When making enquiries or bookings,
a stamped addressed envelope is always appreciated.

CHIPPING CAMPDEN. Mrs Gené Jeffrey, Brymbo, Honeybourne Lane, Mickleton, Chipping Campden GL55 6PU (01386 438890; Fax: 01386 438113). ETC

COTSWOLD COUNTRY BED AND BREAKFAST

◆◆◆. A warm and welcoming farm building conversion with large garden in beautiful Cotswold countryside, ideal for walking and touring. Close to Stratford-upon-Avon, Broadway, Chipping Campden and with easy access to Oxford and Cheltenham. All rooms are on the ground floor, with full central-heating. The comfortable bedrooms all have colour television and tea/coffee making facilities. Sitting room with open log fire. Breakfast room. Children and dogs welcome. Parking. Maps and guides to borrow. Sample menus from local hostelries for your information. Home-made preserves a speciality. FREE countryside tour of area offered to three-night guests. Rooms: two double, two twin, one family. Three en suite bathrooms, two shared. Bed and Breakfast from £17.50 per person, en suite £20.00. Brochure available.
e-mail: brymbo@barclays.net

CHIPPING CAMPDEN. Lucy King, Manor Farm, Weston Sub-Edge, Chipping Campden GL55 6QH (01386 840390; mobile: 07885 108812; Fax: 0870 1640638; Int. Fax: 4487 01640638). 👑👑 COMMENDED.

Working farm, join in. 17th century farmhouse on a 600 acre mixed farm. An excellent base for touring the Cotswolds, Shakespeare country and Hidcote Manor Gardens. Warm, friendly atmosphere. Lovely walled garden. All rooms are en suite with tea/coffee making facilities, TV/radio. Children and dogs most welcome. Lots of excellent walks around beautiful countryside. Only one-and-a-half miles from Chipping Campden which is not only a lovely old market town, but also has a good selection of pubs, restaurants and shops. Open all year round. AA QQQQ Selected. Bed with full English Breakfast from only £20 per person.
e-mail: lucy@manorfarmbnb.demon.co.uk

CIRENCESTER. Ann and Martin Shewry-Fitzgerald, Manby's Farm, Oaksey, Malmesbury SN16 9SA (01666 577399; Fax: 01666 577241). AA/ETC ◆◆◆◆.

Our new farmhouse, situated within stunning countryside on the Wiltshire/Gloucestershire border is close to the Cotswold Water Park. We offer luxury accommodation from where you can enjoy the peace and quiet or plan a visit to one of the many places of interest, such as Malmesbury, Castle Combe, Oxford, Stratford-upon-Avon, Stonehenge, Longleat and many more. Our farmhouse has full central heating and snooker room with indoor swimming pool adjacent. Three double/twin en suite bedrooms with tea/coffee making facilities, radio and colour TV; family room also available. A log fire in the inglenook will ensure our winter guests are kept warm. A hearty English breakfast is served, with three-course dinner and packed lunches available by arrangement. Bed and Breakfast from £20 per person, discount for more than three nights. Visa and Access accepted.
e- mail: DJHackle@compuserve.com

This charming 13th Century farmhouse Hotel is set within its own extensive grounds (14 acres) ideal for dog walking. The Hotel is situated in the village of Clearwell bordering the Forest of Dean. The accommodation comprises 14 en suite bedrooms including Four-Posters and Cottage Suites. The award-winning restaurant serves a selection of traditional food and a comprehensive wine list.

B&B from £30.00pp. DB&B from £44.50pp. Please phone for brochure and information

Tudor Farmhouse Hotel & Restaurant, Clearwell, Near Coleford, Gloucestershire GL16 8JS (01594 833046)

👑👑👑
Commended
WTB ★★★ Hotel

— *See colour advertisement on page 18.* —

DURSLEY. Burrows Court, Nibley Green, North Nibley, Dursley GL11 6AZ (Tel & Fax: 01453 546230).

ETC ◆◆◆. This 18th century mill is idyllically set in an acre of garden surrounded by open country with beautiful views of the Cotswolds. Decorated and furnished in the country style. The house has six bedrooms, all with private bathroom, colour TV, beverage facilities and radio. Other facilities include two lounges, one with residents' bar; central heating. There is a good choice of restaurants and pubs nearby. Children over five years welcome. Bed and breakfast from £20 to £25 per person. Close to M5 motorway between Junctions 13 and 14. RAC Highly Acclaimed.

DURSLEY near. Gerald and Norma Kent, Hill House, Crawley Hill, Uley, Near Dursley GL11 5BH (01453

860267). Cotswold stone house situated on top of a hill with beautiful views of the surrounding countryside, near the very pretty village of Uley. Ideal spot for exploring the various walks in the area including the Cotswold Way and there are many places of interest within reasonable driving distance of Uley. Choice of bedrooms with or without en-suite facilities, all with washbasins, central heating, shaver points, tea/coffee making facilities and TV. Your hosts' aim is to make your stay in the Cotswolds an enjoyable and memorable one, with comfort and hospitality of prime importance. Bed and Breakfast from £18 per person; Evening Meals are normally available if required. Non Smoking Please phone or write for brochure.

DURSLEY near. Mrs Catherine Bevan, Hodgecombe Farm, Uley, Near Dursley GL11 5AN (01453

860365). AA ◆◆◆◆ Situated in the lower Cotswolds, Hodgecombe Farm lies in a quiet valley between Uley and Coaley, tucked under the Uley Bury Roman Fort with spectaular views across open countryside to the River Severn and beyond. The Cotswold Way winds lazily past Hodgecombe Farm and visitors find this the perfect place to relax in unspoilt surroundings. Three double rooms, one en suite, are comfortably furnished with armchairs, tea/coffee, clock radios and central heating. Bed and Breakfast from £17 to £21 per person; Evening Meal £9.50. Sorry no smokers, animals or under five-year-olds. Open March to October.

FALFIELD. John and Janet Buxton, Green Farm Country House, Falfield GL12 8DL (Tel & Fax 01454

260319). Tourist Board Listed. A warm welcome is assured at our 16th century farmhouse offering style and traditional charm. Open all year, we are the ideal touring centre with Bath, Bristol, Cheltenham, Cardiff, Cheddar, the Cotswolds and Forest of Dean within easy reach. Excellent access to M5 motorway (Junction 14) and M4. Comfortable accommodation with pleasant countryside views. Tea/coffee making facilities with colour TV and en suites also available. Completely non-smoking. Ample parking. Bed and Full English Breakfast from less than £19 per person. We look forward to meeting you.
e-mail: info@greenfarmcountryhouse.freeserve.co.uk
website: www.greenfarmcountryhouse.freeserve.co.uk

GLOUCESTER near. S.J. Barnfield, "Kilmorie Smallholding", Gloucester Road, Corse, Staunton,

Gloucester GL19 3RQ (Tel & Fax: 01452 840224) "Kilmorie" is Grade II Listed (c1848) within conservation area in a lovely part of Gloucestershire, deceptively spacious yet cosy, tastefully furnished all ground floor accommodation. Double, twin, family or single bedrooms, all having tea tray, colour TV, radio, mostly en suite. Very comfortable guests lounge, traditional home cooking is served in the separate dining room overlooking lage garden where there are seats to relax, watch our ducks and hens (who provide excellent eggs for breakfast!) or the wild birds and butterflies we encourage to visit. Perhaps walk waymarked farmland footpaths which start here. Children may "help" with our sheep, poultry, child's pony, Pygmy goats whose tiny pretty kids arrive in Spring. Rural yet ideally situated to visit Cotswolds, Royal Forest of Dean, Wye Valley and Malvern Hills. Children over five years. Bed, full English Breakfast and Evening Dinner from £23.50; Bed and Breakfast from £16. Ample parking.

LECHLADE near. Mrs Elizabeth Reay, Apple Tree House, Buscot, Near Faringdon, Oxfordshire SN7 8DA (01367 252592). 👑👑 17th century Listed house situated in small interesting National Trust village, two miles Lechlade, four miles Faringdon on A417. River Thames five minutes' walk through village to Buscot lock and weirs. Ideal touring centre for Cotswolds, Upper Thames, Oxford, etc. Good fishing, walking and cycling area. Access at all times to the three guest bedrooms all of which have washbasins, razor points, tea/coffee facilities and central heating when necessary. En suite room available. Residents' TV lounge with log fire in winter. Bed and Breakfast from £18 per person per night; choice of many restaurants, etc within five mile radius of Buscot. I look forward to welcoming you to Apple Tree House.

e-mail: emreay@aol.com

LYDNEY. Marion Allen, "Woodcroft", Lower Meend, St. Briavels, Lydney GL15 6RW (01594 530083). Welcome Home. Woodcroft is a secluded house set in a five acre smallholding on the side of the Wye Valley near Tintern. A peaceful spot surrounded by woods and lovely walking country, including the Offa's Dyke Path half a mile away. We have two en suite family rooms with tea and coffee making facilities and a guest lounge with colour TV, books, games, maps, etc. To help you enjoy your stay breakfast is served at a time of your choice and includes our own free-range eggs; home-made bread and home-made jams and marmalade. Children and pets welcome. Bed and Breakfast £18. Brochure available.

MINCHINHAMPTON, near Stroud. Mrs Margaret Helm, Hunters Lodge, Dr Brown's Road, Minchinhampton Common, Near Stroud GL6 9BT (01453 883588; Fax: 01453 731449). AA ◆◆◆◆. Hunters Lodge is a beautiful stone-built Cotswold country house set in a large secluded garden adjoining 600 acres of National Trust common land at Minchinhampton. Accommodation available - one double room en suite; two twin/double bedded rooms both with private bathrooms. All have tea/coffee making facilities, central heating and colour TV and are furnished and decorated to a high standard. Private lounge with TV and a delightful conservatory. Car essential, ample parking space. Ideal centre for touring the Cotswolds - Bath, Cheltenham, Cirencester, with many delightful pubs and hotels in the area for meals. You are sure of a warm welcome, comfort, and help in planning excursions to local places of interest. Bed and Breakfast from £22 per person. Non-smokers preferred. Children over 10. No dogs. SAE please for details, or telephone.

SAUL. Mrs Wendy Watts, Saul Farm, Saul GL2 7JB (01452 740384). 👑👑 **Working farm, join in.** Take a break and relax in the comfort and homely atmosphere of our 17th century house overlooking a lake. Guests are welcome to lend a hand around the farm, which is situated between the River Severn and the Berkeley Canal. Many interesting places to visit nearby. TV lounge with open fire, spacious en suite bedrooms and home cooking are waiting for you and your family; children and pets welcome. Two miles from M5 Junction 13. Bed and Breakfast from £18. Open all year.

STOW-ON-THE-WOLD. Graham and Helen Keyte, The Limes, Evesham Road, Stow-on-the-Wold GL54 1EN (01451 830034/831056; Fax: 01451 830034). 👑👑 Over the last 24 years this RAC Listed and AA QQQ guesthouse has established a reputation for its homely and friendly atmosphere. It is just four minutes' walk from the town centre; central for visiting Stratford-upon-Avon, Burford, Bourton-on-the-Water, Cirencester, Cheltenham, etc. The Limes overlooks fields and has an attractive large garden with ornamental pool and waterfall. Single, double, twin and family rooms with washbasins. All rooms en suite, one four-poster and family room; other doubles. All rooms have tea/coffee making facilities and colour TV; hairdryers available. Central heating. TV lounge. Diningroom. Children welcome, cot. Pets welcome. Car park. Fire Certificate held. Bed and full English Breakfast from £18 to £22 per person. Reductions for children. Vegetarians catered for. Open all year except Christmas.

ASTON HOUSE
ENGLISH TOURISM COUNCIL ◆◆◆◆

Aston House is a chalet bungalow overlooking fields in the peaceful village of Broadwell, one-and-a-half-miles from Stow-on-the-Wold. It is centrally situated for all the Cotswold villages, while Blenheim Palace, Warwick Castle, Oxford, Stratford-upon-Avon, Cheltenham, Cirencester and Gloucester are within easy reach. Accommodation comprises a twin-bedded and a double/twin room, both en suite on the first floor, and a double room with private bathroom on the ground floor. All rooms have tea/coffee making facilities, radio, colour TV, and electric blankets for the colder nights. Bedtime drinks and biscuits are provided. Guests and children over 10 years are welcomed to our home February to November. No smoking. Car essential, parking. Pub within walking distance. Bed and good English Breakfast from £21.50 to £23 per person daily; weekly from £150 per person.
Mrs F.J. Adams, Aston House, Broadwell, Moreton-in-Marsh GL56 0TJ
Telephone: 01451 830475   e-mail: fja@netcomuk.co.uk
Website: www.netcomuk.co.uk/~nmfa/aston_house.html

STOW-ON-THE-WOLD. Robert and Dawn Smith, Corsham Field Farmhouse, Bledington Road, Stow-on-the-Wold GL54 1JH (01451 831750). ☙☙ Homely farmhouse with traditional features and breathtaking views, one mile from Stow-on-the-Wold. Ideally situated for exploring all the picturesque Cotswold villages such as Broadway, Bourton-on-the-Water, Upper and Lower Slaughter, Chipping Campden, Snowshill, etc. Also central point for places of interest such as Blenheim Palace, Cotswold Wildlife Park, Stratford and many stately homes and castles in the area. Twin, double and family rooms, most with en suite facilities, other with washbasins, TV and tea/coffee making facilities. Pets and children welcome. Good pub food five minutes' walk away. AA Listed. Bed and Full English Breakfast from £15 to £22 per person.

STOW-ON-THE-WOLD. Mrs S. Davis, Fairview Farmhouse, Bledington Road, Stow-on-the-Wold, Cheltenham GL54 1JH (Tel and Fax: 01451 830279). ☙☙

HIGHLY COMMENDED. You are assured of a warm welcome at Fairview Farmhouse situated one mile from Stow-on-the-Wold on a quiet B road with outstanding panoramic views of the surrounding Cotswold Hills. Ideal base for touring the pretty villages of Bourton-on-the-Water, The Slaughters, Broadway, Chipping Campden, also famous Stratford etc. The cosy bedrooms are furnished to a high standard with a king-size four-poster de luxe for that special occasion; all are en suite with colour TV and tea/coffee making equipment. Lounge and additional lounge area with books, maps, etc. Central heating. Ample parking. Open all year. Prices from £45 to £55 (two people sharing).

STROUD. Mrs Salt, Beechcroft, Brownshill, Stroud GL6 8AG (01453 883422). ☙ *COMMENDED.* Our

Edwardian house is quietly situated in a beautiful rural area with open views, about four miles from Stroud. The house is set in an attractive garden with mature trees, shrubs and herbaceous borders. We are in the midst of good walking country, for which we can lend maps and guides. We provide a full cooked breakfast or fruit salad and rolls with home-made bread and preserves. We welcome the elderly and small children. We are within easy reach of Cheltenham, Gloucester, Cirencester and Bath, also Berkeley Castle, Slimbridge and the North Cotswolds. We are a non-smoking establishment. Evening meal by prior arrangement. Bed and Breakfast from £18 to £22.

FHG
FHG PUBLICATIONS
publish a large range of well-known accommodation guides. We will be happy to send you details or you can use the order form at the back of this book.

TEWKESBURY. Mrs Bernadette Williams, Abbots Court, Church End, Twyning, Tewkesbury GL20 6DA (Tel & Fax: 01684 292515). ♛♛ **Working farm.** A large,

quiet farmhouse set in 350 acres, built on the site of monastery between the Malverns and Cotswolds, half a mile M5-M50 junction. Six en suite bedrooms with colour TV and tea making facilities. Centrally heated. Open all year except Christmas. Large lounge with open fire and colour TV. Spacious diningroom. Licensed bar. Good home cooked food in large quantities, home produced where possible. Children's own TV room, games room and playroom. Tennis lawn. Play area and lawn. Cot and high chair available. Laundry facilities. Ideally situated for touring with numerous places to visit. Swimming, tennis, sauna, golf within three miles. Coarse fishing available on the farm. Bed and Breakfast from £17.00 to £19.00. Reduced rates for children and Senior Citizens.

TEWKESBURY. Mick and Anne Meadows, Home Farm, Bredons Norton, Tewkesbury GL20 7HA (Tel

& Fax: 01684 772322). ♛♛ *COMMENDED.* You will find a friendly and warm welcome at our 18th century farmhouse. The family-run farm is situated in an extremely quiet, unspoilt little village nestling under famous Bredon Hills, a superb position for walking, touring or simply relaxing. All bedrooms have en suite bathrooms, central heating, tea making facilities and TV. Guests' lounge, garden, separate dining room. Choice of breakfast. Excellent pubs nearby serving food. Open mid January to mid-December.

FOR THE MUTUAL GUIDANCE OF GUEST AND HOST

Every year literally thousands of holidays, short breaks and overnight stops are arranged through our guides, the vast majority without any problems at all. In a handful of cases, however, difficulties do arise about bookings, which often could have been prevented from the outset.

It is important to remember that when accommodation has been booked, both parties – guests and hosts – have entered into a form of contract. We hope that the following points will provide helpful guidance.

GUESTS: When enquiring about accommodation, be as precise as possible. Give exact dates, numbers in your party and the ages of any children. State the number and type of rooms wanted and also what catering you require – bed and breakfast, full board etc. Make sure that the position about evening meals is clear – and about pets, reductions for children or any other special points.

Read our reviews carefully to ensure that the proprietors you are going to contact can supply what you want. Ask for a letter confirming all arrangements, if possible.

If you have to cancel, do so as soon as possible. Proprietors do have the right to retain deposits and under certain circumstances to charge for cancelled holidays if adequate notice is not given and they cannot re-let the accommodation.

HOSTS: Give details about your facilities and about any special conditions. Explain your deposit system clearly and arrangements for cancellations, charges etc. and whether or not your terms include VAT.

If for any reason you are unable to fulfil an agreed booking without adequate notice, you may be under an obligation to arrange suitable alternative accommodation or to make some form of compensation.

While every effort is made to ensure accuracy, we regret that FHG Publications cannot accept responsibility for errors, omissions or misrepresentations in our entries or any consequences thereof.

Prices in particular should be checked because we go to press early. We will follow up complaints but cannot act as arbiters or agents for either party.

HAMPSHIRE

BEAULIEU near. Mick and Alexis McEvoy, Langley Village Restaurant, Lepe Road, Langley, Beaulieu,

Southampton SO45 1XR (023 8089 1667; Mobile: 07803 019469). A friendly family atmosphere will greet you in this large detached property on the edge of the beautiful New Forest. Ample off road parking. Each day begins with a hearty full English breakfast. Accommodation comprises one twin, one double and two single rooms, all tastefully decorated and having washbasins, central heating, colour TV and tea-making facilities. A restaurant is attached offering meals all day. Conveniently situated for golf, fishing, horse riding and walking. Close to Exbury Gardens, Lepe Country Park and Beaulieu Motor Museum. Open all year. Bed and Breakfast from £18.50. Special diets catered for by arrangement.

BROCKENHURST (NEW FOREST). Mrs Pauline Harris, Little Heathers, Whitemoor Road, Brockenhurst

SO42 7QG (01590 623512; Fax: 01590 624255; Mobile: 07885 141523). ◆◆◆. A friendly welcome awaits you at our spacious bungalow situated on the outskirts of Brockenhurst, in the heart of the New Forest, where ponies roam free. Wonderful countryside for walking, cycling, riding, touring etc. Golf courses nearby. Four miles from Lymington with its Yacht Haven and Isle of Wight ferry. Colour TV, hairdryer and beverage facilities in double and twin bedded ground-floor bedrooms with en suite facilities; guest lounge, large garden in quiet location. Full English or Vegetarian Breakfast, special diets or smaller appetites catered for. NO SMOKING. Children welcome. Brochure available. From £21 per person per night (special short breaks reduced rates).
e-mail: little_heathers@hotmail.com

CADNAM (NEW FOREST). Simon and Elaine Wright, Bushfriers, Winsor Road, Winsor, Southampton

SO40 2HF (023 80 812552). Bushfriers is situated in the peaceful farming village of Winsor within the unique location of the New Forest Heritage Area. Our individual character cottage offers a comfortable double bedroom with countryside views and private bathroom with an adjoining sitting/single bedroom. One extra double bedroom is available if required. Tea/coffee making facilities in both rooms. Guests may enjoy the TV/sitting room with log fire in winter and our delightful secluded garden. Our highly-rated breakfasts are freshly prepared from local farm produce with home-made breads and preserves. Bed and Breakfast from £20 per person per night. 17th century village pub four minutes' walk away serving excellent good value food.

LYMINGTON. Mrs Patricia Ellis, Efford Cottage, Everton, Lymington SO41 0JD (01590 642315; Fax:

01590 641030/642315). ETC ◆◆◆◆◆ GOLD AWARD. Our friendly, award winning guest house is a spacious Georgian cottage, standing in an acre of garden. All rooms are en suite with many extra luxury facilities. We offer a four course, multi-choice breakfast, with homemade bread and preserves. Patricia is a qualified chef and uses our homegrown produce. An excellent centre for exploring both the New Forest and the South Coast with sports facilities, fishing, bird watching and horse riding in the near vicinity. Private parking. Dogs welcome. Bed and Breakfast from £23 per person. Sorry no children under 14 years. RAC Sparkling Diamond and Warm Welcome Accolades, Welcome Host, FHG Diploma Winner 1997 and 1999.
e-mail: effcottage@aol.com

FHG Please mention *The Farm Holiday Guide* when enquiring about accommodation featured in these pages.

LYMINGTON. Our Bench, Lodge Road, Pennington, Lymington SO41 8HH (Tel & Fax: 01590 673141) ETC ◆◆◆◆. A warm welcome awaits you in this non-smoking and 'no children' award-winning home. This quiet bunglaow is situated between the New Forest and the coast. All rooms are en suite with colour television and tea/coffee facilities; a four-course breakfast and optional evening meals are served in the dining room. There is an indoor heated pool, jacuzzi and sauna within the grounds for your enjoyment, and mountain bikes are available for hire. National Accessibility Scheme 3. Tariff from £22 per person. FHG Diploma winner.
e-mail: ourbench@newforest.demon.co.uk
website: www.newforest.demon.co.uk/bench.htm

LYMINGTON. Mrs R. Sque, Harts Lodge, 242 Everton Road, Lymington SO41 0HE (01590 645902). AA ◆◆◆◆ Bungalow (non-smoking) set in three acres. Large garden with small lake and an abundance of birdlife. Quiet location, convenient for A337. Three miles west of Lymington. Friendly welcome and high standard of accommodation comprising double, twin and family en suite rooms. Each with tea and coffee making facilities and colour TV. Delicious four-course English breakfast. The sea and the forest are five minutes away by car. Horse riding, fishing and golf are nearby. The village pub serving excellent home-made meals is a half-mile away. Children and pets welcome. Bed and Breakfast from £20 per person.

LYNDHURST. Penny Farthing Hotel, Romsey Road, Lyndhurst SO43 7AA (023 8028 4422; Fax: 023 8028 4488). AA/RAC/ETC ◆◆◆◆. The Penny Farthing is a cheerful small Hotel ideally situated in Lyndhurst village centre, the capital of "The New Forest". The Hotel offers en suite single, double, twin and family rooms with direct dial telephones, tea/coffee tray, colour TV and clock radios. We also have some neighbouring cottages available as Hotel annexe rooms or on a self-catering basis. These have been totally refitted, much with "Laura Ashley" decor, and offer quieter, more exclusive accommodation. The hotel has a licensed bar, private car park and bicycle store. Lyndhurst has a charming variety of shops, resturants, pubs ,and bistros and "The New Forest Information Centre and Museum". All major credit cards accepted.
website: SmoothHound.co.uk/hotels/pennyf.html.

NEW FOREST. Orchard House, New Lane Orchard, New Lane, Bashley, Near New Milton BH25 5TD (01425 612404). Orchard House is set in 60 peaceful acres on the edge of the New Forest. We have coarse fishing lakes as featured in Anglers Mail (day tickets), ancient woodland, paddocks, lovely gardens and an abundance of wildlife. Visitors are free to roam and enjoy. Our very pretty double en suite rooms have colour TV and tea/coffee facilities. Within walking distance of the New Forest, it is ideally situated for cycling, horse riding and touring. Bikes and horses can be hired locally. Why not bring your own horse? We have stables, grazing and ample parking. Bed and full English Breakfast from £18 per person. Special rates for low season breaks.

NEW FOREST. Mrs Sandra Hocking, Southernwood, Plaitford Common, Salisbury Road, Near Romsey (01794 323255 or 322577). Tourist Board Listed COMMENDED. Modern country family home, surrounded by farmland, on the edge of the New Forest. Two double, one family and one twin bedrooms; lounge. Full English breakfast. Cots and high chairs available for babies. Four miles from M27 off A36. Salisbury, Southampton 11 miles, Stonehenge 17 miles, Portsmouth half-an-hour, Winchester 14 miles, Romsey five miles and within easy reach of Continental ferries. Large garden. Ample parking. TV. Tea/coffee always available. Horse riding, golf, fishing, swimming, walking in New Forest 10 minutes. Local inns for good food. Terms from £15. Open all year.

NEW FOREST (Fritham). John and Penny Hankinson, Fritham Farm, Fritham, Lyndhurst SO43 7HH (Tel & Fax: 023 8081 2333). ETC/AA ◆◆◆◆ Lovely farmhouse on working farm in the heart of the New Forest. Dating from the 18th century, all three double/twin bedrooms have en suite facilities and provision for tea/coffee making. There is a large comfortable lounge with TV and log fire. Fritham is in a particularly beautiful part of the New Forest, still largely undiscovered and with a wealth of wildlife. It is a wonderful base for walking, riding, cycling and touring. No smoking. Children 10 years and over welcome. Come and enjoy peace and quiet in this lovely corner of England. Bed and Breakfast £19 to £21.

PETERSFIELD. Mrs Mary Bray, Nursted Farm, Buriton, Petersfield GU31 5RW (01730 264278). Working farm. This late 17th century farmhouse, with its large garden, is open to guests throughout most of the year. Located quarter-of-a-mile west of the B2146 Petersfield to Chichester road, one-and-a-half-miles south of Petersfield, the house makes an ideal base for touring the scenic Hampshire and West Sussex countryside. Queen Elizabeth Country Park two miles adjoining picturesque village of Buriton at the western end of South Downs Way. Accommodation consists of three twin-bedded rooms (two with washbasin), two bathrooms/toilets; sitting room/breakfast room. Full central heating. Children welcome, cot provided. Sorry, no pets. Car essential, ample parking adjoining the house. Bed and Breakfast only from £17 per adult, reductions for children under 12 years. Open all year except Christmas, March and April. No smoking.

RINGWOOD, New Forest. Mrs M.E. Burt, Fraser House, Salisbury Road, Blashford, Ringwood BH24 3PB (01425 473958). ♛♛ COMMENDED. Fraser House is situated one mile from the market town of Ringwood, overlooking the Avon Valley. This comfortable family guest house is on the edge of the New Forest, famous for its ponies, deer and pleasant walks. It is ten miles from Bournemouth and the south coast, and is convenient for visiting Southampton, Stonehenge and the Cathedral city of Salisbury. All rooms have central heating, hot and cold water, shaver points, comfortable beds, colour TV, tea/coffee making facilities. Some en suite rooms available at extra charge. Guest lounge with TV. Fishing and water sports available nearby. Non-smokers preferred. Ample parking space. Open all year. Bed and Breakfast from £20 per night.

FHG PUBLICATIONS LIMITED
publish a large range of well-known accommodation guides.
We will be happy to send you details or you can use the
order form at the back of this book.

ROMSEY. Mrs Christina Pybus, Pyesmead Farm, Plaitford, Romsey SO51 6EE (01794 323386).

♨♨ COMMENDED. A warm welcome awaits you on the northern edge of the New Forest, at our family-run stock farm with its own coarse fishing lakes and heated indoor swimming pool and sauna. Many activities locally including horse riding, trout fishing, golf and forest walks. Within easy reach of Salisbury, Winchester, Southampton and the coast. Excellent pubs providing good food within quarter-of-a-mile. Children and pets welcome. Open all year except Christmas. Bed and Breakfast from £17.

SOUTHAMPTON. Mrs Rose Pell, Verulam House, 181 Wilton Road, Shirley, Southampton SO1 5HY (023 8077 3293 or 07778 563096). Tourist Board

Listed. Rose and Dick warmly welcome guests to their comfortable, warm, roomy Edwardian establishment, in a nice residential area. Good cuisine. One double or family, one twin, one single bedrooms all with TV and tea/coffee making facilities; two bathrooms – plenty of hot water. Car parking space. Five minutes by car to historic Southampton city noted for its parks; railway station 10 minutes. Airport, Cross Channel ferries and Isle of Wight within easy reach and not far from M27, M3, Portsmouth, Winchester, Bournemouth, New Forest and coast. Bed and Breakfast from £18 per person; Evening Meal from £8 per person. Bed and Breakfast £120 weekly. Non-smokers only.

WINCHESTER near. Mays Farm, Longwood Dean, Near Winchester (01962 777486; Fax 01962

777747). Twelve minutes' drive from Winchester, (the eleventh century capital city of England), Mays Farm is set in rolling countryside on a lane which leads from nowhere to nowhere. The house is timber framed, originally built in the sixteenth century and has been thoroughly renovated and extended by its present owners, James and Rosalie Ashby. There are three guest bedrooms, (one double, one twin and one either), each with a private bathroom or shower room. A sitting room with log fire is usually available for guests' use. Ducks, geese, chickens and goats make up the two acre "farm". Prices from £23 per person per night for bed and breakfast. Booking is essential. Please telephone or fax for details.

Terms quoted in this publication may be subject to increase if rises in costs necessitate

HEREFORDSHIRE

©MAPS IN MINUTES™(1998)

POWYS
Knighton
ayader
Llandrindod Wells
A488
A44
A483
A481
A438
A470
A470
Builth Wells
Hay-on-Wye
A438
econ
A479
Brecon Beacons
Crickhowell
Abergavenny
Ebbw Vale
Brynmawr
Blaenavon
hyr
dfil
Rhymney
MONMOUTHSHIRE
A40
A40

Presteigne
Kington
A4112
A44
Leominster
HEREFORDSHIRE
Hereford
A465
A49
Monmouth
A40
A466

Ludlow
A49
A456
Bromyard
A44
Worcester
A4103
Great Malvern
A438
Ledbury
A4103

Ross-on-Wye
A40

Kiddermins
Stourport-on-Severn
Droitwich
M5
WORCESTERSHIRE
A442
Pershore
A44
A46

Tewkesbury
M50
M5
GLOUCESTERSHIRE
Chelter
Sto
Gloucester
GLOUCESTERSHIRE
Stroud
A436

BREDENBURY. Mrs G. Evans, Red Hill Farm, Bredenbury, Bromyard HR7 4SY (01885 483255 or 01885 483535). Tourist Board Listed. 17th century farmhouse situated in the beautiful peaceful countryside, within easy driving distance of Worcester, Hereford, Malvern, Ledbury and Ludlow. Guest accommodation includes one family room, two double bedrooms, one twin-bedded room all with washbasins and TV; bathroom and shower; lounge with colour TV; central heating throughout. Good food at local pub (one mile) at reasonable prices (small hot evening meals available on premises also – optional). Home from home. Children and pets welcome. Equestrian Horse Centre (all-weather gallop half-a-mile). Bed and Breakfast from £16 to £17 per person. Situated on A44. From Worcester take A44 to Bromyard, proceed towards Leominster for one and a half miles; farm on right with Tourist Board sign at farm entrance. You will receive a very warm welcome on arrival.

BROADWAY. Mrs Helen Perry, Mount Pleasant Farm, Childswickham, Broadway WR12 7HZ (01386 853424). ◆◆◆◆. Working farm. Large Victorian farmhouse set in 850 acres of mixed farm with cattle and horses. Excellent views. Open all year round, guests are offered a warm welcome and a good, traditional farmhouse breakfast. An ideal centre for touring the Cotswolds - three miles from Broadway, 15 miles from Stratford-upon-Avon, within easy reach of Warwick, Oxford, Cheltenham, Buxford and many other attractions. All the bedrooms are en suite with TV, tea/coffee facilities and central heating. Bed and Breakfast from £23 per person. Superior self-catering accommodation also available in converted barns sleeping two to eight persons. Graded 4 KEYS by Tourist Board.

Terms quoted in this publication may be subject to increase
if rises in costs necessitate

BROMYARD. Sheila Steeds, Linton Brook Farm, Bringsty, Bromyard WR6 5TR (01885 488875). A warm welcome to our substantial, fascinating early 17th century home with comfortable en suite accommodation in glorious countryside; wonderful views, walks and wildlife. The area is rich in history with ruined castles, Iron Age and Roman hill forts recalling a turbulent past. Market towns and pretty villages abound in the area. Pets welcome by arrangement, outside kennels available. Terms from £20 to £25.

FELTON HOUSE
Felton, Near Hereford HR1 3PH
Tel/Fax: (01432) 820366
Internet: http://www.SmoothHound.co.uk/hotels/felton.html

Marjorie and Brian Roby offer guests, children and pets a very warm welcome to their home, a country house of immense character set in beautiful tranquil gardens in the heart of unspoilt rural England. Relax with refreshments in the library, drawing room or garden room. Taste excellent evening meals at local inns. Sleep in an antique four poster or brass bed and awake refreshed to enjoy, in a superb Victorian dining room, the breakfast you have selected from a wide choice of traditional and vegetarian dishes. Felton House is 20 minutes by car from Hereford, Leominster, Bromyard and Ledbury, off A417. Children and pets welcome.

B&B £23 per person with en suite or private bathroom. AA & ETC ◆◆◆ NON-SMOKING

GOLDEN VALLEY. Mrs Joyce Powell, The Old Vicarage, Vowchurch, Hereford HR2 0QD (Tel & Fax: 01981 550357). ETC ◆◆◆◆ *SILVER AWARD*. Warm hospitality guaranteed in this Victorian house of character, once the home of Lewis Carroll's brother. Ideal for walking/cycling through rich agricultural land, by historic churches and castles, near the Black Mountains (Welsh Border) and Offa's Dyke Path. Visit Hay-on-Wye, world famous town of books, or the Mappa Mundi; golf course five minutes away. Enjoy our attractively presented quality breakfasts after restful nights in individually decorated rooms. Single, double, family, twin, (en suites/private bathrooms) with refreshment trays from £19.50 per person. Delightful candlelit dinners available from £13 (including vegetarian and special diets) may be ordered in advance. Fresh, local and home-grown produce used. Small celebratory groups most welcome. Non-smoking.

HEREFORD. Mrs Diana Sinclair, Holly House Farm, Allensmore, Hereford HR2 9BH (01432 277294; Fax: 01432 261285; mobile 07885 830223). ♛♛ *COMMENDED*. Spacious luxury farmhouse and over 10 acres of land with horses, situated in beautiful and peaceful open countryside. Bedrooms en suite or with private bathroom, central heating, TV and tea/coffee making facilities. We are only five miles south of Hereford city centre. Ideal base for Welsh Borders, market towns, Black Mountains, Brecon and Malvern Hills and the Wye Valley. We have a happy family atmosphere and pets are welcome. Brochure on request. From £20 per person per night and with our delicious English breakfast you will be fit for the whole day!

HEREFORD. David and Emma Jones, Sink Green Farm, Rotherwas, Hereford HR2 6LE (01432 870223). ♛♛ **Working farm, join in**. Warm and friendly atmosphere awaits your arrival at this 16th century farmhouse, on the banks of the River Wye. Three miles south of the cathedral city of Hereford, with Ross-on-Wye, Leominster, Ledbury, Malvern and the Black Mountains within easy reach. All rooms en-suite, tea/coffee making facilities and colour TV. One room with four-poster, family room by arrangement. Guests' own lounge. Pets by arrangement. Bed and Breakfast from £19 per person. AA QQQQ.

KINGTON. Mrs E.E. Protheroe, Bucks Head House, School Farm, Hergest, Kington HR5 3EW (01544

231063). Working farm. Newly modernised farmhouse on 290-acre mixed farm which has been worked by the Protheroe family since 1940 and carries cattle, sheep and crops. Wye Valley, Black Mountains, Elan Valley, Ludlow, Hereford Cathedral, Black and White villages all within easy reach. Two double, two single, two family bedrooms, with washbasins; two bathrooms, two showers, four toilets; two sitting rooms; tea/coffee making facilities in all rooms; diningroom. Snooker room with full size table. Cot, high chair and reduced rates for children; babysitting by arrangement. Pets free of charge, by arrangement only. Car essential, parking. Central heating. Peaceful walks around the farm and its sheep walk "Hergest Ridge". Evening Dinner/Meal, Bed and Breakfast or Bed and Breakfast only. Two six-berth mobile homes also available.

LEDBURY. Mrs Jane West, Church Farm, Coddington, Ledbury HR8 1JJ (01531 640271). Church Farm

is a Black and White Listed farmhouse on a working farm in quiet hamlet. Oak beamed accommodation in two double and one twin. Close to Malvern Hills. Ideal touring base being equidistant between Ross-on-Wye, Hereford, Worcester and Gloucester. Plenty of space and fields for walking dogs. Warm hospitality assured in a quiet, relaxed atmosphere. Plenty of good English fare. Evening meals if required. Log fires, TV. Bed and Breakfast from £22. Excellent self-catering unit also available.

See also Colour Display Advertisement

LEDBURY near. Moor Court Farm, Stretton Grandison, Near Ledbury HR8 2TR (01531 670408). ETC ◆◆◆◆. Relax and enjoy our attractive 15th century timber-framed farmhouse with its adjoining oast-houses, whose picturesque location will ensure a peaceful stay. The Godsall family run a traditional hop and livestock farm situated in the beautiful countryside of Herefordshire, being central to the local market towns, with easy access to the Malverns, Wye Valley and Welsh Borders. Guests will enjoy spacious bedrooms, all with en suite facilities, their own oak beamed lounge, dining room and the peaceful setting of the garden or walks through surrounding woods and farmland with their rural views. Fishing is available in our own pool and there are stables on the farm. Bed and Breakfast from £19.00, Evening Meal £12.50. Residential licence.

LONGTOWN. Mrs I. Pritchard, Olchon Cottage Farm, Longtown, Hereford HR2 0NS (Tel & Fax: 01873 860233). ETC ◆◆◆. Working farm. Small working farm. An ideal location for a peaceful holiday in lovely walking country close to Offa's Dyke Path and Welsh Border. The farmhouse is noted for its good, wholesome, home produced food and many guests return to enjoy the homely, relaxing atmosphere. Magnificent views and many places of interest to visit. Accommodation comprises two family bedrooms (also used as singles/doubles) both en suite with colour TV, radio, hairdryer and tea/coffee facilitiies. Guests' sitting room and dining room with separate tables. Towels provided. Reductions for children under 10 years; cot, high chair and babysitting offered. Open all year except Christmas. Bed, Breakfast and Evening Meal or Bed and Breakfast from £20. Car essential, parking. Terms on application with stamp for brochure, please. Welcome Host Award.

FREE and REDUCED RATE Holiday Visits!
Don't miss our Readers' Offer Vouchers

MONNINGTON-ON-WYE. Clare and Edward Pearson Gregory, Dairy House Farm, Monnington-on-Wye HR4 7NL (01981 500143). A superbly appointed farmhouse

situated down a long drive off the A438 between Hereford and Hay-on-Wye. On a working farm, this large, luxury farmhouse is close to the river and Wye Valley walk. Lovely bedrooms with wonderful views of the farm and surrounding countryside. One double bedroom en suite and one twin bedroom with private bathroom and power shower, both rooms furnished to a very high standard with TV, and tea/coffee facilities. Pets by arrangement only. Guest will enjoy a happy family atmosphere and a traditional hearty breakfast cooked on the Aga. A wonderful spot to relax and explore the Welsh Borders, Black Mountains, Hay-on-Wye (Town of Books), Mappa Mundi, Ludlow and Black and White Villages. Fishing, canoeing and riding can be arranged. Bed and Breakfast from £18 per person. Evening meals by prior arrangement.

ROSS-ON-WYE. Jean and James Jones, The Arches Hotel, Walford Road, Ross-on-Wye HR9 5PT (01989 563348). 👑👑👑 Small family-run hotel, set in half-

an-acre of lawned garden, ideally situated only 10 minutes' walk from town centre. All rooms are furnished and decorated to a high standard and have views of the garden. Tea/coffee making facilities and colour TV are available in bedrooms; some en suite rooms, also one ground floor en suite bedroom available. Full central heating. There is a delightful Victorian-style conservatory to relax in and the garden to enjoy in the summer months. Licensed. Ample parking in grounds. A warm and friendly atmosphere with personal service. Generous weekly reductions. Bed and Breakfast £20, en suite rooms £24. Dinner by arrangement. AA QQQQ Selected, RAC Acclaimed, Les Routiers Award. Please telephone or send SAE for colour brochure.

ROSS-ON-WYE. Mrs M.E. Drzymalska, Thatch Close, Llangrove, Ross-on-Wye HR9 6EL (01989 770300). 👑👑 *COMMENDED.* **Working farm, join in.**

Secluded peaceful Georgian farmhouse set in large colourful gardens in 13 acres of pasture situated in the beautiful Wye Valley between Ross and Monmouth. Thatch Close offers a comfortable, homely atmosphere where guests are welcome to help feed the pigs, cows, calves, or just relax and enjoy this traditionally run farm. Places of scenic beauty and historic attractions nearby include Forest of Dean, Black Mountains, Cathedral Cities, old castles and buildings. Guests have their own lounge and diningroom with colour TV. Twin bedroom and one double room, both with bathrooms en suite, one double room with private bathroom; all bathrooms have showers and bath. Central heating. Non-smokers please. Breakfast and optional Evening Meal are prepared using mainly home grown produce. Vegetarian and diabetic meals arranged. Bed and Breakfast from £17 to £20 with reductions for longer stays. Reduced rates for children. SAE for further details.

Key to Tourist Board Ratings

👑 **The Crown Scheme**

The **English Tourism Council** (formerly the English Tourist Board) has joined with the **AA** and **RAC** to create a new, easily understood quality rating for serviced accommodation. **Hotels** will receive a grading ranging from **one to five STARS (★)**. Other serviced accommodation such as **guest houses** and **B&B establishments** will be graded from **one to five DIAMONDS (◆)**. These ratings represent Quality, Service and Hospitality not just facilities. *NB.Some properties had not been assessed at the time of going to press and in these cases the publishers have included the old CROWN gradings.*

 The Key Scheme

The Key Scheme covering self-catering in cottages, bungalows, flats, houseboats, houses, chalets, etc remains unchanged. The classification from **One to Five KEYS** indicates the range of facilities and equipment. Higher quality standards are indicated by the terms APPROVED, COMMENDED, HIGHLY COMMENDED AND DE LUXE.

ROSS-ON-WYE. Geoffrey and Josephine Baker, Brookfield House, Ledbury Road, Ross-on-Wye HR9 7AT (01989 562188). ETC ◆◆◆. Early 18th century Listed house only five minutes' walk from town centre. Licensed. All bedrooms with TV and tea-making. Room only or with Continental or full breakfast. Ideal for golfers and walkers.

WINFORTON. Mrs Jackie Kingdon, Winforton Court, Winforton HR3 6EA (Tel & Fax 01544 328498). AA ◆◆◆◆. A warm welcome and country hospitality at its best awaits you at historic Winforton Court - circa 1500. Relax and be pampered in the beautiful Wye Valley - close to Hay-on-Wye "Town of Books" Beautifully furnished with antiques, interesting collections and bygones, Winforton Court offers luxury accommodation for the discerning visitor. Spacious drawing room, log fires in winter, library, hearty breakfasts (vegetarian available) served in former court room. Large bedrooms, all en suite. For special occasions try the De Mortimer Suite with king-size oak four-poster. Delightful old world gardens; garaging available. We also have a self-catering cottage. Bed and Breakfast from £25.00 per person.

ISLE OF WIGHT

COWES. Judith Shanks, Youngwoods Farm, Whitehouse Road, Porchfield, Newport PO30 4LJ (Tel & Fax: 01983 522170). Tourist Board Listed *COMMENDED.* Enjoy a friendly welcome at our grassland farm set in open countryside, among the ancient oak trees with magnificent views of the West Wight. The 18th century stone farmhouse is peacefully situated well off the road and retains its original character, with two spacious twin/double bedrooms and one single bedroom. Tea/coffee making facilities and central heating throughout. Close to Newtown Nature Reserve with red squirrels and good bird watching hides. Cowes sailing centre four miles, historic Carisbrooke Castle three miles and beaches all round. Children from eight years and non-smokers welcome. Open all year. Terms from £15 to £22 per person per night.

PLEASE MENTION THIS GUIDE WHEN YOU WRITE

OR PHONE TO ENQUIRE ABOUT ACCOMMODATION.

IF YOU ARE WRITING, A STAMPED,

ADDRESSED ENVELOPE IS ALWAYS APPRECIATED.

KENT

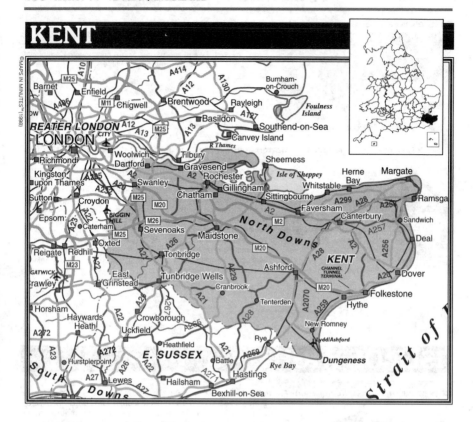

ALDINGTON. Ros and John Martin, Hogben Farm, Church Lane, Aldington, Ashford TN25 7EH (01233 720219). ETC ◆◆◆◆. This farmhouse, dating from the 16th century, lies in a very quiet location down its own drive, set amongst extensive gardens and lawns. It is an ideal centre for visits to Canterbury, Rye, Tenterden, etc, and handy for the ferries, the Channel Tunnel and Eurostar Ashford International Station. Accommodation includes one double room and two twin rooms with en suite facilities. A sittingroom with inglenook fireplace and colour TV is available for guests. Conservatory for guests' use. Good home cooking for your Evening Meal by arrangement. Open all year. Bed and Breakfast from £19.50. No smoking in bedrooms.

ASHFORD. Mrs Lilly Wilton, Bulltown Farmhouse, West Brabourne, Ashford TN25 5NB (01233 813505). An attractively restored 15th century timber-framed Kentish Farmhouse situated on the southwestern side of the North Downs and Pilgrim's Way offering unspoilt countryside and superb walks. The Cathedral City of Canterbury is only 12 miles, Ashford seven miles and the Channel Ports of Folkestone and Dover are 10 and 18 miles respectively. The M20 Junction 10 is only five miles away giving access to other motorways and Gatwick and Heathrow airports. There is an excellent award-winning country inn close by. Accommodation offered in two double and one twin bedded rooms, all en suite and with tea/coffee facilities. Children welcome, cot and reduced terms available. Terms from £20 per person, £19 for three nights or more.

ASHFORD. Mrs Feakins, Old Farm House, Soakham Farm, Whitehill, Bilting, Ashford IN25 4HB (01233 813509). Soakham is a working farm situated on the North Downs Way between Boughton Aluph and Chilham and adjoining Challock Forest. It is ideally located both for walking and visiting many places in the south-east area. Canterbury and Ashford are 10 miles and five miles away respectively. The farmhouse was originally a Hall House and is Grade II Listed with much exposed woodwork. It offers the following accommodation: two double rooms, including one with a four-poster bed, and a twin-bedded room. Prices are from £16 per person for Bed and Breakfast. Ample parking is available, and we are open all year around.

ASHFORD near. Caroline and Paul Boucher, Hillside Farm, Stowting Hill, Stowting, Near Ashford TN25 6BE (01303 863520; Fax: 01303 863683). Set in extensive gardens and with five acres of grounds adjoining a traditional village cricket ground, Hillside Farm is a 17th century farmhouse full of character and beautifully decorated. In an Area of Outstanding Natural Beauty, close to the North Downs way, yet only 10 minutes' drive from the Channel Tunnel terminal. An ideal stop-over for visits to and from France; a country break or for visiting Canterbury (10 minutes), Ashford (10 minutes) and other coastal towns. There are two double and one twin bedrooms, with fabulous hand-painted guest bathroom. Guests' lounge with TV and video. Families welcome, cot and high chair available. Local pubs within easy reach. Bed and Full English Breakfast £18 per person.
e-mail: pboucher@globalnet.co.uk

CANTERBURY. Mrs A. Hunt, Bower Farmhouse, Stelling Minnis, Near Canterbury CT4 6BB (01227 709430). ✹✹ *HIGHLY COMMENDED*. Anne & Nick Hunt welcome you to Bower Farm House, a traditional 17th-century Kentish farmhouse situated in the midst of Stelling Minnis, a medieval common of 125 acres of unspoilt trees, shrubs and open grassland; seven miles south of the cathedral city of Canterbury and nine miles from the coast; the countryside abounds in beauty spots and nature reserves. The house is heavily beamed and maintains its original charm. The accommodation comprises a double room and a twin-bedded room, both with private facilities. Full traditional English breakfast is served with home-made bread, marmalade and fresh free-range eggs. Children welcome; pets by prior arrangement. Open all year (except Christmas). Car essential. Excellent pub food five minutes away. Bed and Breakfast from £21.00 per person.

CANTERBURY. Mrs Lewana Castle, Great Field Farm, Misling Lane, Stelling Minnis, Canterbury CT4 6DE (01227 709223). Listed *HIGHLY COMMENDED*. Situated in beautiful countryside, our spacious farmhouse is about eight miles from Canterbury and Folkestone, 12 miles from Dover and Ashford. We are a working farm with some livestock including friendly ponies and chickens. We provide a friendly and high standard of accommodation with full central heating and double glazing, traditional breakfasts cooked on the Aga, courtesy trays and colour TV in each of our suites/bedrooms. Our annexe suite has a private staircase, lounge, kitchen, double bedroom and bathroom and is also available for self-catering holidays. Our cottage suite has its own entrance, stairs, lounge, bathroom and twin-bedded room. Our large double/family bedroom has en suite bathroom and air-bath. There is ample off-road parking and good pub food nearby. Bed and Breakfast from £18pp; reductions for children. Non-smoking establishment.

CANTERBURY. Mr and Mrs R. Linch, Upper Ansdore, Duckpit Lane, Petham, Canterbury CT4 5QB (Tel & Fax: 01227 700672). Tourist Board Listed. Beautiful secluded Listed Tudor farmhouse with various livestock, situated in an elevated position with far-reaching views of the wooded countryside of the North Downs. The property overlooks a Kent Trust Nature Reserve, it is five miles south of the cathedral city of Canterbury and only 30 minutes' drive to the ports of Dover and Folkestone. The accommodation comprises three double and one twin bedded rooms and family room. All have shower, WC en suite and tea making facilities. Dining/sitting room, heavily beamed and with large inglenook. Car essential. Bed and Full English Breakfast from £20 per person. AA QQQ.

English Tourist Board
Listed

CANTERBURY. N.J. Ellen, Crockshard Farmhouse, Wingham, Canterbury CT3 1NY (01227 720464; Fax: 01227 721125).  Exceptionally attractive farmhouse in beautiful gardens, pasture and woodlands on a 20 acre smallholding with lots of different animals to see. Ideally situated for visiting any part of Kent – Canterbury 15 minutes, Dover 20 minutes, Folkestone 30 minutes. Accommodation comprises three family rooms, one en suite and one double en suite. Tea/coffee making facilities, hairdryer and ironing faciltiies. Separate guest lounge with log fire, TV and pianola. Excellent eating facilities near at hand. Children welcome, reduced rates if sharing with parents. Well behaved pets welcome. Prices from £20.

CANTERBURY. Mrs Joan Hill, Renville Oast, Bridge, Canterbury CT4 5AD (01227 830215).  Renville Oast is a 150-year-old building previously used for drying hops for the brewery trade. It is situated in beautiful Kentish countryside, only two miles from the Cathedral City of Canterbury; 10 miles from the coast and-one-and-a half hours' drive from London. Many interesting castles, historic houses, gardens and Howletts Wildlife Park within easy reach. All rooms are comfortably furnished, with tea making facilities. One family room en suite, one double en suite and one twin-bedded room with private bathroom. TV lounge for guests. Ample parking space. Friendly welcome. Excellent pub food nearby. Bed and Breakfast from £22.50 per person.

FAVERSHAM. N.J. and C.I. Scutt, Leaveland Court, Leaveland, Faversham ME13 0NP (01233 740596).  ◆◆◆. Guests are warmly welcomed to our enchanting timbered 15th century farmhouse which nestles between Leaveland Church and woodlands in rural tranquillity. Offering high standards of accommodation whilst retaining their original character, all bedrooms are en suite with colour TV and hot drinks trays. Traditional breakfasts, cooked on the Aga, are available with a choice of alternatives. There is a large attractive garden with heated outdoor swimming pool for guests' use and ample car parking. Ideally situated for visiting Kent's historic cities, castles, houses and gardens with Canterbury only 20 minutes by car and also easy access to Channel ports, 30 minutes. Good walking country, being close to both the Pilgrim's Way and the coast. Open February to November. Terms from £24 for Bed and Breakfast.

FREE and REDUCED RATE Holiday Visits!
Don't miss our Readers' Offer Vouchers

MARDEN. Mrs L. Mannington, Tanner House, Tanner Farm, Goudhurst Road, Marden TN12 9ND (01622 831214; Fax: 01622 832472). ETC ◆◆◆◆.

Working farm. For a break, holiday or stopover we are ideally placed in the beautiful Weald countryside. Our Tudor farmhouse in the centre of our farm offers comfortable accommodation and homely cuisine. All our rooms have en suite shower/WC, colour TV, tea/coffee facilities and radio/alarms. Our double room boasts a genuine Hepplewhite Fourposter. You can stroll at leisure around our farm and meet our Shire horses, ducks, goats, pigs and hens. Or you can venture further afield and visit the many attractions close by. We are open all year except Christmas. Bed and Breakfast £20 to £22.50 per person per night. We accept Visa, Mastercard, Switch. Sorry we cannot accommodate pets.

SUTTON VALENCE. Mrs Stephanie Clout, Sparks Oast Farm, Forsham Lane, Sutton Valence, Maidstone ME17 3EW (01622 842213). Sparks Oast is a characteristic converted Kentish Oasthouse, on a small sheep farm in quiet country lane overlooking the Weald of Kent. Ideally situated for visiting the many attractive castles, famous gardens such as Sissinghurst, Leeds and Scotney Castle, etc. and other places of interest in the Garden of England, or just rambling amid orchards and hop gardens. There is a wealth of excellent pubs offering good food. A warm welcome by the family including the animals, waterfowl, barn owls, etc. Bed and Breakfast from £19 per person per night. One double room, one twin and one en suite. TV. Guests' bathroom and beverage facilities. ALSO SELF CATERING SUITE from £190 per week.

TENTERDEN. Mrs M.R. O'Connor, The Old Post House, Stone-in-Oxney, Tenterden TN30 7JN (01233 758258). Experience the peace and tranquillity of rural England at its best. This guest house overlooks the historic expanse of Romney Marsh and nestles against the hill of the Isle-in-Oxney in the heart of Kentish farmland. Only about ten minutes' drive to the delightful market towns of Rye and Tenterden, where excellent meals can be enjoyed. All rooms are equipped with central heating, washbasins, razor points, tea/coffee making facilities. One room with en suite facilities. Bathroom and shower room. Open all year round. Children over eight years welcome. Pets must be left in car. Bed and traditional English Breakfast from £20 to £23 per person; delicious food can also be had in the village. Car essential, ample parking

PUBLISHER'S NOTE

While every effort is made to ensure accuracy, we regret that FHG Publications cannot accept responsibility for errors, omissions or misrepresentations in our entries or any consequences thereof. Prices in particular should be checked because we go to press early. We will follow up complaints but cannot act as arbiters or agents for either party.

LANCASHIRE

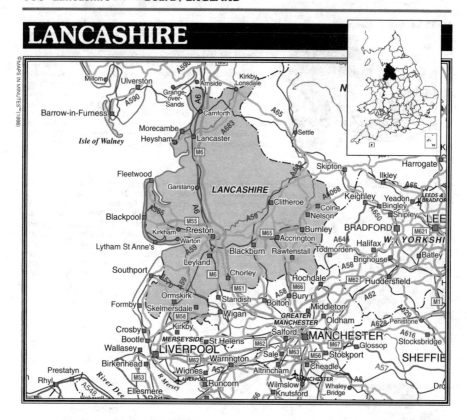

©MAPS IN MINUTES™ (1998)

BACUP. Ann Isherwood, Pasture Bottom Farm, Bacup OL13 9UZ (Tel & Fax: 01706 873790). ETC

◆◆◆. Pasture Bottom Farm is situated at the head of the Rossendale Valley on the Lancashire–Yorkshire border. It is set in an elevated position with panoramic views. It is a working beef farm. We are within a short distance from the main road on a private lane with no passing traffic. All rooms are centrally heated. Two twin rooms, one en suite, one with private bathroom, and one double room en suite. TV in each room and tea/coffee facilities. Tariff from £15 per person per night.
e-mail: ha.isherwood@zen.co.uk

BLACKPOOL near. Mrs Joan Colligan, High Moor Farm, Weeton, Kirkham PR4 3JJ (Tel & Fax: 01253 836273). 👑👑 High Moor Farm is situated six miles from Blackpool and is within easy reach of Lytham St. Annes, Lancaster, Morecambe, the Lake District and the Dales of Yorkshire. Local attractions include sea fishing, golfing, sand yachting, riding schools, Isle of Man ferry (July/August) Fleetwood. Guest accommodation comprises one double, one family, one twin-bedded and one single rooms; the double and family rooms have central heating, colour TV and tea-making facilities. Bed and Breakfast from £15 per person. Special family room (for four) at £35. Reductions for children under 12 years. Closed January until mid February. Travellers cheques accepted.

When making enquiries or bookings,
a stamped addressed envelope is always appreciated.

CARNFORTH. Mrs Gillian Close, Cotestones Farm, Sand Lane, Warton, Carnforth LA5 9NH (01524 732418). Situated on the North Lancashire coast near the M6 (junction 35) on the Carnforth to Silverdale road, this is a 200 acre family-run dairy farm near Leighton Moss RSPB Reserve. Lying between Lancaster, Morecambe and the Lake District, it is an ideal base for touring the area. Tea/coffee facilities and washbasins in all rooms. Bed and Breakfast from £15 per person. Reductions for children. Pets welcome. Open all year (closed Christmas).

CARNFORTH. Mrs Vera Casson, Galley Hall Farm, Shore Road, Carnforth LA5 9HZ (01524 732544). Tourist Board Listed. A 17th century farmhouse on a stock rearing farm on the North Lancashire coast, near Junction 35 M6, close to Leighton Moss RSPB, historic Lancaster; ideal base for touring the Lake District or the coastal resorts. Double, twin and single rooms; tea/coffee, washbasin and radio in all rooms; TV available. Sorry, no pets or smoking. Central heating, log fires. Lounge with TV. Evening meals on request. Good golf courses and fishing in the area. We offer a homely and friendly atmosphere. Open all year except Christmas. Bed and Breakfast from £16 per person.

CLITHEROE. Mrs Frances Oliver, Wytha Farm, Rimington, Clitheroe BB7 4EQ (01200 445295). Working farm, join in. Farmhouse accommodation on stockrearing farm in Ribble Valley with extensive views. Within walking distance of Pendle Hill. Ideal touring centre for Lake District, Yorkshire Dales, Bronte Country, interesting and historic Clitheroe. Children welcome. Babysitting service. Beautiful picnic area. Packed lunches available. Farm produce when possible, and home cooking. Accommodation comprises family and double rooms; TV lounge; central heating. Ample car parking. Pets by prior arrangement (£1 per day). Bed and Breakfast from £14; Evening Meal £8. Reduced rates for children under 11 years. Open all year.

CLITHEROE. Mrs M.A. Berry, Lower Standen Farm, Whalley Road, Clitheroe BB7 1PP (01200 424176). 👑👑 This farmhouse is situated 20 minutes' walk from town centre, one mile from A59 road. Convenient for M6, 20 minutes drive from Junction 31. There are two double rooms en suite, one twin-bedded room with washbasin only and an additional single room if required. TV and tea/coffee making facilities; cot also available. Own lounge with electric fire and TV; dining room. Full central heating. Pets and children are welcome, reduced rates for children under 12 years. Open all year except Christmas and New Year. Golf club nearby. Bed and Breakfast from £17 per person, en suite rooms £20 per person.

See also Colour Display Advertisement   **CLITHEROE. Mrs P. M. Gifford, Rakefoot Farm, Chaigley, Near Clitheroe BB7 3LY (01995 61332/07885 279063).** Working family farm offering accommodation in standard and en suite rooms, some with private lounge. Panoramic views of Longridge Fell and Pendle Hill, ideally situated for walking or touring the Dales, Lakes and coast. Excellent cooked breakfasts; other meals by arrangement. Also self-catering. Bed and Breakfast from £14 to £20 per person per night depending on room and length of stay. Children welcome, reductions for sharing.

FHG Please mention *The Farm Holiday Guide* when enquiring about accommodation featured in these pages.

CLITHEROE near. Miss J.M. Simpson and Mr N.E. Quayle, Middle Flass Lodge, Settle Road, Bolton-by-Bowland, Clitheroe BB7 4NY (01200 447259; Fax: 01200 447300). AA/ETC ◆◆◆◆**.** A warm and friendly welcome awaits in this family-run tastefully converted barn. Unrivalled views across the countryside. Situated in the Forest of Bowland at the heart of the Ribble Valley, ideal base for the Dales and Lakes. We are a small guest house with four en suite bedrooms, all with tea/coffee making facilities, colour teletext TV and room controlled central heating. Residents' lounge. Full English breakfast and four-course table d'hôte dinner served in our dining room using fresh local produce whenever possible, all chef prepared. Licensed. Gardens. Ample private parking. Bed and Breakfast from £20 per person. Please telephone for further details.

LUNE VALLEY. Mrs Shirley Harvey, Low House Farm, Claughton, Lancaster LA2 9LA (015242 21260). English Tourist Board grading applied for. Working farm, join in. Low House is a mixed dairy working farm set in the heart of the beautiful Lune Valley, yet easily accessible from M6 Motorway. Within easy reach of Lake District, North West coast and Yorkshire Dales. Convenient for fishing, golf, waymarked walks and country cycle track. Accommodation in large comfortable farmhouse with guests' own sittingroom. Colour TV and tea/coffee making facilities in bedrooms, two of which have own bath/shower room. Visitors are welcome to relax in large beautiful garden which also has some play facilities for children. Country Pub serving meals approximately 150 yards. Bed and Breakfast £18.

LUNE VALLEY. Mrs Janet Woodhouse, Brow Top Farm, Quernmore, Lancaster LA2 0QW (01524 66833). Working farm. Family-run farmhouse accommodation, convenient for Trough of Bowland. Quiet position in lovely countryside. Excellent range of walks nearby, including Clougha Pike. Outstanding views to Lancaster (three miles) and Morecambe Bay. Three miles from Lancaster University. TV and tea/coffee making facilities. One double and one family bedroom. Both are en suite. Children welcome. Cot available.We have a guests' sittingroom. Parking available. Full English Breakfast and central heating. Brow Top Craft Centre has local crafts and tea-room. Bed and Breakfast from £20.

See also Colour Display Advertisement

LUNE VALLEY. Lancaster Tourist Information Centre (01524 582397). Come and stay on a farm in the Lune Valley. This lovely area of North Lancashire and South Cumbria is known for its stunning countryside and unspoilt villages. There is a variety of farmhouse accommodation to stay in, including B&B and self-catering. Excellent location for visiting The Lake District, Yorkshire Dales, Forest of Bowland, Historic Lancaster and the nearby coast. For general information on the Lune Valley, please contact the Lancaster Tourist Information Centre.

MANCHESTER. Margaret and Bernard Satterthwaite, The Albany Hotel, 21 Albany Road, Chorlton-cum-Hardy, Manchester M21 0AY (0161-881 6774; Fax: 0161-862 9405). ♕♕♕ *COMMENDED.* AA/RAC**.** The Albany Hotel, having recently undergone a major refurbishment, offers luxurious and elegant period accommodation with all the comforts of a modern deluxe hotel, plus the personal attention of the owners. Facilities include Erica's Restaurant, licensed bar, games room and full conference facilities. A choice of single, double or family rooms, all with shower or en suite bathroom, direct dial telephone, colour TV, hair dryer, radio and tea/coffee. Conveniently located being only 10 minutes from the city and Airport, five minutes Manchester United, L.C.C.C., Trafford Shopping Centre, Salford Quays, Trafford Park and Universities. Directions:- just off the A5143 Wilbraham Road, approx. one mile Metrolink, Junction 7 M60 from M61, M6 north. M62 east and west, two miles Junction 3 M56 from M6 south.

PILLING. Beryl and Peter Richardson, Bell Farm, Bradshaw Lane, Scronkey, Pilling, Preston PR3 6SN

Bell Farm

(01253 790324). Beryl and Peter welcome you to their 18th century farmhouse situated in the quiet village of Pilling, which lies between the Ribble and Lune Estuaries. The area has many public footpaths and is ideal for cycling. From the farm there is easy access to Blackpool, Lancaster, the Forest of Bowland and the Lake District. Accommodation consists of one family room with en suite facilities, one double and one twin with private bathroom. Tea and coffee making facilities. Lounge and dining room. All centrally heated. Children and pets welcome. Full English Breakfast is served. Open all year, except Christmas and New Year. Bed and Breakfast from £20.00.

SOUTHPORT. Mrs Wendy E. Core, Sandy Brook Farm, 52 Wyke Cop Road, Scarisbrick, Southport PR8

5LR (01704 880337). ♛♛ Bill and Wendy Core offer a homely, friendly atmosphere at Sandy Brook, a small working farm situated three-and-a-half miles from the seaside resort of Southport and five miles from the historic town of Ormskirk. Motorways are easily accessible, and the Lake District, Trough of Bowland, Blackpool and North Wales are within easy reach. Six en suite bedrooms with colour TV and tea/coffee making facilities. Central heating throughout. Sittingroom with colour TV; diningroom. High chair, cots, and babysitting available. Room available for wheelchair/disabled guest. Open all year round. Bed and Breakfast from £17. Reductions for children. Weekly terms on request. NWTB Silver Award Winner "Place to Stay" Farmhouse Category.

Key to Tourist Board Ratings

♛   **The Crown Scheme**

The English Tourism Council (formerly the English Tourist Board) has joined with the AA and RAC to create a new, easily understood quality rating for serviced accommodation. Hotels will receive a grading ranging from **one to five STARS (★)**. Other serviced accommodation such as **guest houses** and **B&B establishments** will be graded from **one to five DIAMONDS (◆)**. These ratings represent Quality, Service and Hospitality not just facilities. *NB.Some properties had not been assessed at the time of going to press and in these cases the publishers have included the old CROWN gradings.*

   The Key Scheme

The Key Scheme covering self-catering in cottages, bungalows, flats, houseboats, houses, chalets, etc remains unchanged. The classification from **One to Five KEYS** indicates the range of facilities and equipment. Higher quality standards are indicated by the terms APPROVED, COMMENDED, HIGHLY COMMENDED AND DE LUXE.

FHG PUBLICATIONS

publish a large range of well-known accommodation guides. We will be happy to send you details or you can use the order form at the back of this book.

LEICESTERSHIRE including Rutland

BELTON-IN-RUTLAND, Near Oakham. The Old Rectory, Belton-in-Rutland, Oakham LE15 9LE (01572

717279; Fax: 01572 717343). ♛♛ *COMMENDED.* Smallholding with horses and sheep on the edge of this picturesque conservation village overlooking the Eyebrook valley and rolling Rutland countryside. 10 minutes from Rutland Water, Rockingham Castle, Kirby Hall, Launde Abbey and numerous other historical and tourist landmarks including the late Geoff Hamilton's TV gardens at Barnsdale. Excellent walks, cycling, golf, bird watching, water sports and riding locally. A relaxed atmosphere to come and go as you like, offering Bed and Breakfast £22 per person (en suite), and from £18 per person (shared facilities). Children half price, under 3's free. Pets by arrangement. Sorry, no smoking in rooms.
e.mail: bb@stablemate.demon.co.uk.

MELTON MOWBRAY. Mrs D.N. Mellows, Somerby House Farm, Somerby, Near Melton Mowbray

LE14 2PZ (01664 454225). Bed and Breakfast in 18th century farmhouse. Single and double rooms and bath. Family room with bath, WC. TV. Central heating. Children and dogs welcome. Open all year. Stabling for horses May to August. Inns and riding school in village. Nearby places of interest include Rutland Water for boating and water sports, Oakham Castle, Belvoir Castle, Rockingham Castle and Burghley House. The Nene Valley Railway is also close by.

AMBERLEY ◆◆◆
4 Church Lane, Ashfordby, Melton Mowbray, Leicestershire
LE14 3RU Tel: 01664 812314 Fax: 01664 813740

Large modern ranch-style bungalow with river frontage set in one acre of floodlit lawns and gardens in the conservation area of the village. Comfortable en suite bedrooms available all with colour TV and tea making facilities. Centrally heated throughout. Ample parking. Enjoy breakfast in the garden room with the interest of swans and birdlife in the riverbank – and in the evenings watch for foxes and fox cubs on the floodlit lawns. Registered with the EMTB. Shop in the bustling street markets of Melton Mowbray on Tuesdays and Saturdays.
Within half-an-hour car ride of Leicester, Nottingham and Rutland Water.
Excellent meals at the local Inns. Bed & Breakfast from £17.50 per person.
Self-catering holiday annex also available. *Full details on request from* **Mrs D. Brotherhood.**

FREE and REDUCED RATE Holiday Visits!
Don't miss our Readers' Offer Vouchers

LINCOLNSHIRE

BENNIWORTH. Kay Olivant, Skirbeck Farm, Panton Road, Benniworth LN3 6JN (01507 313682; Fax: 01507 313692). Enjoy a stay on a working farm whilst visiting the beautiful Lincolnshire Wolds. The peaceful location is surrounded by good walking country including the Viking Way. It is 16 miles east of the cathedral City of Lincoln and only a few miles from the interesting market towns of Louth, Norcastle and Market Rasen. The east coast and South Yorkshire (via the Humber Bridge), all within easy touring distance. The farm has its own coarse and fly fishing lakes and over four miles of natural lakes. Local atractions include Benniworth Springs off-road driving track, Hemswell antiques, Market Rasen Races and Cadwell racing circuit. The farmhouse is comfortably furnished, has central heating and log fires. All bedrooms have colour TV, Teasmaid and own bathroom. Sun lounge overlooking secluded garden. Children welcome. Non-smokers please. Self-catering cottages also available.

HOLBEACH. Mrs M. Biggadike, Cackle Hill House, Cackle Hill Lane, Holbeach PE12 8BS (01406 426721; Fax: 01406 424659). ◆◆◆◆. We welcome you to our farm situated in rural position just off the A17. Comfortable accommodation (en suites and private facilities) and traditional farmhouse fare. Farm walks, large patio and gardens. Close to the shores of the Wash with its marshes, trails and nature reserves. Spalding, Boston, Norfolk and Cambridgeshire. Prices from £20–£24. Open all year.

LANGTON-BY-WRAGBY. Miss Jessie Skellern, Lea Holme, Langton-by-Wragby, Lincoln LN8 5PZ (01673 858339). Tourist Board Listed. Ground floor accommodation in comfortable, chalet-type house set in own half-acre peaceful garden. All amenities. Central for touring Wolds, coast, fens, historic Lincoln etc. So much to discover in this county with wonderful skies and room to breathe. Attractive market towns, Louth, Horncastle (famed for antiques), Boston, Spilsby, Alford, Woodhall Spa (noted for golf). Accommodation offered in two double bedrooms (can be let as single, no supplement), with washbasins; bathroom, toilet adjoining; lounge with colour TV always available to guests, separate dining room. Drinks provided. Children welcome at reduced rates. Pets welcome (no charge). Car almost essential, parking. Basically room and breakfast, but limited number of evening meals may be available. Numerous eating places nearby. Bed and Breakfast from £20 per person. Open all year.

LINCOLN. Dave Barnes, Ridgeways Guest House, 243 Burton Road, Lincoln LN1 3UB (Tel & Fax: 01522 546878). Ridgeways is an attractive detached guest house with a private car park and pleasant gardens for guests' use. Situated in uphill Lincoln within easy walking distance of the historic heart of Lincoln Cathedral, castle and Lawn Conference Centre. En suite twin, double and family rooms available, all with colour TV, tea/coffee trays, hair dryers; a ground floor room is available for disabled guests. Centrally heated throughout and a non-smoking rule applies for your safety and comfort. Vegetarians are catered for. Bed and Breakfast from £20 to £30. Credit cards accepted. Further information available on request.

When making enquiries or bookings, a stamped addressed envelope is always appreciated.

MARTIN. Mr and Mrs N. Forman, Beechwood Barn, North Moor Lane, Linwood Road, Martin LN4 3RA

(01526 378339). Listed *COMMENDED*. Beechwood Barn, built in 1853 and now managed as a small-holding, has been tastefully converted into a comfortable home retaining its original character. There are many exposed beams together with an imposing spiral staircase winding its way to a double en suite bedroom which was originally the old hay-loft. The pretty twin-bedded room has a washbasin and adjoining private bathroom. Both rooms have colour TV and tea/coffee making facilities. An ideal location for a peaceful and relaxing break. There are numerous places of interest to visit in this area with the Wolds and coast just a short drive away. A full English breakfast is served using our own free-range eggs served to your liking. Dogs are not allowed and Beechwood Barn is a non-smoking Guest House. You are however always assured of a warm welcome.

SPALDING. Mrs C. Cave, Sycamore Farm, 6 Station Road, Gedney Hill, Spalding PE12 0NP (01406

330445; Mobile: 07885 147001). A warm welcome awaits you at Sycamore Farm, a comfortable period farmhouse situated by the B1166 in pleasant rural surroundings. Crowland, with its famous abbey and triangular bridge, is within easy reach as are Stamford, Spalding, Boston and Kings Lynn. The accommodation comprises of double/family rooms with private lounge/ diningroom. Situated in the farm's woodland garden is a fully equipped mobile home to sleep eight. Touring caravans and tents welcome. Also available on the North Norfolk coast, an eight-berth luxury caravan on its own private site of award-winning woodland park. Reasonable terms. Telephone, write or e-mail for further details.
e-mail: sycamore.farm@virgin.net.

THORPE FENDYKES. Mrs S. Evans, Willow Farm, Thorpe Fendykes, Wainfleet, Skegness PE24 4QH.

(01754 830316). In the heart of the Lincolnshire Fens, Willow farm is a working smallholding with free range hens, goats, horses and ponies. Situated in a peaceful hamlet with abundant wildlife, ideal for a quiet retreat – yet only 15 minutes from the Skegness coast, shops, amusements and beaches. Bed and Breakfast is provided in comfortable en suite rooms at £28 per room per night (suppers and sandwiches can be provided in the evening on request). Rooms have tea and coffee making facilities and a colour TV and are accessible to disabled guests. Friendly hosts! Ring for brochure.

MERSEYSIDE

PARKGATE. The Ship Hotel, The Parade, Parkgate L64 6SA (Tel & Fax: 0151-336 3931). ETC ★★ A

character pub serving real ales, guest beers, lagers, fine wines and spirits in our refurbished bar with panoramic views across the Dee to North Wales. The finest food is served in the bar at lunchtimes and early evenings while our restaurant is open every night and serves a traditional lunch on Sundays. En suite accommodation is available at modest prices to suit most pockets.
website: www.scoot.co.uk/ship_hotel

NORFOLK

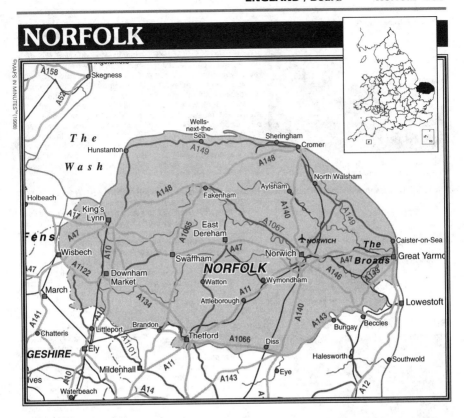

©MAPS IN MINUTES™ (1998)

ATTLEBOROUGH. Hill House Farm, Deopham Road, Great Ellingham, Attleborough NR17 1AQ (01953

453113). 👑 *COMMENDED.* A working farm in quiet rural setting situated within easy reach of all local attractions. We offer our guests a warm welcome, children welcome, pets by arrangement only. Attractions include Banham Zoo, world famous Butterfly Gardens, Snetterton Racing Circuit, riding stables and fishing lakes are close by; seaside resorts and Norfolk Broads are approximately 40 miles distance. Comfortable rooms with washbasins, tea/coffee facilities and colour TV. Ample parking. Open all year. Awarded Good Food Hygiene Certificate. Terms from £18 per person per night. Reduction for children up to 12 years.

ATTLEBOROUGH. Mrs Liz Rivett, Manor Farm, Hingham Road, Great Ellingham, Attleborough NR17

1JE (Tel & Fax: 01953 453388). Manor Farm is situated in a rural location only five minutes from the A11 (20 minutes from Norwich). We are within easy reach of the many and varied places of interest East Anglia has to offer. Set in a large garden backing on to a young woodland, the farmhouse offers a peaceful, relaxing environment. The house has great character with inglenook fireplace and exposed beams. Every effort is made to ensure guests' comfort and the rooms are spacious and well appointed. Further details and terms on request.

BECCLES near. Mrs Rachel Clarke, Shrublands Farm, Burgh St. Peter, Near Beccles, Suffolk NR34 0BB

(01502 677241; mobile 07798 784018). ◆◆◆◆This attractive homely farmhouse offers a warm and friendly welcome, is peacefully situated in the Waveney Valley on the Norfolk/Suffolk border, and is surrounded by one acre of garden and lawns. The River Waveney flows through the 550 acres of mixed working farmland; opportunities for bird-watching. Ideal base for touring Norfolk and Suffolk; Beccles, Lowestoft, Great Yarmouth and Norwich are all within easy reach. The house has two double rooms with en suite facilities and one twin bedded room with private bathroom, shower room and toilet. All have satellite colour TV and tea/coffee making facilities; dining room, lounge with colour satellite TV. Non-smoking rooms available. No pets. Car essential, ample parking. Tennis court available. Swimming pool and food at River Centre nearby. Open all year except Christmas. Bed and Breakfast from £20 per person. Reductions for longer stays. SAE please.

BROOKE. Mrs Daphne Vivian-Neal, Welbeck House, Brooke, Near Norwich NR15 1AT (Tel & Fax: 01508

550292). We would welcome you to our quiet 300 year old farmhouse surrounded by interesting garden and trees. We cater for vegetarians/vegans given notice. We have one double, one twin and one single room, all with tea-making facilities, and charge from £18 per person, evening meals if required. Dogs welcome. No smoking. Good pubs nearby. Excellent theatres, shopping in new Castle Mall, museums, Otter Trust, churches, beaches, two fishing lakes, specialist nurseries and garden centres, nature reserves, National Trust houses and walks are all within easy distance. We are situated off the B1332 between Norwich and Bungay near Brooke Church.

See also Colour Display Advertisement

CROMER. Mrs Ann Youngman, Shrublands Farm, Northrepps, Cromer NR27 0AA (Tel & Fax: 01263 579297). ETB/AA
◆◆◆◆. Shrublands Farm is an arable farm set in the village of Northrepps, two-and-a-half miles south east of Cromer and 20 miles north of Norwich. This is the ideal situation for exploring the wonderful coast of Norfolk, National Trust Properties and the Norfolk Broads. The Victorian/Edwardian house has three bedrooms all with private facilities, colour TV and tea/coffee facilities. There is full central heating and plenty of parking space. Evening Meal by arrangement. This is a no smoking house. Children over 12 years welcome. Sorry, no pets. From £21 to £27 per person per night. Recommended by "Which?" Magazine.
email: youngman@farming.co.uk
website: www.broadland.com/shrublands

DEREHAM. Mrs Pam Gray, Sycamore House, Yaxham Road, Mattishall NR20 3PE (01362 858213).

A guesthouse offering friendly, personal service, ideal for overnight stops and short breaks. Quiet rural location in central Norfolk within easy reach of Norwich, The Broads, beaches, country houses, etc. All rooms with colour TV, washbasins, tea/coffee making facilities. Separate WC and shower for guests' use. Traditional home cooking with fruit and vegetables from the garden in season. Early breakfasts if required, served with a smile. Village pub within walking distance. Ample off road parking. We regret no pets. Bed and Breakfast from £16.50; three-course Evening Meal £9.50.

DICKLEBURGH. Mrs Somerville, 'Avalon', Norwich Road, Near Diss IP21 4NJ (01379 741906).

Attractive 17th century beamed house with inglenook in lounge. We welcome our guests and provide comfortable rooms – twin or double – with private facilities, television, hostess tray and full English breakfast. Situated near Norwich, the Broads and the historic market town of Diss. Excellent centre for touring and cycling, or visiting Bressingham Gardens and Steam Museum. Terms from £20 per person.

DOCKING. Mrs S.J. Williams, Staffordshire House, Station Road, Docking, King's Lynn PE31 8LS (01485 518709; Mobile 07774 609357). AA ◆◆◆◆. A small, stylish guest house, Staffordshire offers privacy or 'en famille' company. A choice of single or double bedrooms, residents' drawing and dining rooms, together with a pretty garden for the summer and roaring fires in the winter. Five miles from Burnham Market, six from Sandringham and four-and-a-half-miles from the coast and glorious deserted beaches. Bird-watching, golf, sailing, historic houses and shrines are all in the vicinity and Staffordshire House offers an ideal base to explore North Norfolk. Bed and Breakfast prices from £26 single room, £19.50 per person sharing a double room. e-mail: vrwsjw@talk21.com

FAKENHAM. Mrs Maureen Walpole, "Hardlands", East Raynham, Fakenham NR21 7EQ (01328 862567; Mobile: 07710 232441). 👑👑 *HIGHLY COMMENDED.* A friendly welcome and relaxing atmosphere await you at "Hardlands". Peaceful countryside surrounds the centrally heated house and its pleasant one-acre gardens. Furnished to high standards we offer superior en suite double and twin-bedded accommodation with tea/coffee making facilities, colour TV and teletext. East Raynham is a hamlet four miles from Fakenham on A1065. "Hardlands" is an ideal base for North and West Norfolk and the Breckland areas including the Royal Sandringham Estate, Norwich, King's Lynn and several historic houses. Residents' lounge with log fires on those cool or miserable evenings. Bed and full English Breakfast from £20 per person per night. Evening meal by arrangement. Ample Parking.

HOLT. Mrs Lynda-Lee Mack, Hempstead Hall, Holt NR25 6TN (01263 712224). 👑👑 *COMMENDED.* **Working farm.** Enjoy a relaxing holiday with a friendly atmosphere in our 19th century flint farmhouse, beautifully set on a 300 acre arable farm with ducks, donkeys and large gardens. Close to the North Norfolk Coast and its many attractions. Take a ride on the steam train or a boat trip to Blakeney Point Seal Sanctuary. There is a five mile circular walk through our conservation award winning farm to Holt Country Park. Large en suite family room, double with private bathroom. Colour TV, tea/coffee facilities. Large lounge with log burning stove. Non-smoking. Sorry, no pets indoors. Bed and Breakfast from £20.00 per person. Children's reductions. Member of Farm Holiday Bureau. website: www.broadland.com/hempsteadhall

KING'S LYNN, Central Norfolk. Mrs G. Davidson, Holmdene Farm, Beeston, King's Lynn PE32 2NJ 01328 701284). Working farm, join in. Holmdene Farm is a mixed farm with rare breeds situated in central Norfolk within easy reach of the coast and Broads. Sporting activities are available locally, and the village pub is nearby. The 17th century farmhouse is comfortable and welcoming with log fires and beams. One double room, one twin room and two single rooms, all with beverage trays. Pets welcome. Bed and Breakfast from £18 per person; Evening Meal from £10. Weekly terms available and child reductions. Two self-catering cottages, one sleeping four the other sleeping up to eight persons. Terms on request. Please telephone for further details.

KNAPTON. Colin and Fiona Goodhead, White House Farm, Knapton NR28 ORX (Tel & Fax: 01263 721344). Enjoy a taste of country living at White House Farm, our Grade II Listed farmhouse. Whether walking along the nearby sandy beaches or just relaxing in our peaceful gardens, you can certainly get away from it all. The quiet village location combines the historic character of a traditional flint and brick home with the modern touches you need to relax – en suite facilities, four-poster bed, colour TV, log fires/central heating, tea/coffee making facilities. Our full English breakfast includes home-made bread and jams, and Fiona will be delighted to cook your evening meals by arrangement. Bed and Breakfast £20. Self-catering cottages also available. We want you to enjoy and remember your visit; please telephone to discuss your booking or to obtain our brochure. e-mail: GOODHEAD@whfarm.swinternet.co.uk

LONG STRATTON, near Norwich. Mrs Joanna Douglas, Greenacres Farmhouse, Woodgreen, Long Stratton, Norwich NR15 2RR (01508 530261). 👑👑

COMMENDED. Period 17th century farmhouse on 30 acre common with ponds and natural wildlife, 10 miles south of Norwich (A140). The beamed sitting room with inglenook fireplace invites you to relax. A large sunny dining room encourages you to enjoy a traditional leisurely breakfast. All en suite bedrooms (two double/twin) are tastefully furnished to complement the oak beams and period furniture, with tea/coffee facilities and TV. Full size snooker table and all-weather tennis court for guests' use. Families welcome, reductions for three nights or more. Come and enjoy the peace and tranquillity of our home. When sunny, you can sit in the garden; when cold, warm yourself by the fire. Bed and Breakfast from £18. Non-smoking.

NORFOLK BROADS/NEATISHEAD. Alan and Sue Wrigley, Regency Guest House, The Street, Neatishead, Near Norwich NR12 8AD (Tel & Fax: 01692 630233). ◆◆◆

An 18th century guest house in picturesque, unspoilt village in heart of Broadlands. Personal service top priority. Long established name for very generous English Breakfasts. 20 minutes from medieval city of Norwich and six miles from coast. Ideal base for touring East Anglia - a haven for wildlife, birdwatching, cycling and walking holidays. Number One centre for Broads sailing, fishing and boating. Guesthouse, holder of "Good Care" Award for high quality services, has five bedrooms individually Laura Ashley style decorated and tastefully furnished. Rooms, including two king-size doubles, and family room have TV and tea/coffee making facilities and most have en suite bathrooms. Two main bathrooms. Separate tables in beamed ceiling breakfast room. Guests' sitting room. Cot, babysitting, reduced rates children and all stays of more than one night. Pets welcome. Parking. Open all year. Fire Certificate held. AA QQQ. Also self catering cottage, sleeps six available next to guest house. Bed and Breakfast from £22.

SLOLEY (Norfolk Broads). Mrs Ann Jones, Sloley Farm, Sloley, Norwich NR12 8HJ (01692 536281; Fax: 01692 535162). 👑👑 *COMMENDED.* **Working farm.**

Relax and enjoy warm hospitality with good food in our peaceful farmhouse, on our working mixed farm. Comfortable, centrally heated accommodation, three bedrooms (one double/twin ground floor room with shower, one double/twin en suite, one double with private bathroom) tastefully furnished to high standard. Explore nearby Norfolk Broads and the coast. Countryside walks with golf, riding and fishing. National Trust properties, Norwich with its splendid Cathedral and Norman castle are all close by. Open all year (closed Christmas and New Year). Sorry, no pets and no smoking. Bed and Breakfast from £19 to £20 per person. Campers and caravanners welcome. e-mail: sloley@farmhotel.u-net.com

THETFORD. Mrs Cynthia Huggins, Malting Farm, Blo Norton Road, South Lopham, Diss IP22 2HT (01379 687201). 👑👑 *COMMENDED.* **Working farm.**

Malting Farm is situated on the Norfolk/Suffolk border amid open countryside. It is a working dairy farm where it is possible to see the cows being milked and there are farmyard pets. The farmhouse is Elizabethan timber-framed (inside) with inglenook fireplaces. Central heating. Some four-poster beds. Easy reach of Norfolk Broads, Norwich, Cambridge, Bressingham Steam Museum and Gardens. Cynthia is a keen craftswoman in embroidery, patchwork/quilting and spinning. Bed and Breakfast from £20.

Terms quoted in this publication may be subject to increase if rises in costs necessitate

THURSFORD. Mrs Sylvia Brangwyn, The Heathers, Hindringham Road, Thursford, Fakenham NR21  **0BL (01328 878352).** Very quiet country location ideal for touring, walking and visiting stately homes (i.e. Sandringham, Holkham Hall, Blickling and Felbrigg), bird watching at Cley, Titchwell and Blakeney Point; Walsingham Shrine four miles. There is one ground floor double room with one twin and one double on first floor; all rooms have private en suite with shaver points, colour TV and tea/coffee making facilities. Full central heating. Christmas and New Year Breaks. Car is essential; ample parking facilities. Bed and Breakfast from £19 to £21 per person per night on two people sharing; optional Evening Meals by prior arrangement.

"The Heathers"

WYMONDHAM. Mrs J. Durrant, Rose Farm, School Lane, Suton, Wymondham NR18 9JN (01953  **603512). ETC & RAC Listed.** 17th Century farmhouse set in eight acres of pasture where our donkeys graze. Rose Farm is situated two-and-a-half miles from Attleborough and the charming market town of Wymondham, with its historic twin-towered abbey church and three-quarters-of-a-mile from A11 London to Norwich trunk road, giving easy access to coastal resorts. All bedrooms are ground floor and have colour TV and beverage making facilities. Central heating throughout. Convenient for Snetterton Race Course. Bed and Breakfast from £19. Reductions for children under 10 years.

WYMONDHAM. Mrs Joy Morter, Home Farm, Morley, Wymondham NR18 9SU (01953 602581).  Comfortable accommodation set in four acres, quiet location, secluded garden. Conveniently situated off A11 between Attleborough and Wymondham, an excellent location for Snetterton and only 20 minutes from Norwich and 45 minutes from Norfolk Broads. Accommodation comprises two double room and one twin-bedded room, all with TV, tea/coffee facilities and central heating. Children over five years old welcome, but sorry no animals and no smoking. Bed and Breakfast from £18 per person per night.

Key to Tourist Board Ratings

 ### The Crown Scheme

The English Tourism Council (formerly the English Tourist Board) has joined with the AA and RAC to create a new, easily understood quality rating for serviced accommodation. Hotels will receive a grading ranging from **one to five STARS (★)**. Other serviced accommodation such as **guest houses** and **B&B establishments** will be graded from **one to five DIAMONDS (◆)**. These ratings represent Quality, Service and Hospitality not just facilities. *NB.Some properties had not been assessed at the time of going to press and in these cases the publishers have included the old CROWN gradings.*

The Key Scheme

The Key Scheme covering self-catering in cottages, bungalows, flats, houseboats, houses, chalets, etc remains unchanged. The classification from **One to Five KEYS** indicates the range of facilities and equipment. Higher quality standards are indicated by the terms APPROVED, COMMENDED, HIGHLY COMMENDED AND DE LUXE.

NORTHAMPTONSHIRE

KETTERING. Mrs A. Clarke, Dairy Farm, Cranford St. Andrew, Kettering NN14 4AQ (01536 330273).

👑👑👑 *COMMENDED*. Enjoy a holiday in our comfortable 17th century farmhouse with oak beams and inglenook fireplaces. Four-poster bed now available. Peaceful surroundings, large garden containing ancient circular dovecote. Dairy Farm is a working farm situated in a beautiful Northamptonshire village just off the A14, within easy reach of many places of interest or ideal for a restful holiday. Good farmhouse food and friendly atmosphere. Open all year, except Christmas. Bed and Breakfast from £22 to £30 (children under 10 half price); Evening Meal £12.50.

LONG BUCKBY. Carrie and Brian Hart, Murcott Mill, Long Buckby NN6 7QR (01327 842236). 👑👑👑

COMMENDED. Murcott Mill is an imposing Georgian mill house set within a working farm. It has a large garden and lovely outlook over open countryside. All rooms are en suite with colour TV. Central heating throughout and visitors have their own lounge and dining room with open log fires. An ideal stopover, close to M1 and good location for touring the area. Children and pets welcome. Bed and Breakfast from £20; Evening Meal from £7.50. Open all year.

PETERBOROUGH. Trudy Dijksterhuis, Lilford Lodge Farm, Barnwell, Oundle, Peterborough PE8 5SA (01832 272230). ◆◆◆◆. Mixed farm set in the attractive Nene Valley, situated on the A605 three miles south of Oundle and five miles north of the A14. Peterborough and Stamford are within easy reach. Guests stay in the recently converted original 19th century farmhouse. All bedrooms have en suite bathrooms, central heating, TV, radio and tea/coffee making facilities. Comfortable lounge and separate dining room. Open all year except Christmas and New Year. Children welcome. Coarse fishing available. Bed and Breakfast from £20. Reductions for children and for longer stays.

e-mail: trudy@lilford-lodge.demon.co.uk

QUINTON. Mrs Margaret Turney, Quinton Green Farm, Quinton NN7 2EG (01604 863685; Fax: 01604 862230). ETC/AA ◆◆◆◆ *SILVER AWARD* The Turney family look forward to welcoming you to their comfortable, rambling 17th century farmhouse only 10 minutes from Northampton, yet overlooking lovely rolling countryside. We are close to Salcey Forest with its wonderful facilities for walking. M1 Junction 15 is just five minutes away; central Milton Keynes 20 minutes. All rooms en suite. Children and pets welcome. Piano and billiards room. Open all year. Bed and Breakfast from £25 single, £45 double.

NORTHUMBERLAND

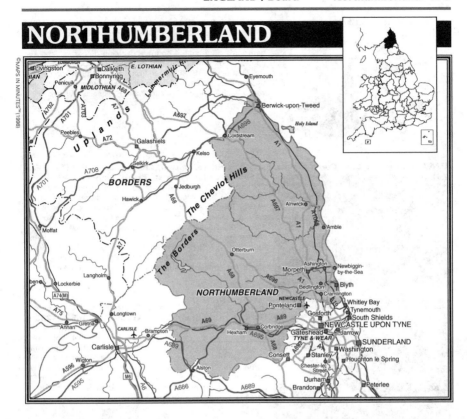

ALNMOUTH. Mrs A. Stanton, Mount Pleasant Farm, Alnmouth, Alnwick NE66 3BY (01665 830215). Mount Pleasant is situated on top of a hill on the outskirts of the seaside village of Alnmouth, with spectacular views of the surrounding countryside. We offer fresh air, sea breezes, green fields, beautiful beaches, country roads and peace and quiet. There are two golf courses and a river meanders around the farm with all its bird life. There are also historic castles, Holy Island, the Farnes and the Cheviots to explore. Farmhouse has large rooms, with washbasins, TV, tea-making and en suite facilities. Guest bathroom. Ample parking. Prices from £20.

ALNMOUTH. Janice and Norman Edwards, Westlea, 29 Riverside Road, Alnmouth NE66 2SD (Tel: 01665 830730) ETC ◆◆◆◆ We invite you to relax in the warm, friendly atmosphere of "Westlea" situated at the side of the Aln Estuary. We have an established reputation for providing a high standard of care and hospitality. Guests start the day with a hearty breakfast of numerous choices and in the evening a varied and appetising four-course traditional meal is prepared using local produce. All bedrooms are bright, comfortable and en suite with colour TVs, hot drinks facilities, central heating and electric blankets. Two bedrooms on the ground floor. Large visitors' lounge and diningroom overlooking the estuary. Ideal for exploring castles, Farne Islands, Holy Island, Hadrian's Wall. Fishing, golf, pony trekking, etc within easy reach. Private parking. Bed and Breakfast from £20; Bed, Breakfast and Evening Meal from £32. Numerous Hospitality awards.

**ALNMOUTH. John & Christina Tanney, Marine House Private Hotel, Marine Road, Alnmouth NE66
2RW (01665 830349). ETC/AA** ◆◆◆◆.Charming hotel in
fine sea front location. Ten individually appointed en suite
bedrooms, four-course gourmet candlelit dinner, cocktail bar,
games room. Dinner, Bed and Breakfast. Low Season from £38
Daily per person: High Season from £44. Northumbrian Log Fire
Breaks: October/April. Children over seven years and pets very
welcome. RAC Highly Acclaimed and Hospitality Awards..

**ALNWICK near. Mrs Celia Curry, Howick Scar Farm House, Craster, Alnwick NE66 3SU (Tel & Fax:
01665 576665). Tourist Board Listed** *COMMENDED.*
Comfortable farmhouse accommodation on working mixed farm
situated on the Heritage Coast between the villages of Craster and
Howick. Ideal base for walking, golfing, bird-watching or exploring
the coast, moors and historic castles. The Farne Islands famous for
their colonies of seals and seabirds, and Lindisfarne (Holy Island)
are within easy driving distance. Accommodation is in two double
rooms with washbasins. Guests have their own TV lounge/dining
room with full central heating. Bed and Breakfast from £16. Open
May to November. Also member of Farm Holiday Bureau.

See also Colour Display Advertisement **AMBLE near. Mrs L.A. Marshall, Togston Hall Farm House,
North Togston, Near Amble NE65 0HR (01665 712699).**
♨♨♨ *COMMENDED.* Tranquil farmhouse atmosphere and
personal service in country setting. En suite bedrooms plus
adjacent cottage for four or more. Colour TV. Varied breakfast
menu using our own eggs, Craster kippers, etc and traditional
home cooked food served for our ever popular five course
evening meal at 7pm. Private parking. Bed and Breakfast from £19
per person per night; Dinner, Bed and Breakfast from £29 per
person per night. Weekly rates available.

**CORBRIDGE. Mrs M.J. Matthews, The Hayes, Newcastle Road, Corbridge NE45 5LP (01434
632010).** ◆◆. Large spacious stone-built country house set in
seven acres of gardens and woodland, on the edge of this historic
village, and with easy nearby access to the A69 and A1M. All
rooms with tea/coffee facilities and TV, and most en suite. Stair lift
available. Well furnished throughout. Plenty of car parking. Bed
and Breakfast from £18.50 with reductions for children. Self-
catering cottages also available (3 Keys Commended). Further
details and brochure on request.
e-mail: MJCT@mmatthews.fsbusiness.co.uk

**HADRIAN'S WALL. Pauline and Brian Staff, Holmhead Guest House on Thirlwall Castle Farm,
Hadrian's Wall, Greenhead, Via Carlisle CA6 7HY (Tel &
Fax: 016977 47402). ETC** ◆◆◆◆ AA QQQ Recommended.
This former farmhouse is not only built on Hadrian's Wall but
also of it. It has stone arches, exposed beams and antique
furnishings. Your host was a former Tour Guide and is an expert
on Hadrian's Wall. Guests dine together for fantastic breakfasts
and candlelit evening meals. A good wine list is available. Guide
books, tea/coffee etc are available in the upstairs lounge which
has an open fire. Four cosy bedrooms with shower/toilet. No
smoking. Bed and Breakfast from £26, Evening Meal £19. Special
breaks and discount ticket available. Winter Ghost Trail weekends.
e-mail: Holmhead@hadrianswall.freeserve.co.uk

HALTWHISTLE. Mrs Pat Murray, Oaky Knowe Farm, Haltwhistle NE47 0NB (01434 320648). Tourist Board Listed *COMMENDED*. A 300 acre working hill farm situated only half a mile from Haltwhistle and approximately two miles from Hadrian's Wall itself. Set in an abundance of hills and trees, you will find your stay here a most peaceful and idyllic one with only the sound of the odd sheep or cow in the distance. We can offer you a home from home atmosphere and rooms are very spacious, each with TV, tea/coffee making facilities and breath-taking views. Private facilities available. Traditional English breakfast and farmhouse evening dinner (if required). Children welcome. Bed and Breakfast from £17.50 each in double room, £20 single. Reductions for children. £2.50 supplement per person for private bathroom.

HALTWHISTLE. Mrs K. McNulty, Saughy Rigg Farm. Twice Brewed, Haltwhistle NE49 9PT (01434 344120) ETC ◆◆◆ A warm welcome awaits you at our beautifully converted farm buildings complex situated in the Northumberland National Park close to Hadrian's Wall and central for touring the Scottish Borders and the Lake District with Newcastle only 35 miles away. Fishing, walking and bird-watching are only a few of the local attractions for your enjoyment. Stabling is available on the farm. We offer comfortable accommodation of the highest standard comprising one twin room and one family room (sleeps five). Rooms are en suite and include tea/coffee making facilities. Read a book, watch television or just relax in our cosy guests' lounge. Short Breaks available. Children and pets are most welcome. Bed and Breakfast £15 per person. Evening Meal optional.

HAYDON BRIDGE. Mrs Eileen Stephenson, West Mill Hills, Haydon Bridge NE47 6JR (01434 684387). Tourist Board Listed *APPROVED*. 17th century farm house in beautiful garden on a working farm. Visitors are met with a warm welcome. Very central for Hadrian's Wall and Kielder. Accommodation comprises one single, one double/family and one twin-bedded room, all have tea/coffee making facilities and TV. Central heating. Children welcome. Bed and Breakfast from £18. Open May to November.

HEXHAM. Judy Stobbs, High Dalton Farm, High Dalton, Hexham NE46 2LB (01434 673320). Listed *COMMENDED*. **Working farm**. Stone-built, family-run working farm in a beautiful setting. An ideal touring base for local attractions including the busy nearby market town of Hexham and Hadrian's Wall. In addition to our comfortable bedrooms we have a guest sitting room with log fires. Children welcome. Bed and breakfast from £15 per person per night.

HEXHAM. Mrs Valerie Gibson, Gibbs Hill Farm, Bardon Mill, Hexham NE47 7AP (Tel & Fax: 01434 344030). 👑👑 *COMMENDED*. Spacious farmhouse accommodation on traditional 700 acre hill farm/nature reserve in National Park. The beautifully furnished en suite rooms, one twin and one double, have tea/coffee facilities and colour TV and enjoy spectacular views. Excellent breakfasts are served in the farmhouse kitchen, and there is a guests' lounge. Private fishing on own small lake, walking, riding, birdwatching from bird hide overlooking Greenlee Lough. Five minutes to Roman Wall and main Roman sites. Open April to October. Children over 12 welcome. Bed and Breakfast from £17.50.

HEXHAM. Mrs Ruby Keenleyside, Struthers Farm, Catton, Allendale, Hexham NE47 9LP (01434

683580). *TOURIST BOARD INSPECTED.* Struthers Farm offers a warm welcome in the heart of England, with many splendid local walks from the farm itself. Panoramic views. Situated in an area of outstanding beauty. Double/twin rooms, en suite, central heating. Good farmhouse cooking. Ample safe parking. Come and share our home and enjoy beautiful countryside. Children welcome, pets by prior arrangement. Open all year. Bed and Breakfast from £18; Evening Meal from £10. Farm Holiday Bureau Member.

HEXHAM. Shirley and John Richardson, High Yarrow Farm, Falstone, Bellingham, Hexham NE48 1BG

(01434 240264). Yarrow is a quiet hamlet on the banks of the River North Tyne near to Kielder Water Reservoir. This area is ideal for leisure pursuits: walking, fishing, sailing, cycling, etc. and in general is a picturesque rural setting. There are two pubs half-a-mile away for evening meals. The farmhouse has one twin and one single bedroom, tea making facilities, comfortable sitting room with TV and a lovely garden. Private bathroom for both rooms. Bed and Breakfast from £16 per person per night.

NINEBANKS. Mrs Mavis Ostler, Taylor Burn, Ninebanks, Hexham NE47 8DE (01434 345343). Warm welcome, good food on quiet working hill farm with spectacular views of Pennine Dales, three miles above Ninebanks. Large, comfortable, centrally heated farmhouse with spacious bedrooms, hospitality trays; guests' bathroom; guests' lounge with log fires and colour TV; you will be our only visitors. Excellent for walkers, ornithologists, country lovers - but no smoking. Pets welcome. Guests free to join in farm activities, observe cattle, sheep, free range hens - even learn to work a sheep dog or build a stone wall. Bed and Breakfast £18 per adult; Evening Meal £9. Special diets catered for, home produce whenever available. 10% reductions for one week's stay. Write or ring for personal reply.

ROTHBURY. Mrs Helen Farr, Lorbottle West Steads, Thropton, Morpeth NE65 7JT (01665 574672).

Listed *COMMENDED.* Situated in the quite beautiful Whittingham Vale, five miles from Rothbury on a 320 acre farm. Stone-built spacious farmhouse with panoramic views of Thrunton Craggs, Simonside and Cheviot Hills, a perfect base for exploring Northumberland's natural beauty and heritage. Many facilities within four miles, e.g. golf, pony trekking, mountain bikes, fishing and woodland walks. The farmhouse offers spacious TV lounge/diningroom with open fires in colder weather. Bedrooms have tea/coffee making and TV facilities. Guests' bathroom and use of garden. Bed and Breakfast from £16.50. Evening Meal negotiable. Self-catering cottage, sleeps five, also available. Further details on request.

WARKWORTH. Mrs Sheila Percival, Roxbro House, 5 Castle Terrace, Warkworth NE65 0UP (01665 711416). ☻ A small family guest house overlooking historic Warkworth Castle, and in the centre of this unspoilt village. Half-a-mile from sandy beach in a designated Area of Outstanding Natural Beauty. Central for touring Northumberland. Plenty of eating places within walking distance. The accommodation is comfortable and includes one family room and two double rooms. All have private shower and washbasin, are centrally heated and have locks on the doors. There is a lounge with TV, and tea/coffee is available. Open all year. Bed and Breakfast from £17.00, reduced rates for children. Non-smokers only.

NOTTINGHAMSHIRE

FARNSFIELD. Ken and Margaret Berry, Lockwell House, Lockwell Hill, Old Rufford Road, Farnsfield, Newark NG22 8JG (01623 883067). Set in 25 acres with 10 acres of woodland and situated on the edge of Sherwood Forest near Rufford Park on the A614, we are within easy reach of Nottingham, Newark, Mansfield, Worksop and all local country parks and tourist attractions. Small family-run Bed and Breakfast offering friendly service and comfort. All bedrooms are en suite and have tea/coffee making facilities. TV room. Full English breakfast. Ample car parking. Good pubs and restaurants nearby. Brochure available. Rates from £19.

MANSFIELD. Mrs L. Palmer, Boon Hills Farm, Nether Langwith, Mansfield NG20 9JQ (01623 743862). Working farm. Farmhouse accommodation in stone-built farmhouse standing in 155 acres of mixed farmland, 300 yards back from A632 on edge of the village. Comfortably furnished with fitted carpets throughout, the house has electric heating and open fire. Large sitting/diningroom with colour TV. Two double rooms and one twin-bedded room. Children welcome and there are many pets for them on the farm. Babysitting arranged. No Pets. Situated on edge of Sherwood Forest, six miles from Visitors' Centre; eight miles M1; 10 miles A1. Places of interest include Hardwick Hall, Thoresby Hall, Chatsworth House, Newstead Abbey. Pleasant half-mile walk to picturesque village inn serving evening meals. Car essential, ample parking. Bed and Breakfast only from £16 per night. Non-smokers only. Reductions for children. Open March to October inclusive.

STANTON-ON-THE-WOLDS. Mrs V. Moffat, Laurel Farm, Browns Lane, Stanton-on-the-Wolds, Nottingham NG12 5BL (0115 9373488). ETC ◆◆◆. Laurel Farm is an old farmhouse in paddocks with many pets and a National Garden Schemes standard garden. All rooms are spacious and newly refurbished, with en suite or private facilities. have shower and washbasin, four rooms have full private facilities. Teatrays, TV, hair dryer and bath robes for non en suite room. Laurel Farm is on a quiet lane with easy access from M1, A46 and A606. Convenient for tourist attractions. Breakfast is served in a specious dining room and only local produce and our own free-range eggs used. Strictly no smoking. Bed and Breakfast from £21.00 double/twin, £25.00 single per person per night

PUBLISHER'S NOTE

While every effort is made to ensure accuracy, we regret that FHG Publications cannot accept responsibility for errors, omissions or misrepresentations in our entries or any consequences thereof. Prices in particular should be checked because we go to press early. We will follow up complaints but cannot act as arbiters or agents for either party.

OXFORDSHIRE

BANBURY near. Mrs E.J. Lee, The Mill Barn, Lower Tadmarton, Near Banbury OX15 5SU (01295 780349). ♨♨ Tadmarton is a small village, three miles south-west of Banbury. The Mill, no longer working, was originally water powered and the stream lies adjacent to the house. The Mill Barn has been tastefully converted, retaining many traditional features such as beams and exposed stone walls, yet it still has all the amenities a modern house offers. Two spacious en-suite bedrooms, one downstairs, are available to guests in this comfortable family home. Base yourself here and visit Stratford, historic Oxford, Woodstock and the beautiful Cotswolds, knowing you are never further than an hour's drive away. Open all year for Bed and Breakfast from £17.50, reductions for children. Weekly terms available.

FARINGDON. Mr D. Barnard, Bowling Green Farm, Stanford Road, Faringdon, Oxfordshire SN7 8EZ (01367 240229; Fax: 01367 242568). ◆◆◆ Attractive 18th century farmhouse offering 21st century comfort. Situated in the Vale of White Horse, just one mile south of Faringdon on the A417. Easy access to M4 Exit 13 for Heathrow Airport. An ideal place to stay for a day or longer. A working farm of cattle, horse breeding, poultry and ducks. Large twin-bedded/family room on ground floor, en suite. All bedrooms have colour TV, tea/coffee making facilities and full central heating throughout. Perfect area for riding, golf, fishing and walking the Ridgeway. Interesting places to visit include Oxford, Bath, Windsor, Burford, Henley, Blenheim Palace and the Cotswolds. Open all year. Member of the Farm Holiday Bureau.
website: www.leading.co.uk/bgfarm

FARINGDON. Mrs Pat Hoddinott, Ashen Copse Farm, Coleshill, Faringdon SN6 7PU (01367 240175; Fax: 01367 241418). ♨♨ *COMMENDED*. **Working farm.** Perfect place to tour or relax. Our 650 acre National Trust farm is set in wonderful, peaceful countryside, teeming with wildlife. The quiet, comfortable accommodation is a great centre for walking or visiting Cotswolds, Vale of the White Horse, Oxford, Bath, Stratford and all little places in between! So much to see and do. Facilities locally for fishing, golfing, riding, boating and swimming. Many places to eat out nearby. Open all year. One family en suite, one twin and one single bedroom. Bed and Breakfast from £21 to £24. Reduction for children sharing. No smoking please.
e-mail: pat@hodd.demon.co.uk
website: www.hodd.demon.co.uk

FREELAND. Mrs B.B. Taphouse, Wrestlers Mead, 35 Wroslyn Road, Freeland, Witney OX8 8HJ (Tel & Fax: 01993 882003). A warm welcome awaits you at the home of the Taphouses. We are conveniently situated for Blenheim Palace (10 minutes), Oxford (20 minutes), and the Cotswolds (25 minutes). Accommodation is available in one en suite double/twin and one single room with washbasin on the ground floor; one first floor triple room also en suite. All rooms have tea/coffee making facilities. The double and triple rooms have colour TV. Large garden for guests' use. Parking. Visa and Mastercard accepted. Bed and Breakfast from £21.00.

HENLEY-ON-THAMES. Mrs Liz Roach, The Old Bakery, Skirmett, Near Henley-on-Thames RG9 6TD (01491 638309). This welcoming family house is situated on the site of an old bakery, seven miles from Henley-on-Thames and Marlow; half an hour from Heathrow and Oxford; one hour from London. It is in the Hambleden Valley in the beautiful Chilterns with many excellent pubs selling good food. Riding school nearby; beautiful walking country. Two double rooms with TV, one twin-bedded and two single rooms; two bathrooms. Open all year. Parking for five cars (car essential). Children and pets welcome. Bed and Breakfast from £25 to £30 single, £45 to £50 double.

LONG HANBOROUGH. Miss M. Warwick, The Close Guest House, Witney Road, Long Hanborough

OX8 8HF (01993 882485). 👑👑 *COMMENDED.* We offer comfortable accommodation in house set in own grounds of one-and-a-half acres. Two family rooms, one double room; all are en suite and have colour TV and tea/coffee making facilities. Lounge. Full central heating. Use of garden and car parking for eight cars. Close to Woodstock, Oxford and the Cotswolds. Babysitting. Open all year except Christmas. Bed and Breakfast from £15.

MINSTER LOVELL. Mrs Katherine Brown, Hill Grove Farm, Crawley Road, Minster Lovell OX8 5NA

(01993 703120; Fax: 01993 700528). 👑👑 *HIGHLY COMMENDED.* Hill Grove is a mixed family-run 300 acre working farm situated in an attractive rural setting overlooking the Windrush Valley. Ideally positioned for driving to Oxford, Blenheim Palace, Witney (Farm Museum) and Burford (renowned as the Gateway to the Cotswolds and for its splendid Wildlife Park.). New golf course one mile. Hearty breakfasts. One double/ private shower, one twin/double en suite. Children welcome. Open all year except Christmas. Bed and Breakfast from £21 per person per night for double/private shower; £23 per person per night for double or twin en suite.

SOULDERN. Toddy and Clive Hamilton-Gould, Tower Fields, Tusmore Road, Near Souldern, Bicester

OX6 9HY (01869 346554; Fax: 01869 345157). ETC ◆◆◆. Tower Fields is in an unspoilt elevated position with outstanding views, situated half-a-mile from the village of Souldern. A recently renovated farmhouse and barn provide comfortable en suite bedrooms on the ground floor, all with colour TV and tea/coffee making facilities. This is a working smallholding where you will see rare breeds of cattle, sheep, poultry and pigs. Full English breakfast using home produce is available. Stabling and garaging available on request. No smoking. Disabled guests accommodated. Three miles Junction 10 M40. Ideally situated Cotswolds, Silverstone, Birmingham, Oxford. Bed and Breakfast from £24. Full details on request.
e-mail: hgould@souldern.powernet.co.uk

TETSWORTH, near THAME. Mrs Julia Tanner, Little Acre, Tetsworth, Thame, Oxford OX9 7AT

(01844 281423). Charming country retreat with pretty landscaped gardens and waterfall. Quiet location but only two miles from J6 M40. Near Chilterns, Oxford, Cotswolds, Heathrow Airport. Comfy beds, hearty breakfasts, 'olde worlde' style dining room. Open all year with friendly, relaxed atmosphere. En suite rooms; ground floor bedrooms. Tea/coffee making and TV in rooms. Pets welcome. Highly recommended by previous guests. Bed and Breakfast from £18.

WATERPERRY. Allie and Guy Jones, Common Leys Farm, Waterperry Common, Waterperry OX33

1LQ (01865 351266 or 0802 960651; Fax: 01865 358005). We take great pride in offering our guests this delightful accommodation comprising twin, family and double rooms in our Grade II Listed Tudor Farmhouse set in picturesque countryside. Friendly, relaxed and informal, the house is ideal for anyone wanting a restful break or a longer holiday. The "Oxfordshire Way' is right on the doorstep and Oxford is not far. Superb food prepared in the farmhouse kitchen which was previously the milking parlour. Duck pond with resident ducks. Self catering units also available. Children over ten years welcome. Sorry, no pets. No smoking in bedrooms. Vegetarian and special diets catered for. Credit cards accepted. Open all year.

WOODSTOCK near. Mrs B. Jones, Gorselands Farmhouse Auberge, Long Hanborough, Near Woodstock OX8 6PU (01993 881895; Fax: 01993 882799).

♕♕ Situated in an idyllic location in the Oxfordshire countryside, Gorselands has its own grounds of one acre. This Cotswold stone farmhouse has exposed beams, flagstone floors, billiards room (full size table), guest lounge, dining conservatory and tennis court. En-suite rooms, family room, double/twin rooms available. Near to Oxford, Blenheim Palace, East End Roman Villa, Cotswold villages. Children welcome; reduced rates. Bed and Breakfast from £19.25 per person; Evening Meal £11.95. Pets welcome. Licensed. RAC Listed. Elizabeth Gundrey Recommended.

Formal water gardens at Blenheim Palace, near Oxford

SHROPSHIRE

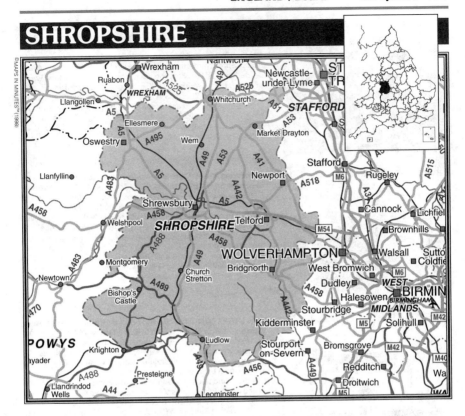

BISHOP'S CASTLE. Mrs Ann Williams, Shuttocks Wood, Norbury, Bishops Castle SY9 5EA (01588 650433; Fax: 01588 650492). Shuttocks Wood is a Scandinavian house in woodland setting situated within easy travelling distance of the Long Mynd and Stiperstone Hills. Accommodation consists of one double and two twin-bedded rooms, all en suite and with tea/coffee facilities and colour TV. Good walks and horse riding nearby and a badger set just 20 yards from the door! Ample parking. Non-smoking establishment. Children over 12 years welcome. Sorry, no pets. Open all year. Bed and Breakfast from £20 per person per night. Credit Cards accepted.

BISHOP'S CASTLE. Mrs Kate Bason, Broughton Farm, Near Bishops Castle, Montgomery SY15 6SZ (01588 638393). ◆◆◆. A warm welcome with tea and home-made cakes awaits you at our lovely Tudor home where you can relax amidst the beautiful South Shropshire countryside. The house has considerable character with its original oak frame structure. Bedrooms are spacious, comfortable and have wash basins and beverage trays. We are a traditional livestock farm and have a pretty garden which guests are welcome to enjoy. Located near the historic town of Bishop's Castle, where good food and drink can be found in some excellent pubs, two of which brew their own beer. Open Febuary to December. Bed and Breakfast from £17, en suite from £19. Sorry, no smoking.

BUCKNELL. Mrs Christine E. Price, The Hall, Bucknell SY7 0AA (Tel & Fax 01547 530249). 👑👑

COMMENDED. You are assured of a warm welcome at The Hall, which is a Georgian farmhouse with spacious accommodation. The house and gardens are set in a secluded part of a small South Shropshire village, an ideal area for touring the Welsh Borderland. Offa's Dyke is on the doorstep and the historic towns of Shrewsbury, Hereford, Ludlow and Ironbridge are within easy reach as are the Church Stretton Hills and Wenlock Edge. Three bedrooms – one twin en suite, two doubles with washbasins. All have tea-making facilities and TV. Guest lounge. Ample parking. Bed and Breakfast from £20 to £22; Evening Meal £10. SAE, please, for details.

CHURCH STRETTON. Mrs Josie Griffiths, Gilberries Farm Cottage, Wall-under-Heywood, Church Stretton SY6 7HZ (01694 771400; Fax: 01694 771663).

ETC ◆◆◆◆. Country cottage adjoining family farm. Quoted as 'an oasis – a haven of peace and tranquillity'. One double en suite bedroom, one twin bedded with private bathroom; both with tea making facilities, radios and hairdryers. Guests' lounge with colour TV and separate dining room are available to guests at all times. Log fires, central heating, spacious parking. A warm welcome awaits. Bed and Breakfast from £18 per person. Excellent evening meals available within a five minutes' drive.

See also Colour Display Advertisement

CHURCH STRETTON. Mrs Lyn Bloor, Malt House Farm, Lower Wood, Church Stretton SY6 6LF (01694 751379). 👑👑
COMMENDED. Olde worlde beamed farmhouse situated amidst specatular scenery on the lower slopes of the Long Mynd hills. We are a working farm producing beef cattle and sheep. One double and one twin bedrooms, both with en suite bathrooms, colour TV, hair dryer and tea tray. Good farmhouse cooking is served in the dining room. Private guests' sitting room. Non smoking. Regret no children or pets. Bed and Breakfast from £18.50 per person per night; Evening Meal from £15.00 per person. Now fully licensed.

CHURCH STRETTON. Mrs Mary Jones, Acton Scott Farm, Acton Scott, Church Stretton SY6 6QN (01694 781260). ETC ◆◆◆. Working farm. Lovely 17th

century farmhouse in peaceful village amidst the beautiful hills of South Shropshire, an area of outstanding natural beauty. The house is full of character; the rooms, which are all heated, are comfortable and spacious. Bedrooms have washbasins and tea/coffee making facilities; en suite or private bathroom. Colour TV lounge. Children welcome, pets accepted by arrangement. We are a working farm, centrally situated for visiting Ironbridge, Shrewsbury and Ludlow, each easily reached within half-an-hour. Visitors' touring and walking information available. Bed and full English Breakfast from £19 per person. No smoking. Farm Holiday Bureau member. Open all year excluding November, December and January.

CHURCH STRETTON. Mrs J. Brereton, Brereton's Farm, Woolston, Church Stretton SY6 6QD (Tel & Fax: 01694 781201). ETC ◆◆◆. Working farm. Peace,

tranquillity and unforgettable views of rambling countryside (including working of sheep dogs) can be enjoyed from extensive gardens surrounding our elegant red brick farmhouse; an ideal base for visiting Ludlow, Ironbridge, Shrewsbury and Powis Castle, or walk onto the Long Mynd from our working farm. Twin and two double bedrooms (one with pine four-poster), all en suite, with tea making facilities and fresh milk. Residents' lounge with log burner. Hearty English Breakfast. Bed and Breakfast from £20, Evening Meal £10.

CLUN. Mrs M. Jones, Llanhedric, Clun, Craven Arms SY7 8NG (01588 640203). 👑👑. Working farm.

Put your feet up and relax in the recliners as the beauty of the garden, the trickle of the pond, and the views of Clun and its surrrounding hills provide solace from the stress of modern day life. Receive a warm welcome at this traditional oak-beamed farmhouse set back from the working farm. Three bedrooms, double en suite, tea/coffee facilities and good home cooking. Visitors' lounge with inglenook fireplace; separate dining room. Walks, history and attractions all close by. Bed and Breakfast from £17.50, Bed, Breakfast and Evening Meal from £27.00. Reductions for children. Non-smoking household. Regret no dogs in house. Open April to October.

CLUN. Miriam Ellison, New House Farm, Clun SY7 8NJ (01588 638314). ETC ◆◆◆◆◆ *GOLD*

AWARD. AA Selected. Isolated, peaceful 18th century farmhouse set high in the Clun Hills near the Welsh Border. Large spacious bedrooms furnished to a high standard with scenic views. One twin en suite and one double with large private bathroom, both rooms have tea/coffee facilities and TV. Hill Farm includes an Iron-age hill fort, "Caer-di-Ring". Many walks start on our doorstep. We provide books to browse through in our large country garden. No smoking. Pets by arrangement. Open April - October. Bed and Breakfast from £25 per person per night. Please ring for brochure.

CRAVEN ARMS. Mrs S.J. Williams, Hurst Mill Farm, Clun, Craven Arms SY7 0JA (01588 640224). 👑👑 *COMMENDED*. **Working farm**. Winner "Great Farm

Breakfast". Hurst Mill Farm is situated in the prettiest part of the Clun Valley, renowned as a completely unspoilt part of England. One mile from the small town of Clun, which has a Saxon church and a Norman castle. Legend says one is wiser after crossing Clun Bridge. Within easy reach are Ludlow, Newtown, Elan Valley, Ironbridge and Long-Mynd Hills. Through the fields runs the River Clun where one can bathe. Woods and hills provide wonderful walks, which can be organised. Fishing and pony trekking locally. The farm has cattle, sheep, two quiet riding ponies. Three double bedrooms, one is en suite, all with washbasins and tea/coffee making facilities; guests' lounge, diningroom. Parking. Children and pets welcome; cot and babysitting. Good food, pretty garden. Dinner, Bed and Breakfast from £27; Bed and Breakfast from £19. Lunches. Open all year. AA Recommended. Mrs Williams is the Winner of "Shropshire's Great Farm Breakfast Challenge". Also two holiday cottages available.

CRAVEN ARMS. Mrs Thirza Watkins, Broadward Hall, Clungunford, Craven Arms SY7 0QA (01547 530357). Listed *COMMENDED*. **Working farm.** Broadward Hall

is a mixed working farm set in the beautiful Clun Valley, nine miles west of historic Ludlow and eight miles east of Clun. The house is an 18/19th century castellated rebuild of an early 12th century residence. The area is ideal for walking and bird-watching. Ironbridge Museums, Central Wales and Severn Valley Railways, National Trust Houses, Border castles and hillforts are all nearby. Two rods available for fly fishing. Two twin rooms (one with washbasin) and one double room are available. Two guest bathrooms, one with shower. Smoking restrictions. £16 per person, £15 for three or more nights. Open Easter (or April 1st) to October.

DORRINGTON. Ron and Jenny Repath, Meadowlands, Lodge Lane, Frodesley, Dorrington SY5 7HD (01694 731350). ETC ◆◆◆. Former farmhouse attractively

decorated, set in eight acres of gardens, paddocks and woodland. Horses and sheep kept. Quiet location in a delightful hamlet seven miles south of Shrewsbury. The guest house lies on a no through road to a forested hill rising to 1000ft. Meadowlands features panoramic views over open countryside to the Stretton Hills. Guest accommodation includes en suite facilities and every bedroom has a colour TV. Guests lounge with maps and guides for loan. Drinks on arrival. Central heating. Plenty of parking space. Strictly no smoking. Bed and Breakfast from £18; Evening Meal from £10 by arrangement. Brochure available

See also Colour Display Advertisement **LUDLOW. Mrs Lewis, Line Farm, Tunnel Lane, Orleton, Near Ludlow SY8 4HY (01568 780400). ETC/AA** ◆◆◆◆◆ Gold Award Tourist Council. Situated five miles south of Ludlow in glorious unspoilt open countryside. Spacious en suite bedrooms, friendly atmosphere, beautiful gardens with panoramic scenery and delicious breakfasts. All this makes Line Farm somewhere truly special to stay. No smoking establishment.

LYDBURY NORTH. The Powis Arms, Lydbury North SY7 8PR (01588 680232). Bed and Breakfast available in country pub. Good food from snacks to full à la carte with friendly and professional service. Accommodation comprises four en suite bedrooms; sittingroom with TV, lounge bar and diningroom. Parking. Fishing and walking. Ideally situated for exploring Shropshire and the Welsh Borders and mediaeval towns of Ludlow and Shrewsbury. Nearby are the world famous Ironbridge and walking or bicycling country of Offa's Dyke, the Long Mynd, Stiperstones and Wenlock Edge. Prices from £25. Self-catering flats and caravan site accommodation also available.

LYDBURY NORTH. Mr and Mrs R. Evans, "Brunslow", Lydbury North SY7 8AD (01588 680244).

Working farm, join in. "Brunslow" is a beautiful Georgian style farmhouse, centrally heated throughout, ideal for walking and those who enjoy the peace and quiet of unspoiled countryside. The house is set in large gardens with lovely views in all directions and the farm produces mainly milk; pigs, poultry and calves are reared and "feeding time" is very popular with younger guests. One double, one single and two family rooms, all having washbasins. Bathroom, toilets; separate sittingroom and diningroom; colour TV, high chair and babysitting available. Open all year, except Christmas, for Bed and Breakfast from £18; Evening Dinner £8 if required. SAE, please, for terms. Packed lunches available. Car essential, parking.

NEWPORT. Lane End Farm, Chetwynd, Newport TF10 8BN (Tel & Fax: 01952 550337). ETC ◆◆◆◆.

Our friendly, interesting farmhouse is set in wonderful Shropshire countryside. The large and comfortable bedrooms are equipped with tea tray and TV. En suite rooms have shower, toilet and washbasin. Relax in our guests' sitting room with log fire. Good woodland walks adjacent to the farm. On A412two miles north of Newport, 15 minutes from Telford centre. Ideal for Ironbridge, Cosford, Weston Park, Hawkstone Park, Potteries and Chester. Bed and Breakfast from £19, reductions for stays of three nights or more, single room supplement applies. Other meals by arrangement, £11 per person. Dogs welcome. For reservations or more information please contact **Mrs Jan Park.**
e-mail: www.go2.co.uk/lef

NEWPORT. Sambrook Manor, Sambrook, Newport TF10 8AL (01952 550256). ETC ◆◆◆. Sambrook

is centrally situated in the heart of Shropshire,15 minutes from Telford and Market Drayton, and 30 minutes from Shrewsbury, Potteries, Stafford, and 40 minutes from Birmingham, Alton Towers and the Welsh Borders. The Manor House, which is a Listed building, is the focal point of the farm which has beef and dairy cattle, sheep, horses and of course the farm dogs. On the ground floor is a large sitting room and conservatory for guests' use, while upstairs are three guest bedrooms. Full English Breakfast cooked to your individual taste. Visitors' room with colour TV. Tea and coffee facility in bedrooms. Private parking. Stabling available for horses – many accessible bridle paths. website: ww.go2.co.uk/sambrookmanor

OSWESTRY. Mrs Margaret Jones, Ashfield Farmhouse, Maesbury, Near Oswestry SY10 8JH (Tel & Fax: 01691 653589). ETC ◆◆◆◆ *SILVER AWARD.* This

warm and friendly old house was once a coach house and later a Georgian farmhouse originating in the 16th century. Full of warmth, charm and character; set in large gardens and orchard just one mile from Oswestry, A5 and A483 roads. All the spacious rooms are fully equipped and have en suite or luxury bathrooms, decorated and furnished in a true country style with lovely views of Welsh mountains; double with connecting family room. Payphone and cot available. Log fires in winter. Wealth of castles, mountains, lakes and valleys to explore. Chester, Shrewsbury and Llangollen about 30 minutes' drive. Excellent food, canal and boat hire only five minutes' walk. Relaxing, welcoming atmosphere. Children and well behaved pets welcome. Bed and Breakfast from £19.50 per person per night. Special terms for short breaks. Details on request.

SHREWSBURY. E.W. and J.A. Bottomley, Lythwood Hall, Bayston Hill, Shrewsbury SY3 0AD (Tel & Fax: 01743 874747). ✿ *COMMENDED*. Quality Bed and Breakfast accommodation in a comfortable, spacious Georgian house. Enjoy the peaceful rural surroundings, our beautiful gardens or the log fire in winter. Relax in the guests' lounge, visit our spotted horses or walk on the Shropshire Way. We are centrally placed for guests to tour Shropshire and the Welsh Borders. The medieval town of Shrewsbury is just three miles away and we offer a collection service from the railway station. There is easy access to all main routes, e.g. A5, A49, M54, M6. We are open all year. Bed and Breakfast £19.50, Evening meal £10. Home-GROwn produce, vegetarians welcome.

See also Colour Display Advertisement

TELFORD. Mrs Mary Jones, Red House Farm, Longdon-on-Tern, Wellington, Telford TF6 6LE (01952 770245). Red House Farm is a late Victorian farmhouse in the small village of Longdon-on-Tern, noted for its aqueduct, built by Thomas Telford in 1796. Two double bedrooms have private facilities, one family room has its own separate bathroom. All rooms are large and comfortable. Excellent breakfast. Farm easily located, leave M54 Junction 6, follow A442, take B5063. Central for historic Shrewsbury, Ironbridge Gorge museums or modern Telford. Several local eating places. Open all year. Families most welcome, reductions for children. Pets also welcome. Bed and Breakfast from £16 to £20..
Website: www.go2.co.uk/redhousefarm

TELFORD. John and Rosemarie Hawkins, Hill View Farm, Buildwas, Near Ironbridge, Telford TF8 7BP (01952 432228). Hill View Farm is set in open countryside with splendid views of the Severn Valley, situated on the A4169 road between the historic town of Much Wenlock and also convenient for Telford and Shrewsbury. Accommodation is non-smoking, peaceful, clean and friendly offering guests hearty breakfasts or lighter options if preferred. Bedrooms are traditional in decor with beverage trays, washbasins with bathrooms next door. Rates from £16 to £20 per person per night. Reductions for three nights or more.

WELSH/SHROPSHIRE BORDER. Mrs Hibbert, Corner House Farm, The Cadney, Bettisfield, Near Whitchurch SY13 2LD (01948 710572). Smallholding in idyllic surroundings, peacefully situated with lovely walks. Easy access to Mid Wales and North Wales coastal resorts and within easy reach of Chester, Shrewsbury and Whitchurch. One single, one twin or family suite with bathroom. Rates start at £16 per person; Evening Meal on request. Open all year except Christmas.

WHITCHURCH. Miss J. Gregory, Ash Hall, Ash Magna, Whitchurch SY13 4DL (01948 663151). Tourist Board Listed. Working farm. An early 18th century house set in large garden with ample room for children to play, on a medium-sized farm with pedigree Friesians. Situated in the small North Shropshire village of Ash, approximately one-and-a-half miles from A41. Within easy reach of Chester and Shrewsbury (about 20 miles); Crewe 15 miles. Interesting features of this house are two oak-panelled reception rooms and an oak staircase; one of the two guest bedrooms is also panelled. One bedroom has en suite facilities. Bathroom, toilet; sittingroom; diningroom. Children welcome, cot, high chair and reduced rates available. Open all year for Bed and Breakfast.

SOMERSET

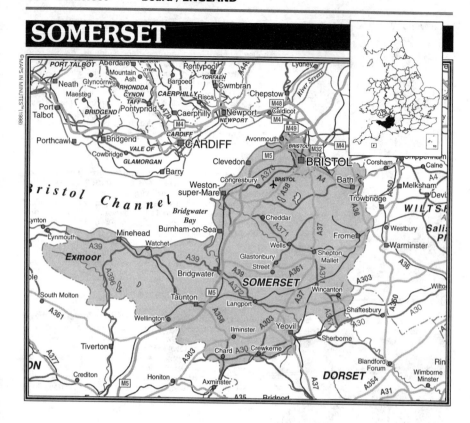

©MAPS IN MINUTES™ (1999)

ASHBRITTLE. Mrs Ann Heard, Lower Westcott Farm, Ashbrittle, Wellington TA21 0HZ (01398 361296). 👑👑 *COMMENDED.*

On Devon/Somerset borders, 230 acre family-run farm with Friesian herd, sheep, poultry and horses. Ideal for walking, touring Exmoor, Quantocks, both coasts and many National Trust properties. Pleasant farmhouse, tastefully modernised but with olde worlde charm, inglenook fireplaces and antique furniture, set in large gardens with lawns and flower beds in peaceful, scenic countryside. Two family bedrooms with private facilities and tea/coffee making. Large lounge, separate dining room offering guests every comfort. Noted for relaxed, friendly atmosphere and good home cooking. Brochure by request. Bed and Breakfast from £18; Dinner £8 per person. Reductions for children.

BATH. Mrs Colin Smart, Leigh Farm, Pensford, Near Bristol BS39 4BA (01761 490281; Fax: 01761 490270). Working farm.

Close to Bath, Bristol, Cheddar, Mendip Hills. Spacious, comfy, stone-built farmhouse with lawns. Twin, family, double rooms, en suite; cot and high chair available. Guests' private lounge with night storage heating and open log fires in cold weather. Traditional farmhouse breakfasts. Tea/coffee facilities, hair dryer. Carp and tench fishing. Close to Blagdon and Chew Valley lakes, both renowned for trout fishing. No pets. Car park. Bed and Breakfast from £22. Also self catering accommodation available (all units with night storage heating) from £150 to £375 weekly.

BATH. Mrs Chrissie Besley, The Old Red House, 37 Newbridge Road, Bath BA1 3HE (01225 330464; Fax: 01225 331661). Welcome to our romantic Victorian "Gingerbread" house which is colourful, comfortable and warm; full of unexpected touches and intriguing little curiosities. The leaded and stained glass windows are now double glazed to ensure a peaceful night's stay. Each bedroom is individually furnished with canopied or king size bed, colour TV, complimentary beverages, radio alarm clock, hair dryer and either en suite shower or private bathroom. Generous four course breakfasts are served. Waffles, pancakes or kippers are just a few alternatives to our famous hearty English grill. Dinner is available at the local riverside pub, just a short stroll away. We are non-smoking and have private parking. Prices range from £20 to £33 per person.

BATH near. Pat Hellard, Pantiles, Bathway, Chewton Mendip, Near Bath BA3 4NS (01761 241519). 👑👑 *HIGHLY COMMENDED*. Delightful house with views over Mendip countryside. Sample the locally baked bread and free range eggs. Ideal base for visits to Bath, Wells, Cheddar, Glastonbury. We offer three rooms, all with private facilities, colour TV and hospitality trays. Early booking advised. Bed and Breakfast from £19 to £23. Open all year.

See also Colour Display Advertisement

BREAN. Mrs Helen Perrett, The Old Rectory, Church Road, Brean, Burnham-on-Sea TA8 2SF (01278 751447: Fax: 01278 751800). ETC Listed. A friendly welcome awaits you at The Old Rectory, situated next to the village church, within a five minute walk of five miles of golden sandy beach. Comfortable ground floor rooms available with en suite facilities. All rooms have colour TV and tea/coffee making facilities. Large walled gardens, with children's play area. Private car park. Golf and swimming 10 minutes' walk. Horse Riding one mile. Hair and Beauty Salon 75 yards. Restaurants nearby. An ideal base from which to explore local places of interest such as Cheddar Caves, Wookey Hole, Secret World, Animal Farm, Fishing and many more.

BRIDGWATER. Mrs Mary Rowe, Wembdon Farm, Hollow Lane, Wembdon, Bridgwater TA5 2BD (01278 453097; Fax: 01278 445856; Mobile: 07702 272755); ◆◆◆◆ **Working farm.** Enjoy a refreshing and memorable stay at our 17th century farmhouse near the Quantock Hills. Quietly and ideally situated for visiting Somerset, Bath and Wells, North Devon, National Trust properties, excellent golf nearby. Ramble some beautiful walks in the hills or join the Parret Trail at our back gate. Warm romantic en suite rooms with TV, beverage trays etc. Superb gardens. Off-road parking. Tucked away yet easy to find. A place for all seasons. Open all year except Christmas. Bed and Breakfast from £20.00 per night. Non smoking. Sorry no pets.
e-mail: mary.rowe@btinternet.com
website:www.btinternet.com/~accomodation.wembdonfarm/index.htm

BRIDGWATER. Mr and Mrs D. Chappell, Cokerhurst Farm, 87 Wembdon Hill, Bridgwater TA6 7QA (Tel 01278 422330 Mobile: 0850 692065). ETC ◆◆◆◆ Working farm. We would like to welcome you to our "Cheerful" home, Cokerhurst Farm a 16th century Somerset longhouse situated just a few yards from the River Parrett Trail. We have three pretty en suite bedrooms, all with comfortable beds, TV, central heating and tea/coffee facilities. A good hearty breakfast is served to you in the diningroom which overlooks the lake and fields beyond. You may then just like to relax in the walled garden, away from all the stress and strain, add a backdrop of cornfields and the rolling Quantock Hills, perhaps this is your idea of tranquillity. Non-smoking. Bed and Breakfast £24 per person per night. Farm Holiday Bureau Member.

The Cottage
Fordgate, Bridgwater,
Somerset TA7 0AP
Tel: 01278 691908
Beverley & Victor Jenkins

A charming country cottage set in two acres of garden in an area of outstanding natural beauty and special interest, close to rivers and canal where birds and wildlife flourish.

A centre for the famous Somerset Levels and all of this historic county.

We offer you privacy, comfort and tranquillity, staying in king-size antique four-poster or twin-bedded en suite rooms with TV and heating. Easy access with all rooms at ground level opening directly onto the gardens.

Evening Meals available by arrangement. English country cooking at its best, using our own fresh vegetables, fruit, honey and free-range eggs.

Bed and Breakfast from £18pp per night

Easy access Junction 24 M5. Ample secure parking. No smoking in house please. A delightful place to stay which is highly recommended.
Phone or write for brochure and map.

Open all year.
e-mail: Jenkins@thecottage.fsnet.co.uk

BRIDGWATER. Nicky and Harry Sanders, 1 Priory Cottages, Chilton Polden Hill, Bridgwater TA7 9AH (01278 723054). Nicky and Harry Sanders invite you to enjoy Bed and Breakfast in their 200-year-old country cottage, which is situated next to the interesting "Chilton Priory", in the heart of England's beautiful West Country. Visit the Tor Hill at Glastonbury, the ancient seat of Christianity, with its Abbey and legends of King Arthur and his Knights of the Round Table, a mere eight miles distant en route to Wells and Bath. The Quantock Hills and Exmoor, Lorna Doone country, the enchanting North Devon and Somerset coast are within easy reach. Several nearby Inns offer an excellent variety of reasonably priced meals. Bed and Breakfast from £18 per person.

BRIDGWATER. Mr and Mrs Sally and Norman Hunt, West Town Farm, Greinton, Bridgwater TA7 9BW (01458 210277). ETC ◆◆◆. A warm welcome awaits you at West Town Farm, a comfortable 17th century country house in the village of Greinton. Ideally situated on the A361 Street-Taunton road for exploring the beauties of the Somerset countryside and within easy reach of coastal resorts. Breakfast is served in the flag-stoned diningroom and each bedroom has en suite shower and toilet, tea/coffee making facilities and colour TV. Guest lounge with inglenook fireplace. Bed and Breakfast from £20 to £24. Reductions for children sharing. Open March to September. Car essential - parking. Non-smokers please.

When making enquiries or bookings,
a stamped addressed envelope is always appreciated.

Brinsea Green Farm

Brinsea Green is a 500 acre dairy, beef and sheep farm situated at the end of a quiet country lane surrounded by open fields. Easy access from M5 exit 21, A38 and Bristol International Airport. Period farmhouse with comfortable dining room lounge with TV both featuring inglenook fireplaces. The accommodation comprises two en suite bedrooms and two with basins sharing a bathroom. All with hot drinks facilities. The historic towns of Bath, Bristol and Wells, the natural wonders of Cheddar and Wookey Hole are nearby.

Mrs Delia Edwards,
Brinsea Green Farm
Brinsea Lane, Congresbury,
Near Bristol BS19 5JN
Tel: (01934) 852278

BRISTOL. Mrs M. Hasell, The Model Farm, Norton Hawkfield, Pensford, Bristol BS39 4HA (01275 832144). ETC ◆◆◆. Working farm. Model Farm is situated two miles off the A37 in a peaceful hamlet, nestling under the Dundry Hills. A working arable and beef farm in easy reach of Bristol, Bath, Cheddar and many other interesting places. The spacious accommodation is in two en suite rooms, one family and one double, with tea/coffee facilities. Separate dining room and lounge with colour TV for visitors. Private parking. Open all year (except Christmas and New Year). Bed and Breakfast from £20.

BRUTON. E. Lemon & N. Daniel, Steps Farmhouse, Wyke Champflower, Bruton BA10 0PW (01749 812788). A delightful, comfortable farmhouse set in picturesque Somerset countryside. No longer a working farm, Steps is a small-holding of goats, sheep, horses and hens. We provide a high standard of vegetarian home-cooking using where possible our own organic produce. Steps is on a quiet country lane but there is easy access to Glastonbury, Wells and Bath. An ideal centre for anyone interested in walking, cycling, horse riding or for those who simply need a restful break. A warm welcome awaits you. One double/one twin (both en suite). Guest sitting room with open fire. Bed and Breakfast from £18.00. Evening meal £7.00.

BURNHAM-ON-SEA. Mrs F. Alexander, Priors Mead, 23 Rectory Road, Burnham-on-Sea TA8 2BZ (Tel & Fax: 01278 782116; Mobile: 0799 0595585). ♛♛ *APPROVED.* "Which?" Recommended. Peter and Fizz welcome guests to enjoy their enchanting Edwardian home set in half-an-acre of beautiful gardens with weeping willow trees and croquet and swimming pool. All three rooms have either twin or king-size beds, en suite/private facilities, washbasins, hospitality tray, colour TV, etc. Peaceful location, walk to the sea, town, golf and tennis clubs. Ideal touring base for Bristol, Bath, Wells, Glastonbury, Wookey Hole, Cheddar and Dunster. A no smoking home. Parking. Easy access to Junction 22 of M5 for Wales, Devon and Cornwall. Bed and Breakfast from £17 to £18. Reductions for three nights.

CHARD. Mrs Sue Eames, Wambrook Farm, Wambrook, Chard TA20 3DF (01460 62371). ETC ◆◆◆. Family farm in the beautiful countryside of the Blackdown Hills. Listed farmhouse and buildings situated in a peaceful and rural village two miles from Chard. An ideal base for visiting Devon, Dorset and Somerset, Forde Abbey and gardens, Lyme Regis and Honiton for antiques. Excellent pub food in village. Tea/coffee facilities in rooms. One double and one family room, both en suite. Double from £40, single £25. No smoking.

CONGRESBURY. Robin and Lucy Stewart, The Old Telephone Exchange, Wrington Road, Congresbury

BS49 5AN (01934 876456). *SILVER AWARD.* Set in the Mendips, we are 20 minutes from Cheddar and Bristol so you can enjoy countryside and culture. We have a large comfortable double room with television, drinks tray and private bathroom. Also single room, campbed available. We can direct you to glorious walks from the house and have spare wellies (sizes 2-10), so there is no excuse! We are both chefs and know Bristol's restaurants (and the local pubs) well so there is no shortage of recommendations. Breakfast is an art at which we excel - you will be well set up with a healthy, hearty breakfast before you leave. Terms from £20 single, £40 double.
e-mail: theold@telephoneexchange.freeserve.co.uk

CREWKERNE. Mr and Mrs A. Emery, Manor Farm, Dunsham Lane, Wayford (01460 78865; mobile:

04676 20031). AA ◆◆◆◆. Beautiful Victorian country home (Portman style) in peaceful location with superb views within easy reach of the coast at Lyme Regis (12 miles), Forde Abbey and Cricket St. Thomas Wildlife Park (three miles). Approximately 20 acres of land with three small coarse fishing lakes, stabling. All bedrooms have en suite facilities, colour TV, tea/coffee tray and are centrally heated. Open all year. Excellent eating establishments close by. Bed and full English Breakfast £22 per person. Reduced rates for children. There is also a self-catering annexe, fully equipped for up to five persons from £150 per week.

DULVERTON. Mrs Carole Nurcombe, Marsh Bridge Cottage, Dulverton TA22 9QG (01398 323197).

This superb accommodation has been made possible by the refurbishment of this Victorian former ex-gamekeeper's cottage on the banks of the River Barle. The friendly welcome, lovely rooms, delicious (optional) evening meals using local produce, and clotted cream sweets are hard to resist! Open all year, and in autumn the trees that line the river either side of Marsh Bridge turn to a beautiful golden backdrop. Just off the B3223 Dulverton to Exford road, it is easy to find and, once discovered, rarely forgotten. From outside the front door footpaths lead in both directions alongside the river. Fishing available. Terms from £16.50 per person Bed and Breakfast or £28.00 per person Dinner, Bed and Breakfast.

DULVERTON. Mrs P. Vellacott, Springfield Farm, Ashwick Lane, Dulverton TA22 9QD (01398

323722). ETC ◆◆◆◆. At Springfield we offer you wonderful hospitality and delicious food. We farm 270 acres within the Exmoor National Park rearing sheep and cattle. Peacefully situated, one-and-a-half mile walk from the famous beauty spot of Tarr Steps, four miles from the market town of Dulverton (film location of The Land Girls). Much wildlife including red deer can be seen on the farm. An ideal base for walking or touring Exmoor and North Devon coastal resorts. Riding and fishing nearby. One double with private WC and shower, one twin en suite and one double en suite - all with drinks making facilities. Guests' lounge with TV, spacious dining room leading to patio and large garden. Access to rooms at al times. Ample parking (garage by request). Pets by arrangement. No smoking in the farmhouse please. Bed and Breakfast from £19.50 to £23.00; Evening Meals with 24 hours notice. £13.00 . Reductions for weekly bookings. FHB Member. WCTB Member. Welcome Host.

See also Colour Display Advertisement

DULVERTON. Mrs A.M. Spencer, Dassels, Dulverton TA22 9RZ

(01398 341203). Superb Georgian style country guest house magnificently situated on the edge of Exmoor, three miles west of Dulverton. Set in nine-and-a-half acres of tranquil grounds with panoramic views. A spacious house with large dining room, separate lounge and log fires. Ten en suite bedrooms with colour TV and tea and coffee making facilities. Dassels is noted for its high standard of comfort and excellent home cooked food. Near the Exmoor National Park with many beauty spots within easy reach, where guests may enjoy horse riding, walking, fishing and nature study. Also places of archaeological and historic interest. Residential licence. Ample parking. Stabling. Open all year. Children welcome.

DUNSTER. Mr & Mrs W.A. Greenfield, Burnells Farm, Knowle Lane, Dunster TA24 6TX (01643 821841). Comfortable and friendly farmhouse accommodation, one mile from Dunster, two miles from sea, with glorious views of Exmoor. Ideal walking or touring centre for the National Park. Accommodation comprises one double, one family and one single bedroom, all with washbasins; one public bathroom and one shower room, toilet upstairs and down; lounge with TV and diningroom. Guests are requested to refrain from smoking indoors. Ample parking. Packed lunches on request. Open Easter to October. Bed and Breakfast £17. Evening Meal, Bed and Breakfast £24. Weekly £154.

EXMOOR. Mrs Blackshaw, North Down Farm, Pyncombe Lane, Wiveliscombe, Taunton TA4 2BL (Tel & Fax: 01984 623730) ETC ◆◆◆. In tranquil surroundings

on the Somerset/Devon Border, traditional working farm set in 103 acres of natural beauty with panoramic views of over 35 miles. M5 motorway only seven miles away and Taunton ten miles. All rooms tastefully furnished. Family rooms, en suite, TV and tea/coffee facilities.Dining room and lounge with log fires for our guests' comfort; central heating and double glazed throughout. Drying facilities. Home produced food and a warm friendly atmosphere await you. Numerous local attractions. Fishing, golf, horse riding and country sports nearby. Dogs welcome. Bed and Breakfast £20pp, Evening Meal £10pp. Weekly Bed, Breakfast and Evening Meal £175pp. North Down Breaks - three nights Bed, Breakfast and Evening Meal £80pp.

GLASTONBURY. Mrs D.P. Atkinson, Court Lodge, Butleigh, Glastonbury BA6 8SA (01458 850575). AA/RAC Recommended. A warm welcome awaits at attractive,

modernised 1850 Lodge with homely atmosphere. Set in picturesque garden on the edge of Butleigh, three miles from historic Glastonbury. Only a five minute walk to pub in village which serves lovely meals. Accommodation in one double, one twin and two single bedrooms; constant hot water, central heating. Bathroom adjacent to bedrooms. TV lounge. Tea/coffee served. Bed and Breakfast from £15.50; Evening Meal by arrangement. Children welcome at reduced rates.

GURNEY SLADE. Mrs Jacqueline Hawkins, Cockhill Farm, Marchants Hill, Gurney Slade, Near Bath BA3 4TY (01749 840125). Farmhouse accommodation on a

working farm keeping a small beef suckler herd in the heart of the Mendips. A friendly atmosphere is assured in this Victorian farmhouse. Excellent home cooking using local produce. We also cater for vegetarians. Bed and Breakfast, optional Evening Meal. Spacious rooms with period furnishings, TV, tea/coffee making facilities. Ideally situated for the Cathedral City of Wells, Glastonbury, Cheddar, Georgian Bath and historic Bristol. Royal Bath and West Showground 10 minutes. Magnificent Chew Valley Lake for bird-watching, fly fishing and picnicking 20 minutes. Good local pubs and peaceful country walks. Children welcome, baby facilities available. One family, three double and one twin room. Open all year. Bed and Breakfast from £17.50.

LANGPORT. Mrs Ann Woodborne, Muchelney Ham Farm, Muchelney Ham, Langport TA10 0DJ (01458 250737). Working farm. ◆◆◆◆◆ *GOLD AWARD.* A

warm welcome awaits you at this 17th century farmhouse situated near the historic village of Muchelney with its Abbey and Priest's House. We are in an excellent centre for exploring Somerset and its wide variety of places of interest. Each room has its own unique character with oak and elm beams, period furniture and comfortable furnishings. All bedrooms are en suite, and guests may also enjoy our large, peaceful garden. A traditional English/Continental breakfast is included. The combination of comfortable surroundings and modern conveniences will ensure that your stay is enjoyable and memorable. Please telephone or write for brochure. Self-catering wing sleeping four/five also available.

MARK. Mrs B.M. Puddy, "Laurel Farm", Mark Causeway, Near Highbridge TA9 4PZ (01278 641216; Fax: 01278 641447). ETC ◆◆. Laurel Farm is on the B3139 road; M5 Junction 22 only two miles and 12 miles from the cathedral city of Wells and five miles from Burnham-on-Sea. Nicely furnished and decorated with large well kept lawn and flower garden at the rear. Doubles, singles and family rooms available ,all en suite with tea/ coffee facilities. Ideal for overnight or short breaks to tour our lovely area. Large sitting room with colour TV, central heating; electric blanket and log fire for cooler evenings.

MARTOCK. Mrs Judith Peach, Falconers Farm, Milton, Ash, Martock TA12 6AL (01935 823363; mobile: 07808 960668). Working farm. A Georgian farmhouse belonging to the Prince of Wales Estates, just off A303 in the quiet hamlet of Milton, one mile from Martock. A working family farm where a warm welcome is assured and a true farmhouse breakfast is waiting for you to sample. Ideal for walking, horse riding or coarse fishing, also just right for breaking a long journey. Near to Montacute House. Accommodation in three guest rooms (one family room sleeping five). Guest bathroom. All children most welcome, cot and high chair available. Bed and Breakfast from £15 per person per night. Telephone or write for further details. We look forward to welcoming you into our house.

MARTOCK. Mrs H. Turton, "Wychwood", 7 Bearley Road, Martock TA12 6PG (Tel & Fax: 01935 825601) ETC/AA ◆◆◆◆. One of the top 20 finalists for 'Landlady of the Year 1999'. Comfortable accommodation in our small pleasant B&B located in quiet position just off the A303. Two double rooms en suite, one twin room with private bathroom. Tea/coffee facilities and TV in bedrooms. Close to the ten 'Classic' Gardens of South Somerset including Montacute House, Tintinhull Gardens, Barrington Court and Lytes Cary (National Trust Properties). Visit Wells Cathedral, Glastonbury Abbey, Lyme Regis and the coast. From £21 per person. parking. NO SMOKING. Credit Cards accepted. Recommended by 'Which? Good Bed and Breakfast'.

NORTH PETHERTON. Mrs Sue Milverton, Lower Clavelshay Farm, North Petherton, Near Bridgwater TA6 6PJ (01278 662347). Working farm. Buzzards, badgers and beautiful countryside surround our traditional 17th century farmhouse on a 250-acre dairy farm. Peaceful, with a relaxed "home from home" atmosphere. Two doubles and one family room, all with tea-making facilities. Sitting/dining room with beams, TV and log fire. Games, books, maps and guide books all freely available. Central heating. Ideally situated for exploring the Quantock Hills, Exmoor, Somerset Levels and coast. Perfect for walking, riding, fishing or just relaxing. Children welcome; cot and high chair available; babysitting. Generous helpings of delicious home cooking using our own produce when possible. Discover why our guests keep returning! B&B from £17 to £20; Evening Meal £10.

QUANTOCK HILLS. Susan Lilienthal, Parsonage Farm, Over Stowey, Bridgwater TA5 1HA (01278 733237; Fax: 01278 733511). Traditional 17th century farmhouse and organic smallholding in quiet location in Quantock Hills with delightful walled gardens, orchard, and walks to explore. Delicious meals are prepared using the farm's produce - fresh eggs, home-made breads and jams - and served before an open fire. Three double bedrooms include colour TV and tea/coffee facilities, en suite available. Guests are invited to enjoy the gardens or relax in the log-fired sitting room. Spacious and welcoming, this is an ideal base for rambling and exploring the Quantock Hills, Exmoor, North Somerset Coast, as well as Glastonbury and Wells. No smoking. Bed and full Breakfast from £18, reductions for children. Optional Evening Meal £15.

SHEPTON MALLET. Mrs M. White, Barrow Farm, North Wootton, Shepton Mallet BA4 4HL (01749

890245). Working farm. This farm accommodation is AA QQQ Listed. Barrow is a dairy farm of 146 acres. The house is 15th century and of much character, situated between Wells, Glastonbury and Shepton Mallet. It makes an excellent touring centre for visiting Somerset's beauty spots and historic places, for example, Cheddar, Bath, Wookey Hole and Longleat. Guest accommodation consists of two double rooms, one family room, one single room and one twin-bedded room, each with washbasin, TV and tea/coffee making facilities. Bathroom, two toilets; two lounges, one with colour TV; diningroom with separate tables. Guests can enjoy farmhouse fare in generous variety, home baking a speciality. Bed and Breakfast, with optional four course Dinner available. Car essential; ample parking. Children welcome; cot and babysitting available. Open all year except Christmas. Sorry, no pets. Bed and Breakfast from £15 to £16. Dinner £10.

SHERBORNE near. Mrs Sue Stretton, Beech Farm, Sigwells, Charlton Horethorne, Near Sherborne,

Dorset DT9 4LN (01963 220524). Comfortable farmhouse with relaxed atmosphere on our 137 acre dairy farm carrying beef and horses in an area with wonderful views and excellent for walking, cycling and horse riding (guests' horses welcome). Located on the Somerset/Dorset border, six miles from Wincanton, four miles from Sherborne and just two miles off the A303. A comfortable, spacious, centrally heated farmhouse with a double room en suite, a twin room and family room with guest bathroom, all with tea/coffee trays. Pets welcome. Bed and Breakfast £16 per person. Less 10% for three or more nights. Evening meals at village inn or by prior arrangement. Open all year.

WEDMORE. Mrs Sarah Willcox, Townsend Farm, Sand, Near Wedmore BS28 4XH (01934 712342;

Fax: 01934 712405). 👑👑 Townsend Farm is delightfully situated in peaceful countryside with extensive views of the Mendip Hills. Set on the outskirts of the picturesque Georgian village of Wedmore with easy access to many places of natural and historic interest, such as the famous Cheddar Gorge, Wells Cathedral, Glastonbury Tor and Abbey ruins and only six miles from the M5 motorway, Junction 22 (one night stops welcome). All bedrooms have tea/coffee making facilities and some have portable TVs. Guests can be assured of a warm and pleasant atmosphere. We offer Bed and Breakfast from £15.50 per person, en-suite from £20. Phone for availability. Farm Holiday Bureau member.
e-mail: smewillcox@farmersweekly.net

Key to Tourist Board Ratings

 The Crown Scheme

The **English Tourism Council** (formerly the English Tourist Board) has joined with the AA and RAC to create a new, easily understood quality rating for serviced accommodation. **Hotels** will receive a grading ranging from **one to five STARS (★)**. Other serviced accommodation such as **guest houses** and **B&B establishments** will be graded from **one to five DIAMONDS (◆)**. These ratings represent Quality, Service and Hospitality not just facilities.

NB. Some properties had not been assessed at the time of going to press and in these cases the publishers have included the old CROWN gradings.

ℙ   **The Key Scheme**

The Key Scheme covering self-catering in cottages, bungalows, flats, houseboats, houses, chalets, etc remains unchanged. The classification from **One to Five KEYS** indicates the range of facilities and equipment. Higher quality standards are indicated by the terms APPROVED, COMMENDED, HIGHLY COMMENDED AND DE LUXE.

WELLS near. Mrs H.J. Millard, Double-Gate Farm Holidays, Godney, Near Wells BA5 1RX (01458 832217; Fax: 01458 835612; 👑👑 *HIGHLY COMMENDED.*

AA QQQQ RAC ACCLAIMED. Accessability Category 1. Located in the heart of Somerset, Double-Gate nestles on the banks of the River Sheppey. This Listed Georgian farmhouse offers guest lounge with colour TV and fully equipped games room; spacious bedrooms with complimentary tea/coffee, all en suite with TVs. Lovely garden; breakfast served outside, weather permitting. Family pets include two golden retrievers and a loving moggy. No restrictions on access. Home from home! Fire Certificate. No smoking, except for gardens. Laundrette available, Ideal for touring Wells Cathedral, Glastonbury Abbey, Wookey Hole Caves, Cheddar Gorge, Bath, Weston-super-Mare. Bed and Breakfast from £22.50; Evening Meals available at village inn next door.

Guide/hearing dogs accepted. Excellent cycling, bird watching area. Self Catering vailable. Credit cards accepted. e-mail:hilary@doublegate.demon.co.uk

---

EXMOOR   Ann & Philip Durbin, 'Cutthorne', Luckwell Bridge,
Wheddon Cross TA24 7EW   Tel: 01643 831255   Website: www.cutthorne.co.uk

Set in the heart of Exmoor, one of the last truly unspoilt areas of the country. Cutthorne is beautifully secluded and dates from the 14th century. It is an ideal base for exploring the coast and countryside – good touring, walking and riding. Fly-fishing is also available in our well-stocked trout pond. The house is spacious and comfortable with log fires and central heating. The three bedrooms have en suite bathrooms and the master bedroom has a four-poster bed. Candlelit dinners with traditional and vegetarian cooking and an excellent choice of breakfasts. Bed and Breakfast from £22.00. Dogs welcome. No smoking.

👑👑👑 **Highly Commended**

The
GOLF
GUIDE
Where to Play
Where to Stay
2000

Available from most bookshops, the 2000 edition of **THE GOLF GUIDE** covers details of every UK golf course – well over 2500 entries – for holiday or business golf. Hundreds of hotel entries offer convenient accommodation, accompanying details of the courses – the 'pro', par score, length etc.

In association with 'Golf Monthly' and including the Ryder Cup Report as well as Holiday Golf in Ireland, France, Portugal, Spain, The USA and Thailand .

£9.95 from bookshops or £10.50 including postage (UK only) from FHG Publications, Abbey Mill Business Centre, Paisley PA1 ITJ

PLEASE MENTION THIS GUIDE WHEN YOU WRITE

OR PHONE TO ENQUIRE ABOUT ACCOMMODATION.

IF YOU ARE WRITING, A STAMPED,

ADDRESSED ENVELOPE IS ALWAYS APPRECIATED.

STAFFORDSHIRE

ECCLESHALL. M. Hiscoe-James, Offley Grove Farm, Adbaston, Eccleshall ST20 0QB (01785 280205).

AA/RAC ◆◆◆ You'll consider this a good find! Quality accommodation and excellent breakfasts. Small traditional mixed farm surrounded by beautiful countryside. The house is tastefully furnished and provides all home comforts. En suite rooms available. Whether you are planning to book here for a break in your journey, stay for a weekend or take your holidays here, you will find something to suit all tastes among the many local attractions. Situated on the Staffordshire/Shropshire borders we are convenient for Stoke-on-Trent, Ironbridge, Alton Towers, etc. Just 15 minutes from M6 and M54; midway between Eccleshall and Newport, four miles from the A519. Reductions for children. Play area for small children. Open all year. Bed and Breakfast from £18. Many guests return. Self-catering cottages available. Brochure on request.
e-mail: accomm@offleygrovefarm.freeserve.co.uk
website: offleygrovefarm.freeserve.co.uk

KINGSLEY. Mrs Jane S. Clowes, The Church Farm, Holt Lane, Kingsley, Stoke on Trent ST10 2BA

(Tel & Fax: 01538 754759). ◆◆◆. A warm and friendly welcome awaits guests on our family dairy farm. Our much loved farmhouse was built in 1700 and has oodles of charm and character, complemented by oak beams and log fires. All rooms are beautifully decorated, spacious and relaxing. Guinevere's Room is a double en suite and quite romantic. Our private family suite consists of a double with brass and iron bed and pine furniture. Next door are pine bunkbeds and family bathroom. Hospitality trays and many extras provided for your comfort. Cottage garden, large lawn, friendly farm animals. Close to Alton Towers, Potteries, Peak District and Churnet Valley.

LEEK. Gwen Sheldon, Middle Farm, Apesford, Bradnop, Leek ST13 7EX (01538 382839). ETC ◆◆◆.
Middle Farm is situated next to Coombes Valley off the A523 Leek to Ashbourne Road at Apesford, near Bradnop. Within easy reach of Alton Towers, Leek town centre, Peak District National park and the Potteries where you will find the famous makes. i.e. Royal Doulton, Wedgwood and others. All rooms en suite, tea/coffee making facilities, TV, radio. Private parking. The dairy has recently been converted into a family room with the elderly and disabled in mind. Bed and Breakfast from £18.

LEEK. Mrs P. Simpson, Summerhill Farm, Grindon, Leek ST13 7TT (01538 304264). ETC/AA ◆◆◆

Traditional family farm set in the Peak District amid rolling countryside with panoramic views. Wonderful for walkers. All three rooms are en suite and have tea and coffee making facilities, colour TV, clock radios. Children welcome. Alton Towers only 15 minutes away, 35 minutes to Potteries. Open all year for Bed and Breakfast from £17.50 to £19; Dinner from £10. Directions – Leek to Ashbourne Road A523 through Onecote, first right for Grindon, three-quarters of a mile up no through road.

SUFFOLK

BURY ST EDMUNDS. Mrs Roberta Truin, Brighthouse Farm, Melford Road, Lawshall, Near Bury St Edmunds IP29 4PX (Tel & Fax: 01284 830385). ETC ◆◆◆◆. A warm welcome awaits you at this Georgian farmhouse with three acres of beautiful gardens, set in glorious Suffolk countryside. We offer quality accommodation in our en suite double (two) and twin rooms. Central heating throughout, TV and tea/coffee facilities. Bury St Edmunds, Lavenham and Long Melford, etc. nearby. Plenty of pubs and restaurants locally. The perfect place to unwind and relax. Bed and Breakfast from £20 to £30 per person per night. Self catering also available.

BURY ST. EDMUNDS. Kate Over, Elmswell Hall, Elmswell, Bury St. Edmunds IP30 9EN (Tel & Fax: 01359 240215). ETC ◆◆◆◆ A fine Georgian house set in open countryside. Large newly refurbished heated rooms with en suite bathrooms. Tea/Coffee making facilities and colour TV. Separate guests' lounge with open fire; hearty breakfasts, relaxed family atmosphere. Heated swimming pool open in summer. Easy access A14 (Cambridge, Lavenham, Aldeburgh) for touring. One double/family and one twin. Open all year. Bed and Breakfast from £20.00.

BURY ST. EDMUNDS. Jenny Pearson, Hay Green Farm, Whepstead, Bury St. Edmunds IP29 4UD (01284 850567). Hay Green Farm, a typical Listed Suffolk farmhouse, is quietly situated off the A143 five miles south of Bury St. Edmunds, close to the National Trust property of Ickworth Park. Ideal base for exploring East Anglia, being close to the picturesque villages of Clare, Kersey, Long Melford and Lavenham to the south; Newmarket and Cambridge to the west. Accommodation comprises an en suite family room, double room and twin room, all with TV and tea making facilities. Open all year. As there are horses, sheep and other livestock on the farm, sorry no pets. Paddock and stabling available for horses. Bed and Breakfast from £20. Good evening meals in local pubs.

Hay Green Farm

EYE. Mrs Sheila Webster, Elm Lodge Farm, Chippenhall Green, Fressingfield, Eye IP21 5SL (01379 586249). ETC ◆◆◆◆. This 112-acre working farm, with early Victorian farmhouse, overlooks a large common (SSSI) where animals graze in summer - the perfect spot for an after dinner stroll. Spacious bedrooms (one en suite), separate dining and sitting rooms, log fires and excellent food ensure that a comfortable, relaxing holiday is enjoyed by all those we warmly welcome to this attractive and peaceful corner of Suffolk. Open March to November. Children over 10 years and pets welcome. Bed and Breakfast from £17 to £21; Evening Meal £12.

FRAMLINGHAM. Mrs J.R. Graham, Woodlands Farm, Brundish, Near Framlingham, Woodbridge IP13 8BP (01379 384444). ♛♛ HIGHLY COMMENDED. Woodlands Farm has a cottage-type farmhouse set in quiet Suffolk countryside. Near historic town of Framlingham with its castle and within easy reach of coast, wildlife parks, Otter Trust, Easton Farm Park and Snape Maltings for music lovers. Open all year. Twin room wih private shower, washbasin and WC; two double bedrooms with bathroom en suite. Diningroom and sittingroom with inglenook fireplaces for guests' use. Good home cooked food assured. Full central heating. Car essential, good parking. Sorry, no pets. Bed and Breakfast from £19 to £20; Evening Meal by arrangement £12.50. SAE or telephone. FHB Member.

FRAMLINGHAM. Mrs Ann Proctor, Grove Farm, Laxfield, Framlingham, Woodbridge IP13 8EY (01986

798235). This is a Georgian farmhouse standing in a 30 acre mixed farm with pigs and sheep, ponies and pedigree breeding dogs. Beautiful view of village and only 12 miles from the coast. Within easy reach of Norwich, Norfolk Broads, historic houses and quaint unspoilt villages. The accommodation is in two double and two family bedrooms (with washbasins); diningroom; lounge with colour television; bathroom, three toilets; full central heating. Children welcome, cot, high chair and babysitting. Sorry, no pets. Open March to November. The emphasis is on a friendly atmosphere with good home cooking – meat, vegetables, honey, etc., mainly produced on farm. Car essential, ample parking. Bed and Breakfast or Bed, Breakfast and Evening Meal; children under 12 years reduced rates. Please phone or send SAE for terms.

FRAMLINGHAM. Mr and Mrs Kindred, High House Farm, Cransford, Framlingham, Woodbridge IP13

9PD (01728 663461; Fax: 01728 663409). Working farm. 👑👑 *COMMENDED*. Beautifully restored 15th Century Farmhouse on Family-run arable farm, featuring exposed oak beams and Inglenook fireplaces with spacious and comfortable accommodation. One double room, en suite and one large family room with double and twin beds and private adjacent bathroom. A warm welcome awaits all, children's cots, high chairs, books, toys, and outside play equipment available. Attractive semi-moated gardens, farm and woodland walks. Explore the heart of rural Suffolk, local vineyards, Easton Farm Park, Framlingham and Orford Castles, Parham Air Museum, Saxtead Windmill, Minesmere, Snape maltings, Woodland trust and the Heritage Coast. Bed and Breakfast from £20. Reductions for children and stays of three nights or more. Self catering available in three-bed Gamekeeper's house set in woodland.

FRAMLINGHAM. Mrs C. Jones, Bantry, Chapel Road, Saxtead, Woodbridge IP13 9RB (01728 685578).

👑👑👑 Bantry is set in half an acre of gardens overlooking open countryside in the picturesque village of Saxtead, which is close to the historic castle town of Framlingham. Best known for its working windmill beside the village green, Saxtead is a good central base from which to discover East Anglia. Accommodation is offered in self-contained apartments (one ground floor), each comprising its own private diningroom/TV lounge and bathroom for secluded comfort. Terms: Bed and Breakfast from £19.50 per night. Non smoking.

FRAMLINGHAM. Mrs Jennie Mann, Fiddlers Hall, Cransford, Near Framlingham, Woodbridge IP13

9PQ (01728 663729). Working farm, join in. Signposted on B1119, Fiddlers Hall is a 14th century, moated, oak-beamed farmhouse set in a beautiful and secluded position. It is two miles from Framlingham Castle, 20 minutes' drive from Aldeburgh, Snape Maltings, Woodbridge and Southwold. A Grade II Listed building, it has lots of history and character. The bedrooms are spacious; one has en suite shower room, the other has a private bathroom. Use of lounge and colour TV. Plenty of parking space. Lots of farm animals kept. Traditional farmhouse cooking. Bed and Breakfast terms from £20.

FRAMLINGHAM. Mr and Mrs D. Strachan, Rendham Hall, Rendham, Saxmundham IP17 2AW (Tel &

Fax: 01728 663440). Tourist Board Listed. A warm red brick Suffolk farmhouse with guests' rooms overlooking the dairy herd's grazing pasture and beyond over tranquil countryside. The bedrooms, one double en suite and one family, both with washbasins, are delightfully furnished and very peaceful. The guests' lounge and dining room have been carefully renovated and are traditionally furnished. Just two miles from the A12, it is an ideal setting for touring the Heritage coastline from Southwold to Aldeburgh; also convenient for Norfolk Broads. We offer comfort and warm hospitality, as well as excellent food. Non-smokers preferred. Bed and Breakfast from £20 to £25.

FRAMLINGHAM. Brian and Phyllis Collett, Shimmens Pightle, Dennington Road, Framlingham,

Woodbridge IP13 9JT (01728 724036). Listed COMMENDED. Shimmens Pightle is situated in an acre of landscaped garden, surrounded by farmland, within a mile of the centre of Framlingham, with its famous castle and church. Ideally situated for the Heritage Coast, Snape Maltings, local vineyards, riding, etc. Cycles can be hired locally. Many good local eating places. Double and twin bedded rooms, with washbasins, on ground floor. Comfortable lounge with TV overlooking garden. Morning tea and evening drinks offered. Sorry, no pets or smoking indoors. Bed and traditional English Breakfast, using local cured bacon and home made marmalade. Vegetarians also happily catered for. SAE please. Open mid March to November. Bed and Breakfast from £20 per person. Reduced weekly rates.

FRAMLINGHAM. John and Liz Bellefontaine, Colston Hall, Badingham, Woodbridge IP13 8LB (01728

638375; Fax: 01728 638084). ETC ◆◆◆. FARM BUREAU MEMBER. You are welcome to share our Elizabethan farmhouse with its ancient oak beams and idyllic setting overlooking the Alde Valley. Comfortable en suite bedrooms, some ground floor; tea and coffee making facilities in all bedrooms. Ample private parking. Well stocked coarse fishing lakes. Two full length indoor bowls rinks. Delicious wholesome breakfasts. Wide variety of things to see and do nearby. Holiday cottage also available (5 KEYS COMMENDED). You will find Colston Hall just half-a-mile from the A1120, surrounded by beautiful quiet countryside and only a short drive from the Heritage Coast. We look forward to meeting you!

HALESWORTH. Mrs Patricia Kemsley, Broad Oak Farm, Bramfield, Halesworth IP19 9AB (01986

784232). ETC ◆◆◆◆. Relax in our modernised 16th century farmhouse and enjoy the peace and quiet of a farm situated where the countryside meets the North-East Heritage Coast, eight miles from Southwold. Surrounded by attractive gardens and meadowland. Tennis court. One double and two twin rooms (two en suite and one private bathroom). Separate guests' sitting room and beautiful beamed dining room. Good home cooking, evening meal by arrangement. Friendly, informal atmosphere. Bramfield Village is on the A144. Open all year. Pets welcome. Bed and Breakfast from £18.

Key to Tourist Board Ratings

     The Crown Scheme

The English Tourism Council (formerly the English Tourist Board) has joined with the AA and RAC to create a new, easily understood quality rating for serviced accommodation. Hotels will receive a grading ranging from **one to five STARS (★)**. Other serviced accommodation such as **guest houses** and **B&B establishments** will be graded from **one to five DIAMONDS (◆)**. These ratings represent Quality, Service and Hospitality not just facilities. *NB.Some properties had not been assessed at the time of going to press and in these cases the publishers have included the old CROWN gradings.*

ꝯ   **The Key Scheme**

The Key Scheme covering self-catering in cottages, bungalows, flats, houseboats, houses, chalets, etc remains unchanged. The classification from **One to Five KEYS** indicates the range of facilities and equipment. Higher quality standards are indicated by the terms APPROVED, COMMENDED, HIGHLY COMMENDED AND DE LUXE.

STOKE-BY-NAYLAND. Ryegate House, Stoke-by-Nayland, Colchester CO6 4RA (01206 263679).

ETC ◆◆◆◆ *SILVER AWARD*. Situated on the B1068 within the Dedham Vale, in a quiet Suffolk village, Ryegate House is a modern property built in the style of a Suffolk farmhouse. It is only a few minutes' walk from the local shops, post office, pubs, restaurants and church and an ideal base for exploring Constable country. A warm welcome, good food and comfortable accommodation in a peaceful setting with easy access to local historic market towns, golf courses and the East Coast. Comfortable en suite bedrooms with colour TV, radio alarms, tea/coffee making facilities, shaver points and central heating. Children welcome. Parking for six cars. Open all year except Christmas. Bed and Breakfast from £28.00 to £33.50 per night single, £40.00 to £48.00 double.
e-mail: ryegate@lineone.net

RED HOUSE FARM

A warm welcome and homely atmosphere awaits you at our attractive farmhouse set in the beautiful surroundings of mid Suffolk. Comfortably furnished bedrooms with en suite shower rooms and tea/coffee making facilities. One double, one twin and two single rooms. Central heating. Guests' own lounge with TV and dining room. Ideal location for exploring, walking, cycling and bird watching. No smoking or pets. Open January to December except Christmas.

ETC ◆◆◆◆

Mrs Mary Noy, Red House Farm, Station Road, Haughley, Stowmarket IP14 3QP
Tel: 01449 673323; Fax: 01449 675413

The **GOLF GUIDE** *Where to Play Where to Stay* **2000**

Available from most bookshops, the 2000 edition of **THE GOLF GUIDE** covers details of every UK golf course – well over 2500 entries – for holiday or business golf. Hundreds of hotel entries offer convenient accommodation, accompanying details of the courses – the 'pro', par score, length etc.

In association with 'Golf Monthly' and including the Ryder Cup Report as well as Holiday Golf in Ireland, France, Portugal, Spain, The USA and Thailand .

£9.95 from bookshops or £10.50 including postage (UK only) from FHG Publications, Abbey Mill Business Centre, Paisley PAI ITJ

Visit the **FHG** website
www.holidayguides.com
for details of the wide choice of accommodation featured in the full range of FHG titles

SURREY

LINGFIELD. Mrs Vanessa Manwill, Stantons Hall Farm, Eastbourne Road, Blindley Heath, Lingfield

RH7 6LG (01342 832401). Stantons Hall Farm is an 18th century farmhouse set amidst 18 acres of farmland and adjacent to Blindley Heath Common. Family, double and single rooms, most with toilet, shower and washbasin en suite. Separate bathroom. All rooms have colour TV, tea/coffee facilities and are centrally heated. There are plenty of parking spaces. We are conveniently situated within easy reach of M25 (London Orbital), Gatwick Airport (car parking facilities for travellers) and Lingfield Park Racecourse. Enjoy a traditional English Breakfast in our large farmhouse kitchen. Bed and Breakfast from £21 per person, reductions for children sharing. Cot and high chair available. Well behaved dogs welcome by prior arrangement.

LINGFIELD. Mrs Vivienne Bundy, Oaklands, Felcourt Road, Lingfield RH7 6NF (01342 834705).

Oaklands is a spacious country house of considerable charm dating from the 17th century. It is set in its own grounds of one acre and is about one mile from the small town of Lingfield and three miles from East Grinstead, both with rail connections to London. It is convenient to Gatwick Airport and is ideal as a "stop-over" or as a base to visit many places of interest in south east England. Dover and the Channel Ports are two hours' drive away whilst the major towns of London and Brighton are about one hour distant. One family room en-suite, one double and one single bedrooms with washbasins; three bathrooms, two toilets; sittingroom; diningroom. Cot, high chair, babysitting and reduced rates for children. Gas central heating. Open all year. Parking. Bed and Breakfast from £20; Evening Meal by arrangement.

SUSSEX

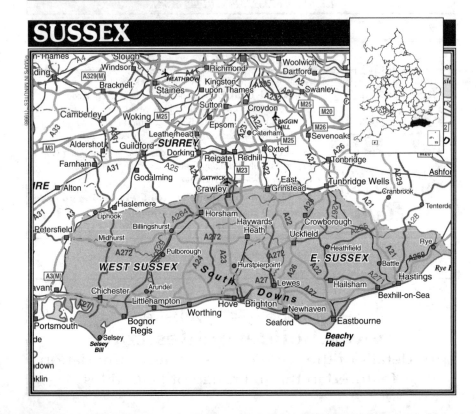

EAST SUSSEX

BATTLE. Mrs June Ive, Moonshill Farm, The Green, Ninfield, Battle TN33 9LH (Tel & Fax: 01424 892645) ☸☸ *COMMENDED*.

Every comfort in quiet, peaceful farmhouse situated in 10 acres of garden, orchard and stables, in the centre of the village of Ninfield. Enjoy beautiful, walks, golf and riding arranged. Comfortable rooms with hospitality tray and TV, three en suite, central heating, electric fires, lounge. Parking. Babysitting service. Bed and Breakfast from £17.50-£20.00. Open January to November.

BATTLE. Monty and Amanda Worssam, Kitchenham Farm, Ashburnham, Battle TN33 9NP (Tel & Fax: 01424 892221).

Monty and Amanda offer a friendly family atmosphere in a beautiful Georgian farmhouse built in 1770. The house is surrounded by an Oasthouse and traditional farm buildings which offer a lovely backdrop to the spectacular views. The farm is an 820 acre working farm with sheep and cattle but is mainly arable. There are three large comfortable rooms furnished with antiques. Two rooms share a shower room and the third is en suite. All have tea/coffee making facilities. There are plenty of walks around the farm, to the river or to the "Ash" which is half-an-hour away. Reductions for children under 12 years.

BURGESS HILL. Mr M. Mundy, The Homestead, Homestead Lane, Valebridge Road, Burgess Hill RH15 0RQ (Tel & Fax: 01444 246899; Mobile 07808 567241). ETC ◆◆◆◆.

Tranquil, country setting in seven-and-a-half acres at end of a private lane. Home also to a variety of wildlife, including foxes, badgers, squirrels, rabbits, the occasional deer and our own free-range hens. Close to Wivelsfield Station - frequent trains to Gatwick, London, Brighton, Lewes and Eastbourne. Centrally situated for Glyndebourne, South Downs Way, numerous NT locations, gardens, Bluebell Railway and the Lavender Line. Opportunities for fishing, walking and golf. All rooms en suite and fully equipped. Wheelchair access to ground-floor bedrooms. Extensive breakfast menu; vegetarian option available. Strictly non-smoking. Children over 12 years welcome. Unlimited parking.
e-mail: homestead@burgess-hill.co.uk
website: www.burgess-hill.co.uk

BURWASH. Mrs E. Sirrell, Woodlands Farm, Burwash, Etchingham TN19 7LA (Tel & Fax: 01435 882794). Working farm, join in.

Woodlands Farm stands one third of a mile off the road surrounded by fields and woods. This peaceful and beautifully modernised 16th century farmhouse offers comfortable and friendly accommodation. Sitting/dining room; two bathrooms, one en suite, double or twin bedded rooms (one has four poster bed) together with excellent farm fresh food. This is a farm of 108 acres with mixed animals, and is situated within easy reach of 20 or more places of interest to visit and half an hour from the coast. Open all year. Central heating. Literature provided to help guests. Children welcome. Dogs allowed if sleeping in owner's car. Parking. Evening Meal optional. Bed and Breakfast from £19 to £23 per person per night. AA QQ. Telephone or SAE, please.
e-mail: liz_sir@lineone.net

Terms quoted in this publication may be subject to increase
if rises in costs necessitate

HASTINGS. Mr and Mrs S. York, Westwood Farm, Stonestile Lane, Hastings TN35 4PG (Tel & Fax: 01424 751038). Working farm. ETC ◆◆◆ Farm with pet sheep, chickens, etc. Quiet rural location off country lane half a mile from B2093 approximately two miles from seafront and town centre. Golf course nearby. Central position for visiting places of interest to suit all ages. Elevated situation with outstanding views over Brede Valley. Double, twin, family rooms with en suite and private facilities. Colour TV, tea/coffee in all rooms, two bedrooms on ground floor. Full English breakfast. Off-road parking. Bed and Breakfast from £18 to £25 per person for two persons sharing. Reduced rates for weekly booking. Also available six-berth self catering caravan – details on request.

HERSTMONCEUX. Mr and Mrs R.E. Gentry, The Stud Farm, Bodle Street Green, Near Hailsham BN27 4RJ (Tel & Fax: 01323 833201). 🏵🏵 *COMMENDED*. **Working farm.** The Stud Farm keeps mainly cattle and sheep. It is peacefully situated between A271 and B2096 amidst beautiful undulating countryside. Ideal for walking and touring lovely East Sussex, being within easy reach of Eastbourne (12 miles), Bexhill (10 miles) and Hastings (15 miles). There are many places of historic interest in the vicinity and the coast is only eight miles away at Pevensey. Upstairs there is a family unit (only let to one set of guests – either two, three or four persons – at a time), consisting of one twin-bedded room and one double-bedded room, both with TVs, handbasins and shaver points and their own bathroom with toilet. There is also downstairs one twin-bedded with shower, handbasin and toilet en suite, tea/coffee making facilities, TV. Guests have their own sittingroom with TV and diningroom and sunroom. Sorry, no pets. No Smoking. Open all year. Central heating in winter. Car essential – parking available. Bed and Breakfast from £20; Evening Meals from £11 by arrangement. SAE, please.

RYE. Jackie & Robert Hollands, Riverhaven, 60 New Winchelsea Road, Rye TN31 7TA (01797 223267; Fax: 01797 227075). Jackie and Robert Hollands invite you to Riverhaven, our lovely home in the beautiful town of Rye. Full central heating; TV and washbasins all rooms, four-poster room available. Wonderful English breakfasts. Parking on forecourt. 25 years experience in Bed and Breakfast accommodation. Please ring for details.

RYE. Pat and Jeff Sullivin, Cliff Farm, Iden Lock, Rye TN31 7QE (Tel & Fax: 01797 280331). Long ring please). Our farmhouse is peacefully set in a quiet elevated position with extensive views over Romney Marsh. The ancient seaport town of Rye with its narrow cobbled streets is two miles away. We are an ideal touring base although the town and immediate district have much to offer – golden beaches, quaint villages, castles, gardens etc. Comfortable guest bedrooms with washbasins and tea/coffee making facilities; two toilets; own shower; diningroom and sittingroom. Home produce. Open March to October for Bed and Breakfast from £16. Reduced weekly rates. AA and RAC Recommended.

WEST SUSSEX

BOGNOR REGIS. Mrs M. Hashfield, Taplow Cottage, 81 Nyewood Lane, Bognor Regis PO21 2UE

(01243 821398). The Cottage lies in a residential part, west of the town centre, 600 yards from the sea and shops. Proximity to many beaches and contrasting towns and countryside make for an ideal touring centre. Chichester, Goodwood Racecourse, Arundel Castle, Brighton, Portsmouth and Southsea are but a few of the places of interest within easy reach. Accommodation comprises one double, one twin-bedded and one family bedroom, all with vanity units, tea/coffee making facilities and colour TV. Lounge, diningroom. The cottage is well appointed and the area is served by public transport. Parking space available. Bed and Breakfast from £16. Dogs by prior arrangement.

"TAPLOW COTTAGE"

CHICHESTER. Mrs Sue Kemble, 47 Mid Lavant, Lavant, Chichester PO18 0AA (01243 785883). ETC

◆◆◆ Situated in the pretty village of Lavant, accommodation is offered in a flint cottage surrounded by fields and peaceful walks. Only a short drive to Goodwood with its scenic views or go back in time and visit the Weald and Downland open air museum. Perhaps you prefer to see the historic city of Chichester, or Fishbourne Roman Palace, the choice is yours. Accommodation consists of a twin bedded room, private bathroom, tea/coffee facilities, colour TV. No smoking please. Open January to December. Bed and Breakfast from £20 per person per night.

CHICHESTER near. Mrs Melanie Bray, Compton Farmhouse, Church Lane, Compton, Nr Chichester, West Sussex PO18 9HB (01705 631597). Listed

COMMENDED. We are situated 200 yards up a track from the village square next door to the church. Large family room with double bed, single bed, bunk beds, cot and basin. Private bathroom with bath/shower and basin. Private sitting/dining room with TV, fridge and drink making facilities. Central heating and log fires. Woods and fields right behind the house for walking. Excellent base for visiting Chichester, Portsmouth, Goodwood, Arundel, Winchester, Petersfield and the coast. Open all year except Christmas. Plenty of parking space. Children welcome at half price. Single occupancy £20. Otherwise £18 per person per night.

HENFIELD. Mrs J. Forbes, Little Oreham Farm, off Horne Lane, Near Woodsmill, Henfield BN5 9SB

(01273 492931). Delightful old Sussex farmhouse situated in rural position down lane, adjacent to footpaths and nature reserve. One mile from Henfield village, eight miles from Brighton, convenient for Gatwick and Hickstead. Excellent base for visiting many gardens and places of interest in the area. The farmhouse is a listed building of great character; oak-beamed sittingroom with inglenook fireplace (log fires), and a pretty diningroom. Three comfortable attractive bedrooms with en-suite shower/bath; WC; colour TV; tea-making facilities. Central heating throughout. Lovely garden with views of the Downs. Situated off Horne Lane, one minute from Woodsmill Countryside Centre. Winner of Kellogg's award: "Best Bed and Breakfast" in the South East. You will enjoy a friendly welcome and pleasant holiday. Sorry, no children under 10. Bed and Breakfast from £20 per person. Evening Meals by arrangement. No smoking. Open all year.

When making enquiries or bookings,
a stamped addressed envelope is always appreciated.

WARWICKSHIRE

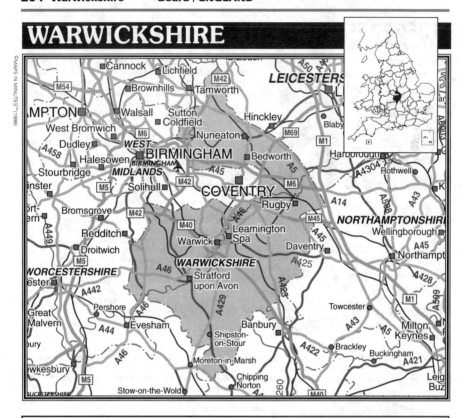

ALCESTER. John and Margaret Canning, Glebe Farm, Exhall, Alcester B49 6EA (Tel & Fax: 01789 772202). ☙ *COMMENDED*. Shakespeare named our village "Dodging Exhall" and it has somehow "dodged" the passing of time, so if you want a true taste of rural England, come and relax in our quaint old farmhouse - parts of it dating from Tudor times - with its log fires, four-poster bed and country hospitality. One double, one twin and two single rooms, all with tea/coffee trays, electric blankets. Smoking in lounge. Payphone. Laundry. Children and pets welcome. Ample parking. Bed and Breakfast from £19 to £22. Open all year except Christmas and New Year.

BRAILES. Mrs M. Cripps, Agdon Farm, Brailes, Banbury OX15 5JJ (Tel & Fax: 01608 685226).

Working farm. A warm welcome awaits all our guests. Our comfortable Cotswold stone farmhouse is set in 500 acres of mixed farming, in an unspoilt part of the countryside. Two miles from B4035, five miles from A422. Within walking distance of Compton Wynyates, in close driving range of the Cotswolds, Warwick, 10 miles Stratford-upon-Avon and Banbury Cross. Many local village pubs. Accommodation with TV room, separate diningroom, guests' bathroom, pleasant bedrooms with tea/coffee facilities. Central heating. Evening Meals available.

Cooperage Farm

Old Road, Meriden, Near Coventry CY7 7JP
Telephone 01676 523493

Cooperage Farm is a 300 year old Listed farmhouse situated in the very heart of England in the attractive village of Meriden. A friendly, family-run establishment with full central heating, tea/coffee making facilities, full English Breakfast etc. Transport available for guests. All-in-all, first class, homely accommodation with a friendly welcome for all.

COVENTRY near. Mrs Sandra Evans, Camp Farm, Hob Lane, Balsall Common, Near Coventry CV7 7GX

(01676 533804). Tourist Board Listed *COMMENDED*. Camp Farm is a farmhouse 150 to 200 years old. It is modernised but still retains its old world character. Nestling in the heart of England in Shakespeare country, within easy reach of Stratford-upon-Avon, Warwick, Kenilworth, Coventry with its famous Cathedral, and the National Exhibition Centre, also the National Agricultural Centre, Stoneleigh. Camp Farm offers a warm homely atmosphere and good English food, service and comfortable beds. The house is carpeted throughout. Diningroom and lounge with colour TV. Bedrooms – three double rooms or three single rooms, all with washbasins. The house is suitable for partially disabled guests. All terms by letter or telephone.

FRANKTON. Mrs Mary Pritchard, Frankton Grounds Farm, Frankton, Near Rugby CV23 9PD (01926

632391). Listed *APPROVED*. Working farm. Beautifully situated in a mixed farm of horses, sheep, pedigree and commercial cattle. A warm welcome for the visitor who enjoys peace and quiet, yet with the benefit of easy access to Warwick, Leamington and Stratford. Two-and-a-half miles from M45. Full central heating, log fires, excellent food. One double with bathroom, one twin. Open all year. Bed and Breakfast from £15 to £17.50, Evening Meal from £8.50.

LEAMINGTON SPA. Mrs Kate Liggins, Stonehouse Farm, Leicester Lane, Cubbington Heath,

Leamington Spa CV32 6QZ (01926 336370). A warm and friendly Grade II Listed Queen Anne farmhouse, set in the peaceful surroundings of a mature garden and orchard, overlooking the Warwickshire countryside. Ideally situated for visitors to the National Exhibition Centre, the Royal Showground at Stoneleigh or Business and Technology Parks in the area. Warwick Castle, Stratford-upon-Avon and the Cotswolds are also within easy reach. A high standard of accommodation is offered in three twin-bedded rooms (one en suite, one with vanity basin and two with colour TV). All have central heating and tea/coffee making facilities. There is a sitting room with television and a traditional diningroom. Bed and Breakfast from £21 per person.

LEAMINGTON SPA. Miss Deborah Lea, Crandon House, Avon Dassett, Leamington Spa CV33 0AA (Tel: 01295 770652/626458; Fax: 01295 770632).

◆◆◆◆◆ *SILVER AWARD.* **Working farm.** Guests receive a specially warm welcome at our comfortable farmhouse offering an exceptionally high standard of accommodation. Set in 20 acres, with beautiful views over unspoilt countryside, this small working farm has rare breeds of cattle, sheep and poultry. Five attractive no smoking bedrooms with en suite/private facilities (one ground floor), tea/coffee making equipment and colour TV. Guests' dining room and sitting rooms, one with colour TV. Full central heating and log fire in chilly weather. Extensive breakfast menu. Car essential. Ample parking. Peaceful and quiet. Easy access for touring the Heart of England, Warwick, Stratford-upon-Avon, the Cotswolds, NAC and NEC. Open all year. Bed and Breakfast from £19.50 to £25. Winter Breaks available. Farm Holiday Bureau member. Write or ring for further details. Children over ten years welcome.
e-mail: crandonhouse@talk21.com

LEAMINGTON SPA. Mrs R. Gibbs, Hill Farm, Lewis Road, Radford Semele, Leamington Spa CV31 1UX

(01926 337571). ETC/AA ◆◆◆◆. Working farm. Guests are welcome all year round to this comfortable, centrally heated farmhouse on a 350-acre mixed farm. Ideally situated for Warwick, Coventry, Stratford-upon-Avon, Leamington Spa, Royal Showground, Birmingham, the NEC and the Cotswolds. Three pretty double bedrooms and two twin rooms with washbasins, tea and coffee facilities and TV. Some are en suite. Guests' sittingroom with colour TV; lovely conservatory for breakfast dining and excellent breakfast menu. Car preferable, ample parking. Spacious five van site also available. Farm Holiday Bureau member. FHG past Diploma Winner. Bed and Breakfast from £18 to £25 per person.

OXHILL. Mrs Sue Hutsby, Nolands Farm, Oxhill CV35 0RJ (01926 640309; Fax: 01926 641662).

Working farm. AA ◆◆◆◆. 'Which? Hotel Guide', 'Great Bed & Breakfast'. A working farm situated in tranquil valley surrounded by fields, woods and wildlife . All bedrooms are annexed, some ground floor and overlooking the old stableyard or fields and garden. All rooms are en suite, TV, tea/coffee, radio alarm, hairdryers. We have superior four-posters, doubles, twins, family and single rooms. We can offer clay pigeon shooting, fishing, bikes or horse riding at nearby stables. Plenty of peace and quiet for a relaxing break. Licensed bar, dinner by arrangement. Ample parking. Stratford-upon-Avon eight miles. Credit cards taken. Restricted smoking. No children under seven
e-mail: nolandsfm@compuserve.com
website: www.stratford-upon-avon.co.uk/nolandsfm.htm

PRIORS HARDWICK. Mrs A. Darbishire, Hill Farm, Priors Hardwick, Rugby CV23 8SP (01327 260338; mobile: 07710 457262). ETC ◆◆◆.

Hill Farm is a mixed farm situated in South Warwickshire, very close to the borders of Oxfordshire and Northamptonshire. Our relaxed, friendly farmhouse is in the middle of beautiful, rolling countryside, with outstanding views and a large garden. Close to Banbury, Stratford-upon-Avon, Warwick, the NAC Stoneleigh; numerous walks and good country pubs nearby. We have one double and one twin room, both with full central heating, tea/coffee facilities, colour TV and log fire on request. Open all year except Christmas and New Year. Bed and Breakfast available from £20 per person per night.

SHIPSTON-ON-STOUR. Mrs Fox, Kirby Farm, Whatcote, Shipston-on-Stour CV36 5EQ. (01295

680525). Kirby Farm is situated in beautiful countryside within easy reach of Cotswolds, Stratford-upon-Avon, Banbury, Warwick Castle and many other places of interest. Our spacious, stone built, fully centrally heated farmhouse is set in 450 arable acres and a long driveway gives it an "off the beaten track" feel. Visitors will receive a warm welcome. Bedrooms have tea/coffee making facilities and en suite accommodaton is available. Breakfast is served in separate dining room and guests have access to their own drawing room with TV and log fire on cold evenings. Bed and Breakfast from £15.

STRATFORD-UPON-AVON. Mrs Marion J. Walters, Church Farm, Dorsington, Stratford-upon-Avon CV37 8AX (01789 720471; Fax: 01789 720830; Mobile: 0831 504194). COMMENDED. **Working farm.** Situated

on the Heart of England Way. A warm and friendly welcome awaits you all year at our 127-acre mixed farm with woodlands and stream which you may explore. Ideal for walking. Our Georgian Farmhouse is situated on the edge of an extremely pretty village. Stratford-upon-Avon, Warwick, NEC, Royal Showground, Cotswolds, Evesham and Worcester all within easy driving distance. Family, twin and double bedrooms, all with tea/coffee facilities; most en suite with TVs, some in converted stable block. Cot and high chair available. Central heating. Gliding, fishing, boating and horse riding nearby. Full Fire Certificate held. Bed and Breakfast from £18. Write or phone for further details.

STRATFORD-UPON-AVON. Mrs Julia Downie, Holly Tree Cottage, Birmingham Road, Pathlow, Stratford-upon-Avon CV37 0ES (Tel & Fax: 01789 204461). Period cottage dating back to 17th century, with beams,

antiques, tasteful furnishings and friendly atmosphere. Large picturesque gardens with extensive views over the countryside. Situated three miles north of Stratford towards Henley-in-Arden on A3400, convenient for overnight stops or longer stays, and ideal for theatre visits. Excellent base for touring Shakespeare country, Heart of England, Cotswolds, Warwick Castle and Blenheim Palace. Well situated for National Exhibition Centre. Double, twin and family accommodation with en suite and private facilities; colour TV and tea/coffee in all rooms. Full English Breakfast. Restaurant and pub meals nearby. Bed and Breakfast from £24. Telephone for information.

STRATFORD-UPON-AVON. Mrs R.M. Meadows, Monk's Barn Farm, Shipston Road, Stratford-upon-Avon CV37 8NA (01789 293714). AA ◆◆◆◆. Working farm. Two miles south of Stratford-upon-Avon on the A3400 is

Monk's Barn, a 75 acre mixed farm welcoming visitors all year. The farm dates back to the 16th century, although the pretty house is more recent. The double, single and twin rooms, most with en suite facilities, are provided in the main house and the cleverly converted milking parlour. The two ground floor rooms are suitable for some disabled guests. Visitors lounge. Beautiful riverside walk to the village. Tea/coffee facilities and colour TV in rooms. Sorry, no pets. Non smokers preferred. Details on request. Bed and Breakfast from £16.

STRATFORD-UPON-AVON. Mrs Sally Gray, Rectory Farm, Clifford Chambers, Stratford-upon-Avon CV37 8AA (01789 414355). Rectory Farm is a delightful home

converted from attractive farm buildings and barn with self-contained bed and breakfast accommodation with private front door, where you will be our only guests. Double bedroom overlooking Warwickshire countryside, a twin bedded room, bathroom with shower, spacious and tastefully furnished private sitting room for guests with TV, tea/coffee making facilities, ample car parking, childrens outdoor play equipment, gardens, countryside location but only 2 miles from Stratford town centre, Cotswolds close by. Pub within walking distance. Bed and Breakfast from £22.

STRATFORD-UPON-AVON. Mrs M. Turney, Cadle Pool Farm, The Ridgway, Stratford-upon-Avon CV37 9RE (01789 292494). 👑👑👑 **Working farm.**

Situated in picturesque grounds, this charming oak-panelled and beamed family house is part of a 450-acre mixed farm. It is conveniently situated two miles from Stratford-upon-Avon town, between Anne Hathaway's Cottage and Mary Arden's House, also only eight minutes from The Royal Shakespeare Theatre. Ideal touring centre for Warwick, Kenilworth, Oxford, the Cotswolds and Malvern Hills. Accommodation comprises family, double and twin bedrooms, one en suite and one with private bathroom, all with central heating and tea/coffee making facilities. There is an antique oak dining room, and lounge with colour TV. The gardens and ornamental pool are particularly attractive, with peacocks and ducks roaming freely. Children over 10 years welcome at reduced rates. Sorry, no pets. Non-smoking accommodation available. Bed and Breakfast from £20 to £26 per person. Open all year.

STRATFORD-UPON-AVON. Prim and John Finnemore, Walcote Farm, Walcote, Haselor, Alcester B49 6LY (Tel & Fax: 01789 488264). ETC ◆◆◆

Come and enjoy the relaxing atmosphere at our attractive 16th century oak-beamed farmhouse with inglenook fireplaces, set in a tranquil, picturesque hamlet, one-and-a-quarter miles from the A46 near Stratford-upon-Avon. En suite double and twin rooms with TV/Fastext, tea/coffee making facilities and lovely views. Full central heating with log fires in winter. Ideal area for interesting walks, Shakespeare's birthplace and theatre, Warwick Castle, The Cotswolds, NEC and National Trust properties. Open all year except Christmas and the New Year. Bed and Breakfast £19 to £23. No smoking in the house.
e-mail: john_finnemore@csi.com
website: ourworld.compuserve.com/homepages
john_finnemore

WARWICK. Mr and Mrs D. Clapp, The Croft, Haseley Knob, Warwick CV35 7NL (Tel & Fax: 01926 484447). ◆◆◆◆.

Join David and Pat on their country guest house and share the friendly family atmosphere, the picturesque rural surroundings, home cooking and very comfortable accommodation. Bedrooms, most en suite, have colour TV, tea/coffee making equipment. Ground floor en-suite bedrooms available. Bed and Full English Breakfast from £23. Centrally located for touring Warwick (Castle), Stratford (Shakespeare), Coventry (Cathedral), and Birmingham. Also ideal for the businessman visiting the National Exhibition Centre or Birmingham Airport, both about 15 minutes. No smoking inside. Ample parking. Mobile home available, also caravan parking. Large gardens. Open all year. French spoken.

WARWICK. Mrs J. Stanton, Redlands Farm, Banbury Road, Lighthorne, Near Warwick CV35 0AH (01926 651241). 👑👑 A beautifully restored 15th century

farmhouse built of local stone, the "Old Farm House" is set in two acres of garden with its own swimming pool, well away from the main road yet within easy travelling distance of Stratford and Warwick, and handy for the Cotswolds. Guest accommodation is one double (with bathroom), one single and one family bedrooms, all with tea making facilities; bathroom; beamed lounge with TV; diningroom. Rooms are centrally heated and the farmhouse also has open fires. Bed and Breakfast from £17.50. Children welcome – facilities available. No pets. A car is recommended to make the most of your stay. AA QQQ.

When making enquiries or bookings,
a stamped addressed envelope is always appreciated.

WEST MIDLANDS

Boxtrees Farm

Stratford Road, Hockley Heath, Solihull B94 6EA
Telephone: 01564 782039 • Fax: 01564 784661

Boxtrees Farm is on the A3400, just one mile from Junction 4 of the M42 and is within easy reach of Birmingham International Airport/NEC/Rail link (10 minutes) and Stratford-upon-Avon (20 minutes). The 18th Century farmhouse has all the comforts of modern living whilst retaining its traditional features. The delightful farm courtyard has a 12 unit craft centre and coffee shop-bistro. Tastefully converted large twin bedded, family and double rooms available. All rooms are en suite with TV and tea/coffee making facilities. Bed and Breakfast from £45 per room per night.

E-mail: b&b@boxtrees.co.uk   Website: www.boxtrees.co.uk

WILTSHIRE

BIDDESTONE. Mrs Julia Sexton, Elm Farmhouse, The Green, Biddestone, Chippenham SN14 7DG

(Tel and Fax: 01249 713354). 👑👑 *COMMENDED.* A peaceful 17th century Grade II Listed farmhouse now run as a Bed and Breakfast establishment located in the heart of North Wiltshire. Situated opposite the pond and two minutes from the village pub, Elm Farmhouse is traditionally decorated and retains many striking features such as original fireplaces and mullioned windows. Accommodation is offered in three double bedrooms, all en suite with colour TV, tea/coffee making facilities, and good views. Biddestone is only four miles from the M4 and is between the famous villages of Lacock and Castle Combe, just nine miles from Bath, and close to many National Trust properties and beautiful countryside. Ample car parking. Children and pets welcome. Bed and Breakfast from £20 per person.

CHIPPENHAM. Paul & Elaine Sexton, The Old Rectory, Cantax Hill, Lacock, Chippenham SN15 2JZ

(01249 730335; Fax: 01249 730166). Welcome to 'The Old Rectory' and experience a real taste of English life at this inspiring Grade II Listed rectory set on the edge of the beautiful and famous village of Lacock. Built in 1866, it is a superb example of Gothic architecture and is set in its own grounds and gardens. Large elegant bedrooms are offered, two with four-posters, and all are en suite and offering tea and coffee and colour TV. There is also ample private parking. Lacock is a charming village on the edge of the Cotswolds and is also close to Lacock Abbey where William Fox Talbot lived (a pioneer of photography and inventor of the negative). Local too are Bowood House, Avebury and Stonehenge. Bath is 12 miles and the M4 (J17) only six miles. From £25pp. Ask for special offers.
e-mail: Elaine@oldrectorylacock.freeserve.co.uk

Terms quoted in this publication may be subject to increase if rises in costs necessitate

CHIPPENHAM. Caroline Tayler, The Moors, Kington Langley, Chippenham SN14 6HT (01249 750288; Fax: 01249 758814). ETC ◆◆◆.

Family-run dairy farm set in 115 acres. Ideally situated for visiting Bath, Castle Combe, Lacock, Bowood House and the Cotswolds. Only two miles from Junction 17 M4 and a useful overnight stop for Devon, Cornwall, Wales or Ireland. The farmhouse is set away from the farm buildings and accommodation is in double, twin or single rooms. There is a guests' lounge with TV and tea/coffee making facilities. Open all year. Non-smoking. A good breakfast is offered. From £17 per person per night. Caravan and camping facilities also available.

CHIPPENHAM near. Suzanne Candy, Olivemead Farm, Dauntsey, Near Chippenham SN15 4JQ (01666 510205). ✤ COMMENDED.

Working farm. Relax and enjoy the warm informal hospitality at our delightful 18th century farmhouse on a working dairy farm in the Dauntsey Vale. Twin, double and family rooms with washbasins, colour TVs. Tea/coffee making facilities. Generous breakfasts. Oak beamed dining room/lounge for guests' exclusive use. Large garden, children's play area, cot, high chair, baby listening. Excellent food available locally. Convenient for Bath, Cotswolds, Salisbury, M4, South West and Wales. Bed and Breakfast from £18 to £20 per person per night. Reductions for children and long stay guests. Self-catering cottage also available.

DEVIZES. Mr & Mrs Straker, Stroud Hill Farm, Potterne Wick, Devizes SN10 5QR (01380 720371). ETC ◆◆◆◆.

The farm is set in 140 acres of delightful Wiltshire countryside just two-and-a-half miles south of the famous market town of Devizes. Ideal for enjoying peace and tranquillity, or as a base for touring this historic county and for visiting such places as Stonehenge, NT Lacock Village and Castle Combe, or the towns of Malmesbury and Marlborough. Stroud Hill Farm offers accommodation in one double and one twin room; private sitting room with open fire and tea/coffee facilities. Self-catering also available. You are guaranteed a warm Wiltshire welcome combining the best of tradition with the warmth and comfort of modern living.

DEVIZES. Mrs J. Reardon, Home Farm, Close Lane, Marston, Devizes SN10 5SN (01380 725484). ✤✤ HIGHLY COMMENDED.

Home Farm is a Wiltshire longhouse believed to date back to the late 15th century. Located in a quiet, rural setting near the Kennet and Avon Canal in good walking countryside. Fishing available. Three miles from Erlestoke Sands Golf Course. Only 20 minutes' drive from Stonehenge and 25 minutes from Avebury. Devizes is the central market town of Wiltshire and enjoys a rich heritage of fine Georgian houses and a castle which stands on the site of a Norman stronghold. Accommodation is available in one double and one twin room, both with en suite bathroom and tea and coffee making facilities. Central heating. Bed and Breakfast from £24 single, £40 double. Further details on request.

GASTARD. Mrs Dorothy Robinson, Boyds Farm, Gastard, Near Corsham SN13 9PT (Tel & Fax: 01249 713146). ETC ◆◆◆◆ *SILVER AWARD.* Welcome Host. Dorothy and Andrew Robinson warmly welcome guests to Boyds Farm which is a family-run working farm with a pedigree herd of Hereford Cattle. The farmhouse is a delightful 16th century Listed building surrounded by beautiful mature gardens. Near to Bath, Lacock, Bradford-on-Avon, Castle Combe, Stonehenge, etc. Accommodation comprises one double en suite, one family or twin with private bathroom and one double with private shower room, all well furnished with tea/coffee facilities, electric blankets, etc; guest lounge with log fire for cooler nights. Featured in the "Daily Express," "The Sunday Observer," and "Sunday Mail". Rates from £20 to £25 per person.

MALMESBURY. Mrs Claire Read, Leighfield Lodge Farm, Malmesbury Road, Leigh, Cricklade SN6 6RH (Tel & Fax: 01666 860241). ◆◆◆. Imagine a lovely old farmhouse in a truly rural setting; step inside and discover comfortable en suite rooms with crisp cotton bed linen. Relax in the sitting room after exploring the Cotswolds or Wiltshire Downs. Children will enjoy meeting the cows and may even see wild deer! Enjoy staying in a friendly family atmosphere where you will be truly welcomed. Look forward to discovering picturesque villages and elegant towns. We are well situated for visiting Cirencester, Westonbirt Arboretum and the Great Western Designer Outlet Village. Bath, Oxford and Cheltenham are all within easy reach. Open all year.

MALMESBURY near. Mrs Susan Barnes, Lovett Farm, Little Somerford, Near Malmesbury SN15 5BP (Tel & Fax: 01666 823268; mobile: 07808 858612). ETC/AA ◆◆◆. **Working farm.** Enjoy traditional hospitality at our delightful farmhouse on a small working farm with beautiful views from both the one double and one twin en suite bedrooms, each having tea/coffee making facilities, radio and colour TV. Full central heating. Sample a scrumptious farmhouse breakfast in our cosy dining room/lounge with a log fire for those cold winter days. Situated three miles from Malmesbury on B4042 and within easy reach of Bath, Cotswolds and Stonehenge. Excellent food pubs locally. Non-smoking accommodation. Bed and Breakfast from £20 to £25. Reductions for children. Open all year except Christmas. Farm Holiday Bureau Member.
e-mail: lovetts-farm@hotmail.com

MARLBOROUGH. Mrs Judy Davies, Marridge Hill House, Ramsbury, Marlborough SN8 2HG (01672 520237; Fax: 01672 520053). ETC ◆◆◆. The house originated in1750 and is set in glorious countryside, only one hour's drive from Heathrow Airport. You will be warmly welcomed into the relaxed, informal atmosphere of our family home, with its pleasant sitting and dining rooms, books galore, and an acre of garden. There are three comfortable and attractive twin bedrooms (one with en suite facilities). Both bathrooms have power showers. An ideal base for visiting Avebury, Salisbury, Bath, Oxford and the Cotswolds. Good pubs and restaurants nearby. Bed and Breakfast from £19 per person. No smoking. Dogs by arrangement. Open all year except Christmas and New Year. Nearest roads: B4192, M4.
e-mail: dando@impedaci.demon.co.uk

SALISBURY. Mrs Suzi Lanham, Newton Farmhouse, Southampton Road, Whiteparish, Salisbury SP5 2QL (01794 884416).👑👑 *HIGHLY COMMENDED*. This Listed 16th century farmhouse on the borders of the New Forest was formerly part of the Trafalgar Estate and is situated eight miles south of Salisbury, convenient for Stonehenge, Romsey, Winchester, Portsmouth and Bournemouth. All rooms have pretty en suite facilities and are delightfully decorated, three with genuine period four-poster beds. The beamed diningroom houses a collection of Nelson memorabilia and antiques, and has flagstone floors and an inglenook fireplace with an original brick-built bread oven. The superb English breakfast is complemented by fresh fruits, home-made breads and preserves and free-range eggs. Dinner is available by arrangement using home-grown kitchen garden produce wherever possible. A swimming pool is idyllically set in the extensive well-stocked gardens and children are most welcome in this non-smoking establishment. AA QQQQ Selected.
website: www.website.lineone.net/~newton.farmhouse.b-b/

SALISBURY. Mrs Sue Combes, Manor Farm, Burcombe, Salisbury SP2 0EJ (01722 742177; Fax: 01722 744600). ◆◆◆◆ Working farm. An attractive stone built farmhouse with a lovely walled garden, set in a quiet village amid downland and water meadows, five miles west of Salisbury. The two bedrooms are very comfortable with en suite facilities, TV, tea trays and clock radios. Large lounge and access to garden. This is an ideal location for Salisbury, Wilton and Stonehenge and easy access to many places of historic interest and gardens. For those seeking peace this is an idyllic place to stay with various walks and the local pub only a five minute stroll. Children welcome. Bed and Breakfast from £22 to £23.

SWINDON. Mrs Mary Richards, Little Cotmarsh Farm, Broad Town, Wootton Bassett, Swindon SN4 7RA (01793 731322). Little Cotmarsh Farm is a lovely 17th Century farmhouse nestling quietly in the little hamlet of Cotmarsh. Enjoy the relaxed atmosphere of our home, the attractive bedrooms are spacious and well equipped – two en suite, one with private bathroom. We are just seven miles from Avebury, the largest monument in Britain. Hungerford, Tetbury and Bradford-on-Avon are full of glorious antique shops or visit Swindon's new Great Western Designer Outlet Village. Best of all, borrow "100 Walks in Wiltshire" and explore our wonderful countryside. Good local pub food. M4 Junction 16 approximately four miles. Bed and Breakfast from £20 per person. No smoking.

WARMINSTER. Mrs M. Hoskins, Spinney Farmhouse, Chapmanslade, Westbury BA13 4AQ (01373 832412). 👑👑👑 Working farm. Off A36, three miles west of Warminster; 16 miles from historic city of Bath. Close to Longleat, Cheddar and Stourhead. Reasonable driving distance to Bristol, Stonehenge, Glastonbury and the cathedral cities of Wells and Salisbury. Pony trekking and fishing available locally and an 18 hole golf course within walking distance. Washbasins, tea/coffee-making facilities and shaver points in all rooms. Family room available. Guests' lounge with colour TV. Central heating. Children and pets welcome. Ample parking. Open all year. Bed and Breakfast from £17 per night. Reduction after two nights. Evening Meal £11. Farm fresh food in a warm, friendly, family atmosphere.

WORCESTERSHIRE

BROMSGROVE. Mrs C. Gibbs, Lower Bentley Farm, Lower Bentley, Bromsgrove B60 4JB (01527 821286). ◆◆◆. An attractive Victorian farmhouse with modern comforts on a dairy and beef farm is an ideal base for a holiday, Short Break or business stay. Overlooking peaceful countryside, we are situated five miles away from M5 and M42 between Redditch, Bromsgrove and Droitwich. The accommodation comprises spacious double, two twin rooms with en suite or private bathroom, colour TV and tea/coffee making facilities. The comfortable lounge and separate dining room overlook the large garden. Young children are welcome. We are ideally situated for visits to Stratford-upon-Avon, Warwick, Worcester, Stourbridge, Birmingham, the Black Country, the NEC and International Convention Centre. Prices from £19 per person. AA QQQ, RAC Acclaimed.

Lower Field Farm

For enquiries, bookings or a free colour brochure contact:
Jane Hill, Lower Field Farm,
Willersey, Broadway, Worcs WR11
5HF 01386 858273 or 0403 343996
Fax: 01386 854608
e-mail: lowerfield.farm@virgin.net

Lower Field Farm offers genuine farmhouse comfort and hospitality in a late 17th century Cotswold stone and brick farmhouse looking out on to the Cotswold Hills. Broadway two miles. Delightful rooms have tea/coffee making, TV and en suite bathrooms. Ground floor room available for those who find stairs difficult. This peaceful location provides an ideal base from which to explore the Cotswolds, Stratford-upon-Avon, Warwick Castle, Cheltenham, Oxford and beyond. We can provide Evening Meals by arrangement, or there is a wealth of good eating houses nearby, Open all year. Bed with full English Breakfast from £20 per person. Pets and children welcome.   *See also Colour Advertisement*

DROITWICH. David and Tricia Havard, Phepson Farm, Himbleton, Droitwich WR9 7JZ (01905 391205). Working farm. 👑👑 *HIGHLY COMMENDED.* In our 17th century oak beamed farmhouse we offer a warm welcome, good food and a relaxed and informal atmosphere. The recently converted Granary has two ground floor bedrooms, whilst the farmhouse has double and family accommodation. All rooms en suite with colour TV. Peaceful surroundings on family stock farm. Coarse fishing lake. Walking on Wychavon Way. Featured on 'Wish You Were Here'. Open all year except Christmas and New Year. Bed & Breakfast from £20 to £25. Self-catering also available.

GREAT MALVERN. Mrs F.W. Coates, Mill House, 16 Clarence Road, Great Malvern WR14 3EH (01684 562345). Originally a 13th century Water Mill at the foot of the beautiful Malvern Hills. Situated in tranquil grounds with croquet lawns and hill views. A few minutes' walk from the town centre or Great Malvern Station. Malvern is ideal for touring the Cotswolds, Severn and Wye Valleys and Welsh Marches. Comfortable accommodation with full central heating, washbasins and tea/coffee making facilities in all bedrooms. One double en suite, one double with shower, one twin room. Shower room, two separate WCs. Parking within grounds. NO SMOKING! No children and no pets. Bed and English Breakfast from £20. Advance booking only.

Terms quoted in this publication may be subject to increase
if rises in costs necessitate

MALVERN. Nick and Amanda Mobbs, Rock House, 144 West Malvern Road, Malvern WR14 4NJ (01684 574536). ETC/AA ★ *HOTEL.* Attractive, family-run early Victorian guest house situated high on hills in peaceful atmosphere with superb views of over 40 miles. Ideal for rambling on hills or open country. 11 comfortable bedrooms, most overlooking our splendid view, en suite facilities available.TV lounge, separate quiet room. Licensed bar enhances excellent home cooked dinners. Groups welcome. Parking on premises. Open all year. Special Christmas package. Bed and Breakfast from £20. Stamp only, please, for brochure. Also pretty self-catering cottage available.

MALVERN near. Ann and Brian Porter, Croft Guest House, Bransford, Worcester WR6 5JD (01886 832227; Fax: 01886 830037). ETC/AA ◆◆ 16th-18th century part black and white cottage-style country house situated in the River Teme Valley, four miles from Worcester and Malvern. Croft House is central for visiting numerous attractions in Worcester, Hereford, Severn Valley and surrounding countryside. There is fishing close by and an 18 hole golf course opposite. Facilities include three en suite rooms (two double, one family) and two double rooms with washbasins, hospitality trays. Double glazing, central heating, residential licence and home cooked dinners. There is a TV lounge, sauna and large jacuzzi for guests' use. A cot and baby listening service are provided. Bed and Breakfast from £25 to £28 single, £38 to £48 double. Festive Christmas and New Year Breaks available.

MALVERN WELLS. Mrs J.L. Morris, Brickbarns Farm, Hanley Road, Malvern Wells WR14 4HY (016845 61775; Fax: 01886 830037). Working farm. Brickbarns, a 200-acre mixed farm, is situated two miles from Great Malvern at the foot of the Malvern Hills, 300 yards from the bus service and one-and-a half miles from the train. The house, which is 300 years old, commands excellent views of the Malvern Hills and guests are accommodated in one double, one single and one family bedrooms with washbasins; two bathrooms, shower room, two toilets; sittingroom and diningroom. Children welcome and cot and babysitting offered. Central heating. Car essential, parking. Open Easter to October for Bed and Breakfast from £16 nightly per person. Reductions for children and Senior Citizens. Birmingham 40 miles, Hereford 20, Gloucester 17, Stratford 35 and the Wye Valley is just 30 miles.

TENBURY WELLS. Edward and Margaret Yarnold, Court Farm, Hanley Childe, Tenbury Wells WR15 8QY (01855 410265). Listed *COMMENDED.* Family-run Court Farm extends a warm and friendly welcome to you. The 15th century oak-beamed farmhouse is in a perfect position far from the madding crowd in 200 acres with outstanding views of the Teme Valley, Clee Hills and the Welsh mountains. Near to Tenbury Wells, Ludlow and Elgar's Birthplace. Spacious en suite bedrooms, hospitality trays and guests' sitting room. Excellent meals available locally. Children and pets welcome. Terms from £18. Open April to October.

FHG Please mention *The Farm Holiday Guide* when enquiring about accommodation featured in these pages.

WORCESTER near. Sylvia and Brian Wynn, The Old Smithy, Pirton, Worcester WR8 9EJ (01905 820482). Listed *HIGHLY COMMENDED.*

A 17th century half-timbered country house set in peaceful countryside with many interesting walks. Centrally situated, within easy reach of Stratford-upon-Avon, Cotswolds, Warwick Castle, Malvern Hills, Worcester Cathedral and Royal Worcester Porcelain. Four and a half miles from junction 7 of the M5 motorway. Private guests' facilities include lounge with inglenook log fireplace, colour TV and video, bathroom/dressing room and toilet, laundry, tea/coffee, central heating, gardens. One double bedroom and one twin bedroom. Ample parking. Bed and English Breakfast from £18.00; 3 course Evening Meal optional extra £9.95. Fresh local produce and home cooking. Sorry, no pets or children under 12 years. Craft Workshop (Harris Tweed and knitwear).

WORCESTER near. Mrs J. Morris, Knowle Farm, Suckley, Near Worcester WR6 5DJ (01886 884347).

Part timbered 17th century farmhouse with 25 acres grassland, used mainly for horses. Adjacent to a small, quiet country Inn, the house is in an elevated position with unrivalled views of the Malvern Hills and offers accommodation all year round. Large colourful garden. The quaint market towns of Bromyard, Ledbury and Hereford are nearby, and Knowle Farm is in the heart of a fruit-growing area where visitors enjoy the magnificent spring blossom. Superb walking country. One double and one single bedrooms (one with washbasin); bathroom, toilet. Sittingroom with woodburner fire, diningroom. Central heating keeps the house comfortable throughout the year. Car essential – parking. Traditional hearty English Breakfast. Fresh farm eggs. Bed and Breakfast £18 (bedtime drink). No single supplement. This is a non-smoking establishment.

FOR THE MUTUAL GUIDANCE OF GUEST AND HOST

Every year literally thousands of holidays, short breaks and overnight stops are arranged through our guides, the vast majority without any problems at all. In a handful of cases, however, difficulties do arise about bookings, which often could have been prevented from the outset.

It is important to remember that when accommodation has been booked, both parties – guests and hosts – have entered into a form of contract. We hope that the following points will provide helpful guidance.

GUESTS: When enquiring about accommodation, be as precise as possible. Give exact dates, numbers in your party and the ages of any children. State the number and type of rooms wanted and also what catering you require – bed and breakfast, full board etc. Make sure that the position about evening meals is clear – and about pets, reductions for children or any other special points.

Read our reviews carefully to ensure that the proprietors you are going to contact can supply what you want. Ask for a letter confirming all arrangements, if possible.

If you have to cancel, do so as soon as possible. Proprietors do have the right to retain deposits and under certain circumstances to charge for cancelled holidays if adequate notice is not given and they cannot re-let the accommodation.

HOSTS: Give details about your facilities and about any special conditions. Explain your deposit system clearly and arrangements for cancellations, charges etc. and whether or not your terms include VAT.

If for any reason you are unable to fulfil an agreed booking without adequate notice, you may be under an obligation to arrange suitable alternative accommodation or to make some form of compensation.

While every effort is made to ensure accuracy, we regret that FHG Publications cannot accept responsibility for errors, omissions or misrepresentations in our entries or any consequences thereof. Prices in particular should be checked because we go to press early. We will follow up complaints but cannot act as arbiters or agents for either party.

YORKSHIRE

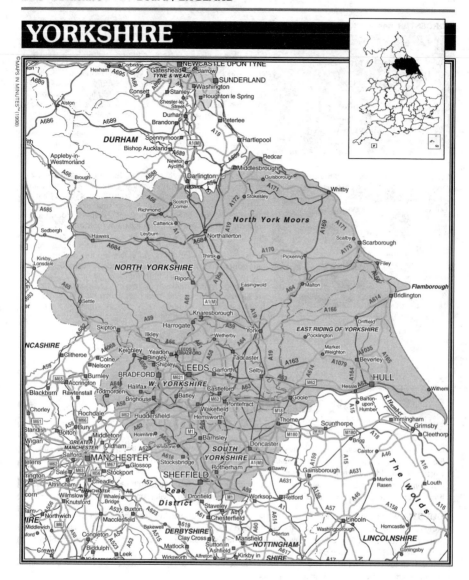

EAST YORKSHIRE

BRIDLINGTON. Mrs Pat Cowton, The Grange, Bempton Lane, Flamborough, Bridlington YO15 1AS

(01262 850207). For a relaxing holiday come and stay in our Georgian farmhouse situated in 450 acres of stock and arable land on the outskirts of Flamborough village. Ideally situated for bird watching at RSPB Sanctuary at Bempton, sandy beaches, cliffs and coves on our Heritage Coast. Golf and sea fishing nearby. Children and pets welcome. Open all year except Christmas Day. Bed and Breakfast from £15. Self Catering cottage – sleeps 6-8 people also available.

DRIFFIELD. Mrs Watson, Skerne Leys Farm, Driffield YO25 9HN (01377 253102). Skerne Leys is a family

farm with beautiful open views south across the plain of Holderness towards Beverley, close to Driffield and convenient for York, The North York Moors and the coast. We welcome all the family to our farmhouse. The garden has a grass tennis court, sometimes! and ornamental pond. We offer family accommodation in two rooms, one for all the family and one twin room, with shared facilities. A cot is available. There are many local pubs providing excellent meals. Terms on application.

GREAT DRIFFIELD. Mrs Tiffy Hopper, Kelleythorpe, Great Driffield YO25 9DW (01377 252297).

Tourist Board Listed *COMMENDED*. **Working farm.** Imagine peacocks strutting, ducks swimming and trout rising. Enjoy a cup of tea on the sun terrace overlooking a crystal clear shallow river. The friendly atmosphere of our lovely Georgian farmhouse with its mellow antique furniture, pretty chintzes and new bathrooms, one en-suite, is sure to captivate you. Delicious country cooking. Children are very welcome, they enjoy playing in our large garden with swings and playcastle. Ideally placed for touring. Bed and Breakfast from £17; optional Evening Meal from £10 by prior arrangement. 10% discount for seven nights or more. Reductions for children under 12 years.

NORTH YORKSHIRE

AMPLEFORTH. Annabel Lupton, Carr House Farm, Ampleforth, Near Helmsley YO6 4ED (01347

868526 or 07977 113197). ETC ◆◆◆. Working farm. 'Which?' Guide; Sunday Observer recommends "Fresh air fiends' dream – good food, good walking, warm welcome". In idyllic 16th century farmhouse, sheltered in Herriot/Heartbeat countryside, half an hour to York, ideal to enjoy moors, Dales, National Parks, coasts, famous abbeys, castles and stately homes. Romantics will love four-poster bedrooms en suite and medieval-styled bedroom in comfortable relaxing home, with large garden. Enjoy full Yorkshire breakfasts with home-made preserves, free-range eggs, hearty evening meals – own produce used whenever possible and served in oak-panelled, beamed dining room with flagstoned floor, inglenook and original brick bread oven. No children under seven and no pets. Bed and Breakfast from £17.50. Evening meal from £10. Open all year.

ASKRIGG. Mrs B. Percival, Milton House, Askrigg, Leyburn DL8 3HJ (01969 650217). ☜☜
COMMENDED. Askrigg is situated in the heart of Wensleydale and is within easy reach of many interesting places – Aysgarth Falls, Hardraw Falls, Bolton Castle. Askrigg is one of the loveliest villages in the dale. This is an ideal area for touring or walking. Milton House is a lovely spacious house with all the comforts of home, beautifully furnished and decor to match. All bedrooms are en suite with colour TV and tea/coffee making facilities. Visitors lounge, dining room. Central heating. Private parking. Milton House is open all year for Bed and Breakfast. Good pub food nearby. You are sure of a friendly welcome and a homely atmosphere. Please write or phone Mrs Beryl Percival for details and brochure.

CARLTON-IN-COVERDALE. (Near Leyburn). Mrs P. Lashmar, Abbots Thorn, Carlton, Leyburn DL8 4AY (01969 640620; Fax: 01969 640304). ☜☜ COMMENDED.
Relax and unwind at our non-smoking home. Friendly faces, fabulous food, superb scenery, terrific touring, wonderful walking! Set in the Yorkshire Dales National Park, Carlton-in-Coverdale is a quiet, peaceful village - yet only a short distance from so many places of interest. To complete your day, why not sample our delicious evening meals served in the informal dining room. The oak beamed guest lounge has an open fire for those chilly evenings. We have three attractive bedrooms, two with en suite facilities and one with private bathroom, and are open all year. Brochure available on request.
e-mail: abbots.thorn@virgin.net
website: http://business.virgin.net/patricia.lashmar

New Inn

YORKSHIRE DALES NATIONAL PARK

Keith and Barbara Mannion invite you to their friendly 18th century residential coaching inn in the picturesque Dales village of Clapham. Ideal centre for walking the three peaks of Ingleborough, Pen-y-ghent and Whernside. Kendal and Skipton 21 miles. All 15 bedrooms have full en suite facilities, colour TV and tea/coffee facilities. Enjoy good wholesome Yorkshire food in our restaurant, or bar meals in either of our two bars. Dogs welcome. Midweek B&B £20 Winter.

Ring Barbara for full details on 015242 51203

Tel: 015242 51203   Fax: 015242 51496
☜☜☜ Commended
Member of Inns of Tradition

See also Colour Display Advertisement

COVERDALE. Mrs Julie A. Clarke, Middle Farm, Woodale, Leyburn DL8 4TY (01969 640271). Middle Farm is a peacefully situated traditional Dales farmhouse, with adjoining stable block for guests accommodation. Situated on the unclassified road linking Wensleydale and Wharfedale. Ideal place to escape the 'madding crowd'. Good base for walking and touring any of the Dales' many beauty spots. Noted for excellent home cooking, offering Bed and Breakfast with optional Dinner. Two double and one twin-bedded rooms all en suite. Separate lounge, dining room. Guests' privacy assured. Pets and children welcome. Ample private off-road parking. Open all year round. Brochure available on request. Directions – 5 miles Kettlewell, 10 miles Leyburn, unclassified road.

DANBY. Mrs B. Tindall, Rowan Tree Farm, Danby, Whitby YO21 2LE (01287 660396). ETC ◆◆◆.

Working farm, join in. Rowan Tree Farm is situated in the heart of the North Yorkshire Moors and has panoramic moorland views. Ideal walking area and quiet location just outside the village of Danby. Accommodation comprises one twin-bedded room and one family room all with washbasins and full oil-fired central heating. Residents' lounge with colour TV. Two residents' bathrooms. Children welcome – cot provided if required. Babysitting available. Pets accepted. Good home cooking. Bed and Breakfast from £16; Evening Meals provided on request £8 each. Ample car parking space.

EASINGWOLD. Mrs Rachel Ritchie, The Old Rectory, Thormanby, Easingwold, York YO61 4NN (01845 501417). 👑👑 A warm welcome awaits you at this interesting Grade II Listed Georgian rectory built in 1737 and furnished with many antiques including a four-poster bed. Three comfortable and very spacious bedrooms with tea/coffee making facilities, two en suite; charming lounge with colour TV and open fire. Separate diningroom. Large mature garden. An excellent base for touring the Moors, Dales and York. This is the centre of "James Herriot" country with many historic houses and abbeys to visit in the area. Thormanby is a small village between Easingwold and Thirsk. Historic York is 17 miles away. Many delightful inns and restaurants serving good food locally. Bed and Breakfast from£16 – reductions for children under 12 years and reduced weekly rates. Ample parking. Open all year. SAE for brochure or telephone.

EASINGWOLD. Mrs L. Glaister, Garbutts Ghyll, Thornton Hill, Easingwold YO6 3PZ (01347 868644).

Georgian working farm set in its own secluded valley but well resourced by many local amenities. Homely, friendly, family atmosphere with home cooking and open log fires. Pets and children welcome; babysitting available. Directions: leave Easingwold market square, ascend hill on your left, at crossroads turn left into Oulston Road marked Oulston/Coxwold; after 0.6 miles take road signposted Thornton; Garbutts is two and a half miles on left. Bed and Breakfast from £17.50 to £20.00 single, £20.00 to £25.00 double. Open from March to November.

See also Colour Display Advertisement

GLAISDALE. Tom and Sandra Spashett, Red House Farm, Glaisdale, Near Whitby YO21 2PZ (Tel & Fax: 01947 897242). Listed Georgian farmhouse featured in "Houses of the North York Moors". Completely refurbished to the highest standards, retaining all original features. Bedrooms have bath/shower/toilet, central heating, TV and tea making facilities. Excellent walks straight from the doorstep. Friendly farm animals – a few cows, horses, geese and pretty free-roaming hens. One-and-a-half acres of gardens, sitting-out areas. Magnificent views. Interesting buildings – listed barns now converted to two holiday cottages. Games room with snooker table. Eight miles from seaside/Whitby. Village pubs within walking distance. Stabling available for horses/dogs. Non-smoking. Please phone Tom or Sandra for more information.

GOATHLAND. Mrs Marion N. Cockrem, Dale End Farm, Goathland, Whitby YO22 5LJ (01947 895371). Working farm. 140-acre working farm, 500-year-old stone-built farmhouse in North York Moors National Park. Generous portions of home-cooked food. Rare breeds of animals kept including llamas, emus, Vietnamese pot-bellied pigs and miniature ponies. Children and pets welcomed. An excellent children's playground. Guests' lounge with TV and log fire. Homely old-worlde interior, oak beams and panelling. Many repeat bookings. Sensible prices. SAE for brochure.

GOATHLAND. Christine Chippindale, Barnet House Guest House, Goathland, Whitby YO22 5NG

(01947 896201). ETC ◆◆◆. Situated in large garden on edge of delightful village of Goathland with magnificent views of the surrounding moors. Overlooking North Yorkshire Moors Railway and Goathland Station. Ideal centre for walking, touring moors, dales and coast. Warm comfortable accommodation, friendly atmosphere, excellent lounge with colour TV. Triple, double, twin and single rooms, some en suite. All with washbasins, razor points, heating and tea/coffee facilities. Reductions for children (minimum six years). Non smoking. Parking in grounds. Open from March to November for Bed and Breakfast from £20, Evening Meal, Bed and Breakfast from £29.50. Brochure on request.

HARROGATE. Anne and Bob Joyner, Anro Guest House, 90 King's Road, Harrogate HG1 5JX (01423 503087; Fax: 01423 561719). AA QQQ, RAC ◆◆◆. "Excellent!", "Exceptional value!", "Good food!", "Quiet!", "Never had it so good!" – just a few testimonials visitors have written in our book on leaving. Situated in a tree-lined avenue in a central position close to all amenities. Conference and Exhibition Centre two minutes' walk. Valley Gardens, town and local swimming baths close by. Our house is centrally heated, with tea/coffee making facilities and colour TV in all rooms, hot and cold throughout. Some rooms en suite. Home cooking. Bed and Breakfast from £22.50pppn; four-course Dinner, plus tea or coffee on request, £13pp. Ideal centre for touring Dales/Herriot country. Well recommended. FHG Diploma Winners.
e-mail: anro@joyner.fsnet.co.uk

HARROGATE. Mrs Alison Harrison, Garden Cottage, Moor Park, Norwood Lane, Beckwithshaw,

Harrogate HG3 1QN (01423 530197). ETC ◆◆◆◆. Set in secluded woodland grounds, three miles west of Harrogate with pastoral views. One luxury twin en suite and one family en suite ground floor apartments with private patio; single room with private bathroom. Purpose built from converted pottery to high standard. Comfy beds, electric blankets, TV, beverage trays, gas and convector heating. Roomy non-slip power showers, large windows, own entrance. Breakfast in Listed cottage dining room. Pub in village and good dining places within five minutes. A good base for touring and walking. Harrogate is 10 minutes' drive, York, Leeds and Dales 25 minutes. Reasonably disabled friendly. Open all year. Bed and Breakfast from £22.50 per person. A warm welcome assured.

HARROGATE. Christine Ryder, Scaife Hall Farm, Blubberhouses, Otley, West Yorkshire LS21 2PL

(01943 880354; Fax: 01943 880374). ETC ◆◆◆◆. Scaife Hall is a working farm set in picturesque countryside on the edge of the Yorkshire Dales. Ideal location for visiting Harrogate, Leeds, York and Dales. Many tourist attractions in the area and ideal for walking. All three rooms are tastefully decorated, all have en suite facilities, central heating, beverage tray and colour TV. Private guest lounge with colour TV and log fires on chilly nights. Recommended by the Which? Good Bed and Breakfast Guide. Local inns provide excellent evening meals. Bed and Breakfast from £23. Farm Holiday Bureau member.
e-mail: christine.a.ryder@btinternet.com

HARROGATE. Mrs A. Wood, Field House, Clint, Near Harrogate HG3 3DS (01423 770638). Field House with its beautiful large gardens is situated five miles from Harrogate commanding lovely views over the Nidd Valley. Ideal for exploring the Dales and Moors with ancient abbeys, castles and country houses. The market towns of Skipton, Ripon and Knaresborough and the historic city of York are all within easy reach. Accommodation is in one twin and one double room with private bathroom. Private sittingroom with TV, etc. Open all year. Car essential - private parking. Bed and Breakfast from £15 with Evening Meals readily available. A warm welcome guaranteed in a peaceful friendly atmosphere. Telephone or SAE, please, for further details.

HAWES. Margaret and Roy Hill, Widdale Foot, Hawes DL8 3LX (Tel & Fax: 01969 667383). ETC ◆◆◆.

Our spacious Dales farmhouse enjoys a superb sheltered position on the side of Widdale fell, just three miles from Wensleydale's popular market town of Hawes. Excellent walking from the house and close to the Three Peaks and Settle to Carlisle Railway. We have our own woodland with abundant wildlife, mountain streams and a flock of primitive Hebridean sheep. The Lake District is within easy reach by car. Two double rooms (one en suite, one with private bathroom). Extra twin room by arrangement. Central heating, lounge with TV and log fire, tea/coffee making facilities in rooms, south facing lawns and patio. Self-catering available in the west wing of the house. Bed and Breakfast from £17.50. Brochure on request.

Working mixed farm, stylish, well-appointed farmhouse accommodation twixt moors and dales in the North Yorks Moors National Park with outstanding views across beautiful countryside. Relax in rural peace and tranquillity, excellent walking country. Warm spacious en suite rooms each with tea and coffee making facilities and colour TV. Substantial whole and hearty breakfast and old fashioned leisurely farmhouse dinners are served. Licensed and open all year. Bed and Breakfast from £28. Dinner, Bed and Breakfast £41.50. Self-catering cottages also available. Please phone for brochure

Telephone: 01439 798221
Fax: 01439 798447
E-mail: sally@valleyviewfarm.com
Website: www.valleyviewfarm.com

ETC
◆◆◆◆

Mrs Sally Robinson,
Valley View Farm,
Old Byland, Helmsley, York,
North Yorkshire. YO6 5LG

HELMSLEY. Mrs J. Milburn, Barn Close Farm, Rievaulx, Helmsley YO6 5LN (01439 798321). 👑👑👑

COMMENDED. **Working farm.** Farm Holiday Bureau member. Farming family offer homely accommodation on mixed farm in beautiful surroundings near Rievaulx Abbey. Ideal for touring, pony trekking, walking. Home-made bread, own home-produced meat, poultry, free range eggs - in fact Mrs Milburn's excellent cooking was praised in the "Daily Telegraph". Modern home - two double bedrooms with washbasins, one family room (one room en suite); all with tea/coffee making facilities. TV lounge; diningroom. Children welcome, babysitting. Sorry, no pets. Open all year round. Open log fires. Storage heaters in bedrooms. Car essential - parking. Bed and Breakfast from £20 to £25; Dinner £12. Reduced rates for children under 10 sharing parents' room.

HELMSLEY. Mrs Sarah Wood, Easterside Farm, Hawnby, Helmsley YO6 5QT (01439 798277). ◆◆◆

A large 18th century Grade II Listed farmhouse nestling on Easterside Hill and enjoying panoramic views. Ideal base for walking, touring, the coast and the city of York. Enjoy good food and a warm welcome in comfortable surroundings. All rooms have en suite facilities. Bed and Breakfast from £21; Evening Meal from £12.50. Children welcome. Open all year except Christmas.

HELMSLEY near. Sue Smith, Laskill Farm, Hawnby, Near Helmsley YO6 5NB (01439 798268). ETC

◆◆◆◆. Amidst beautiful North Yorkshire Moors, in heart of James Herriot Country. Attractive farmhouse with own lake and large walled garden. Own natural spring water. High standard of food and comfort. Two double rooms en suite, two twins en suite, one double and one twin each with shower and washbasins, one single; all with colour TV and beverage tray. Ideal for nearby places of interest and scenic beauty, or simply enjoy peaceful and tranquil surroundings. Open all year except Christmas Day. Pets welcome. Bed and Breakfast from £26.50. Self catering accommodation also available. Brochure on request. Featured on BBC Holiday Programme.

HELMSLEY near. Brenda Johnson, Hill End Farm, Chop Gate, Bilsdale TS9 7JR (01439 798278).

ETC ◆◆◆. Hill End Farm is recommended by "Which?" the Good Bed and Breakfast Guide. If you are looking for a comfortable peaceful break with beautiful views come and join us! Excellent walking country within the North York Moors National Park with way-marked paths from the farm. Near to Captain Cook, Herriot and Heartbeat country. Guests' lounge with TV and open fire; dining room; two pretty en suite bedrooms. Bed and Breakfast £20. Children under 14 years half price.

INGLETON. Mrs Nancy Lund, Gatehouse Farm, Far Westhouse, Ingleton LA6 3NR (015242 41458/41307). ♨♨ *COMMENDED.* Bryan and Nancy invite you to their farm which they run with their son who lives at Lund Holme (next door). You are welcome to wander round and look at the cows, calves and sheep or stroll in the quiet country lanes and enjoy the wild flowers. Gatehouse, situated in the Yorkshire Dales National Park, is in an elevated position with beautiful views over open countryside; it was built in 1740 and retains the original oak beams. Double or twin rooms (families welcome), all with private facilities and tea/coffee trays; guests' diningroom and lounge with colour TV. M6 turnoff 34, 15 miles, one-and-a-half miles west of Ingleton, just off A65. Bed and Breakfast from £20; Evening Meal available.

NUTSTILE

INGLETON. Carol Brennand, Nutstile Farm, Ingleton, Via Carnforth LA6 3DT (015242 41752). Tourist Board Listed *COMMENDED.* Surrounded by the outstanding beauty of the Yorkshire Dales, Nutstile is a typical working farm providing first class accommodation. The mountains, caves and waterfalls of Ingleton are immediately accessible, the Lake District also close by. Try a leisurely ride on the scenic Settle-Carlisle railway. Three bedrooms (all with views) with washbasin and tea/coffee facilities and colour TV, en suite available. Guests' lounge with TV. Children welcome. Open all year. Bed and Breakfast from £17 to £19.

See also Colour Display Advertisement

INGLETON. Mrs Mollie Bell, "Langber Country Guest House", Ingleton, via Carnforth LA6 3DT (015242 41587). Ingleton, "Beauty Spot of the North" in the Three Peaks/Dales National Park area. Renowned for waterfalls, glens, underground caves, magnificent scenery, and Ingleboro' Mountain (2,373 feet), an excellent centre for touring Lakes, Dales and coast. Golf, fishing, swimming, bowls, and tennis in vicinity; pony trekking a few miles away. Guests are warmly welcomed to "Langber", a detached country guest house with beautiful views and 82 acres of gardens, terrace and fields. Lambs and sheep kept. Ample parking space available. Three family, three double/twin and one single bedrooms, all with washbasins and razor points, some en-suite. Bathroom and two toilets. Sunny comfortable lounge and separate diningroom. Central heating; fire precautions. Babysitting offered. Open all year except Christmas. Fire Certificate granted Highly recommended. Bed and Breakfast from £16.50; Bed, Breakfast and Evening Meal from £23.50. Reductions for children under 13 sharing with two parents.

MALHAM (Yorkshire Dales National Park). Peter and Vera Sharp, Miresfield Farm, Skipton BD23 4DA (01729 830414). Miresfield is situated on the edge of the village of Malham in the Yorkshire Dales National Park. An ideal centre for exploring the Dales or for visiting the City of York, Settle and Skipton. Within walking distance is Malham Cove, Gordale Scar with its spectacular waterfalls, and Malham Moor with the famous Field Centre and home of Charles Kingsley's "Water Babies". Miresfield is set in a well-kept garden and offers accommodation in six double rooms, six twin and two large family rooms, most en suite. There are two well furnished lounges with TV, one has open fire. Good, old-fashioned farmhouse cooking is served in the large, beamed diningroom.

NORTHALLERTON. Mary and John Pearson, Lovesome Hill Farm, Lovesome Hill, Northallerton DL6 2PB (01609 772311). Come and enjoy the experience of staying in our 19th century farmhouse amidst a friendly atmosphere. Tastefully converted granary adjoins house with spacious, well-furnished en suite rooms which include TV and beverage facilities. Beamed ceilings are still retained in the two upstairs bedrooms. Our newly converted downstairs accommodation includes a bedroom and dining room, both of which overlook the garden and patio. Locally produced food is used when available. Situated in open countryside overlooking Hambleton Hills, four miles north of Northallerton, this is a perfect base for exploring the Dales, Moors, York and Durham. You'll "love" it. Brochure available

OTLEY. Mrs C. Beaumont, Paddock Hill, Norwood, Otley LS21 2QU (01943 465977). ◆◆ Converted

farmhouse on B6451 south of Bland Hill. Open fires, lovely views, in the heart of the countryside. Within easy reach of Herriot, Bronte and Emmerdale country and with attractive market towns around – Skipton, Knaresborough, Otley and Ripon. Walking, bird watching and fishing on the nearby reservoirs. Residents' lounge with TV. Comfortable bedrooms. Non-smoking accommodation available. Children welcome. Pets by arrangement. Bed and Breakfast £15, en suite £22.

See also Colour Display Advertisement **PICKERING. Mrs Ella Bowes, Banavie, Roxby Road, Thornton-le-Dale, Pickering YO18 7SX (01751 474616). ETC ◆◆◆◆.** Banavie is a large stone built semi-detached house set in Thornton-le-Dale, one of the prettiest villages in Yorkshire with the stream flowing through the centre. Situated in an attractive part of the village off the main road, it is ideal for touring coast, moors, Castle Howard, Flamingo Park, Eden Camp, North Yorkshire Moors Railways and "Heartbeat" country. A real Yorkshire breakfast is served by Mrs Bowes herself which provides a good start to the day. One family en suite bedroom, two double en suite bedroom, all with colour TV, shaver points and tea making facilities; dining room, lounge with TV, central heating. Children and pets welcome, cot, high chair and babysitting available. Own door keys. Car park; cycle shed. Open all year. Bed and Breakfast including tea and biscuits at bedtime from £18. SAE please. Thornton-le-Dale has three pubs, two restaurants and fish and chip shop in the village for meals. Welcome Host, Hygiene Certificate held.

REETH. Richard and Rebecca Keyse, Hackney House, Reeth, Richmond DL11 6TW (01748 884302).

Situated amid the beauty of Swaledale and conveniently astride the coast to coast route, Reeth is a haven for the weary walker, cyclist or motorist. Principal cities and cultural attractions are within easy reach, or simply enjoy the peace and quiet to be found in the Dales and villages, which offer a wealth of leisure facilities and good restaurants. Hackney House offers comfortable accommodation for both the overnight guest or those who wish to stay longer. Ideal touring base. Accommodation comprises double, twin and single rooms, all centrally heated and double glazed, with colour TV and beverage making facilities. Some rooms en suite, guests have own lounge and diningroom. Bed and Breakfast from £17. Packed Lunches available. Private off-street parking.

RICHMOND. Mrs A. Porter, Oxnop Hall, Low Oxnop, Gunnerside, Richmond. DL11 6JJ (Tel & Fax: 01748 886253). ❀❀❀ COMMENDED. Working Farm.

Sleeps 11. Visit our working hill farm where we have beef cattle and Swaledale sheep. Oxnop Hall is of historical interest and has been enlarged with exclusively all en suite rooms. Great walking and touring. Situated in Yorkshire Dales National Park, Herriot Country, an unspolt area of natural beauty famous for its stone walls, barns and flora. Good farmhouse food. Tea/coffee-making facilities. Open all year except Christmas. Bed and Breakfast £23.00 to £24.00. Evening meals from £14.00.

RICHMOND. Mrs Dorothy Wardle, Greenbank Farm, Ravensworth, Richmond DL11 7HB (01325 718334). This 170 acre farm, both arable and carrying livestock,

is four miles west of Scotch Corner on the A66, midway between the historic towns of Richmond and Barnard Castle, and within easy reach of Teesdale, Swaledale and Wensleydale, only an hour from the Lake District. The farm is one mile outside the village of Ravensworth with plenty of good eating places within easy reach. Guests' own lounge; dining room; two double bedrooms, one en suite and one family room. All have washbasins, tea/coffee facilities, heating and electric blankets. Children welcome. Sorry, no pets. Car essential. Bed and Breakfast from £14.00. Reductions for children and Senior Citizens. Open all year. Luxury mobile home also available.

Browson Bank Farmhouse Accommodation

A newly converted granary set in 300 acres of farmland. The accommodation consists of three very tastefully furnished double/twin rooms all en suite, tea and coffee making facilities, colour TV and central heating. A large, comfortable lounge is available to relax in. Full English breakfast served. Situated 6 miles west of Scotch Corner (A1). Ideal location to explore the scenic countryside of Teesdale and the Yorkshire Dales and close to the scenic towns of Barnard Castle and Richmond. Terms £18.00 per night

Browson Bank Farmhouse, Browson Bank, Dalton, Richmond DL11 7HE
Tel: (01325) 718504 or (01325) 718246

See also Colour Display Advertisement

RICHMOND. Mrs Diana Greenwood, Walburn Hall, Downholme, Richmond DL11 6AF (Tel & Fax: 01748 822152). ◆◆◆◆. Walburn Hall is one of the few remaining fortified farmhouses dating from the 14th century. It has an enclosed courtyard and terraced garden. Accommodation for guests includes two double (one with four poster) and one twin bedroom all with en suite facilities. The guests' lounge and dining room have beamed ceilings and stone fireplaces with log fires as required. Your stay at Walburn Hall in the heart of the Yorkshire Dales of Swaledale and Wensleydale gives the opportunity to visit Richmond, Middleham and Bolton Castles and numerous Abbeys. York, Durham and Harrogate are one hour away. Sorry no pets. Non smoking. Bed and Breakfast from £23 per person. Open March – November. Self catering Dales farmhouse available, sleeps seven plus cot. Brochure on request.

RICHMOND. Mrs S. Lawson, Stonesthrow, Dacton, Richmond DL11 7HS (01833 621493; mobile: 09770 655726). ETC ◆◆◆ Welcoming fire, private garden and conservatory – Stonesthrow offers you a friendly family atmosphere. Unmistakable Yorkshire hospitality from the moment you arrive; we greet you with tea or coffee and home-made cakes. Situated midway between the towns of Richmond and Barnard Castle it offers you an ideal base for exploring the Yorkshire Dales, Teesdale and York. Stonesthrow Bed and Breakfast has well appointed bedrooms with TV, tea and coffee facilities and full central heating. Off- road parking. Children over eight are welcome; sorry, no pets. No smoking.

RIPON. Mrs Maggie Johnson, Mallard Grange, Aldfield, Near Fountains Abbey, Ripon HG4 3BE (01765 620242). 💐💐 *HIGHLY COMMENDED.* **Working farm.** Historically linked with nearby Fountains Abbey, Mallard Grange is a rambling 16th century working farm oozing character and charm in a glorious rural setting. Offering a superb level of quality and comfort, spacious rooms furnished with care and some lovely antique pieces. En suite bedrooms have colour TV, hair dryers, beverages and homely extras. Delicious breakfasts complemented by home-made preserves. Yorkshire Dales, historic properties, gardens, York and Harrogate are all within easy reach, making this the perfect centre for a peaceful, relaxing stay in a Designated Area of Outstanding Natural beauty. Open most of the year. Bed and Breakfast from £22.50. Brochure available.

RIPON. Mrs Dorothy Poulter, Avenue Farm, Bramley Grange, Ilton Road, Grewelthorpe, Ripon HG4 3DN (01765 658348). Small dairy farm offering quiet, homely farmhouse accommodation at the foot of the Yorkshire Dales set in lovely countryside with beautiful views. Near James Herriott country. Within easy reach of A1, Ripon, York, Fountains Abbey and just three miles from Masham with the taste of Black Sheep Ale, Golf, fishing and pony trekking nearby. Avenue Farm guarantees a warm welcome with a cup of tea on arrival and bedtime drink. TV lounge. Bed and Breakfast from £14 per night.

ROBIN HOOD'S BAY. Mrs B. Reynolds, 'South View', Sledgates, Fylingthorpe, Whitby YO22 4TZ (01947 880025). Pleasantly situated, comfortable accommodation in own garden with sea and country views. Ideal for walking and touring. Close to the moors, within easy reach of Whitby, Scarborough and many more places of interest. there are two double rooms, lounge and diningroom. Bed and Breakfast from £17, including bedtime drink. Parking Spaces. Phone for further details

ROSEDALE. Mrs B. Brayshaw, Low Bell End Farm, Rosedale, Pickering YO18 8RE (01751 417451). Working farm. The farm is situated in the North Yorkshire Moors National Park about 15 miles from the nearest seaside resort of Whitby. Scarborough and Bridlington are within easy reach, also York, Pickering and Helmsley, all places of historic interest. The farm, a 173-acre beef and sheep farm, is one mile from the village of Rosedale Abbey and there are many lovely walks to be taken in the area. A car is essential with ample parking space. Pets by arrangement. One double, one bunk-bedded, one family rooms; bathroom and toilet; combined sitting/diningroom with colour TV. Children welcome at reduced rates. Cot, high chair, babysitting available. Central heating and open fires. Open all year. Evening Dinner, Bed and Breakfast or Bed and Breakfast. Terms on request.

ROSEDALE EAST. Mr and Mrs Harrison, Moordale House, Dale Head, Rosedale East, Pickering YO18 8RH (01751 417219). Enjoy beautiful views across the historic valley of Rosedale in the heart of the North Yorkshire moors. We offer comfortable accommodation, en suite bedrooms - one family, two double and two twin-bedded. Tea and coffee making facilities, central heating. TV lounge with open fire. Diningroom with separate tables. Good home cooking, traditional English breakfast. Warm and friendly welcome, pets by arrangement. Licensed, good parking, evening meal by arrangement. Excellent area for walking, cycling or visiting the Yorkshire coast, York and the North East.

RUFFORTH. Mrs Helen Butterworth, Wellgarth House, Wetherby Road, Rufforth, York YO23 3QB (01904 738592 or 738595). ETC/AA ◆◆◆ A warm welcome awaits you at Wellgarth House, ideally situated in Rufforth (B1224) three miles from York and one mile from the ring road (A1237). Also convenient for "Park and Ride" into York City. This country guest house offers a high standard of accommodation with en suite Bed and Breakfast from £18.50. All rooms have complimentary tea/coffee making, colour TV. Rooms with four-poster or king-size beds also available. Excellent local pub two minutes' walk away serves lunches and dinners. Large private car park. Telephone or write for brochure.

SCARBOROUGH. Mrs D.M. Medd, Hilford House, Crossgates, Scarborough YO12 4JU (01723 862262). Detached country guest house, quietly situated in own grounds adjoining Scarborough – Seamer road just off A64. Near Scarborough, but handy for touring all coast and countryside of North Yorkshire. Three double, one single and one family bedrooms all with washbasins and central heating. Bathroom, two toilets; diningroom with separate tables and guests' lounge with colour TV. Cot, high chair and babysitting available. Full Fire Certificate held. Open all year round. Personal supervision ensures complete satisfaction of guests. Non-smoking accommodation available. Own home grown fruit and vegetables served in season, also fresh Scarborough cod and local meats. Private car parking. Bed and Breakfast from £18 to £22. Reductions for children sharing.

FHG FREE and REDUCED RATE Holiday Visits! Don't miss our Readers' Offer Vouchers

SCARBOROUGH. Sue and Tony Hewitt, Harmony Country Lodge, Limestone Road, Burniston, Scarborough YO13 0DG (0800 2985840). ◆◆◆◆

DISTINCTIVELY DIFFERENT, HARMONY COUNTRY LODGE is a peaceful and relaxing retreat, octagonal in design and set in two acres of private grounds overlooking the National Park and sea. Two miles from Scarborough and within easy reach of Whitby, York and the beautiful North Yorkshire countryside. Comfortable en suite centrally heated rooms with colour TV and all with superb views. Attractive dining room, guest lounge and relaxing conservatory. Traditional English breakfast, optional evening meal, including vegetarian. Fragrant massage available. Bed and Breakfast from £19.00 to £28.00. Non-smoking, licensed, private parking facilities. Personal service and warm, friendly Yorkshire hospitality. Spacious eight berth caravan also available for self-catering holidays. Open all year. Please telephone or write for brochure. Children-friendly over 7 years old. website: www.spiderweb.co.uk/Harmony

SCARBOROUGH. Mrs M. Edmondson, Plane Tree Cottage Farm, Staintondale, Scarborough YO13 0EY (01723 870796). ◆◆◆ This small mixed farm is situated off

the beaten track, with open views of beautiful countryside and the sea. We have sheep, hens, two ginger cats and special sheep dog "Bess". This very old beamed cottage, small but homely, has one twin, one double and one room en suite with washbasins and tea makers. Meals of very high standard served with own fresh eggs and garden produce as available. Staintondale is about half-way between Scarborough and Whitby and near the North York Moors. Pretty woodland walks nearby. Car essential. Bed and Breakfast from £20 per person per night. Also six-berth caravan available. SAE please for details, or telephone.

SKIPTON. Mrs Heather Simpson, Low Skibeden Farmhouse, Skibeden Road, Skipton BD23 6AB (07050 207787/01756 793849; Fax: 01756 793804). AA

QQQ Recommended. "Welcome Host", "Which?" Detached 16th century farmhouse in private grounds one mile east of Skipton off the A59/A65 gateway to the Dales, eg Bolton Abbey - Malham, Settle. Luxury bed and breakfast with fireside treats in the lounge. All rooms are quiet, spacious, have panoramic views, washbasins, tea facilities and electric overblankets. Central heating October to May. All guests are warmly welcomed and served tea/coffee and cakes on arrival, bedtime beverages are served from 9.30pm. Breakfast is served from 7am to 8.45am in the dining room. No smoking. No pets and no children under 12 years. Safe parking. New arrivals before 10pm. Quality and value guaranteed. Bed and Breakfast from £17 to £22 per person per night; en suite from £22 per person per night; full en suites single occupancy from £25 to £38. Two piece toilet en suite £20 per person per night. A deposit secures a room.

SKIPTON. Mrs Rosie Lister, Bushey Lodge Farm, Starbotton, Upper Wharfedale, Skipton BD23 5HY (01756 760424). Bushey Lodge is a traditional working hill

farm of over 2000 acres set in the heart of the Yorkshire Dales. The lovely old farmhouse nestles on the edge of Starbotton village and has been sympathetically restored to create a haven of peace and tranquillity. Each bedroom has en suite bathroom, TV, hairdryer and tea/coffee facilities. Featured in the Which? Good Bed and Breakfast Guide. Bed and Breakfast from £22.50 per person. website: www.yorkshirenet.co.uk/stayat/busheylodgefarm

---

FHG Please mention *The Farm Holiday Guide* when enquiring about accommodation featured in these pages.

STOKESLEY. Mrs Pat Weighell, Dromonby Hall Farm, Busby Lane, Kirkby in Cleveland, Stokesley TS9 7AP (Tel & Fax: 01642 712312). ETC ◆◆◆. Come and stay in our comfortable modern farmhouse on our 170 acre working farm and explore the National Park. We are situated close to the National Cycle Route, Coast to Coast Walk and the Cleveland Way and can provide locked storage for bicycles, or stabling and grazing for horses - why not bring your horse for a holiday? Mountain biking and horse riding available nearby. Packed lunches and drying facilities available; excellent pub food close by. Guided walking on moors by arrangement - come and learn about the local history and enjoy the beautiful moorland scenery, or visit the coast. B&B from £20. Open all year except Christmas. Log fires in winter. Full central heating.
e-mail: B&B@dromonby.swinternet.co.uk

THIRSK. Mrs Tess Williamson, Thornborough House Farm, South Kilvington, Thirsk YO7 2NP (Tel & Fax: 01845 522103). ◆◆◆. Working farm This is "James Herriot's" town! Situated one and a half miles north of Thirsk, a warm welcome awaits you in this 200 year old farmhouse set in lovely countryside. Ideal location for a walking or touring holiday. The bedrooms are warm and comfortable: one family room, one double room en suite and one twin room with washbasin and private bathroom. Guests' own sitting and dining rooms with colour TV and open fire. Non-smoking. Children most welcome. Pets accepted. Good home cooking is a speciality; special diets catered for. Guests can choose to have Bed and Breakfast or Bed, Breakfast and Evening Meal. The North York Moors, Pennine Dales, York, the East Coast, Scarborough, Whitby, Ripon, Fountains Abbey, Harrogate are all very near. Golf courses, fishing, horse riding available locally. Bed and Breakfast from £16 pp.
e-mail: williamson@thornboroughhousefarm.freeserve.co.uk

THIRSK. Mrs Barbara Ramshay, Garth House, Dalton, Near Thirsk YO7 3HY (01845 577310). Tourist Board Listed. Working farm, join in. Garth House is situated in Herriot country amidst beautiful scenery. Near to York, Harrogate and many historic buildings, this area with its many attractions is ideal for touring. Guest accommodation is in one family room and one twin room, both with washbasins and tea/coffee making facilities; TV in lounge; central heating. Large gardens and lawns, children's pets and toys. Access to badminton court and other sporting facilities. Bed and Breakfast from £12 to £14. Easy access – from A1 turn off onto A168 and follow signposts for Dalton. Brochure on request.

THIRSK. Mrs M. Fountain, Town Pasture Farm, Boltby, Thirsk YO7 2DY (01845 537298). ♛♛ *COMMENDED.* **Working farm, join in.** A warm welcome awaits on a 180 acre mixed farm in beautiful Boltby village, nestling in the valley below the Hambleton Hills, in the midst of Herriot country and on the edge of the North York Moors National Park. An 18th century stone-built farmhouse with full central heating, comfortable en suite bedrooms (one family, one twin) with original old oak beams, and tea/coffee facilities; spacious guests' lounge with colour TV. Children and pets welcome. Good home cooking, hearty English breakfast and evening meals by arrangement. Ideal walking country and central for touring the Dales, York and East Coast. Pony trekking in village. Bed and Breakfast from £17.50.

WHITBY. Mrs A Mortimer, Hollins Farm, Glaisdale, Whitby YO21 2PZ (01947 897516). Hollins Farm is 10 miles from Whitby, surrounded by beautiful countryside and moorland, with lots of walks. Nearby attractions include Steam Railway, Pickering market town and castle, National Parks Centre, Whitby, Staithes, Robin Hood's Bay, pony trekking and fishing. The 16th century farmhouse provides comfortable accommodation comprising two large family or double rooms with washbasins and TV. Also twin room, all with tea making facilities and storage heaters. Bathroom, sitting/diningroom with TV, conservatory. Cot and high chair available. Log fires in winter. Access to rooms at all times. Camping facilties. Phone or send SAE for terms. Property has been inspected.

WHITBY near. Mrs Pat Beale, Ryedale House, Coach Road, Sleights, Near Whitby YO22 5EQ (Tel and Fax: 01947 810534). 😚😚 *COMMENDED.* Welcoming non-smoking Yorkshire house of charm and character at the foot of the Moors, National Park and "Heartbeat" country, three-and-a-half miles from Whitby. Rich in history, magnificent scenery, picturesque harbours, cliffs, beaches, scenic railways, superb walking. Double and single beautifully appointed bedrooms with private facilities. Guests' lounge and dining room (separate tables) with breathtaking views over Eskdale. Enjoy our large sun terrace and gardens, relax, we're ready to pamper you! Long established for delicious Yorkshire fare; extensive breakfast menu, picnics (traditional and vegetarian). Recommended local inns and restaurants. Parking, near public transport. Regret no pets. Bed and Breakfast Double from £18.50 per person per night, Single £21, minimum two nights. Regret no pets or young children.

YORK. Mrs Susan Viscovitch, The Manor Country House, Acaster Malbis, York YO23 2UL (Tel & Fax: 01904 706723). ◆◆◆◆ Atmospheric Manor in rural tranquillity with our own private lake set in five-and-a-half acres of beautiful mature grounds. Close to Racecourse and only 10 minutes' car journey from the city or take the leisurely river bus (Easter to October). Conviently situated for trips to Dales, Moors, Wolds and splendid coastline. Find us via A64 exiting for Copmanthorpe-York, Thirsk, Harrogate or Bishopthorpe (Sim Balk Lane). Centrally heated. 10 en suite bedrooms with full facilities. Cosy lounge and lounge bar; licensed. Conservatory breakfast room. Four-poster. Bed and Breakfast from £25 to £34 per person per night inclusive of VAT. For details SAE or telephone. Also see our advertisement on the Outside Back Cover of this guide.
e-mail: manor.house@mywebpage.net
website: www.mywebpage.net/manor.house

YORK. Mrs K.R. Daniel, Ivy House Farm, Kexby, York YO4 5LQ (01904 489368).Working Farm. Bed and Breakfast on a mixed dairy farm six miles from the ancient city of York on the A1079. Central for the east coast, Herriot country and dales. We offer a friendly service with comfortable accommodation consisting of double or family rooms, all with colour TV and tea/coffee making facilities. We provide a full farmhouse English Breakfast served in separate diningroom; colour TV lounge. Ample car parking with play area for children, who are most welcome. Bed and Breakfast from £15 per person. We are within easy reach of local restaurants and public houses serving excellent evening meals. AA and RAC Listed.

YORK. Mrs Diana Susan Tindall, Newton Guest House, Neville Street, Haxby Road, York YO31 8NP (01904 635627). ETC ◆◆◆. Diana and John offer all their guests a friendly and warm welcome to their Victorian End Town House, a few minutes walk from City centre, York's beautiful Minster, the City Walls and museums. Situated near an attractive park with good bowling greens. York is an ideal base for touring Yorkshire Moors, Dales and coastline. One bedroom (private facilities outside), all other rooms en suite, colour TV, tea/coffee making tray. Full central heating. Fire Certificate. Private car park. Personal attention. We are a non-smoking house.

FHG Please mention *The Farm Holiday Guide* when enquiring about accommodation featured in these pages.

YORK. Mrs L. Manners, Church View, Staddon on the Forest, York (01904 400403; mobile: 07971

431074; Fax: 01904 400325). Situated in a pretty countryside village with local walks, wildlife and animals, our 200-year-old cottage, a former farmhouse, is three miles from York. Ideal location for visiting the moors, Heartbeat Country, Castle Howard and the east coast. Feel at home in our cosy lounge with real fires. A full size snooker table is in our games room and the local golf course and pub are close by. Bed and Breakfast £20 per person per night. Reductions for children and special rates for longer stays.

YORK. Mont-Clare Guest House, 32 Claremont Terrace, Gillygate, York YO31 7EJ (01904 627054;

Fax: 01904 651011). ♛♛*COMMENDED*. Take advantage and enjoy the convenience of City Centre accommodation in a quiet location close to the magnificent York Minster. A warm and friendly welcome awaits you at the Mont-Clare. All rooms are en suite, tastefully decorated and have colour TV (Satellite), radio alarm, direct-dial telephone, hairdryer, tea/coffee tray, shoe cleaning, etc. Some four-poster rooms available. All of York's attractions are within walking distance and we are ideally situated for the Yorkshire Dales, Moors and numerous stately homes. Fire and Hygiene Certificates. Cleanliness, good food, pleasant surroundings and friendliness are our priorities. Private car park with CCTV. Open all year. Reduced rates for weekly stays. Bed and Breakfast from £25 per person per night.
e-mail: montclareY@aol.com
website: www.mont-clare.co.uk/index.htm

YORK. Mr P. Mangham, Scotlee Guest House, 2 Claremont Terrace, Gillygate, York YO31 7EJ (01904

622462; Fax: 01904 643599). Small and friendly guest house situated in the city centre, just round the corner from the Minster. All rooms tastefully appointed and have en suite facilities. Four-poster room is also available for special occassions. Colour TV with Teletext and satellite, tea/coffee making facilities and hairdryer, etc. Open all year. Bed and breakfast from £20 to £35.
e-mail: scotlee@aol.com

YORK. Peggy Swann, South Newlands Farm, Selby Road, Riccall, York YO4 6QR (01757 248203).

Friendliness, comfort and good traditional cooking are always on offer to our guests. The kettle's always on the boil in our kitchen, and the comfortable lounge is yours to relax in at any time. Easy access to York and the Dales and Moors. Our farm is a strawberry and plant nursery with a five-caravan site adjacent. No smoking please. Dogs welcome; day kennelling available.

YORK, near Castle Howard. Sandie and Peter Turner, High Gaterley Farm, Near Welburn, York YP60 7HT (Tel & Fax: 01653 694636). ◆◆◆◆.

High Gaterley enjoys a unique position, located within the boundaries of Castle Howard's magnificent country estate. It is ideally situated for easy access to the City of York, East Coast and the North Yorkshire Moors renowned for ruined abbeys and castles. The tranquil ambience with panoramic views over the Howardian Hills make it a perfect location for a peaceful and relaxing stay in a comfortable well-appointed farmhouse with the option of fine cuisine. En suite facilities with tea and coffee in all rooms, log fire in the drawing room, TV, non-smoking, dogs by prior arrangement. Open all year. Bed and breakfast from £16.00. Optional evening meal and special diets by arrangement.
e-mail: highgaterley@btinternet.com
website: www.highgaterley.com

WEST YORKSHIRE

KEIGHLEY (Bronte Country). Currer Laithe Farm, Moss Carr Road, Long Lee, Keighley BD21 4SL (01535 604387).

An extensive 180 acre Pennine hill farm rearing and pasturing 140 cattle, goats and donkeys. It and the 16th century farmhouse, beamed, mullioned and with inglenook fireplace, offer panoramic views of Airedale and are covenanted to The National Trust. Satisfied guests, still returning after 19 years, create a warm, friendly atmosphere. Food is traditional Yorkshire fare. Pets and children welcome. Ground floor accommodation is frequently used by guests in wheelchairs. Bed and Breakfast en suite from £14.50; Bed, Breakfast and Evening Meal from £18. We also have two self-catering cottage flats from £70 to £160 per week. Group accommodation can be arranged, serviced or self catering.

Visit the FHG website
www.holidayguides.com
for details of the wide choice of accommodation featured in the full range of FHG titles

COUNTRY INNS

DEVON

SEATON. Three Horseshoes Inn, Branscombe, Seaton EX12 3BR (01297 680251). The Sea Mist Bungalow adjoins the famous Three Horseshoes Inn. Accommodation in two bedrooms (one has twin beds and the other a double), bathroom, large sittingroom with bed-settee, kitchen with fridge. Central heating if required. Colour TV. Set in its own little garden, but many guests like to use the full facilities of the Inn. 10 minutes from Sidmouth, Seaton and Beer. Glorious countryside yet close to the sea. Terms range from £100 (low season) to £235 (high season). Open all year.

WARWICKSHIRE

THE FHG DIPLOMA

HELP IMPROVE
BRITISH TOURIST STANDARDS

You are choosing holiday accommodation from our very popular FHG Publications.
Whether it be a hotel, guest house, farmhouse or self-catering accommodation, we think you will find
it hospitable, comfortable and clean, and your host and hostess friendly and helpful.

Why not write and tell us about it?

As a recognition of the generally well-run and excellent holiday accommodation reviewed in our
publications, we at FHG Publications Ltd. present a diploma to proprietors who receive the highest
recommendation from their guests who are also readers of our Guides. If you care to write to us
praising the holiday you have booked through FHG Publications Ltd. – whether this be board, self-
catering accommodation, a sporting or a caravan holiday, what you say will be evaluated and the
proprietors who reach our final list will be contacted.

The winning proprietor will receive an attractive framed diploma to display on his premises as
recognition of a high standard of comfort, amenity and hospitality. FHG Publications Ltd. offer this
diploma as a contribution towards the improvement of standards in tourist accommodation in
Britain. Help your excellent host or hostess to win it!

FHG DIPLOMA

We nominate ....

....

Because

Name ....

Address...

....

Telephone No..

ENGLAND

Self-Catering Accommodation

CAMBRIDGESHIRE

PETERBOROUGH. Mrs J. Singlehurst, Brook Farm, Lower Benefield, Peterborough PE8 5AE (01832 205215). ♛♛♛ *COMMENDED*. **Sleeps 2 adults and 2 children in family room**. At the beginning of a gated road we offer peace and tranquillity with picturesque walks. Granary Cottage is warm, cosy and well equipped with linen provided. Close by are the historic market towns of Oundle and Stamford and the pretty village of Rockingham. Children welcome. Open all year. Weekly terms from £150 to £250.

WATERBEACH. Mrs Lock, Goose Hall Farm, Ely Road, Waterbeach, Cambridge CB5 9PG (Tel & Fax: 01223 860235). Goose Hall Farm is situated between the famous University city of Cambridge and the Cathedral city of Ely. Overlooking the paddock which is home to our small herd of red deer are two semi-detached cottages offering self-catering for the longer stay. Sleeping up to five people, each cottage has a shower room, one double room with king-size bed, and one triple room with 3' single bed and full size bunk beds. Each cottage has full gas central heating, a fitted kitchen with automatic washing machine, full size cooker and fridge, and a colour television in the lounge. Fitted carpets throughout. All linen and towels provided. Electricity and gas are £1 coin meters. Seasonal tariffs: low £150 mid £180 and high £250.

WISBECH ST MARY. Mrs T. Fowler, Common Right Barns, Plash Drove, Tholomas Drove, Wisbech St Mary PE13 4SP (Tel and Fax: 01945 410424). Bookings taken from 1st April 2000. Situated in the unique rural fen landscape, newly renovated barn and stable, wheelchair-friendly. Two self-catering units, traditionally decorated and furnished, sleep four and two persons. Children and one small dog welcome. Enclosed rear gardens and patios. Ideal for walking, cycling, fishing and golf. Numerous attractions locally and within one hour's drive. Local pub and restaurant 500 yards; village, pubs and shop two miles. On site meals and special diets available at additional cost. Barn unit £50 per night; Stable unit £40 per night; special rates for seven and three nights. Businessmen welcome. EETB registered.

CHESHIRE

MACCLESFIELD. Mrs D. Gilman, The Old Byre, Pye Ash Farm, Leek Road, Bosley, Macclesfield SK11 0PN (01260 273650). ⚬♔♔♔. The Old Byre at Pye Ash Farm

is a sympathetic conversion of an unused shippon into accommodation, particularly well designed to suit two families wishing to spend their holidays together in the countryside; smaller groups may book one half if all rooms not required - one half sleeps six, the other four. Fully equipped including electric cookers, fridges, microwave ovens; the rear porch has washing machine, dryer and central heating boiler. All accommodation is on the ground floor, so is suitable for the less able visitor. Many interesting places to visit and plenty to do; Alton Towers is 15 miles away. Brochure giving full details and terms available on request. Bed and Breakfast accommodation also available.

CORNWALL

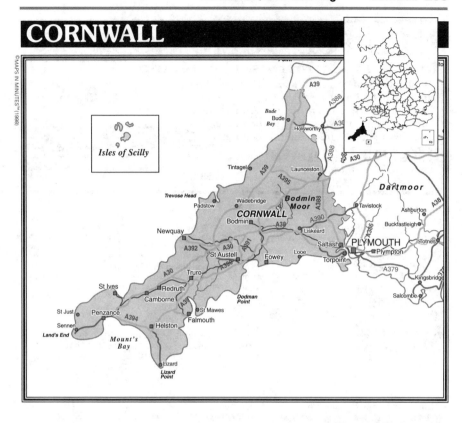

classic cottages

400 select West Country cottages just for the discerning

01326 565 555
www.classic.co.uk

BODINNICK-BY-FOWEY. Penmarlam Quay Cottage, Yeate Farm, Bodinnick-by-Fowey. Sleeps 6. The cottage, carefully converted from a 14th century barn, is situated in an enviable position, overlooking Mixtow Pill and the Fowey Estuary. With its own quay, slip and mooring, it is ideally placed for sailing, boating and fishing. Nearby footpath leads across our fields to the Old Ferry Inn at Bodinnick, and many other walks are available in surrounding countryside which is mainly National Trust land. Cottage stands in own grounds, 120 yards above the river. Open plan living and dining area contains a feature fireplace of Cornish stone; fuel supplied in winter; colour TV; three double bedrooms; shower room with toilet. Electric cooker. Night storage heater. Well behaved pets welcome. Ample parking. Terms from £140 per week. Available all year. Please send SAE (22cm by 11cm) for brochure. **Mrs Angela M. Oliver, Yeate Farm, Bodinnick-by-Fowey PL23 1LZ (01726 870256).**

BODMIN. Polgrain Holiday Cottages, Higher Polgrain, St Wenn, Bodmin PL30 5PR (01637 880637; Fax: 01637 880637). ꞇꞇꞇꞇ COMMENDED. Well off the beaten track, yet superbly positioned to tour the spectacular north coast, this is a holiday destination which offers the best of both worlds. Polgrain is the most perfect place to relax, unwind and enjoy the peace and tranquillity of the surrounding countryside. Once a flourishing farm and mill, the main farmhouse is now our family home, while the granite barns and mill have been converted into comfortable, well equipped holiday cottages – each with its own individual character and features. Adjoining the main farmhouse is the heated indoor swimming pool. Each cottage has a fully fitted kitchen including washing machine and microwave, and each living area is also equipped with colour TV, video recorder and compact disc hi-fi system. Alarm clock radios can be found in the bedrooms and all linen is provided free of charge. Central heating, power and lighting are all included within the price of the holiday. Each cottage also has its own patio, complete with furniture and brick built barbecue. Car parking. Tariffs and booking details on request. Open March - January.

BOSCASTLE. Mrs Ann Harding, Ringford Farm, St. Juliot, Boscastle PL35 0BX (01840 250306). Working farm, join in. A two bedroomed centrally heated converted barn sleeping up to six persons comfortably. Fully equipped and has magnificent sea views. Pure spring water. Set on a 25 acre stock farm with cows, sheep, goats, pigs, ducks and chickens – you are welcome to look around and help with feeding if you so wish. Ideally situated for touring Devon and Cornwall, many footpaths to explore. Children and pets welcome. Weekly terms from £100 to £360.

BOSCASTLE near. Mr D. Clough, Courtyard Farm, Lesnewth, Near Boscastle PL35 0HR (01840 261256). ETB ꙨꙨ/ꙨꙨꙨꙨ *COMMENDED.* **Sleep 2-8.** Picturesque group of 17th century luxury stone cottages overlooking beautiful National Trust valley, some with sea views. All the cottages are individually designed and furnished, and equipped to a high standard with colour TV etc. They are warm and comfortable and are open all year round. Virtually all the coastline around Boscastle is National Trust owned and provides fabulous walks and beaches. Our cottages offer you quality and comfort at reasonable rates. Colour brochure available.

BUDE. Mrs Patricia Nicklen, Creathorne Farm, Near Widemouth Bay, Bude EX23 0NE (01288 361407). Sleeps up to 8. This large detached farmhouse is traditionally built in the Cornish style and is situated on a 200 acre family-run milking goat farm. The south-west wing of the farmhouse is completely self-contained having its own entrance and attractive garden. The farm is midway between Widemouth Bay and the pretty village of Marhamchurch. Bude, only three miles away, is the main holiday resort of the area with spacious beaches and rock pools. Close by are Clovelly, Boscastle and Tintagel.

BUDE. Houndapitt Farm Cottages, Houndapitt Farm, Sandymouth, Bude EX23 9HW (01288 355455). These self-catering cottages are furnished and equipped to the highest standards. Magnificent views of the sea and surrounding countryside. One mile from clean sandy beach. Farm activities include pony rides and feeding of lambs and small animals. Play area, games room and free coarse fishing available. Sorry no pets. Terms include electricity, heating, bed linen and towels. Detailed colour brochure available from Mr and Mrs F. Heard.

CAMBORNE. Mr & Mrs A. S. Blumenau, Cargenwen Farm, Blackrock, Praze, CamborneTR14 9PL (Tel/Fax: 01209 831151). Cargenwen Farm is a 150 acre dairy farm set in the centre of West Cornwall. We are situated in easy reach of both coasts and provide an ideal centre for touring. The cottages sleep two, four and six and have been tastefully converted from a range of granite buildings offering peace and relaxation with a high level of comfort. Each cottage is fully equipped with all bed linen (duvets), shower, colour TV, microwave, storage heater etc. Washing machine and tumble dryer are provided, travel cot and highchair on request. Well behaved pet by arrangement. Visitors welcome to come on the farm.

COVERACK. Brookside, Old Mill Yard, Coverack. Sleeps 4/5. Delightful bungalow within short distance of super beach and picturesque harbour. Situated in an area of outstanding natural beauty, an ideal base for touring, walking, sea fishing, windsurfing. Village store, pub, restaurant and cafes nearby. Comfortably furnished accommodation comprises double bedroom, twin-bedded room, lounge with colour TV; bathroom/toilet, kitchen/diner with microwave, electric cooker, washing machine, fridge. Sun room. Secluded garden, patio. Ample parking, garage. Metered electricity. No linen supplied. Sorry no pets. Weekly terms £195 to £365. Bookings Saturday to Saturday, mid-week out of season breaks available. Cornwall Tourist Board registered. For details phone **01243 841485.**

COVERACK (Helford River area). Lindford House Holidays. Beautifully appointed and fully equipped cottages sleeping 2–8, some with sea views, plus large gardens and ample parking. All the properties have heating and most are available all year. In a superb location in an Area of Oustanding Natural Beauty, close to the rugged coastline of the Lizard Peninsula and the softer, greener landscape of the Helford River. Beautiful beaches, picturesque coves and harbours and superb cliff walks. Ideal for walking, bird-watching, fishing, windsurfing and sailing. Prices from £105 including heating and linen. Sorry no pets. Apply for colour brochure to: **Mrs Linda Askew, Lindford House, Penhallick, Coverack, Helston TR12 6SG (01326 280454).**

CRACKINGTON HAVEN. Mr and Mrs O.H.F. Tippett, Trelay, St. Gennys, Bude EX23 0NJ (01840 230378). Sleep 2/8. Lovely stone cottages converted from traditional barns and period farmhouse (accommodate two, four, six or eight). Idyllic setting on small working sheep farm at the head of a deep wooded valley. Area of Outstanding Natural Beauty. Five minutes to sandy beach at Crackington Haven and coast path along spectacular National Trust cliffs. Ideal area for surfing, walking, bird-watching etc. All cottages furnished in character – much pine and oak, comfortable suites and beds. Log fires, dishwashers, linen, fenced gardens, patios, laundry room and payphone. Pets welcome. Low season from £99 per week, also short breaks. Main season £160 to £715 per week. Colour brochure sent on request. Cornwall Tourist Board registered.

CUSGARNE (near Truro). Sleeps 2. DOGS WELCOME. A cosy single-storey clean, detached dwelling with own garden within the grounds of Saffron Meadow, situated in a quiet hamlet. Secluded and surrounded by wooded pastureland. Bedroom with double bed and twin vanity unit. Fully tiled shower, W.C. and L.B. Comprehensively equipped kitchen/diner. Compact TV room, storage room. Hot water galore and gas included. Metered electricity. Automatic external safety lighting. Ample parking space in drive. Shop, Post Office and Inn only a short walk. Central to Truro, Falmouth and North Coast. Terms from £110 to £220 per week. Contact: **Joyce and George Clench, Saffron Meadow, Cusgarne, Truro TR4 8RW (01872 863171).**

FALMOUTH. Mr and Mrs Lobb, Nangitha Farm, Budock, Near Falmouth TR11 5DA (01326 372514). Sleeps 4/5. Half farmhouse comprises: one double, one twin and convertible bed in dining room, bathroom downstairs - fully fitted kitchen on the outskirts of Falmouth. Magnificent views from all fields. Three beaches within two miles. Terms from £200 to £400 per week.

FALMOUTH (near Helford River). Mrs Anne Matthews, Boskensoe Farm, Mawnan Smith, Falmouth TR11 5JP (Tel & Fax: 01326 250257). Sleeps 6/8. BOSKENSOE FARM HOLIDAY BUNGALOW. Situated in picturesque village of Mawnan Smith, Falmouth five miles, one and a half miles from lovely Helford River famous for beautiful coastal walks, gardens and scenery. Several quiet, safe beaches for bathing, also excellent sailing and fishing facilities. Bungalow has three bedrooms, colour TV, electric cooker, fridge/freezer, washing machine and microwave. Fitted with storage heaters and electric fires. Spacious garden and ample parking for cars and boats. Terms from £140 to £400. Brochure on request.

GWEEK. Mrs Pascoe, Lower Boskenwyn Farm, Gweek, Helston TR13 0QQ (01326 573248). Delightful barn cottage on working farm. Ideally situated to tour Falmouth, Penzance and the Lizard Peninsula with beaches a short drive away. One-and-a-half miles from the town of Helston, famous for Flora Day in May and Flambards Theme Park. One mile from the village of Gweek and the National Seal Sanctuary. Recently converted, the accommodation sleeps six comfortably with a cot available if required. Bed linen is included and towels for hire on request. An enclosed garden and ample parking. Open all year and children welcome. £150 to £450 per week.

HELFORD ESTUARY. Mrs S. Trewhella, Mudgeon Vean Farm, St. Martin, Helston TR12 6DB (01326

231341). Leave the hustle and bustle of town life. Come and enjoy the peace and tranquillity of the Helford Estuary. Three homely cottages sleep four/six, equipped to a high standard. Open all year for cosy winter breaks. Open fires/heating. Set amidst a small 18th century working farm with magnificent views across an extensive valley area, surrounded by fields and woodland - a walk through the woods takes you to the Helford River. A superb location in an area of outstanding natural beauty with the rugged coastline of the Lizard Peninsula and beaches only a short drive away. Children and pets welcome. From £100 to £325 per week

HELFORD RIVER. Mrs J. Jenkin, Mudgeon Farm, St Martin, Helston TR12 6BZ (01326 231202).

Mudgeon Farm runs down to the picturesque Helford River, on the Lizard Peninsula, an Area of Outstanding Natural Beauty. The cottage sleeps eight and is a tastefully restored 17th century wing of the ancient manor house, mentioned in the Domesday Book. It is equipped to a high standard with antique furniture, dishwasher and microwave. One double bedroom is en suite, the other has a four-poster. The spacious lounge has an inglenook fireplace with woodburner, and guests have their own private garden and walled patio. There are numerous safe beaches nearby. Interested visitors can watch the cows being milked, see farmyard animals and visit the ponies. Terms from £100 to £550.

HELSTON. Mrs Julie Bray, Tregevis Farm, St. Martin, Helston TR12 6DN (01326 231265). ♕♕♕♕

HIGHLY COMMENDED. **Sleeps 7 + cot.** Come and relax at Tregevis, a working dairy farm in the picturesque Helford River area, just half a mile from the little village of St. Martin and five miles from sandy beaches. The accommodation is a self contained, spacious part of the farmhouse, very comfortable, well equipped and with a games room. The large lawn area with swings will prove popular with children, as will our farm animals. Open Easter to October. Terms from £220 to £490 per week.

HELSTON. Jan Oates, Rosuick Farm, St. Martin, Helston, Cornwall TR12 6D2 (01326 231302).

Tucked away in our picturesque valley, in an area of outstanding natural beauty, Rosuick Farm offers a special holiday. Our farmhouse and cottages are steeped in history. Each with its individual charm and character, the cottages offer quality and comfort. Four-poster beds, log fires, snooker table, private gardens, dishwasher, microwave, tennis court. Enjoy our family-run beef and sheep farm, meet the ducks and turkeys. Discover the Helford River with its sailing and wonderful walks, and the many coves and beaches on The Lizard. Elmtree Cottage and Rosuick Cottage each sleep six and Rosuick Farmhouse sleeps ten. Open all year. £90-£700 per week.

HELSTON. Delightful Cornish Cottage, Helston. Set in the heart of the Cornish countryside this secluded,

pretty, stone-built, beamed cottage is roughly 200 years old. Having two double bedrooms and a folding bed sleeps four to five. There is a dining area and a charming sitting room with a huge open log fire. The well-equipped kitchen has room to dine with an Aga and electric cooker. Outside are well-maintained private gardens and parking space for three or four cars. Accessing all coasts is easy from the cottage's ideal situation about two miles from Helston. For competitive prices contact **Sue Cox, The Old Dairy, Hollington Lane, Ednaston, Ashbourne DE6 3AE (01335 361325).**

LAUNCESTON. Mrs Heather French, Higher Scarsick, Treneglos, Launceston PL15 8UH (01566 781372) Working farm. Nestled amongst the peace and tranquillity of unspoilt Cornish countryside, this well furnished and comfortable cottage is the ideal retreat. Very convenient for exploring the many beaches and coves on the North Cornwall Coast yet within easy driving distance of Bodmin Moor, Dartmoor and all leisure pursuits. The accommodation has three bedrooms, two double and one twin bedded, bathroom with separate shower cubicle, a fully equipped large farmhouse kitchen, lounge with open fireplace. Pleasantly decorated throughout. Tariff: £120–£350 includes bed linen, night storage heaters, electricity and a very warm welcome. No pets.

LAUNCESTON. Luxury two-bedroomed mobile home set in private site with views of a beautiful valley, with woods, three ponds with wildlife, domestic ducks and geese and sheep grazing in the fields. Fully equipped, colour TV, washing machine and all electrical appliances. Large fenced garden, safe for children, with patio and barbecue. Parking space. Central heating, gas cooker and lounge heater (gas supplied). Electricity by £1 meter. Linen supplied. Cot available. Prices from £160 per week. Apply: **Mrs A.E. Moore, Hollyvag, Lewannick, Launceston PL15 7QH (01566 782309; Fax: 01566 782956).**

LAUNCESTON. Mrs Kathyn Broad, Lower Dutson Farm, Launceston PL15 9SP (Tel & Fax: 01566 776456). Working farm. ETC ◆◆◆ ♛♛♛♛ *COMMENDED*. Sleeps 2/6 Enjoy a holiday on our traditional working farm. A warm welcome awaits you at our 17th century farmhouse, centrally situated for touring Devon and Cornwall. Wander across fields to the River Tamar or carp lake (good fishing available). Well furnished accommodation including fully fitted kitchen with automatic washing machine, tumble dryer, standard electric cooker, microwave and toaster. Sittingroom with colour TV. Storage heaters, bed linen inclusive in price; towels can be hired. Three bedrooms plus cot. Bathroom and shower room. Children welcome. Terms £100 to £350 per week. Bed and Breakfast also available from £17.50 per night.

LAUNCESTON near. Mrs A.E. Moore, Hollyvag, Lewannick, Near Launceston PL15 7QH (01566 782309; Fax: 01566 782956). Working farm, join in. Sleeps 5. Part of 17th century farmhouse, self-contained and full of old world charm with own lawns, front and back. Set in secluded position in wooded countryside with views of the moors. Central for North and South coasts. Family farm with ducks on the pond, horses, sheep and poultry. Sleeps up to five, fully furnished with all modern conveniences, folding bed and cot available. Colour TV, fridge, electric cooker, solid fuel heater if needed. Babysitting available free. Linen not provided. Within five miles of market town; golf, fishing and riding nearby. Terms from £140 to £200. Brochure on request

LAUNCESTON near. Mrs Barbara Sleep, Trevadlock Farm, Congdon's Shop, Launceston PL15 7PW (Tel & Fax: 01566 782239). ETB ♛♛♛♛♛ *HIGHLY COMMENDED*. Sleeps 2-6, cot available. Something special - superbly equipped and tastefully furnished, two character farm cottages set on working farm amidst beautiful Cornish countryside, relax – walk the moors, visit nearby Jamaica Inn, return to cosy rooms with original beams and open fires. We are Ideally placed for both north and south coasts and exploring both counties. Fully equipped kitchen, fridge/freezer, microwave, electric cooker, dishwasher, washing machine, colour TV, video, telephone, garden patio barbecue area. Included in price all electricity, linen and oil central heating. Available all year. Terms from £150. Short Breaks available. Non-smoking properties. Brochure available.

THE COTTAGES
AT
Trefanny Hill Nr. LOOE

GORGEOUS OLD WORLD COUNTRY COTTAGES

Cornish Charm: Enchanting medieval hamlet with cottages dating back to the 15th century. Log fires, antiques and lovely country furnishings, fresh white linen, flowers and the comforts of home – for children, family, friends, or a cosy cottage for two. Nestling on a south facing hillside, with your own private garden, fabulous views, friendly farm animals including shires, lakeside and woodland walks, beautiful heated pool, tennis court and play area. Delicious home cooked cuisine in our own tiny inn (inc. fresh fish), and meals service. Open all year.

O. Slaughter, Trefanny Hill, Duloe, Liskeard, Cornwall PL14 4QF
Telephone: 01503 220622

A COUNTRY LOVERS PARADISE – WITH AN ABUNDANCE OF COUNTRY WALKS FROM YOUR GARDEN GATE AND COASTAL WALKS ONLY FOUR MILES AWAY.

LISKEARD. Trewalla Farm Cottages, Trewalla Farm, Minions, Liskeard PL14 6ED (Tel & Fax: 01579 342385). ♀♀♀ *COMMENDED.* **Sleeps 3/4 plus cot.** Our small, traditionally run farm on Bodmin Moor has rare breed pigs, sheep, hens and geese, all free-range and very friendly. Our three cottages are beautifully furnished and very well equipped. Their moorland setting offers perfect peace, wonderful views, ideal walking country and a good base for exploring – if you can tear yourself away! Linen and electricity included. Open March to December and New Year.

LOOE. Mrs Angela Barrett, Tredinnick Farm, Duloe, Liskeard PL14 4PJ (01503 262997; Fax: 01503 265554) Up to ♀♀♀♀ *HIGHLY COMMENDED.* Enjoy a relaxing and tranquil holiday on our family-run farm situated in rolling countryside only three miles from Looe. The farmhouse is very comfortable and homely including en suite bedrooms. The local pub is renowned for its excellent food, only a short distance away. An ideal base for local and coastal walking. National Trust properties, golf and beaches nearby. Two units sleeping from two to ten people. Prices from £125 to £720.

LOOE. Mrs Alison Maiklem, Katie's Cottage, Bocadden Farm, Lanreath, Looe PL13 2PG (Tel & Fax:

01503 220245). A warm welcome awaits you at Bocadden Farm, a 350 acre dairy farm set in beautiful countryside in East Cornwall, seven miles from Looe. Katie's Cottage, a stone built barn conversion, has a fully equipped kitchen/living area including electric cooker, fridge/freezer, microwave, washing machine and tumble dryer and TV and video. There is a downstairs double bedroom, and upstairs an open plan twin room with vanity unit. The bathroom is specially designed to fit the needs of everyone, including wheelchair users Central heating throughout. Large patio and lawn area, with barbecue if required. Looe, Polperro and Fowey close by, and many attractions within easy reach.

MARAZION near. Mrs W. Boase, Trebarvah Farm, Trebarvah Lane, Perranuthnoe, Penzance TR20 9NG

(01736 710361). Sleeps up to 4. "Tue Brook" is a detached bungalow with magnificent views across Mount's Bay and St. Michael's Mount. It overlooks the village of Perranuthnoe (two-and a-half-miles east of Marazion) in this beautiful holiday area with Penzance the local centre. Perranuthnoe beach is both sandy and sheltered and easily accessible on foot and also by car. Accommodation comprises one double and one twin-bedded room, both with duvets, pillows and blankets; please supply own linen; kitchen/diner, bathroom and sitting room leading to a large conservatory overlooking the sea; front and rear gardens; well behaved dogs welcome; fully equipped electrically with £1 prepayment meter. Colour TV. Terms from £150 to £300 per week. AvailabLE APril to October.

MARAZION near. Jenny Birchall, Mount View House, Varfell, Ludgvan, Near Penzance TR20 8AW

(01736 710179) Sleeps 2/3. Situated three miles from Penzance and five miles from St.Ives, the cottage is conveniently placed for exploring West Cornwall. Formerly the dairy of a Victorian farmhouse it comprises a sittingroom with TV, fully equipped kitchen, shower room WC, one bedroom with double and single beds (a cot or "Z" bed can be provided for additional small children). Outside, guests have their own patio area and use of large gardens overlooking sea. Quiet location, 15 minute walk to nearest shop and beach. Linen provided. Regret no pets. Terms from £130 per week. Short breaks early and late season. Please telephone for brochure.

MEVAGISSEY. Diana Littlejohns, Stanwicke, School Hill, Mevagissey PL26 6TQ (01726 843352). Sleep

4/5. The self-contained flats are right in the centre of the village with harbour and shops close by. Free parking available. Pets welcome. Linen by arrangement. Large bungalow sleeps six to eight also available with delightful gardens and parking five minutes from harbour and shops. Pets welcome. Linen by arrangement. Lost Gardens of Heligan close by. Open all year. Weekly terms for flats from £130 to £250. Weekly terms for bungalow from £180 to £450.

PADSTOW. The Brewer Family, Carnevas Farm Holiday Park, Carnevas Farm, St. Merryn, Padstow PL28 8PN (01841 520230). Bungalow/Chalets sleep 4/6. ✓✓✓✓✓ Rose Award Park 1999. Situated only half-a-mile from golden sandy beach, fishing, golf, sailing etc. Quaint harbour village of Padstow only four miles. Bungalows/chalets sleep four/six, have two bedrooms, bathroom, kitchen/diner, airing cupboard, colour TV. Caravans six berth or eight, all have showers, toilets, fridge, colour TV (also separate camping and caravan facilities). Newly converted barns now available, sleep four/six persons, furnished to a high standard. AA Three Pennant site. Brochure on request.

PENZANCE. Mrs Catherine Wall, Trenow, Relubbus Lane, St. Hilary, Penzance TR20 9EA (01736 762308). Mini bungalow sleeps two within the grounds of an old country house. Lovely garden, surrounding rural area. Lounge/diner with cooking area, fridge, cooker, colour TV etc; shower room. Linen not provided. Beaches within easy reach, sporting activities, bird watching. No pets. Off-road Parking. Terms from £80 per week. Available all year. Please write or phone for further details.

PENZANCE. Mrs James Curnow, Barlowenath, St. Hilary, Penzance TR20 9DQ (01736 710409). Working farm. Cottages sleep 4/5. These two cottages are on a dairy farm, in a little hamlet right beside St. Hilary Church, with quiet surroundings and a good road approach. A good position for touring Cornish coast and most well-known places. Beaches are two miles away; Marazion two-and-a-half miles; Penzance six miles; St. Ives eight; Land's End 16. Both cottages have fitted carpets, lounge/diner with TV; modern kitchen (fridge, electric cooker, toaster, iron); bathroom with shaver point. Electricity by £1 meter, night storage heaters extra. One cottage sleeps five in three bedrooms (one double, twin divans and one single). The second cottage sleeps four in two bedrooms (twin divans in both). Linen not supplied. Cot by arrangement. Available all year. £95 to £320 weekly, VAT exempt.

PERRANPORTH. Mrs S. Rilstone, Seathrift Seaside Flat, 7 Pentreve, Wheal Leisure, Perranporth TR6 0EY (01872 572157). Extensive holiday home in the centre of Perranporth and only 50 yards from the sandy surfing beach. This spacious family flat has all the facilities for two to eight persons to have a seaside holiday in comfort. Four bedrooms (H&C), two bathrooms and a separate shower room, large dining room, modern fully-fitted kitchen with split level cooker, fridge, etc. Large lounge. All rooms (including bedrooms) with TV sockets. Cots available. Completely self-contained and boasting full central heating in every room. Supervised by owner living close by. Colour television. SECLUDED BUNGALOW, centrally heated, with gardens plus garage and parking. Sleeps two to six. From £90 (VAT inclusive). Brochure with pleasure.

PERRANPORTH. "Makhan" and "Kinsi", Liskey Hill Crescent, Perranporth. Two delightful furnished semi-detached houses offering basic accommodation at a budget price. "Makhan" sleeps upto 12 in six bedrooms, and "Kinsi" sleeps up to ten in four bedrooms. They are simply furnished, spacious and particularly suitable for a party of four or five adults and four or five children, with colour TV, crockery, cutlery, saucepans and blankets supplied, but not linen. Cot supplied. Both houses are within a few minutes' walk of the beach, and have a garage and parking space for a second car. Perranporth has a fine sandy beach with high rocky cliffs with caves and pools on one side. There is a magnificent surf and the sea is excellent for surfing. Tennis club, golf club and gliding club all within easy reach. Boating lake, bowling or putting available in the park. Terms from £165 to £415. For further details please contact: **Mrs D.E. Gill-Carey, Penkerris, 3 Penwinnick Road, St Agnes, Cornwall TR5 0PA (01872 552262).**

PORT ISAAC. The Dolphin, Port Isaac. Sleeps 10. This delightful house, originally an inn, is one of the most attractive in Port Isaac. Fifty yards from the sea, shops and pub. Five bedrooms, three with washbasins. Two bathrooms and WCs. Large diningroom. Cosy sittingroom. Spacious and well-equipped kitchen with electric cooker, gas-fired Aga, dishwasher, washing machine. Sun terrace. Port Isaac is a picturesque fishing village with magnificent coastal scenery all round. Nearby attractions include surfing, sailing, fishing, golf, tennis, pony trekking. The Dolphin sleeps ten but reduced rates offered for smaller families and off-peak season. Weekly terms: £440 to £575 inclusive. SAE for details to **Emily Glentworth, 30 Victoria Road, London W8 5RG (0171 937 1954)**

PORT ISAAC. 🏠🏠/🏠🏠 *HIGHLY COMMENDED.* Open all year. Come and enjoy being a part of a working family farm. Stay in one of our beautiful cottages with lovely countryside views, own garden and parking. Tastefully furnished, catering for your every need, each having double glazing, microwave, fridge freezer, washer-dryer, food processor, coffee maker, colour TV and video, etc. All our animals are very friendly; meet "Barney" our Vietnamese Pot-Bellied Pig and our dogs who think visitors come to entertain them! We lamb from Christmas until March and everyone enjoys feeding the lambs. We have tennis and volleyball courts, games room and fitness room on the farm and acres of wildlife habitat to wander through. Sandy beaches, surfing, sailing, golf, riding, fishing, country pubs all within a three mile radius. We also have a large period house overlooking a wooded valley near Camelford, sleeping 12 plus cots. Moors and golf two miles, sea six miles. Out of season Short Breaks available. For details please send SAE to: **Henry and Shirley Symons, Trevathan, St. Endellion, Port Isaac PL29 3TT or telephone/fax (01208 880248).**

PORT ISAAC. The Lodge, Treharrock, Port Isaac. Sleeps 6. Pleasant, south facing and convenient bungalow, set in its own small, natural garden and surrounded by fields and woodland with streams. About two miles inland from Port Isaac, a sheltered, secluded spot at the end of driveway to Treharrock Manor. Rugged North Cornish cliffs with National Trust footpaths and lovely sandy coves in the vicinity. Excellent sandy beach at Polzeath (five miles), also pony trekking, golf etc. in the area. South-facing sun room leads on to terrace; TV. Accommodation for six plus baby. Bathroom, toilet; sittingroom; kitchen/diner. Open all year. Linen extra. Sorry, no pets. Car essential– parking. Terms from £150 to £400 per week (heating included). SAE to **Mrs E.A. Hambly, Willow Mill, St. Kew, Wadebridge, Cornwall PL30 3EP (01208 841806).**

PORTSCATHO. Trewince Manor, Portscatho, Near Truro TR2 5ET. Peter and Liz Heywood invite you to take your self-catering or touring holiday at their Georgian Manor House Estate in this undiscovered and peaceful corner of Cornwall. Luxury lodges, cedarwood cabins, cottage and small touring site available. Spectacular sea views; our own quay and moorings. Relaxing lounge bar and restaurant. Shop, launderette and games rooms. Superb walking and sailing. Abundance of wildlife in the area. Dogs welcome. Please write of telephone for further information. **Freephone: 0800 0190289.** e-mail: bookings@trewince.com.uk

PRAA SANDS. Sandy Cove Bungalows, Praa Sands, Penzance. Sleep 2/6. Five two or three bedroomed bungalows just 75 yards from Praa Sands' lovely mile-long sandy beach. Set in palm-fringed garden with private parking. Our personally supervised bungalows, suitable for couples and families, are comfortably furnished including fitted carpets and colour TV. Free storage heater and double glazing add comfort duringcolder periods. Ideal centre to enjoy the beach and magnificent coastal walks, or visit Land's End, The Lizard, Cornwall's many glorious gardens with sup-tropical species, and numerous attractions only a short journey away. Golf, putting, Post Office/general store and cafes nearby. Sorry no pets. Reductions for couples. Apply: **Mr and Mrs T.J. Holland, 5 Pengersick Parc, Praa Sands, Penzance TR20 9SS (01736 763574).**

FREE and REDUCED RATE Holiday Visits!
Don't miss our Readers' Offer Vouchers

CLASSY COTTAGES
POLPERRO TO FOWEY

ETB up to 🔑🔑🔑🔑🔑 Highly Commended

We are the proud owners of 3 SUPERB coastal cottage locations
Our cottages are of the highest standard

★ Dishwashers, microwaves and washing machines   ★ Open fires and heating
★ Telephone and Fax available   ★ Cleaning/maid services

WE HAVE FARM PETS FOR OUR VISITORS TO ENJOY

★ Daily feeding of farm pets   ★ We are animal lovers.

★ You are very welcome to arrange to bring your pets

Shark Fishing

INDOOR PRIVATE POOL 85°F
Sauna, Spa & Solarium

Golf courses

Please contact FIONA and MARTIN NICOLLE on 07000 423000
website: www.classycottages.co.uk

REDRUTH. Friesian Valley Cottages, Mawla, Redruth TR16 5DW (01209 890901). ETB Registered. Sleeps 2-6. Atlantic Coast between Newquay and St Ives. Charming luxury cottages elegantly furnished and surrounded by rural views. Two miles to sandy beaches of Portreath, Porthtowan, and the National Trust Coastal Path. There is a games room, launderette and cosy bar. Terms from £120 to £480 per week.

ROSELAND PENINSULA. Mrs J.M. Palmer, Caladrick Farm, Veryan Green, Truro TR2 5QQ (01872 501796). On the outskirts of Veryan Green in an area of outstanding natural beauty approximately two miles from Carne and Pendower beaches. The accommodation, on the first floor of a modern house, is approached by an outside railed staircase leading to a lounge with a TV. There is a fitted kitchen with fridge, microwave and cooker. Further accommodation includes two bedrooms (one double and one twin), both have fitted wardrobes and washbasins. The bathroom completes the accommodation with bath, shower and toilet. There is private parking and pets are welcome at the owner's responsibility. Guests are welcome to enjoy a lawned area and 80 acres of farmland which includes 10 acres of woods. Parking area for boat. CTB Approved.

ST AUSTELL. Anita Treleaven, Trevissick Manor, Trevissick Farm, Trenarren, St Austell PL26 6BQ (Tel & Fax: 01726 72954). ῼῼῼ *COMMENDED*. **Sleeps 2/4.** The east wing of the manor farmhouse on our coastal mixed farm is situated between St Austell and Mevagissey Bays. Spectacular views across the gardens down the valley to the sea. Ideal for a couple or family. Meet the animals, view the milking, play tennis or take the farm trail to Hallane Cove. Close to sandy beaches, sailing, watersports, cycling, 18 hole golf. Heligan Gardens 5-10 minutes. Open all year. Terms from £140 to £390.

ST. AUSTELL. Mr C. Mynard, St. Margaret's Park Holiday Bungalows, Polgooth, St. Austell PL26 7AX (01726 74283; Fax; 01726 71680). ✓✓✓✓✓ *BHP APPROVED*. **Sleep 2/8.** Family-owned and run small park set in six acres of tranquil lovely grounds offering good quality accommodation of varying sizes. The attractive timber bungalows are all detached, many on level ground with parking outside or nearby. Two bungalows have wheelchair access and partially adapted toilet facilities. All properties are well equipped including colour TV, microwave and outside furniture. Children's playing field, launderette and payphone in the park and the Polgooth Inn and village shop are a short stroll away. Excellent location to tour all Cornwall. Well controlled pets allowed. Open March to December. Brochure on request.

ST AUSTELL. Mrs Rosemary Adkins, Little Crugwallins Farm, Burngullow, St Austell PL26 7TH (Tel & Fax: 01726 63882; mobile: 07974 791456). Our two newly refurbished cottages THE BARN and THE CABIN sleeping two and five are tastefully furnished and well-equipped with ample parking. Enjoy the peace of our five acre smallholding and wander at will in our large secluded gardens. There is easy access to both North and South coasts and the facilities in St Austell are only three miles away. The famous Lost Gardens of Heligan and Eden Project are nearby as are opportunities for walking, riding, golf, sea and beach fishing and diving. Full central heating and bed linen provided. Short breaks are available also B&B. Further information and brochure on request.

ST. COLUMB. Mrs J.V. Thomas, Lower Trenowth Farm, St. Columb TR9 6EW (01637 880308).

Sleeps 6. This accommodation is part of a large farmhouse, all rooms facing south. Situated in the beautiful Vale of Lanherne, four miles from the sea, eight miles from the holiday resort of Newquay. Golf, horse riding, etc all within easy reach. One double room, one twin-bedded room and one single room with bunk beds, all with washbasins. Bed linen provided. Bathroom. Large lounge with colour TV. Fully equipped kitchen/diner. Electricity included in tariff. Large lawn. Ample parking. Dogs accepted if kept under control. Terms from £200 per week. SAE for further details please.

ST. IVES. J. & P. Husband, Consols Farm, St. Ives TR26 2HN (01736 796151). Properties sleep 4/6/8.

A selection of four properties is available. Large cottage set in garden in quiet surroundings, sleeps eight people, sittingroom with TV; kitchen (fridge, electric cooker, etc); bathroom; five bedrooms. Also annexe flat in garden grounds; one double bed, one set bunk beds in family room; kitchen; lounge; bathroom, toilet, etc; small garden and patio. Ample parking. Situated one mile from St. Ives: Cottage flat sleeping four at end of farmhouse, on working farm. Sittingroom with TV; two bedrooms; kitchen; bathroom, toilet, etc. Flat in town of St. Ives sleeps five. One large attic room with panoramic view, one small double room, one single bedroom; kitchen; lounge; bathroom and toilet. Parking in town car park. Full details on request.

ST IVES area. Mrs S. Britnell, Little Pengelly Farmhouse, Trenwheal, Leedstown, Hayle TR27 6BP (01736 850452). Large single storey 'barn conversion'. Patio and garden. Pets welcome. No smoking. Open all year. Three day off-peak breaks. Please write of telephone for full details.
e-mail: little@pengelly.freeserve.co.uk

ST. KEVERNE. Mrs Rosemary Peters, Trenoweth Valley Farm Cottages, St. Keverne, Helston TR12 6QQ (01326 280910). ETB ↑↑↑ APPROVED. Spacious, comfortable rural cottages, fully furnished and carpeted with well-equipped kitchen, colour TV and laundry facilities. Kitchen/diner, lounge/sittingroom, shower room/toilet. Sleeping upto six persons, each cottage has two bedrooms with duvets and covers for each bed. Surrounded by trees and fields, there is a safe play area for young children and a barbecue. Quiet, relaxing environment, midway between St. Keverne and Porthallow. Pleasant walks; beach, village shops and inns one-and-a-half miles. Open Easter to end October. Sorry, no pets. Attractive early and late prices. Terms from £70 to £345 per week.

TAMAR VALLEY. Mr and Mrs B.J. Howlett, Deer Park Farm, Luckett, Callington PL17 8NW (Tel & Fax:

01579 370292). ↑↑↑↑ APPROVED. Sleeps 4/5. Three character cottages – traditional barn conversions – situated in the delightful rural setting of the Tamar Valley, well away from the traffic. Kit Hill Country Park, Tamar Trail both within one mile, Morwellham Quay, Cotehele House nearby. Free exclusive/ private fishing on the farm – Carp/Roach. Nature and Heritage Trails are on the farm. St. Mellion Golf Club six miles. Also available locally riding schools, pony trekking, swimming, sports centre, south Cornwall beaches and the quaint fishing villages of Looe and Polperro within easy reach making this an excellent base for Cornwall, Dartmoor and South Devon. Prices from £175 to £310. Regret no pets.

FHG PUBLICATIONS LIMITED
publish a large range of well-known accommodation guides.
We will be happy to send you details or you can use
the order form at the back of this book.

TINTAGEL. Mrs Gillian Sanders, Fentafriddle Farm, Trewarmett, Tintagel PL34 0EX (01840 770580).

Enjoy a holiday at Fentafriddle, overlooking Trebarwith, with lovely sunsets and sea views. A spacious flat occupies the first floor of our farmhouse, with its own entrance, garden and picnic table. There are four bedrooms: one family, two double and one single. The kitchen is equipped with an electric cooker, microwave and fridge freezer. We are ideally situated for walking the coastal footpath, surfing and swimming at Trebarwith, Polzeath and Daymer Bay, cycling the Camel Trail and exploring Bodmin Moor. Bed linen supplied. Sorry no pets.

WADEBRIDGE/BODIEVE. Sleeps 6 plus cot.

300 year old farmhouse, converted in 1990, surrounded by sunny gardens, ample parking space in front of house in quiet country crescent. Only three miles from the sandy beaches at Rock and Daymer Bay, the surfing beach at Polzeath, close to the ancient fishing harbour of Padstow. Ideal for surfing, safe bathing, walking, fishing, sailing, golf, cycling (cycle hire in Wadebridge). The excellent shops, pubs, markets at Wadebridge are half-a-mile away. Wadebridge Leisure Centre with its brand new indoor swimming pool is only a five minute walk. The house comprises lounge with wood/coal burner in fireplace, colour TV, comfortable sofa bed (double). large, cosy, well equipped kitchen/diner with fridge, electric cooker, dishwasher, microwave, double aspect windows; laundry room with automatic washing machine, tumble dryer, fridge/freezer. Three bedrooms - large master bedroom (double aspect windows) with king size bed, one twin bedroom and a bedroom with bunk beds (brand new beds, mattresses and bedding). Linen and towels on request at extra charge. Bathroom, shower, toilet. Night storage heaters. Pets by arrangement. Available all year. Terms from £120 to £480 per week (including electricity and cleaning). Saturday to Saturday bookings. Ring or write for further details. **Mr and Mrs Peter Simpson, 32 Wolsey Road, East Molesey, Surrey KT8 9EN (020-8979 2433; Fax: 020-8224 6806; Mobile : 0777 575 8491) or Angela Holder (01208 813024).**

FOR THE MUTUAL GUIDANCE OF GUEST AND HOST

Every year literally thousands of holidays, short breaks and overnight stops are arranged through our guides, the vast majority without any problems at all. In a handful of cases, however, difficulties do arise about bookings, which often could have been prevented from the outset.

It is important to remember that when accommodation has been booked, both parties – guests and hosts – have entered into a form of contract. We hope that the following points will provide helpful guidance.

GUESTS: When enquiring about accommodation, be as precise as possible. Give exact dates, numbers in your party and the ages of any children. State the number and type of rooms wanted and also what catering you require – bed and breakfast, full board etc. Make sure that the position about evening meals is clear – and about pets, reductions for children or any other special points.

Read our reviews carefully to ensure that the proprietors you are going to contact can supply what you want. Ask for a letter confirming all arrangements, if possible.

If you have to cancel, do so as soon as possible. Proprietors do have the right to retain deposits and under certain circumstances to charge for cancelled holidays if adequate notice is not given and they cannot re-let the accommodation.

HOSTS: Give details about your facilities and about any special conditions. Explain your deposit system clearly and arrangements for cancellations, charges etc. and whether or not your terms include VAT.

If for any reason you are unable to fulfil an agreed booking without adequate notice, you may be under an obligation to arrange suitable alternative accommodation or to make some form of compensation.

While every effort is made to ensure accuracy, we regret that FHG Publications cannot accept responsibility for errors, omissions or misrepresentations in our entries or any consequences thereof.

Prices in particular should be checked because we go to press early. We will follow up complaints but cannot act as arbiters or agents for either party.

ENGLAND / Self Catering

Cumbria 249

CUMBRIA

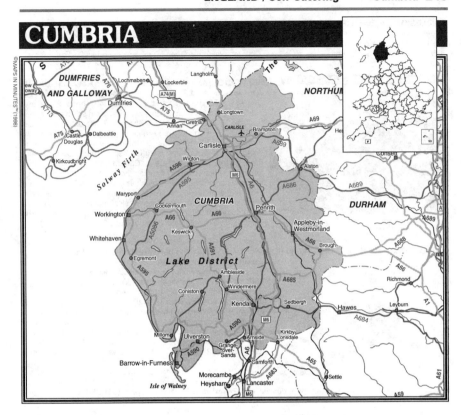

ALSTON. Lorne House, Alston. ♛♛♛ *COMMENDED.* **Sleeps 6.** Lovely old stone house in large garden 200 yards

from centre of England's highest market town. Set in magnificent North Pennines, ideally situated for touring North Yorkshire Dales, Hadrian's Wall, Northumbrian Coast, the Lakes. Walking, cycling, fishing, golf, swimming all available nearby. Accommodation sleeps six in three bedrooms and has two bathrooms; excellent, well-equipped kitchen; living room with wood stove, sitting room with open fire, colour TV. Washing machine. Gas central heating. Open all year. Prices from £150 to £320 per week inclusive of bed linen. Short breaks available. Children very welcome. Contact: **Mr J.H. Kendall, "Bowling Green Lodge", Edenside, Wetheral, Cumbria CA4 8HA (Tel & Fax: 01228 560340)**

AMBLESIDE. Peter and Anne Hart, Bracken Fell Cottage, Outgate, Ambleside LA22 0NH (015394 36289). Sleeps 2/4. Bracken Fell Cottage is situated in beautiful open countryside between Ambleside and Hawkshead in the picturesque hamlet of Outgate. The two bedroomed accommodation has central heating and is immaculately furnished. Fully equipped kitchen. Linen and electricity included. Ideally positioned for exploring the Lake District. All major outdoor activities catered for nearby. Ample parking. Patio area and two acres of gardens. Open all year. Terms from £140 per week. Sorry, no pets or children under eight years. Bed and Breakfast accommodation also available (♦♦♦). Non smoking. Write or phone for brochure and tariff.
e-mail: hart.brackenfell@virgin.net

AMBLESIDE. Mr Evans, Ramsteads Coppice, Outgate, Ambleside LA22 0NH (015394 36583). Six timber lodges of varied size and design set in 15 acres of mixed woodland with wild flowers, birds and native wild animals. There are also 11 acres of rough hill pasture. Three miles south west of Ambleside, it is an ideal centre for walkers, naturalists and country lovers. No pets. Children welcome. Open March to November.

See also Colour Display Advertisement

AMBLESIDE. Mr Marsden, Betty Fold, Hawkshead Hill, Ambleside LA22 0PS (015394 36611). ETC ♀♀♀ **COMMENDED.** Betty Fold is a large country house in its own spacious grounds with magnificent views and set in the heart of the Lake District National Park. The quaint village of Hawkshead is nearby and Coniston and Ambleside are within four miles; the beauty spot of Tarn Hows is 20 minutes' walk away. As well as being a guesthouse Betty Fold offers self-catering accommodation for up to four persons; there is "Garden Cottage" in the grounds and a flat which is part of the main house. All accommodation is centrally heated and facilities such as linen, colour TV and cots are provided, also heating, power and lighting. Pets welcome. Terms approximately £260 to £360 per week in main season, reduction for reduced occupancy. Special packages from November to Easter. Dinner available in guest house.

AMBLESIDE. Hole House, High Wray. HOLE HOUSE is a charming detached 17th century Lakeland cottage set in idyllic surroundings overlooking Blelham Tarn with magnificent panoramic views of the Langdale Pikes, Coniston Old Man, the Troutbeck Fells and Lake Windermere. High Wray is a quiet unspoilt hamlet set between Ambleside and Hawkshead making this an ideal base for walking or touring. This charming cottage which once belonged to Beatrix Potter has the original oak beams and feature stone staircase. It has recently been restored to provide very comfortable accommodation without losing its olde worlde charm. Accommodation consists of one double and two twin bedrooms; bathroom with shower; large spacious lounge with Sky TV and video; fitted kitchen with microwave oven, fridge freezer, tumble dryer, automatic washing machine and electric cooker. Storage heating included in the cost. Play area. Ample parking. Please write, or phone, for further details: **The Proprietor, Tock How Farm (015394 36294).**

APPLEBY-IN-WESTMORLAND. Mrs Edith Stockdale, Croft House, Bolton, Appleby-in-Westmorland CA16 6AW (Tel & Fax: 017683 61264). Sleep 2/5 and 10. Three cosy cottages recently converted from an old Westmorland style barn adjoining the owner's house. With an abundance of open stone work and oak beams and many original features. An excellent base for fell and country walking, horse-riding or as a touring base for the Lake District, beautiful Eden Valley, Scottish Borders, Hadrian's Wall and North Yorkshire Dales. Bed linen, towels, electricity and heating included in rent. Facilities include electric cooker, washing machine, fridge freezer, microwave, colour TV, video, hi-fi and dishwasher. Stabling provided for anyone wishing to bring pony on holiday. Weekly terms from £150. Brochure.

APPLEBY-IN-WESTMORLAND near. "Jubilee Cottage", North End, Bolton, Near Appleby. Sleeps 6/7. 18th century cottage, fully equipped except linen. Two bedrooms (sleeps six plus small child). Bathroom, lounge with colour TV and kitchen/diner with electric cooker, automatic washing machine, fridge, iron, etc. Economy 7 storage heater. Carpeted throughout. Situated between North Lakes and the Pennines. Car essential, off-road parking for two cars in front of cottage. Open Easter until October. Well behaved pets welcome. Terms £150 to £220 inclusive of all electricity. **Miss L. I. Basten.**

BOWNESS-ON-WINDERMERE. Mrs P. M. Fanstone, Deloraine (Dept F), Helm Road, Bowness-on-Windermere LA23 2HS (015394 45557).

COMMENDED. **Disabled Scheme Category 2 (first in Cumbria).** Deloraine spells seclusion, space, convenience and comfort for all seasons, while exploring Lakeland heritage. Parties of two/six have a choice of five apartments within an Edwardian mansion, and a detached cottage with four-poster bed. Set in one-and-a-half acres of private gardens, yet only a few minutes' walk from Bowness centre and water sports, each unit has distinctive qualities and character. Two command dramatic views of the Langdale Pikes and Lake at 300 foot elevation. Ground floor flat and cottage include disabled facilities. All properties have free parking, private entrances, full equipment, colour TV, electric heaters and central heating. Double glazing. Fire Prevention system. Payphone. Washing machine. Barbecue. Sun Room, Cot hire. Linen included. Four-poster beds. FREE SWIM/SAUNA TICKETS. No pets. Resident owners. Brochure on request. Terms from £120 to £415 per week. Winter Breaks available.

CALDBECK near. Croft House, Brocklebank, Wigton, Near Caldbeck. This beautiful farmhouse is in a quiet

country setting with large garden. Easy reach of Lake District, Scottish Borders and the Solway Firth, half-a-mile from open fells. Caldbeck is the nearest village with shops and pub. Lounge, dining room, kitchen, three bedrooms - two double, one twin; bathroom with toilet and shower. Night storage heaters, electric fire, coal, logs, cooker, fridge, colour TV, duvets all included. Bed linen and towels can be hired. Weekly terms from £150 to £250. Sorry no pets. Brochure from **Mrs Joan Todd, Wyndham Farm, Brocklebank, Wigton CA7 8DH (016974 78272).**

CARLISLE. Mrs J Moscrop, Collin Bank, Bewcastle, Carlisle CA6 6PU (Tel & Fax: 01697 748408).

APPROVED. **Sleeps 6.** High on the fells of Bewcastle is Collin Bank Farm which has magnificent views of the surrounding countryside. An ideal area for walking with Hadrian's Wall not far away. Riding and birdwatching. The chalet is well equipped and comfortable. Enjoy a swim in our indoor heated pool. Open all year. Children and pets welcome. Terms from £230 to £390 per week.

CARLISLE. Mrs Georgina Elwen, New Pallyards, Hethersgill, Carlisle CA6 6HZ (01228 577308).

COMMENDED. **Working farm, join in.** GOLD AWARD WINNER. Filmed for BBC TV. Relax and see beautiful North Cumbria and the Borders. A warm welcome awaits you on our 65 acre livestock farm tucked away in the Cumbrian countryside, yet easily accessible from M6 Junction 44. In addition to the surrounding attractions there is plenty to enjoy, including hillside walking, peaceful forests, ponies and sea trout/salmon fishing - or just nestle down and relax with nature. One comfortable well-equipped bungalow, three/four bedrooms. Two lovely, pleasant cottages on a working farm, one/two bedrooms. Terms from £80 to £380 weekly. Also Award Winning Bed and Breakfast and Half Board (ETC Four Diamonds). HWFH, ETB, FHB.
e-mail: info@newpallyards.freeserve.co.uk
website: www.newpallyards.freeserve.co.uk

When making enquiries or bookings, a stamped addressed envelope is always appreciated.

HODYOAD COTTAGES

Hodyoad stands in its own private grounds, with extensive views of the surrounding fells in peaceful rural countryside. Mid-way between the beautiful Lakes of Loweswater and Ennerdale, six miles from Cockermouth and 17 from Keswick. Fell walking, boating, pony trekking and trout fishing can all be enjoyed within a three-and-a-half mile radius. Each cottage is fully centrally heated and has two bedrooms to sleep five plus cot. All linen provided. Lounge with colour TV. Kitchen with fitted units, cooker and fridge. Bathroom with shower, washbasin, toilet, shaver point. Laundry room with washing machine and tumble dryer. Car essential, ample parking. Sea eight miles. Open all year. From £170 to £310 per week. For further details please contact:

Mrs J. A. Cook, Hodyoad House, Lamplugh, Cumbria CA14 4TT   Tel: 01946 861338

CONISTON. Mrs D.A. Hall (FHG), Dow Crag House, Coniston LA21 8AT (015394 41558). Two chalet bungalows to let, sleeping two/six. One mile from Coniston village on A593. Resident owner. Cleanliness assured. First bungalow has sittingroom, kitchen/diningroom, three bedrooms sleeping six; bathroom, separate toilet. Electric cooker, fridge/freezer. Night store heaters. Second bungalow comprises livingroom/kitchen, three bedrooms sleeping five, shower room. All equipped with continental quilts. Please bring own linen. Parking space. These holiday chalets are set in private garden with direct access to the Fells and Hills. Superb views overlooking Lake towards Grizedale Forest. Freedom, yet safe for children. Pets welcome by arrangement. Mountain walks, boating, fishing, tennis and bowls in village. Available March till November. Terms on application with SAE, please.

CONISTON near. Mrs J. Halton, "Brookfield", Torver, Near Coniston LA21 8AY (015394 41328). ♙♙♙ APPROVED/COMMENDED. **Sleeps 2/4.** This attractive, modern Bungalow property in quiet picturesque surroundings has a lovely outlook and extensive views of the Coniston mountains. It is completely detached and stands in its own half-acre of level garden and grounds. The accommodation inside is in two entirely separate self-contained units. The holiday bungalow is spacious but compact, and is suitable for two/four persons (special rate for two persons). It contains large sitting/diningroom, kitchen, utility room, two double bedrooms, bathroom and toilet. Well-equipped except for linen. Good parking space. Village inns are handy (300 yards). Coniston three miles. Available all year. Small dogs only, by arrangement. From £170 to £260 weekly. SAE for further details and terms stating number of persons and dates required.

CONISTON near. Mrs J.F. Halton, Scarr Head Caravans, Torver, Coniston LA21 8BP (015394 41576/41328). Small working farm at the foot of the Coniston mountains offers three modern static holiday caravans for hire, situated in large private garden. Spacious accommodation provides shower room with toilet and washbasin. Galley kitchen, (fully equipped) with fridge and full-sized gas cooker. Large lounge with dining area, gas fire and colour TV. Main bedroom has double bed. Smaller bedroom with twin beds and shaver point. Pillows, blankets and duvets with covers provided. Linen supplied at extra charge (sleeps 4). RTB inspected. Pets welcome by arrangement. Open Easter to end October. Please telephone or write for full details.

DUDDON VALLEY. Mrs M.E. Boyd, High Bigert Mire, Ulpha, Broughton-in-Furness LA20 6EY (01229 716493).

This cosy flat, ideal for two, is situated in a hamlet on the western slopes of the Duddon Valley five miles from Broughton-in-Furness. Attached to the owner's house, it includes a living room/kitchen, a bedroom with double bed and en suite bathroom. There is a wood burning stove with central heating, double glazing, colour TV, combination microwave oven, fridge. It provides a good base for walking, birdwatching or exploring the Lakes. Good views. Car essential, parking. No pets. Price inclusive of gas, electricity, coal, logs, linen and towels. Terms from £185 per week. Telephone for leaflet.

ELTERWATER. Lane Ends Cottages, Elterwater. ♈♈♈ *COMMENDED.*

Three cottages are situated next to "Fellside" on the edge of Elterwater Common. Two cottages accommodate a maximum of four persons: double bedroom, twin bedded room; fully equipped kitchen/dining room; bathroom. Third cottage sleeps five: as above plus single bedroom and separate dining room. Electricity by meters. The cottages provide an ideal base for walking/touring holidays with Ambleside, Grasmere, Hawkshead and Coniston within a few miles. Parking for one car per cottage, additional parking opposite. Open all year; out of season long weekends available. Rates from £175 per week. Brochure on request (SAE please). **Mrs M.E. Rice, "Fellside", Elterwater, Ambleside LA22 9HN (015394 37678).**

GRIZEDALE FOREST. High Dale Park Barn, High Dale Park, Satterthwaite, Ulverston LA12 8LJ.

♈♈♈/♈♈♈♈ **up to** *HIGHLY COMMENDED.* Delightfully situated south-facing barn, newly converted, attached to owners' 17th century farmhouse, with wonderful views down secluded, quiet valley, surrounded by beautiful broadleaf woodland. Oak beams, log fires, full central heating, patio. Grizedale Visitor Centre (three miles) includes the indoor Theatre-in-the-Forest, award-winning sculpture trails, gallery and unique sculptured playground. Grizedale Forest is one of the Lake District's richest areas of wildlife. Accommodation in two self contained units, one sleeping eight, the other two plus baby; available separately or as one unit at a reduced rate. Hawkshead three miles, Beatrix Potter's home three miles. Contact: **Mr P. Brown, High Dale Park Farm, High Dale Park, Satterthwaite, Ulverston LA12 8LJ (01229 860226).**

HAWESWATER/ULLSWATER/EDEN VALLEY. Goosemire Cottages. Over 30 traditional self-catering

holiday homes in size from one to four bedrooms, at sensible prices. Most are rustic 17th or 18th Century Lakeland cottages or lovely barn conversions, where antiquity and modern comforts have been beautifully combined. The majority of our holiday cottages are set on, or very near to Lake Ullswater (the Lake Districts second largest lake), or near Haweswater. We also have a nice selection of properties in the peaceful Eden Valley. An ideal base for walking, fishing, sailing, bird watching, touring or just relaxing in a beautiful and peaceful setting. Local pubs and post office/shop nearby. Furnished and equipped to a high standard. Log fires and central heating. Majority include heating, electric and bed linen in tariff. Pets welcome. Open all year. Short Breaks available. Details and brochure: **Goosemire Cottages, North Lodge, Longtail Hill, Bowness on Windermere. LA23 3JD (015394 47477)** website: www.goosemirecottages.co.uk

HAWKSHEAD. Peter and Anne Hart, Bracken Fell Cottage, Outgate, Ambleside LA22 0NH (015394

Bracken Fell

36289). Sleeps 2/4. Bracken Fell Cottage is situated in beautiful open countryside between Ambleside and Hawkshead in the picturesque hamlet of Outgate. The two bedroomed accommodation has central heating and is immaculately furnished. Fully equipped kitchen. Linen and electricity included. Ideally equipped for exploring the Lake District. All major outdoor activities catered for nearby. Ample parking. Patio area, two acres of gardens. Open all year. Terms from £140 per week. Sorry, no pets or children under eight years. Bed and Breakfast accommodation also available (◆◆◆). Non smoking. Write or phone for brochure and tariff.
e-mail: hart.brackenfell@virgin.net.

HAWKSHEAD. Borwick Fold, Outgate, Near Ambleside LA22 0PU (Tel & Fax: 015394 36742). Tourist

Board ♔♔/♔♔♔ HIGHLY COMMENDED. 3 cottages Very special barn conversion - adjacent to 17th century farmhouse. Stunning setting; away from the madding crowd. Panoramic mountain/valley views. Walks from the door to fell, tarn, valley, pubs and village. Abundant birdlife. Resident elkhounds, hens, geese etc. Character and comfort. Abundance of books and beamed ceilings. Some antiques and local craftsmen furnishings. Excellently equipped. Central heating. Access to two acres fell with benches. Our visitors return again and again."A relaxing, welcoming haven, out of the tourist trap" (NewZealand);"One of the most beautiful places on earth. An experience we shall never forget' (San Fransisco); "The cottage is wonderful – so much character and beautifully furnished" (Lancashire),;"Local walks and views superb. Loved the place" (London). Brochure.

HOLMROOK. G. and H.W. Cook, Hall Flatt, Santon, Holmrook CA19 1UU (019467 26270). Working

farm. Sleeps 7. This comfortably furnished house is set in own grounds with beautiful views. The approach road is a short but good lane off Gosforth/Santon Bridge road. Ideal centre for climbers and walkers. Within easy reach of Muncaster Castle and Narrow Gauge Railway from Ravenglass to Eskdale, about three miles from the sea and Wastwater. Accommodation comprises two double bedrooms, two single and child's bed; bathroom, two toilets; sittingroom, dining room; all electric kitchen with cooker, fridge, kettle, immersion heater, stainless steel sink unit. Fully equipped except for linen. Open Easter to Christmas. Pets by arrangement. Shopping about two miles and car essential. Electricity by 50p meter. SAE, please, for weekly terms.

KENDAL. The Barns, Field End, Patton, Kendal. ♈♈♈♈ *COMMENDED.* Two detached barns converted into

five spacious architect-designed houses. The Barns are situated on 200 acres of farmland, four miles north of Kendal. A quiet country area with River Mint passing through farmland and lovely views of Cumbrian Hills, many interesting local walks with the Dales Way Walk passing nearby. Fishing is available on the river. The Barns consist of four houses with four double bedrooms and one house with three double bedrooms. Each house fully centrally heated for early/late holidays; lounge with open fire, diningroom; kitchen with cooker, fridge, microwave and washer; bathroom, downstairs shower room and toilet. Many interesting features include oak beams, pine floors and patio doors. Central to Lakes and Yorkshire Dales, National Parks. Terms from £140 to £385. Electricity at cost. Pets welcome. For brochure of The Barns apply to **Mr and Mrs E.D. Robinson, 1 Field End, Patton, Kendal (01539 824220 or 07778 596863; Fax:01539 824464**

e-mail: fshawend@globalnet.co.uk
website: www.diva~web.co.uk.fsendhols.

KENDAL. Mrs E. Barnes, Brackenfold, Whinfell, Kendal LA8 9EF (01539 824238). Working farm, join in. Sleeps 5. Brackenfold is a 217-acre dairy farm set in a quiet country area. There are beautiful scenic views from the farm and also a river running through the middle of the farm which is suitable for paddling and picnicking. Brackenfold is situated centrally for touring the Lake District and the Yorkshire Dales. All children are welcome and babysitting is available. Milk can be obtained from the farm. The accommodation is part of the farmhouse and has two double bedrooms, cot; bathroom, toilet; sitting/diningroom; fully equipped kitchen with electric cooker, fridge, etc. Shops four miles, sea 20. Sorry, no pets. Open March to November. SAE, please, for terms.

KENDAL. Mrs E. Bateman, High Underbrow Farm, Burneside, Kendal LA8 9AY (01539 721927). Working farm. Sleeps 4. The cottage adjoins the 17th century farmhouse in a sunny position with wonderful views. Ideal spot for touring the Lake District and Yorkshire Dales, with many pleasant walks around. There are two bedrooms (one with double bed, the other with two singles). Children are welcome and a cot is available. Bathroom with bath, shower, toilet and washbasin. Large livingroom/kitchen with colour TV, fitted units, fridge and cooker. Electricity by £1 coin meter. Storage heaters 50p meter. Understairs store. Fitted carpets throughout. Own entrance porch. Sorry, no pets. Shops at Burneside two miles away, Kendal four miles, Windermere eight miles. Linen provided. Car essential – parking. Terms from £130 weekly. There is also a six-berth holiday caravan to let from £130 per week.

KESWICK. Harney Peak, Portinscale, Near Keswick. We can offer you the very best in self catering

accommodation in our spacious well-equipped apartments in the quiet village of Portinscale - overlooking Derwentwater yet only one mile from Keswick. We have various sized apartments and this makes an ideal location for couples and families. Hot water and central heating included in rental. Laundry facilities. Ample off-street parking. Open all year. Dogs welcome. Short breaks are available off season. For brochure please apply to: **Mr & Mrs Smith, The Leathes Head Hotel, Borrowdale, Cumbria CA12 5UY (017687 77247).**

KESWICK. Derwentwater Manor, Portinscale, Keswick CA12 5RE (01768 772211). ♈♈♈♈ *HIGHLY COMMENDED.* This former gentleman's country residence now provides some of Lakeland's finest self-catering accommodation amid tranquil surroundings on the fringe of a picturesque village. Our tastefully converted one or two bedroomed self-catering apartments and cottages are all superbly appointed and offer a high standard of facilities. Fully fitted feature kitchens (many with dishwashers), central heating, teletext colour TVs with video, CD player and direct dial telephone. Bedrooms are complete with hairdryer, trouser press, radio alarms, welcoming tea tray, bouquet of fresh flowers and fruit baskets. Beds made and towels supplied and to be sure your holiday starts with a sparkle, a bottle of chilled Champagne. Ample free parking, takeaway meals and grocery delivery service, and a special welcome for pets.

e-mail: derwentwater.hotel@dial.pipex.com
website: http://.dial.pipex.com/derwentwater.hotel/

When making enquiries or bookings, a stamped addressed envelope is always appreciated.

KESWICK. Stoney Gill, Newlands, Keswick. Situated three miles from Keswick on the Braithwaite to Buttermere Road, with the most magnificent views across Newlands Valley to Catbells, Stoney Gill flat makes an excellent base for walking directly onto the fells. Also convenient for touring in the Lake District, fishing, sailing, pony trekking and golf. Stoney Gill consists of one single and two double bedrooms, all with washbasins; bathroom; open plan lounge with dining and kitchen area. Electric meter. Central heating included in rent. Weekly terms from £160 to £250. Parking for two cars. One dog only please. Further details apply to:- **Mrs L. Edmondson, Stoney Acre, Newlands, Keswick CA12 5TS (017687 78200).**

KESWICK near. Mrs A.M. Trafford, Bassenthwaite Hall Farm, Bassenthwaite Village, Near Keswick CA12 4QP (Tel & Fax: 017687 76393). Working farm. By

a stream with ducks and a white wooden bridge we have delightful cottages of charm and character, in this tranquil and pretty hamlet, six miles north of Keswick. Children spend many happy hours nearby playing on the swings in the wood whilst the ducks and hens roam freely. Lovely walks to the Lake, Skiddaw, Dash Falls and surrounding hills. Excellent inn nearby serving good food. All cottages are situated around the farmyard. We have small properties for two and family properties sleeping four to 10. Large groups of up to 20 can also be catered for. Pets welcome. Terms from £100 to £695. Reduction off peak. Long weekends, bargain mid-week and weekend breaks from November to May. Also farmhouse Bed and Breakfast. Colour brochure available. Open all year.

KIRKBY LONSDALE near. Mrs M. Dixon, Harrison Farm, Whittington, Kirkby Lonsdale, Carnforth, Lancashire LA6 2NX (015242 71415). Properties sleep 2/8. Near Hutton Roof, three miles from Kirkby Lonsdale and central for touring Lake District and Yorkshire Dales. Coast walks on Hutton Roof Crag, famous lime stone pavings. Sleeps eight people, one room with double and single bed and one room with double and cot, while third bedroom has three single beds. Bathroom. Sittingroom, diningroom and kitchen. Everything supplied but linen. Parking space. Pets permitted. Other cottages available for two to eight people. Electric cooker, fridge, kettle, iron, immersion heaters and TV. Electricity and coal extra. Terms from £150 per week. SAE brings quick reply.

See also Colour Display Advertisement

KIRKOSWALD. Crossfield Cottages with Leisure Fishing. ♈♈♈♈ *COMMENDED.* Tranquil quality cottages overlooking modest lakes amid Lakeland's beautiful Eden Valley countryside. Only 30 minutes' drive from Ullswater, North Pennines, Hadrian's Wall and Scottish Borders. You will find beds freshly made up for your arrival, tranquillity and freedom in your surroundings, and good coarse and game fishing at hand. Accommodation clean, well equipped and maintained; laundry area; pets welcome. Centrally located, good fishing and walking. Relax and escape to YOUR home in the country - why settle for less? No silly rules. Telephone or SAE for terms and full details: **Crossfield Cottages, Kirkoswald, Penrith CA10 1EU (24 hour Brochure Line 01768 898711 (manned most Saturdays). Bookings 8am to 10pm 01768 896275 (Fax available).**

See also Colour Display Advertisement

KIRKOSWALD. Liz Webster, Howscales, Kirkoswald, Penrith CA10 1JG (01768 898666; Fax: 01768 898710). ♈♈♈ and ♈♈♈♈ *HIGHLY COMMENDED.* **Sleep 2/4.** COTTAGES FOR NON SMOKERS. Howscales is a former farm built in local red sandstone with the buildings grouped around a central courtyard. Located in a rural setting one-and-a-half miles from Kirkoswald. Three cottages are two storey, with the lounge, kitchen and dining areas on the first floor; the bedrooms and bathroom are on the ground floor. One is single storey at ground level, suitable for accompanied disabled guests, with two en suite double bedrooms. All cottages have full central heating, are equipped with colour TV and have a fully equipped kitchen/dining area with microwave, electric cooker, gas hob and fridge. Shower room and WC. Everything supplied including linen. gas and electricity paid by meter reading at end of stay. Sorry, but no pets or children under six. Please ring or write for our colour brochure.

FHG Please mention *The Farm Holiday Guide* when enquiring about accommodation featured in these pages.

LAKE DISTRICT. We offer a wide range of self-catering accommodation situated throughout the English Lakes,

North Cumbria and Eden Valley, Northumberland. Many different properties to choose from including houses, cottages and apartments with a range of prices. Please send for our free brochure. **Clark Scott-Harden, 52 King Street, Penrith CA11 7AY (01768 868989; Fax: 01768 865578).** email: post.penrith@csh.co.uk

LOWESWATER. Latterhead Cottage, Loweswater, Cockermouth. Sleeps 4. Charming country cottage retaining many of its original features and charm. Seven miles from Cockermouth, 10 miles from Keswick. Self catering cottage comprising lounge with feature fireplace and colour TV; fully fitted kitchen/dining area including electric cooker, microwave, fridge and kettle. Shower room/WC. Two bedrooms. Cot and high chair available. All very comfortably furnished. Everything supplied except linen. Electricity payable by £1 coin meter. Children and pets welcome. Weekly terms from £165 to £180. Booking forms, etc from: **R.F. Bell, Oakbank, Loweswater, Cockermouth CA13 0RR (01900 85227).**

MORESBY. Swallows Return and Owls Retreat, Moresby. ♙♙♙♙ *HIGHLY COMMENDED.* Sorry no smoking.

Sorry no pets. Maintained with loving care by the owners who live within two minutes' walking distance, converted 19th century farm buildings, very tastefully furnished to provide high standard accommodation in a courtyard setting within a rural hamlet. Two miles from Georgian Whitehaven with its antiquarian bookshop and its new Harbour Heritage Centre and the Meteorological Office Weather Gallery. Half a mile from Rosehill Theatre. Within easy reach of Ennerdale, Wastwater, Loweswater, Crummock and Buttermere, St. Bees with its red sandstone cliffs, Ravenglass and miniature railway, Muncaster Castle and Owl Centre. The properties are kept warm throughout the year providing cosy accommodation in winter. Full gas central heating, living flame gas fires, double glazing. Each property sleeps four, cot available. Ample private parking. Terms from £170 to £320. Brochure available on request from **James and Joyce Moore, Moresby Hall Cottage, Moresby, Whitehaven CA28 6PJ (01946 64078).** website: www.cottageguide.co.uk/moresby.html

PENRITH. Skirwith Hall Cottages. ETC ♙♙♙♙ *COMMENDED.* Escape to Eden! Get away from it all in one of

two comfortable well-equipped cottages on dairy farm in the Eden Valley between the Lake District and the Pennine Dales. Set on the edge of the village of Skirwith in the shadow of Crossfell, the highest mountain in the Pennine range, the properties are maintained to the highest standard with every modern convenience. Accommodating two/four and five/eight people both cottages have riverside gardens and open fires. Well behaved children and pets welcome. Please contact for brochure. **Mrs L. Wilson, Skirwith Hall, Skirwith, Penrith CA10 1RH (Tel & Fax: 01768 88241).** e-mail: idawilson@aol.com

PENRITH. The Cruck Barn, Berrier, Greystoke, Penrith CA11 0XD (017684 83859/016974 76327;

Mobile: 078 3627 2033). Sleeps 2/7. Truly a unique opportunity to stay in this magnificent detached 16th century Listed cruck barn conversion, commanding panoramic views of the Lakeland mountains. Situated in the tranquil hamlet of Berrier, set within the National Park close to Keswick and Ullswater. Easy access to all the Lakes. Tastefully furnished by the caring, friendly owners who live next door. Excellent pubs; one walking distance. Enjoy lake walks, high fell walking, pony trekking and boat trips. Visit Hadrian's Wall. The barn is extremely popular all year round. Three night short breaks from £150 low season. Weekly rates from £190 low season to £395 high season.

PENRITH. Alan and Susan Grave, West View Farm, Winskill, Penrith CA10 1PD (Tel & Fax: 01768 881356). COMMENDED. **Sleeps 2/6.** Three cosy sandstone

cottages, fully centrally heated and well furnished and equipped for all your needs. Situated on a small working farm in the village of Winskill at the foot of the Pennines in the Eden Valley. Here you can enjoy tranquil, relaxing surroundings with scenic views all round from the Lake District hills to the Pennines, and yet the Lakes, Roman Wall and the Borders are all within easy access by car. Children and pets are welcome. We have a games room (snooker and table tennis) on the farm and a play area in the village. Open all year. Short breaks available. Phone for colour brochure.

PENRITH. Rampshowe, Orton, Penrith. Working farm, join in. Sleeps 2/8. Rampshowe is a 150 acre fell

farm with sheep, lambs, beef cattle and calves. Organised pony riding nearby. Delightfully positioned in the peace and quiet of Birbeck Fells, with a river flowing through the fields, lovely waterfall and pool. Ideal area for birdwatchers. Local angling club. Shops, post office, pub serving snacks, Tea room serving home-baking. Unspoilt, rural countryside, yet only five miles from M6 motorway. Accommodates eight people in three double bedrooms, cot; bathroom, toilet; colour TV, sittingroom, diningroom. All downstairs rooms and bathroom with night-store electric heaters and there is an open fire with back-boiler (wood and coal provided). Fully equipped kitchen. Fitted carpets throughout. Pets and children welcome. Car essential, ample car parking space in the farmyard. Open all year. The owner maintained house stands on its own, with garden and large farmyard. Prices from £130 to £275. SAE to **Mrs M.E. Mawson, Bow Brow, Orton, Penrith CA10 3SJ (015396 24244).**

See also Colour Display Advertisement

SILECROFT. Fellside Farm, Near Wastwater. Sleeps 7 plus cot. Working farm. Situated in a peaceful unspoilt part of the Lake District, we offer a truly "get away from it all" holiday. Lounge with open fireplace or electric fire, playroom with table tennis equipment. Kitchen with oil fired Rayburn which runs the central heating, electric cooker and fridge freezer. Three large double bedrooms, bathroom with airing cupboard and two w.c.'s, one upstairs and one downstairs. Cot and high chair available. Large play safe garden, ample parking. Electricity and coal all inclusive. Ten miles from Wastwater, 13 miles from Coniston. Local shop and Post Office 15 minute walk. Price per week from £130 short break to £400 high season. Enquiries to: **Mrs S. Capstick, Whicham Hall, Whicham Valley, Silecroft LA18 5LT (01229 772637).**

SPARK BRIDGE. Dicky Cragg, Spark Bridge, Ulverston. COMMENDED. **Sleeps 14; 2 cots.** Situated

in a quiet country lane, our barn conversion is rural and peaceful but not isolated with easy access to Windermere and the quieter Western Fells. The house has a large lounge with beechwood floor, inglenook fireplace. Full oil-fired central heating and a woodburning stove. Dining kitchen equipped with fridge freezer, microwave, cooker and dishwasher. Three double bedrooms, two twin bedrooms and two bunk rooms. French windows lead onto a terrace with large garden and brick barbecue. There is a quarter size snooker table, a table tennis table and payphone. Parking for six cars. Weekly rates from £550 to £1100. For further details contact **Mrs D. Lever, 27 East Beach, Lytham St Annes, Lancashire FY8 5EX (01253 795905 daytime; Evening & Fax: 01253 736438).**

When making enquiries or bookings,
a stamped addressed envelope is always appreciated.

STAVELY. William, Anne & Linda Batey, Brunt Knott Farm, Staveley, Kendal LA8 9QX (01539 821030;

Fax: 01539 821221). ꝪꝪꝪ *APPROVED.* **Sleep 2/5.** Four cosy cottages on a small 17th century farm. Peaceful, elevated, fellside location, with superb views over Lakeland Fells. Five miles from Windermere and the historic market town of Kendal. One- and-a-half miles from Staveley village. Lovely walks from your door. Three cottages with oil central heating, one with electric storage heaters. Three cottages also have woodburner/fire. Laundry facilities. Gardens, picnic tables and parking. Ideal touring base Lakes and Yorkshire Dales. Caring resident owners. Children and pets welcome. Short breaks in low season. Tariff £160 to £290 per week. Brochure.
e-mail: Linda@Bruntknott.demon.co.uk
website: www.Bruntknott.demon.co.uk

See also Colour Display Advertisement

ULLSWATER. The Estate Office, Patterdale Hall Estate, Glenridding, Penrith CA11 0PJ (Tel & Fax: 017684 82308 24 hours; Coach Houses ꝪꝪꝪ *COMMENDED;* **Cottages** ꝪꝪꝪ *COMMENDED;* **Pine Lodges** ꝪꝪꝪ *COMMENDED;* **Chalets** Ꝫ/ꝪꝪ *COMMENDED;* **The Dairy and Bothies** Ꝫ *COMMENDED.* Our range includes three very comfortable large coach houses, two stone-built cottages with open fires, two three-bedroomed pine lodges, six two-bedroomed cedar chalets, a unique, detached, converted dairy, and two converted Gardener's Bothies which make ideal, low cost accommodation for two people. All set in a private 300 acre Estate between Lake Ullswater and Helvellyn and containing a working hill farm, a Victorian Waterfall Wood, private lake foreshore for guests to use for boating and fishing, and 100 acres of designated ancient woodland for you to explore. Children welcome. Dogs by appointment in some of the accommodation. Colour TV, central heating, launderette, payphone. Day time electricity metered. Linen hire available. Terms from £129 to £440. Please phone for full brochure.
e-mail: patterdalehallestate@phel.demon.co.uk
website: www.phel.demon.co.uk

WINDERMERE. Mr and Mrs F. Legge, Pinethwaite, Lickbarrow Road, Windermere LA23 2NQ (Tel & Fax: 015394 44558). ꝪꝪꝪ & ꝪꝪꝪꝪ *COMMENDED.* **Properties**

sleep 2/7. Pinethwaite offers more than just somewhere to stay for your Lake District holiday. Our unique cottages and apartments nestle in the heart of our private woodland, the haunt of roe deer, red squirrels and extensive bird life. A tranquil location, yet only one mile from Windermere and Bowness villages. Superb viewpoints close by. Lovely walks in our grounds and local footpaths (Cumbrian Way) through surrounding farmland and fell. Well equipped accommodation (colour TVs, microwaves, electric heating, log fires). Central washing machine/dryer. Sauna. Private parking. Children welcome but, sorry, no pets. Open all year. Short Breaks available in the Low Season. Tariffs from £170 to £500 per week. Full details in our brochure, sent on request.

PUBLISHER'S NOTE

While every effort is made to ensure accuracy, we regret that FHG Publications cannot accept responsibility for errors, omissions or misrepresentations in our entries or any consequences thereof. Prices in particular should be checked because we go to press early. We will follow up complaints but cannot act as arbiters or agents for either party.

DERBYSHIRE

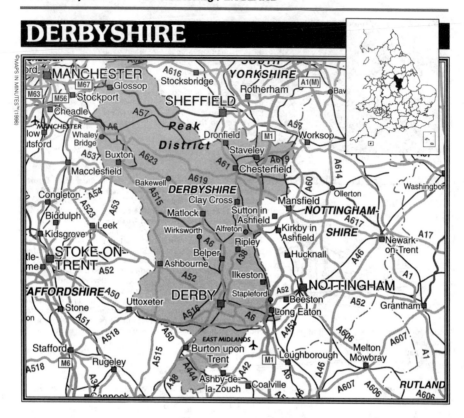

ASHBOURNE. Mrs Louise Tatlow, Ashfield Farm, Calwich, Near Ashbourne DE6 2EB (01335 324279 or 324443). ♛♛♛♛ *COMMENDED.* **Working farm. Sleeps 7.** Ashfield Cottage is a recently renovated oak-beamed cottage on this working farm, well situated for the Peak District and many other places of interest with beautiful views of Dove Valley and Weaver Hills. Accommodation is for seven persons in two bedrooms (one family room and one with twin beds). Well-furnished and equipped with storage heaters, colour TV, automatic washing machine, tumble dryer, fridge/freezer. Coloured bathroom suite and shower. Linen for hire. Parking space. Further details and brochure on request.

ASHBOURNE. Alan and Liz Kingston, Old Boothby Farm, The Green, Ashbourne DE6 1EE (01335 342044). The converted Hayloft and Stables of our 17th century farmhouse are an idyllic location for your stay in the "Gateway to the Peak District". Just a five minute level walk to the centre of Ashbourne with its historic pubs and wide variety of restaurants. Handy for visiting Alton Towers, Dovedale, Buxton, Matlock and numerous stately homes. Excellent walking country. The Hayloft with its verandah, exposed beams, log fire, fully equipped kitchen, lounge with colour TV, two double bedrooms and one twin bunk bedroom is ideal for party or family bookings; cot and high chair available. The Stables studio flat with en suite facilities, king-size bed, colour TV and kitchen is the perfect setting for that romantic break away from it all. Bed and Breakfast also available.

**ASHBOURNE. Mrs M. Large, Overtown Farm, Hognaston, Ashbourne DE6 1NR (01629 540365).
Sleeps 4/6.** Self-catering holiday cottage, beautifully converted from an attractive barn. Surrounded by farmland and overlooking Carsington Water. Situated between Ashbourne and Wirksworth. Sailing, sailboarding and canoeing with instruction are available on Carsington Water; horse riding, fishing, bike riding and bird watching are all within five minutes of the cottage. Chatsworth House and Haddon Hall are just two of the historic houses within easy visiting distance. The cottage has full central heating and facilities include microwave, electric cooker, washing machine, TV, video, payphone. Linen and towels supplied. There is a small garden. Available all year. Brochure on request.

ASHBOURNE near. Throwley Moor Farm and Throwley Cottage, Ilam, Near Ashbourne. ꜛꜛꜛꜛ **Working**

farm, join in. Properties sleep 7/12. Self-catering farmhouse and cottage on this beef and sheep farm near Dovedale and Manifold Valley. Approached by A52/A53 Ashbourne to Leek road, then via Calton and follow signs for Throwley and Ilam. Within easy reach of Alton Towers, cycle hire and places of historic interest. An ideal touring centre. The cottage accommodates seven people and the farmhouse 12. Sittingrooms and diningroom (kitchen/diner in cottage). Electric cookers; fridges; washing machine and dryer. Pay phone. Pets permitted. Car essential – parking. Available all year; terms according to season. Nearest shops three miles away. SAE, please, for further details to **Mrs M.A. Richardson, Throwley Hall Farm, Ilam, Near Ashbourne DE6 2BB (01538 308 202/243).**

ASHBOURNE near. Yeldersley Hall. ꜛꜛꜛꜛ *COMMENDED* **to** ꜛꜛꜛꜛꜛ *DE LUXE.* We have three delightful flats (each

to sleep two) in the stable block and a fabulous apartment (to sleep four) in the East Wing of our historic Georgian house, two miles from Ashbourne. This is an operational country house with 12 acres of gardens and grounds to explore. Each flat is furnished and equipped to a very high standard with full heating, colour TV, microwave, payphone, etc. Use of washing machine and dryer. All linen and electricity included. Cot available. Regret no pets or children under 12 except baby in cot. Terms from £150 per week. Further details and brochure from **Mrs J. Bailey, Yeldersley Hall, Ashbourne, Derbyshire DE6 1LS (01335 343432).**

ASHBOURNE near. Mrs Sylvia Foster, Shirley Hall Farm, Shirley, Ashbourne DE6 3AS (01335

360346). Up to ꜛꜛꜛ *COMMENDED.* Three lovely properties in the Derbyshire Dales. Bungalow on the edge of peaceful Shirley village, overlooking farmland comprises three double bedrooms, bathroom, large lounge/dining room, kitchen with washing machine, fridge, cooker, microwave. Colour TV. Night storage heaters. First floor barn conversion comprises family bedroom, bathroom, livingroom with kitchen, electric cooker, fridge, microwave. Colour TV. Night store heaters. In nearby hamlet of Mercaston, secluded farmhouse (pictured here) in gentle rolling countryside sleeping up to eight in four bedrooms. Bathroom and cloakroom with toilet. Modern kitchen with washing machine, cooker, fridge, microwave. Colour TV in beamed sitting room, log burner. Night store heaters. All properties have free coarse fishing. From £150 to £360 per week.

BARLOW. Mr and Mrs R. Ward, Barlow Trout, Mill Farm, Barlow, Dronfield S18 7TJ (0114 289 0543).
ꜛꜛꜛꜛ *COMMENDED.* **Units sleep 2/6.** Mill Farm Holiday Cottages are situated in a conservation area with post office and pub/bar meals just 300 yards away; bus stop at gate. Horse riding can be arranged and coarse and fly fishing is available on site. Children and pets welcome. Central heating. Four-poster bed in three of the five units. Weekly terms from £109 to £210. Linen provided free of charge. Short break bookings accepted October – April. Please write or phone for full details.

FHG

Visit the FHG website
www.holidayguides.com
for details of the wide choice of accommodation
featured in the full range of FHG titles

BELPER. Mr and Mrs Postles, Chevin Green Farm, Chevin Road, Belper DE56 2UN (Tel & Fax: 01773 822328). ETC ŤŤŤŤ COMMENDED**.** The four bungalows have been attractively converted from farm buildings to provide well-equipped accommodation with character for two to six people in a quiet situation with glorious views over the hillside known as "The Chevin". One bungalow has been thoughtfully adapted for disabled visitors. Terms from £100 to £320 per week. Also available Bed and Breakfast accommodation (4 Star) from £20 to £26 per person. Reductions for children sharing family room. There is so much for visitors to do in Derbyshire.

BUXTON. Mrs V Lawrenson, Grove House, Elkstone, Near Warslow, Buxton SK17 0LU (01538 300487). ŤŤŤ COMMENDED**. Sleeps 2/3 plus baby.** STABLE COTTAGE is a character stone country cottage, sympathetically modernised to retain original oak beams with attractive galleried landing. In quiet Peak District village near Manifold Valley with Dovedale six miles away. Comfortable and very well-equipped including bed linen and towels. Patio garden with sunny aspect and parking close to cottage. Good walking and cycling area with five country parks within a 12 mile radius. Convenient for Alton Towers, Staffordshire Potteries factory shops, National Trust properties in Derbyshire and Staffordshire and RSPB Reserve. Pub/restaurant nearby. Dog by arrangement. The perfect location for the true country lover. Weekly terms from £140 to £210. Short winter breaks available.

BUXTON. Sue Flower, Old House Farm Cottage, Old House Farm, Newhaven, Hartington, Buxton SK17 0DY (01629 636268). ETC ŤŤŤŤ COMMENDED**. Sleeps 6+cot.** Join us in our warm, well-appointed cottage and explore 'Peak Practice' country. Stay on a real working dairy and sheep farm where a high standard is maintained. We run a busy family farm, still having time to answer your questions and delighted to let you watch our farm activities – lambing time in April is a must! An off-road cycling trail leads from our farm. Children and pets welcome. Open all year. Terms from £190 to £350 per week, with short breaks available November to March. Please write or phone for our brochure.
e-mail: s.flowerfarmaccom@btinternet.com

CHINLEY (Near Chapel-en-le-Frith). Stephen and Kath Drabble, Brook View, Slack House Farm, Chapel-en-le-Firth SK23 0QL (01663 750320). Working farm. Sleeps 8. ŤŤŤŤ COMMENDED**.** Large detached bungalow, set in its own grounds, close to Kinder Scout, the Edale Moors and Jacob's Ladder. Excellent walking country. Accommodation comprises entrance hall, large comfortable lounge with open fire and TV. Diningroom with TV which leads to fully fitted kitchen and utility room with freezer, washer, tumble dryer. Bathroom with shower cubicle, bath, washbasin and w.c. Single bedroom. Double bedroom with adult size bunks. Double bedroom with single bed with en suite shower/bath, washbasin, bidet and w.c. Suitable for people with mobility problems. Cot and high chair available. Linen included. Sorry, no pets. Terms from £160 to £350.

CROMFORD. Mrs Beardsley, Woodseats Farm, Willersley Lane, Cromford, Near Matlock DE4 5JG (01629 56525). Built in Derbyshire stone, Woodseats Cottages have been converted from the original cowshed. Situated on our 75 acre family-run working farm which sits on a hillside overlooking the Derwent Valley with its panoramic views. About two miles from Cromford village and Matlock Bath. Many attractions include Chatsworth House, Crich Tramway Museum, Carsington Water, Alton Towers and Bakewell. The two cottages each have two double bedrooms that sleep four plus two. They both have a shower room on the first floor, and well-equipped dining kitchens with electric cooker and fridge/freezer, microwave, etc. Lounge with feature stone wall and exposed beams, TV and video. Central heating, electricity and bed linen are inclusive. Ample parking. No pets. Terms from £200 to £350 per week. Bed and Breakfast also available. Open all year.

EDALE. ♔♔♔ *COMMENDED.* **Cottages sleep 2/4.** Edale, in the heart of the Derbyshire Peak District, well-known

as the start of the Pennine Way, is renowned for its beautiful scenery, and is a paradise for walking, climbing and touring. Two cottages on working hill farm sleep two/four, plus cot. Bathroom, one bedroom with double bed and bunk beds, kitchen/lounge. Well equipped, with central heating, double glazing, colour TV, immersion heater. Bed linen and towels provided. Electricity by meter reading. Children welcome. Terms from £170 to £210 per week. Weekend and short breaks out of season. Details from **Mrs S. Gee, Cotefield Farm, Edale, Near Sheffield S30 2ZG (01433 670273).**

HARDSTOFT. Pear Tree Cottage, Locke Lane, Hardstoft, Near Chesterfield. A delightful, fully refurbished

cottage on a smallholding in country surroundings, offering quality accommodation ground floor:– conservatory, WC, well equipped dining kitchen, sitting room with colour TV. 1st floor:– two bedrooms [one double bed, three singles]. Fully equipped bathroom. Enclosed garden. Ample parking. Children welcome, cot and high chair available. Pets by arrangement. There are many local walks and trails and the Peak District with its wonderful scenery and many attractions is just a short distance away. Also ideal for "Robin Hood Country" and American Adventure. Terms £130–£220 (includes central heating, electricity, bed linen]. **Mrs C. Beckett, Laburnum Cottage, 46 Hardstoft Road, Pilsley, Chesterfield S45 8BL (01773 872767).**

HARTINGTON. P. Skemp, Cotterhill Farm, Biggin-by-Hartington, Buxton SK17 0DJ (01298 84447;

Fax: 01298 84664). ♔♔♔♔ *HIGHLY COMMENDED.* Two recently converted cottages, one sleeping four, the other two. Exposed beams, two-person cottage has galleried bedroom, log burner, five piece suite in bathroom and more. High and tasteful specification. Patio, substantial garden area, wild flower meadows and barbecue. Laundry room. Phone. Glorious location in rolling countryside. Excellent views with privacy. Half-a-mile from village and pub. Tissington Trail three-quarters of a mile, two other cycle/footpath trails within three miles, nature reserve on our land leading after one-and-a-half miles to River Dove, four miles down river is Dovedale. Footpaths/bridleways surround our farm. Highly praised, personalised information pack in each cottage giving loads of advice on attractions, walks, etc. Terms from £150 to £320 per week.
website: www.skemp.u-net.com

HOPE. Crabtree Cottages, Crabtree Meadow, Aston Lane, Hope Valley S33 6SA (Tel & Fax: 01433

620291). ♔♔♔♔ *HIGHLY COMMENDED.* **Four cottages sleep 2/6.** Four beautifully converted, well-equipped cottages in the grounds of a country house in Peak District National Park, sleeping two to six persons. Beautifully fitted kitchens with microwave ovens. Colour TVs. Laundry. Payphone. Central heating, fuel and linen included in rental. Ample off road parking but car not essential. Superb walking country and facilities in the area for golf, tennis, climbing, gliding, fishing, pony trekking and caving. Convenient for shops and pubs, visiting historic houses. Weekly all year £160 to £365. Short breaks in winter from £60. Contact: **Mrs P.M. Mason.**

MATLOCK. **Honeysuckle, Jasmine and Clematis Cottages, Middlehills Farm, Grange Hill, Matlock DE4 4HY (01629 650368).** ♔♔♔♔ *COMMENDED/HIGHLY COMMENDED.* Relax, unwind, enjoy the peace and tranquillity in one of our warm, welcoming cottages or static caravan. JASMINE - two bedroomed, and HONEYSUCKLE - three bedroomed, both Four Keys Commended, are full of character - stone mullions, exposed beams, oak parquet floors, rustic rose arches and enclosed south facing patios. CLEMATIS - two bedroomed and Four Keys Highly Commended, Accessible Category 2, is on one level and especially converted for less-able and wheelchair users. Large bathroom with support rails, wheel-in shower with shower seat. Also fully equipped static caravan for bargain breaks. Meet our friendly pot-bellied pig and Bess and Ruby are ideal playmates for children of all ages.

PEAK DISTRICT. **Angela Kellie, Shatton Hall Farm, Bamford, Hope Valley S33 0BG (01433 620635; Fax: 01433 620689).** ♔♔♔♔ *HIGHLY COMMENDED.* Three self-catering cottages each sleeping four in two bedrooms, plus sofa bed. The Elizabethan Farmstead in a superbly peaceful setting has extensive gardens, waymarked walks through ancient woodland, wetland and trout lake, streamside and new plantations. We welcome groups wishing to stay in our comfortable accommodation and use our resource centre Townfield Barn to pursue their special interest, such as photography, art, craft or nature studies - in our "Programme 2000". Cot and high chair. A visitors' laundry, payphone and hard tennis court are available. Each stone self-contained cottage is finished in pine with open fires and full central heating, also over bath showers and newly refurbished kitchens. Terms from £190 to £375. Open all year.
e-mail: a.j.kellie@virgin.net
website: http://freespace.virgin.net/a.j.kellie/home.htm

Key to Tourist Board Ratings

    The Crown Scheme

The **English Tourism Council** (formerly the English Tourist Board) has joined with the AA and RAC to create a new, easily understood quality rating for serviced accommodation. Hotels will receive a grading ranging from **one to five STARS (★)**. Other serviced accommodation such as **guest houses** and **B&B establishments** will be graded from **one to five DIAMONDS (◆)**. These ratings represent Quality, Service and Hospitality not just facilities.
NB.Some properties had not been assessed at the time of going to press and in these cases the publishers have included the old CROWN gradings.

♟   **The Key Scheme**

The Key Scheme covering self-catering in cottages, bungalows, flats, houseboats, houses, chalets, etc remains unchanged. The classification from **One to Five KEYS** indicates the range of facilities and equipment. Higher quality standards are indicated by the terms APPROVED, COMMENDED, HIGHLY COMMENDED AND DE LUXE.

DEVON

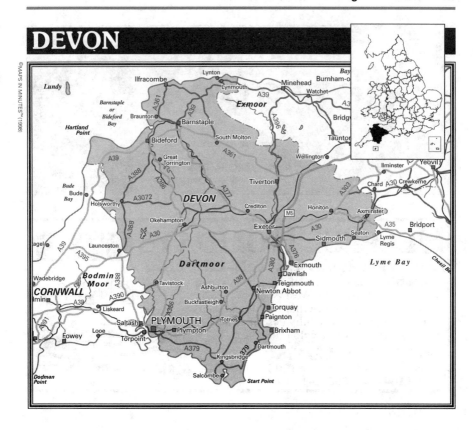

Toad Hall Cottages

100 outstanding waterside & rural properties
from cosy cottages - large farmhouses,
in truly beautiful locations in Devon.
Call for our highly acclaimed brochure.
Video also available.

Tel: **01548 853089**

www.toadhallcottages.com

WEST COUNTRY TOURIST BOARD
MEMBER

FHG

FREE and REDUCED RATE
Holiday Visits!
Don't miss our
Readers' Offer Vouchers

APPLEDORE. Sea Birds Cottage, Appledore. Sea edge, pretty Georgian cottage facing directly out to the open sea. Sea Birds is a spacious cottage with large lounge, colour TV; dining room with French windows onto garden; modern fitted kitchen; three double bedrooms; bathroom, second WC downstairs; washing machine. Lawned garden at back overlooking the sea with garden furniture. Own parking. Dog welcome. Sea views from most rooms and the garden is magnificent; views of the open sea, boats entering the estuary, sunset, sea birds. Appledore is still a fishing village - fishing trips from the quay, restaurants by the water. Area has good cliff and coastal walks, stately homes, riding, swimming, golf, surfing, excellent beaches. Off peak heating. From £95. Other cottages available. Send SAE for colour brochure to **F.S. Barnes, 140 Bay View Road, Northam, Bideford EX39 1BJ (01237 473801).**
Photo shows view of sea from garden.

ASHBURTON. Mrs Angela Bell, Wooder Manor, Widecombe-in-the-Moor, Near Ashburton TQ13 7TR (01364 621391). ☆☆☆☆ *COMMENDED.* Modernised granite cottages and converted coach house, on 150 acre working family farm nestled in the picturesque valley of Widecombe, surrounded by unspoilt woodland, moors and granite tors. Half-a-mile from village with post office, general stores, inn with dining room, church and National Trust Information Centre. Excellent centre for touring Devon with a variety of places to visit and exploring Dartmoor by foot or on horseback. Accommodation is clean and well equipped with colour TV, central heating, laundry room. Children welcome. Large gardens and courtyard for easy parking. Open all year, so take advantage of off-season reduced rates. Short Breaks also available. Two properties suitable for disabled visitors. Brochure available.

BARNSTAPLE. Mrs M. Balman, Tidicombe Farm, Arlington, Near Barnstaple EX31 4SP (01271 850300). ♈♈♈♈.

Comfortable farmhouse wing for two to eight persons. Three bedrooms - one family room, one twin-bedded room and one room with three singles. Two bathrooms, one with shower, large living room with log fire and galley kitchen. Linen, towels and central heating inclusive. Cot and high chair. Plenty of safe parking. Dogs allowed downstairs - £10 per week. Adjoining National Trust open countryside to explore. Ten minutes drive from coast to Exmoor or Barnstaple. garden for children. Fishing one-and-a-half miles, horse riding on the premises. Terms from £100 to £400 according to number of people.

BARNSTAPLE. Mrs R. Gard, Brinscombe Farm, Arlington, Barnstaple EX31 4SW (01271 850529). Working farm. Sleeps 6.

An 18th century farmhouse situated on a 180-acre hill farm in a peaceful location approached by a concrete drive. This is ideal for walking and touring the countryside, exploring the Exmoor National Park, National Trust properties, Devon beaches, also a wealth of good local inns. Barnstaple Leisure Centre. The large, very spacious self-contained wing of the farmhouse comprises one family bedroom and one double room, both with washbasins, diningroom, bathroom and fitted kitchen and you can relax in the comfortable TV lounge, which has an electric fire. Fully carpeted. Night storage heaters. It has its own beautifully enclosed garden, ideal for the children to play in. Bed linen supplied. Adequate car parking. Open April to end October. No pets. It has everything you need for a comfortable carefree stay. Children welcome. From £170 to £260.

BARNSTAPLE. Mrs Kate Price, Country Ways, Little Knowle Farm, High Bickington, Umberleigh, Near Barnstaple EX37 9BJ (Tel & Fax: 01769 560503). ♈♈♈♈

HIGHLY COMMENDED. Beautifully converted stone barns, all with lovely gardens and magnificent views, hidden away on a small farm. Incredibly peaceful. Walks in ancient woodland and within easy reach of Barnstaple, Exmoor and coast. The farm has rare breeds, friendly animals, play area including huge trampoline and barbecue. THE CUCKOO'S NEST has two double rooms and one bunk room, also sofa bed, THE STABLES has two bedrooms - one with king size bed and the other with two singles. THE DEN has one double bedroom and fold-out bed if required. Open all year. One unit suitable for disabled guests. Warm and well equipped. Cots on request. Short breaks available most of the year. Please telephone for further details. e-mail: kate.price@virgin.net

See also Colour Display Advertisement

BARNSTAPLE. North Devon Holiday Homes, 19 Cross Street, Barnstaple EX31 1BD (01271 376322 24-hour brochure service; Fax: 01271 346544). With our Free Colour Guide and unbiased recommendation and booking service, we can spoil you for choice in the beautiful unspoilt region around Exmoor and the wide sandy beaches and coves of Devon's beautiful National Trust Coast. Choose from over 500 selected properties including thatched cottages, working farms, beachside properties with swimming pools, luxury manor houses, etc. From only £89 to £890 per week. First class value assured.

FHG PUBLICATIONS LIMITED

publish a large range of well-known accommodation guides. We will be happy to send you details or you can use the order form at the back of this book.

BARNSTAPLE. Mr and Mrs C.L. Hartnoll, Little Bray House, Brayford, Barnstaple EX32 7QG (01598 710295). ⍟⍟⍟. Properties sleep 2/6. Situated nine miles east

of Barnstaple, Little Bray House is ideally placed for day trips to East Devon, Somerset and Cornwall, the lovely sandy surfing beaches at Saunton Sands and Woolacombe, and many places of interest both coastal and inland. Exmoor has much charm. Lovely walks abound, and there is a large garden with lawn and woodland, ducks and hens, fun for children. Indoor badminton and ping-pong rooms. The accommodation is in three cottages sleeping from four to six people and a flatlet which sleeps two, all self-contained and fully furnished with well-equipped kitchens and colour TV. Cot and high chair available on request. Bring own linen and towels. Linen hire on request. Well behaved dogs allowed, on lead. Terms range from £130 to £300 per week, depending on season. Telephone or write for brochure.

BIDEFORD near. West Titchberry Farm Cottage, Hartland, Near Bideford. Sleeps 5 adults, 1 child.

Situated on the coast near Hartland Point (follow signs to Hartland Point Lighthouse), this recently renovated farm cottage comprises (upstairs) double and family rooms (plus cot); bathroom, toilet. Downstairs is a fully fitted kitchen with dining area. Electricity for the cooker, fridge/freezer, microwave oven and washing machine is on a £1 meter. In the lounge the settee converts into a single bed; colour TV, video, wood-burning stove (logs provided free), central heating downstairs (no charge), portable heaters upstairs. The lounge door opens onto a small enclosed garden. The cottage is carpeted throughout and well appointed. Open all year. Guests have freedom of this 150-acre mixed farm. Easy access to costal footpath - quiet, unspoilt surroundings. Clovelly six miles, Hartland three miles. Sorry, no pets. Terms approximately £90 to £340 weekly according to season. SAE please **Mrs Yvonne Heard, West Titchberry Farm, Hartland, Near Bideford EX39 6AU (01237 441287).**

BIGBURY near. Miss C.M. Hodder, Bennicke Farm, Modbury, Ivybridge PL21 0SU (01548 830265). Sleeps 8. The main part of Bennicke Farmhouse is self-contained and reached from the Plymouth to Kingsbridge main road A379, by a lane quarter-of-a-mile long. Set in a quiet valley with a variety of wildlife, usually a tame lamb, and a large garden. Within easy reach of beaches (five miles), Dartmoor National Park (six miles) and Cornwall (15 miles). Terms from £200 to £265 per week.

BOVEY TRACEY. Jon and Sue Peters, Lookweep Farm, Liverton, Newton Abbot TQ12 6HT (01626 833277). ⍟⍟⍟⍟ *COMMENDED.* **Sleeps 5.** Lookweep Farm is set

within Dartmoor National Park and is perfectly placed for exploration of Dartmoor, the stunning coastline, charming villages and towns of South Devon. Shippen and Dairy cottages are two attractive, well-equipped stone cottages surrounded by open farmland and woods in this tranquil setting near Bovey Tracey and just a two mile drive from Haytor. Own gardens, ample parking, heated pool and outstanding walks right on your doorstep. Children welcome (high chairs and cots available). Pets also welcome. Short breaks available. Please phone or write for brochure.

BRATTON FLEMING. Mrs A. Douglas, Friendship Farm, Bratton Fleming, Barnstaple EX31 4SQ (01598 763291 evenings). Friendship Bungalow is quietly situated down a short drive from the farmhouse, in its own garden, and surrounded by fields. There is ample parking space. The farm is situated 12 miles from Barnstaple and Ilfracombe, at the junction of roads A399 and B3358, within easy reach of the beaches of Woolacombe and Combe Martin. Exmoor is literally on the doorstep. The accommodation comprises three bedrooms (sleep six), plus cot. Linen supplied. Lounge with colour TV. Well equipped kitchen/diningroom. Bathroom, laundry room, spin dryer. Metered electricity. Weekly terms, low season from £100, high season £250.

BRAUNTON. Mrs J.M. Barnes, Denham Farm Holidays, North Buckland, Braunton EX33 1HY (Tel & Fax: 01271 890297). ꙮꙮꙮ COMMENDED. Friendly folk required to fill our cottages with fun and laughter. Beautifully furnished accommodation just right for your holiday. Only two and a half miles from golden sandy beaches of Croyde and Woolacombe. One cottage will sleep eight with four bedrooms and the other sleeping four in one bedroom. Spacious lounges and kitchens with all you require for an easy holiday. Have home cooked meals in farmhouse or in your cottage, be spoilt. Large garden and play area. Small pets for children to enjoy. Prices from £160 to £595 all inclusive. You can't afford to miss the hospitality at Denham. Farm Holiday Bureau member.

BRAUNTON. Marsdens Cottage Holidays, 2 The Square, Braunton EX33 2JB (01271 813777; Fax: 01271 813664). ꙮꙮꙮ/ꙮꙮꙮꙮꙮ. There is no better way to experience the charms of North Devon than from the comfort and luxury of a Marsdens Cottage Holiday. Romantic white-washed cottages nestling in the heart of the countryside; secluded beach houses just a stone's throw away from some of Britain's most spectacular coastlines - whatever your idea of a perfect holiday we can help make it reality. And, as an extra bonus, our prices will come as a pleasant surprise too. Call or write today for your free brochure. Choose from a one-bed cottage with swimming pool from £70 for four nights up to a beach house for 17 from £295 for four nights.

CHALLACOMBE. Mrs L. Nash, Little Swincombe Farm, Challacombe, Near Barnstaple EX31 4TU

(01598 763506). Experience Exmoor and the wonderful North Devon beaches by staying in a pretty stone cottage on the edge of open moorland. Swincombe Cottage is in a secluded but not isolated position within a working farm with a pub, shop and cream teas within walking distance. It has two comfortable bedrooms sleeping four plus two either on a sofa bed or on single beds in an attic bedroom. The kitchen and living room are light, spacious and well equipped. Outside there is ample parking and a private rear garden. Children are most welcome, as are your dog or horse by arrangement.
e-mail: nash@lineone.net
website: www.jcjdatacom.co.uk/nash

Little Swincombe Farm Cottage

CHALLACOMBE. Mrs Rosemarie E. Kingdon, Whitefield Barton, Barnstaple EX31 4TU (01598

763271). ꙮꙮꙮ COMMENDED. Working farm, join in. We are a 200 acre working Exmoor farm surrounded by glorious countryside. There are animals to see and freedom for children to play. Spacious characteristic accommodation in half of 16th century farmhouse with modern luxuries. Tastefully furnished to high standard. Warm, cosy lounge with colour TV, video recorder; large kitchen; family and twin bedrooms; bathroom with shower. Babysitting and equipment available. Ample parking. Private patio/barbecue. Garden with stream. Inclusive of all linen and electricity. Peaceful surroundings with scenic walks and footpath direct to Exmoor. The best sandy beaches of North Devon are within easy reach and we are central for touring around Lynton and Lynmouth. Terms from £100 to £375.

CHALLACOMBE. Mrs Christine Johnson, Shorland Old Farm, Challacombe, Bratton Fleming EX31

4TX (01598 763505). Our 16th century farmhouse and adjoining barn is beautifully and peacefully situated in 14 acres overlooking Exmoor, nine miles from the sea. The farmhouse provides Bed and Breakfast accommodation while the barn is tastefully converted, retaining much character, to provide self catering accommodation for six people. It has two bedrooms, comfortable lounge and well equipped kitchen, all with beautiful views across the Moors. Bed linen is provided, cot and high chair available, babysitting by arrangement. Terms from £190. Please telephone for brochure.

COMBE MARTIN. Mr and Mrs T. Massey, Wheel Farm Country Cottages, Berrydown 12, Combe Martin EX34 0NT (01271 882100). ÏÏÏÏ *HIGHLY COMMENDED*. COTTAGES WITH A DIFFERENCE. Enjoy the freedom of self-catering with friendly five star service. Gold Award gardens surround watermill and pretty cottages, lovely Exmoor views, near superb beaches. Inclusive indoor pool, fitness room, maid service, linen, flowers, four posters, log fires. Plus sauna, central heating, dishwashers, home baking, tennis with tuition. Families welcome, riding, cycling, golf, walking arranged. Open March - October. Spring short breaks, midweek discounts.

DREWSTEIGNTON. Mrs A. Bowden, Bowbeer Farm, Drewsteignton, Exeter EX6 6PD (01647 281239). Working farm, join in. Sleeps 4 plus cot or camp bed. Wing of old Devon farmhouse, full of character and charm. Spacious accommodation consists of one double and one twin room, bathroom, lounge/kitchen/diner. Central heating. Garden with swing, slide and trampoline. Linen and towels provided. Colour TV, microwave, fridge, electric cooker, washing machine. Evening meals provided on request. Situated one mile from picturesque village of Drewsteignton on the edge of Dartmoor National Park. Peaceful, tranquil surroundings. Fishing available on nearby farm, and guests are welcome to join in the activities on the working farm and see Santa the pony. Children welcome. Sorry, no pets. Terms from £80 to £250. Further details available on request.

HOLSWORTHY. Mr & Mrs Charles and Pat Clarke, Thorne Manor Holiday Cottages, Holsworthy

EX22 7JD (Tel & Fax: 01409 253342). ÏÏÏ **Sleep 4- 6.** Ten self-catering cottages in courtyard on working dairy farm. Eight miles to Bude and beaches. Outdoor swimming pool, squash courts, tennis court, play area. Nature walks and reserve. Short breaks available. Cycling, walks, golf, fishing, within easy reach. Pets by arrangement.

HOLSWORTHY. Pauline and Tony Blight, Blagdon Farm Country Holidays, Ashwater, Beaworthy

EX21 5DF (01409 211509; Fax: 01409 211510). ÏÏÏ *HIGHLY COMMENDED*. Superb south-facing holiday bungalows which overlook our own lake and are set within 38 acres of glorious countryside. Each one has been designed to be fully wheelchair accessible, as have all of the facilities which include an indoor swimming pool, a nature trail, adventure playground, pets corner, large games room and tea room/shop. A takeaway service and equipment loan are also available. We can assure you of the warmest of welcomes. Free colour brochure available.

HOPE COVE. Mike and Judy Tromans, Hope Barton Barns, Hope Cove, Near Salcombe TQ7 3HT (01548 561393). ETB ÏÏÏÏ *HIGHLY COMMENDED*. **Sleep 2/10.** Nestling in its own valley, close to the sandy cove, Hope Barton Barns is an exclusive group of 17 stone barns in two courtyards and three luxury apartments in the converted farmhouse. Heated indoor pool, sauna, gym, lounge bar, tennis court, trout lake and a children's play barn. We have 35 acres of pastures and streams with sheep, goats, pigs, chickens, ducks and rabbits. Superbly furnished and fully-equipped, each cottage is unique and they vary from a studio to four bedrooms, sleeping two to ten. Farmhouse meals from our menu. Ample parking. Golf, sailing and coastal walks nearby. Open all year. A perfect setting for family Summer holidays, a week's walking in Spring/Autumn or just a get away from it all break. Free range children and well behaved dogs welcome. For a colour brochure and rental tariff, please contact Mike or Judy.

ILFRACOMBE near. Mrs M. Cowell, Lower Campscott Farm, Lee, Near Ilfracombe EX34 8LS (01271

863479). Four excellent holiday cottages on a 90 acre dairy farm with a delightful one mile walk down to the beach at Lee Bay. The cottages have been newly converted from the original farm buildings to a high standard. Two of the cottages will accommodate four people, one will accommodate up to six people and the large one will take eight/ten people; laundry room; linen included in the price. We also have a large, self-contained six-berth caravan to let, with Bed and Breakfast in the farmhouse. Children welcome but regret no pets. Terms from £140 to £421 weekly. Spring Mini Breaks (three nights) from £80.

INSTOW. Beach Haven Cottage. Sleeps 5. Seafront cottage overlooking the sandy beach. Instow is a quiet yachting village with soft yellow sands and a pretty promenade of shops, old houses, pubs and cafes serving drinks and meals. Beach Haven has extensive beach and sea views from the house and garden, own parking, gas fired central heating, colour TV, washing machine. Lawned garden overlooking sea with terrace and garden furniture. Coastal walks and cycle trails, boat to Lundy Island. Dog welcome. Please send SAE for colour brochure of this and other cottages to **F. I. Barnes, 140 Bay View Road, Northam, Bideford EX39 1BJ (01237 473801).**
Photo shows view from balcony of beach and sea.

KINGSBRIDGE. Mrs Pam Lidstone, Centry Farm, Kingsbridge TQ7 2HF (01548 852037). Working farm.

Cottage adjoining farmhouse which is ideal for two or family of four with views across garden and fields. Centry is located in a peaceful, secluded valley just a mile from Kingsbridge - the centre of the South Hams. The area is well known for its scenery, beaches, cliff and moorland walks and many places of interest. The cottage at Centry offers comfort, cleanliness and well equipped accommodation including washer/dryer, microwave, colour TV, video, radio/cassette, hair dryer. There is one bedroom with a double and two single beds - duvets and linen supplied. Bathroom with bath/shower, etc. Upstairs there is a large living room with kitchen corner. Electricity by £1.00 meter. Ample car and boat parking. No smoking or pets. Terms £140 to £250, Easter to October. Brochure available.

KINGSBRIDGE. Mr and Mrs M.B. Turner, Cross Farm, East Allington, Kingsbridge TQ9 7RW (01548

521327). Working farm, join in. Sleeps 11 plus 2 cots. Get away from the hustle and bustle of everyday life and enjoy the peace and tranquillity of Cross Farm, surrounded by South Hams countryside of outstanding natural beauty. Children love to help feed the animals while you take a leisurely farm walk or relax in the garden. Lovely 17th century part farmhouse and delightfully converted barn; both sleep 11 in four bedrooms; equipped to very high standard including colour TV, dishwasher, microwave, washing machine, dryer, fridge freezer, showers, duvets and linen. Cleanliness guaranteed. Play area and recreation barn. Heating included for early/late holidays. Only four miles to Kingsbridge (one mile to village pub!) and close to many lovely coves and beaches. Central for Dartmoor, Salcombe, Dartmouth, Torbay; riding, fishing, golf, etc. Ideal touring area. Rough shooting on farm in season. Brochure available.

KINGSBRIDGE. Allan and Marcia Green, Gara Mill, Slapton, Kingsbridge TQ7 2RE (01803 770295).

Sleep 1-7. Set in an idyllic wooded valley, we offer two cosy flats in the 16th C mill plus eight cedar lodges along the River Gara. All are well-equipped, including microwaves and colour TVs. Four acre site off quiet lane, sheltered and peaceful, yet convenient for Dartmouth, Kingsbridge, Totnes. Swings, outdoor badminton court, games room, launderette. Cots available. Dogs welcome. Woodland walk on your doorstep. Two miles to beaches and spectacular coastline. From £150-£300 per week. Please ring for brochure.

KINGSBRIDGE. West Charleton Grange, Kingsbridge, South Devon TQ7 2AD (01548 531779; Fax:

01548 531100). ETC ♀♀♀♀ up to *HIGHLY COMMENDED*. Secluded oasis on the outskirts of Kingsbridge and central for local beaches. Superb indoor heated pool and comprehensive leisure facilities for all ages. Large safe children's playfield, with Wendy House. Wildlife lake, ideal for bird-watching and coarse fishing. Phone or fax for colour brochure.
e-mail: colbet@globalnet.co.uk
website: www.users.globalnet.co.uk/colbet
use Altvista/inforseek.

KINGSBRIDGE near. Mrs J. Tucker, Mount Folly Farm, Bigbury-on-Sea, Near Kingsbridge TQ7 4AR

(01548 810267). Working farm. Sleeps 6. A delightful family farm, situated on the coast, overlooking the sea and sandy beaches of Bigbury Bay. Farm adjoins golf course and River Avon. Lovely coastal walks. Ideal centre for South Hams and Dartmoor. The spacious wing comprises half of the farmhouse, and is completely self-contained. All rooms attractively furnished. Large, comfortable lounge with bay windows overlooking the sea; colour TV. There are three bedrooms – one family, one double and a bunk bed; two have washbasins. The kitchen/diner has a fridge/freezer, electric cooker, microwave, washing machine and dishwasher. There is a nice garden, ideal for children. Cot and babysitting available. Sorry no smoking. Reduction for two people staying in off peak weeks. Please write or telephone for a brochure.

KING'S NYMPTON. Venn Farm Cottages. ♀♀♀♀ *COMMENDED.* **Sleep 2/6 adults; 2/4 children.** Delightful

holiday cottages converted from old stone barn on small working farm set in beautiful Devon countryside. The children will love to feed the lambs and goat kids. Nearly 50 acres of rolling fields to wander over with views to Exmoor and Dartmoor. The cottages are furnished and equipped to a high standard and have patios with a picnic table and barbecue. Cottages have two or three bedrooms sleeping up to six persons plus cot. One cottage is suitable for disabled visitors. Bed linen provided. Laundry room and children's play area. Pets welcome. Weekly terms from £120 to £450. For brochure apply to: **Mrs Martin, Venn Farm, King's Nympton, Umberleigh EX37 9TR (01769 572448).**

When making enquiries or bookings,
a stamped addressed envelope is always appreciated.

LYNTON. Mrs Marilyn Purchase, Bridwick Farm, Kentisbury, Barnstaple EX31 4NN (01598 763416).

Sleeps 12 plus 2 cots. Farmhouse on working livestock farm, beautifully set in quiet Exmoor Valley. Every care taken to ensure you enjoy your stay. Situated on A39 near Blackmoor Gate crossroads midway between Woolacombe and Lynton. Excellent location for touring. Particularly well-equipped large farmhouse kitchen, dishwasher, microwave, washing-machine, tumble dryer. Spacious accommodation with seven bedrooms, three bathrooms, including en suite and separate shower room. Large conservatory with far reaching views down the valley. Full central heating, linen and electricity included. Many of our guests enjoy accompanying the farmer in the Land Rover on his morning round to see the sheep and cattle. Terms from £200. B&B also available.

NEWTON ABBOT. Mrs M. A. Gale, Twelve Oaks Holiday Cottages, Twelve Oaks Farm, Teigngrace, Newton Abbot TQ12 6QT (Tel & Fax: 01626 352769). Working farm, join in. Sleeps 4. ⚲ COMMENDED. Join us

at one of the two carefully converted cottages on our 220 acre beef farm, bordered by the River Teign, on the edge of the village of Teigngrace. Each self-contained cottage has one double and one twin room with bathroom and shower room. Heating, TV fridge, microwave and laundry facilties. Parking. Children welcome. Non-smoking accommodation available. Find us off the A38 Expressway. Prices from £230 to £400. Also Twelve Oaks Caravan Park (✓✓✓✓✓) with electric hook-ups, TV hook-ups and awnings available. Hot water, shower, pets and swimming pool free of charge.

NEWTON FERRERS. Mary Steps and Morningside. Two delightful properties situated in the village

MARY STEPS

of Newton Ferrers on the beautiful tidal estuary of the River Yealm. MORNINGSIDE (⚲ COMMENDED) is only a short walk from shops, restaurants and pubs. Secluded courtyard at rear and garden running down to a waterside jetty. One double bedroom and one twin, bathroom with bath and shower, fully equipped kitchen and living room with colour TV and payphone. MARY STEPS (in the same vicinity as Morningside) sleeps six in comfort; bed settee in the dining room sleeps two. Downstairs it has a large kitchen, separate dining room, lounge with small conservatory area, utility room and toilet. Upstairs are three bedrooms and bathroom. Spectacular views of the river; garden For further information please contact: **Mrs Edwards, 4 Butts Park, Newton Ferrers, Plymouth PL8 1HY.**

NORTH MOLTON. Mrs Gladys Ayre, Pitt Farm, North Molton EX36 3JR (01598 740285). ⚲

COMMENDED. **Sleeps 5/6.** Enjoy peaceful surroundings at our charming cottage set in lovely Exmoor countryside. One mile from village of North Molton with local pubs, shops, garage. Accommodation has recently been converted and is equipped to high standard throughout with night storage heating. Three bedrooms, bath/shower room, beamed lounge with colour TV, woodburner, oak fitted kitchen/diner with automatic washing machine, fridge, microwave, etc. Your own patio overlooking the valley with garden furniture and barbecue. There is a small pond nearby with ducks and geese. Our guests are welcome to explore our sheep farm and to observe seasonal activities. Cot and high chair available and babysitting by arrangement. Dog by arrangement. Linen available. Electricity by coin meter. Terms from £160 to £395 per week. Short Breaks available end October to Easter. Illustrated brochure on request.

OKEHAMPTON. East Hook Cottages, Okehampton. Cottages sleep 2/6. In the heart of Devon on the fringe of Dartmoor, with woodland surroundings, two comfortably furnished holiday cottages. One mile north of the A30 at Okehampton, quiet and peaceful, 50 yards from a country road. Ample car parking space. The accommodation comprises a pleasant sitting room with a TV set; kitchen with electric cooker and refrigerator; modern bathroom with shaver point; three bedrooms. Visitors are requested to supply their own bed linen. Electricity by £1 meter. Children and pets welcome. Terms from £95 to £185 per week. Open all year. Midweek/weekend breaks possible. **Mrs M.E. Stevens, West Hook Farm, Okehampton EX20 1RL (01837 52305).**

PENNYMOOR (Near Tiverton). Miss N. Croft, Lower Yedbury Farm, Pennymoor, Tiverton EX16 8LH (01363 866243). COMMENDED. Sleeps 5 plus cot.

Situated in beautiful Mid-Devon, ideal for visiting both north and south coasts, Exmoor and Dartmoor. The south-facing self contained cottage has lovely views and is part of the old farmhouse on a 28 acre working farm with cows, sheep, pigs, poultry and donkeys. You are welcome to wander in the fields or help on the farm. Children love feeding the animals. Home produced milk, cream, butter, eggs and meat usually available. Two bedrooms, bathroom, kitchen/diner, lounge with woodburner and entrance lobby. Full central heating extra. Electricity by meter. Bed linen, colour TV. One dog by arrangement. Non-smokers only please. Shop five miles; horse riding three, swimming and golf seven. Terms from £156 to £402.

SEATON. Mrs Elsie Pady, Higher Cownhayne Farm, Cownhayne Lane, Colyton, Near Seaton EX13 6HD (01297 552267). Working farm. Properties sleep 4/8.

Higher Cownhayne is a family working farm. Accommodation consists of three self-catering farmhouse holiday apartments which are open all year round. Each apartment has all modern conveniences, with its own dining room, kitchen, bathroom and WC (no linen is provided). Tourist Caravan and Camping site across lane - four berth fully equipped caravan available. Animals on farm. Baby-sitting can be arranged. Fishing Holidays from the 1st March to end of October - trout fly fishing on the River Coly on farm. Leisure facilities available to visitors include badminton, squash, gymnasium, sauna, solarium, swimming pool and licensed restaurant. Air strip on farm for small plane enthusiasts. No pets. Terms on application, at a price families can afford to pay. Open all year.

SEATON. Mrs E.P. Fox, "West Ridge", Harepath Hill, Seaton EX12 2TA (Tel & Fax: 01297 22398). COMMENDED. **Sleeps 3/4.** " West Ridge" bungalow stands on elevated ground above the small coastal town of Seaton. It has one-and-a-half acres of lawns and gardens and enjoys wide panoramic views of the beautiful Axe Estuary and the sea. Close by are Axmouth, Beer and Branscombe. The Lyme Bay area is an excellent centre for touring, walking, sailing, fishing, golf, etc. This comfortably furnished accommodation is ideally suited for three to four people. Cot can be provided. Available March to October, £165 to £375 weekly (fuel charges included). Full gas central heating. Colour TV. SAE for brochure.

SIDMOUTH. Mr Nigel Hunt, Langsford Farm and Cottages, High Street, Newton Poppleford, Sidmouth EX10 0DU (01395 568249; Fax: 01395 568969). HIGHLY COMMENDED. **Sleeps 2 to 6 and cot.** Six cottages tastefully converted from 1874 courtyard farm buildings in the Otter Valley. Swimming pool with patio area, children's play area, laundry room. Some cottages have patios overlooking stream. Link to East Devon Way footpath, within walking distance RSPB nature reserve. Electricity and heating included in the price. Linen provided. Electric cooker, washing machine, microwave oven, payphone, tumble/spindryer, colour TV, video. Welcome Pack on arrival. Barbecue. Gardens. Baby-sitting by arrangement, high chair, children's stairgate. Shops nearby. Non-smokers preferred. Parking for 14 cars. Start day Saturday 2.30pm. For brochure ring Nigel or Daphne
e-mail: Cottages@Langsford.com
Website: www.langsford.com

When making enquiries or bookings,
a stamped addressed envelope is always appreciated.

SOUTH DEVON. Lower Coombe Farm and Studio. Working farm. Cottage sleeps 5. Twixt moor and sea.

Cottage, split level, courtyard with small garden. TV, central heating, wood burner, microwave. From £120 to £185 per week. Mobile Home (only two on site) sleeping two adults and two children, toilet, shower, TV, small garden. From £85 to £110 per week including electricity. Working farm (sheep and horses) in secluded valley one mile from Bovey Tracey. Professional artist gives personal tuition £50 per week. Riding instruction available. Dogs by arrangement £7 per week. Quiet and peaceful. Details **Mrs S.D. Ansell, Lower Coombe, Bovey Tracey TQ13 9PH (Tel & Fax: 01626 832914).**

SOUTH MOLTON. Mike and Rose Courtney, West Millbrook, Twitchen, South Molton EX36 3LP (01598 740382). ÏÏÏ up to *COMMENDED*. **Properties sleep 2/8.** Adjoining Exmoor. Two fully-equipped bungalows and one

farmhouse annexe in lovely surroundings bordering Exmoor National Park. Ideal for touring North Devon and West Somerset including moor and coast with beautiful walks, lovely scenery and many other attractions. North Molton village is only one mile away. All units carpeted, have electric cookers, fridge-freezers, microwaves and colour TVs; two bungalows also have washing machines. Children's play area; cots and high chairs available free. Linen hire available. Games room. Car parking. Central heating if required. Electricity metered. Out of season short breaks. Weekly prices from £70 to £320. Colour brochure available.

SOUTH MOLTON. North Lee Holiday Cottages. ETB ÏÏÏÏ *HIGHLY COMMENDED*. **Working farm**. Southern edge of Exmoor, tastefully decorated barn conversions, sleep two-eight. Full working dairy farm. Courtyard setting. Easy reach of Exmoor and Coast. Open all year. Pets welcome at £5 per week. Weekend and short breaks available. **North Lee Farm, South Molton EX36 3EH (01598 740248/740675; Fax: 01598 740248).**

SOUTH MOLTON. Ruth Ley, Drewstone Farm, South Molton EX36 3EF (01769 572337). ÏÏÏÏ and

ÏÏÏÏÏ *COMMENDED*. Our 300 acre family run farm is set in the foothills of Exmoor surrounded by a wooded valley with breathtaking views and full of wildlife. We offer a superb farmhouse and barn conversion with beams, four bedrooms, oak fitted kitchens, electric cooker, autowasher, dryer, freezer, microwave and phone. Heating throughout and log fires and woodburner. Furnished and equipped to the highest standards with real country cottage charm. Guests may wander amongst the farm animals, enjoy country walks, small games room, clay shooting, own trout fishing or just relax in the garden. South Molton two miles, beaches 25 minutes' drive. From £160 to £395.

SOUTH MOLTON. Carol Woollacott, Nethercott Manor Farm, Rose Ash, South Molton EX36 4RE (01769 550483). ℡℡℡ *APPROVED.* Denis and Carol assure a warm welcome at Nethercott, a 17th century thatched house on a 200 acre working farm. Three comfortable self-contained wings sleeping four and seven. Pleasant views overlooking woods and trout pond. Extensive games room and laundry. Also barbecuing facilities. Six miles from the market town of South Molton, ideal for touring Exmoor and coast. Horse riding nearby. Children and pets welcome. Terms from £110 to £400. Open all year.

SOUTH MOLTON near. Court Green, Bishop's Nympton, Near South Molton. Sleeps 5. A most attractive well-equipped, south facing cottage with large garden, on edge of the village of Bishop's Nympton, three miles from South Molton. Ideal holiday centre, within easy reach of Exmoor, the coast, sporting activities and places of interest. Three bedrooms – one double, one twin-bedded, one single with washbasins. Two bathrooms with toilet. Sitting and dining rooms, large kitchen. Central heating, wood-burning stove, TV. One mile sea trout/trout fishing on River Mole. Well behaved pets welcome. Terms April to October £180 to £220. **Mrs J. Greenwell, Tregeiriog, Near Llangollen, North Wales LL20 7HU (01691 600672).**

See also Colour Display Advertisement

TRENTISHOE. Mr and Mrs Wright, The Old Farmhouse, Trentishoe, Near Parracombe EX31 4QD (01598 763495). Sleeps 2/4. ℡℡℡ *COMMENDED.* On the north-west tip of Exmoor where heather-clad moors, wooded valleys and spectacular coastline meet, lies the tiny hamlet of Trentishoe. Dating from at least the 17th century, and for many generations home to smugglers, The Old Farmhouse, is ideally situated for exploring this beautiful corner of England. Here time runs slowly and peace and tranquillity can still be found. The original stone barns have been tastefully converted to form five cottages sleeping two, three or four. Each is maintained to a high standard by the resident owners. Free Cream Tea on arrival for bookings of one week or more. From £110 to £390 weekly. Short breaks available. Open March to mid November. Sorry, no pets. Please contact us for brochure.
email: info@oldfarmhouse.co.uk
website: www. oldfarmhouse.co.uk

WELLINGTON. Mr and Mrs L.J. Tristram, West End, Holcombe Rogus, Wellington, Somerset TA21 0QD

(01823 672384). Working farm, join in. Sleeps 6. This 16th century olde worlde farm cottage in Devon has an inglenook fireplace and bread oven. It is approached by a private tarmac road and surrounded by a large garden. Situated on 180-acre family farm, over which guests are free to wander. Half-a-mile from the small village of Holcombe Rogus which has general store with post office, garage, public house, church. Within easy reach of Exmoor, Taunton, Exeter and the coast. Excellent walks in unspoilt countryside; extensive views. Six people accommodated in three double rooms, cot; bathroom, toilet; sitting/diningroom. Kitchen with electric cooker, fridge, microwave, washing machine, kettle, iron, etc.; glass conservatory at front of house. Linen by arrangement. Pets allowed. Car an advantage, ample parking. Open all year. TV provided. SAE, please, for terms.

WOOLACOMBE. Mrs B.A. Watts, Resthaven Holiday Flats, The Esplanade, Woolacombe EX34 7DJ (01271 870248). Situated on the sea front opposite the beautiful Combesgate Beach, with uninterrupted views of the coastline. Two self-contained flats – ground floor sleeps five, first floor sleeps nine. Family, double and single bedrooms, all with washbasins. Comfortable lounges with sea views, colour TV and videos. Fully equipped electric kitchens. Bathrooms have bath and shower. Electricity by £1 meter. Payphone. Free lighting, parking, hot water and laundry facility. Terms from £100 to £550 per week. Please write, or phone, for brochure.

WOOLACOMBE. Europa Park, Station Road, Woolacombe (01271 870159). Self-catering holiday park,

with superb views of this lovely area in North Devon. Accommodation available in luxury bungalows, or with touring caravans and tents. Full facilities on site, including indoor heating swimming pool. Pets are welcome, and there is a six acre dog park. Please write or phone for further information.

Key to Tourist Board Ratings

The Crown Scheme

The English Tourism Council (formerly the English Tourist Board) has joined with the AA and RAC to create a new, easily understood quality rating for serviced accommodation. Hotels will receive a grading ranging from **one to five STARS (★)**. Other serviced accommodation such as **guest houses** and **B&B establishments** will be graded from **one to five DIAMONDS (◆)**. These ratings represent Quality, Service and Hospitality not just facilities. *NB.Some properties had not been assessed at the time of going to press and in these cases the publishers have included the old CROWN gradings.*

♀ The Key Scheme

The Key Scheme covering self-catering in cottages, bungalows, flats, houseboats, houses, chalets, etc remains unchanged. The classification from **One to Five KEYS** indicates the range of facilities and equipment. Higher quality standards are indicated by the terms APPROVED, COMMENDED, HIGHLY COMMENDED AND DE LUXE.

DORSET

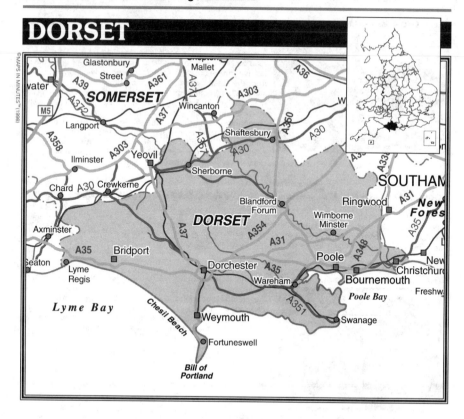

ABBOTSBURY. **Mrs Mary Pengelly, Gorwell Farm, Abbotsbury, Weymouth DT3 4JX (01305 871401; Fax: 01305 871441).** ♛♛♛♛ *COMMENDED.* **Sleep 2/8.** You can relax, unwind and enjoy peaceful surroundings at Gorwell, a family farm situated in its own secret wooded valley. We are only one-and-a-half miles north of the historical thatched village of Abbotsbury, famous for its Swannery, Subtropical Gardens and World Heritage coastline. Central for Weymouth, Dorchester and Bridport. Very well equipped cottages are comfortable for any time of the year, with open fireplaces, central heating and double glazing. Spindle Cottage has wheelchair access and is suitable for the disabled. Enjoy Gorwell's abundance of wildlife, birdlife and flora, explore the pretty villages or wonderful footpath network, or actively enjoy watersports and golf locally. Something for all in this Area of Outstanding Natural Beauty.
e-mail: gorwell@wal.co.uk
website: gorwellfarm.co.uk

When making enquiries or bookings, a stamped addressed envelope is always appreciated.

ABBOTSBURY near. Character Farm Cottages, Langton Herring, Near Abbotsbury. ♔♔♔♔ *HIGHLY COMMENDED*. **Sleep 2-8. Working farm.** Four character farm cottages situated in the villages of Langton Herring and Rodden, nestling on the coastline between picturesque Abbotsbury and Weymouth. This unique part of Dorset's Heritage Coast is ideal for walking, touring, bird-watching and fishing with the added attractions of Abbotsbury's world famous Swannery, The Fleet and Weymouth's safe sandy beaches. The four cottages are all comfortably furnished with features such as open fires, beams, inglenooks, walled gardens and ample parking. Pets and children welcome. Logs and linen available. Prices from £130. Enquiries: **Mrs J. Elwood, Lower Farmhouse, Langton Herring, Weymouth DT3 4JB (01305 871187; Fax: 01305 871347).** e-mail: elwood0205@netscapeonline.co.uk

BEAMINSTER. 33A St. Mary Well Street, Beaminster. Sleeps 5. Lovely two-bedroomed bungalow peacefully located on the outskirts of a small market town, nestled in the beautiful rolling hills of West Dorset. 200 metres from the square with shops, restaurants, pubs, etc. Each bedroom has a washbasin, one contains a double bed, the second two singles; Z-bed and cot available. Separate toilet and bathroom. Lounge has Hamstone fireplace. Well furbished kitchen/dining room with separate utility room. Patio, garden, car park and private drive. Hardy's Cottage, Parnham House, Forde Abbey, Cricket St. Thomas and many places of interest nearby. The picturesque, unspoilt coast is eight miles away. Terms £120 to £270. Sorry, no pets. For brochure please send SAE to **Mrs L. Watts, 53 Hogshill Street, Beaminster DT8 3AG (01308 863088)**

BEXINGTON. Mrs Josephine Pearse, Tamarisk Farm, West Bexington, Dorchester DT2 9DF (01308 897784). ♔♔♔ *APPROVED.* **Sleeps 4/6.** On slope overlooking Chesil Beach between Abbotsbury and Burton Bradstock. Three large (one suitable for Disabled Category 1) and two smaller cottages; properties sleep fours/six. Terms from £105 to £495. Each one stands in own garden. Glorious views along West Dorset and Devon coasts. Lovely walks by sea and inland. Mixed organic farm with arable, sheep, cattle, horses and market garden – vegetables available. Sea fishing, riding in Abbotsbury, lots of tourist attractions and good markets in Bridport (six miles), Dorchester, Weymouth and Portland, all 13 miles. Good centre for touring Thomas Hardy's Wessex. Safe for children and pets can be quite free.

BLANDFORD. Orchard Cottage, Deverel Farm, Milborne St Andrew, Blandford. ♔♔♔♔ *COMMENDED.* In the midst of Hardy Country, one mile from Milborne St. Andrew and just two miles from the picturesque village of Milton Abbas, the cottage is within easy reach of the coast. Situated at the edge of the farmyard, 150 yards from the A354, this modern three bedroom semi-detached cottage has a large, well fenced garden and views of rolling countryside. Children welcome. Open all year. Weekly terms from £120 to £380. Contact: **Charlotte Martin, Deverel Farm, Milborne St. Andrew, Blandford DT11 0HX (Tel & Fax: 01258 837195)**

BLANDFORD. Mrs M.J. Waldie, The Old Rectory, Lower Blandford St. Mary, Near Blandford Forum DT11 9ND (01258 453220). Sleeps 6. Completely self-contained wing of Georgian Old Rectory, one mile from the market town of Blandford Forum, within easy reach of the south coast, Poole, Bournemouth, Salisbury and Thomas Hardy country around Dorchester. Local fishing and many places of historical interest. Accommodation for six in three rooms, one double bedded, one twin bedded and smaller room with bunk beds, cot. Large well equipped kitchen, spacious sitting/diningroom with colour TV; cloakroom downstairs; bathroom and separate toilet upstairs. Pets allowed by prior arrangement. Children welcome. Parking spaces. Use of secluded garden. Everything provided except bed linen and towels. Terms from £170 to £225 per week. May to September. SAE, please, for further details.

Organic Farm Annexe

Childe Okeford, Blandford Forum, Dorset DTI I 8HB
Telephone: 01258 860293

Self-catering ground floor flat suitable for 2 or 4 adults (non-smokers) and child over 5 years. Light and airy, tastefully furnished and set in peaceful surroundings. Well equipped kitchen. Sitting room with colour TV. Central heating. Toilet with basin and separate shower. Bedroom No.2 upstairs with en suite bathroom. Lovely garden with summerhouse. Gold Hill is a 60 acre working farm specialising in vegetable and salad crops, and raising rare breed British White Cattle. We also work Shire Horses. Childe Okeford is in Dorset's beautiful Blackmore Vale, with its associations with Thomas Hardy and Lawrence of Arabia. Only 20 miles from the nearest coast at Poole. Ideal for walking, riding (own horses taken), National Trust Properties and places of historical interest. Short breaks available during winter. Prices from £140 to £345 per week.
Contact D.N. & A.D. Cross for further details. ETB ♇♇♇ Commended.

Superior Self-Catering Holiday Accommodation

A working farm set in the heart of the beautiful and unspoilt Dorset countryside with stunning views and a peaceful, traffic free environment. Luccombe offers quality accommodation for 2-7 people in a variety of converted and historic farm buildings, with original timbers and panelling.
Well equipped kitchens. Large shower or bath. Cosy lounge/dining with colour TV. Bed linen, duvets, towels provided. Laundry room. Children and well behaved pets welcome. Ample parking. Disabled access. Riding, tennis, games room, Clay pigeon shooting and fishing nearby. Post office and stores in local village. Open throughout the year. Group/family enquiries welcome. Short breaks available

Luccombe Farm

Murray and Amanda Kayll, Luccombe, Milton Abbas, Blandford Forum, Dorset DT11 0BE
Tel:(01258) 880558 Fax: (01258) 881384   * See also colour advertisement*

BLANDFORD near. Jasmine and Plumtree Cottage. Sleeps 4/6. ETB ♇♇♇♇ COMMENDED. Working Farm. Two attractively furnished and well equipped character cottages with open fires and night storage heating. Gardens with garden furniture. Set in a peaceful location with natural woodlands for exploring wildlife and a small lake for coarse fishing, a wonderful base from which to explore Dorset's beautiful countryside with its superb views, properties and coastline. Personally supervised to a high standard. Excellent value low season. Cots and highchairs supplied. Pets welcome. Linen available. Prices from £130 to £400. Contact: **Mrs Penny Cooper, Dairy House Farm, Woolland, Blandford Forum, Dorset DT11 0EY (01258 817501; Fax: 01258 818060)**

BOURNEMOUTH. Bournemouth Holiday Bureau, Unit 1, Uplands Way, Blandford Heights Industrial Estate, Blandford DT11 7UZ (01258 858580). For more than thirty-five years Bournemouth's oldest self-catering holiday accommodation agency has been providing a booking service for a broad selection of properties comprising houses, bungalows, cottages, flats and caravans in the Bournemouth, Poole, Dorset, Christchurch, Mudeford and New Forest areas. All are personally inspected for quality. Prices vary widely. Many units welcome children and some accept pets. FREE COLOUR BROCHURE on request.

LANCOMBES HOUSE HOLIDAY COTTAGES

Carol & Karl Mansfield
West Milton
Bridport. DT6 3TN

Tel: 01308 485375

English Tourist Board
COMMENDED

Lancombes House is a 200-year-old stone barn built 300 feet above sea level set in 10 acres; there are tame animals for children to play and help with including horses, ponies, goats and ducks. Farm has panoramic views to the sea only four miles away. There are four superbly converted cottages, each with its own sitting-out area, barbecue and garden furniture. They have spacious open plan living areas, most with wood burning stoves. Modern fitted kitchens, double and twin-bedded rooms. Electric central heating, shared laundry. Deep in the heart of Hardy country, this is a delightful area to explore whether on foot or horseback. There are many things to do and pets and children are very welcome. Prices start at £140 for mini-breaks; open all the year round.

★★★ # MANOR FARM HOLIDAY CENTRE   ♀♀♀
Charmouth, Bridport, Dorset DT6 6QL   *Approved*

Situated in a rural valley, ten minutes' level walk from the beach.

1983 Built Two-Bedroomed Houses: *Sleep 4-6 *Lounge with colour TV *Fully fitted kitchen/diner *Fitted carpets *Double glazing *Central heating *Parking space.

Three-Bedrooms House and Bungalow: *Sleep 4-6 each *Lounge with colour TV *Central heating available *Parking within grounds *Enclosed garden.

Luxury six-berth Caravans: *One or two bedrooms *Toilet *Shower *Refrigerator *Full cooker *Television *Gas fire.

FULL CENTRE FACILITIES AVAILABLE INCLUDING SWIMMING POOL, SHOP, BAR (BAR FOOD AVAILABLE), LAUNDERETTE ETC.

*Send SAE for colour brochure to **Mr R. E. Loosmore** or Tel: 01297 560226*
See also Colour Display Advertisement in this Guide.

BRIDPORT. Mrs Sue Diment, Rudge Farm, Chilcombe, Bridport DT6 4NF (01308 482630). ♀♀♀♀

HIGHLY COMMENDED. **Sleep 2/6.** Peacefully situated livestock farm in the beautiful Bride Valley, just two-and-a-half miles from the sea. The old farm buildings have been converted into superbly comfortable cottages around a flower-decked cobbled yard, enjoying open views towards our lakes and the countryside beyond. Ideal for a family holiday or a relaxing break. Barbecues, rowing boat, sand pit, climbing frame, indoor games room. One cottage adapted for wheelchair users. £200 to £550 per week. Open all year. Short breaks available all year.
website: www.rudge-farm.co.uk

BRIDPORT. Mrs Sandra Huxter, Strongate Farm, Strongate Lane, Salwayash, Bridport DT6 5JD (01308 488295). ♀♀♀♀

A picturesque thatched cottage off the beaten track in peaceful surroundings. Situated on a small working family farm with cows, sheep, geese, ducks, stream, etc. Seaside five miles, within easy reach of charming Dorset villages, beautiful walking areas. Ideal for recharging batteries in relaxing unspoilt countryside. Families especially welcome, children can play freely. Secluded garden and space for cars. Cottage has two bedrooms, one with double bed, the other with two single beds, cot available; bathroom; fitted carpets. Price includes electricity and bedding. Dogs by arrangement. Non smokers only please. Further details on request.

BERE FARM

Winsham, Chard, Somerset TA20 4JQ
Telephone 01460 30207
Fax: 01460 30850

Peaceful quality cottages
in a quiet valley
*Rates from £150 – £500
per week*

Bed & Breakfast
AA QQQ

Surrounded by lawns,
trees, the stream,
meadows and the lake

Children and pets
welcome.

A place for 'Adventures'.

A place to sit and dream.

NEAR FORDE ABBEY

Mr & Mrs John Jeffery   *VISA*

E-mail: john@berefarm.freeserve.co.uk   Website: www.berefarm.freeserve.co.uk

**BRIDPORT near. Mrs S. Norman, Frogmore Farm, Chideock, Bridport DT6 6HT (01308 456159).
Working farm. Sleeps 6.** Delightful farm cottage on ninety acre grazing farm set in the rolling hills of West Dorset. Superb views over Lyme Bay, ideal base for touring Dorset and Devon or rambling the many coastal and country footpaths of the area. This fully equipped self-catering cottage sleeps six. Three bedrooms. Bed linen supplied. Cosy lounge with woodburner and colour TV, French doors to a splendid columned sun verandah. Children and well behaved dogs welcome. Car essential. Open all year. Short breaks available, also Bed and Breakfast in the 17th century farmhouse. Brochure and terms free on request.

DORCHESTER near. Pitt Cottage, Ringstead Bay, Near Dorchester. Sleeps 6. An attractive thatched stone cottage, surrounded by farmland and situated on the edge of a small wood about a quarter mile from the sea, commanding outstanding views of Ringstead Bay on the Dorset Heritage Coast. The cottage is equipped to sleep six; three bedrooms (two beds in each), two bathrooms, sitting room with open fire and large kitchen/dining area. Cot/high chair; washing machine; TV; night storage heaters/electric radiators in all rooms. Car essential. Available from £150 per week. For details please send SAE (reference FHG) to: **Mrs S.H. Russell, 49 Limerston Street, London SW10 0BL or telephone 0171 351 9919.**

PITT COTTAGE

FHG Please mention *The Farm Holiday Guide* when enquiring about accommodation featured in these pages.

DORCHESTER near. Old Dairy Cottage, sleeps 6; Clyffe Dairy Cottage, sleeps 3. ♈♈♈ *COMMENDED.*

Two attractively furnished character cottages with beams and inglenook fireplaces. Personally supervised to a high standard. Central heating. Gardens. Quiet location with beautiful woodland walks, wildlife on the streams close by. Within easy reach of the coast, historic houses, golf, fishing, trekking or leisure centre. Ideal cycling location to suit families or Senior Citizens. Four miles from Dorchester. Excellent value low season. Prices from £195 to £475. Contact: **Rosemary Coleman, Clyffe Farm, Tincleton, Dorchester DT2 8QR (01305 848252; Fax: 01305 848702).**

GILLINGHAM. Mrs J. Wallis, Meads Farm, Stour Provost, Gillingham SP8 5RX (01747 838265). ETC ♈♈♈♈ *COMMENDED.* **Working farm, join in. Sleeps 6.** Mead

Bungalow is a superior property enjoying outstanding views over Blackmore Vale. Situated one mile from A30 at the end of the lovely village of Stour Provost. Shaftesbury with its famous Gold Hill is nearby and within easy reach are Bournemouth, Weymouth and Bath. Many attractive and interesting places lie a short car ride away. Over one mile of private coarse fishing 160 yards from bungalow. Spacious accommodation sleeps six plus cot. Large lounge with colour TV, diningroom, three double bedrooms, bathroom, luxury oak kitchen with automatic washing machine etc; all electric (no meters), full central heating; linen supplied. Quarter acre lawns. Sorry no pets.

HOLDITCH. Old Forge Cottage, Holditch, Chard. Sleeps 4. Ideal for peace and seclusion in glorious

unspoilt countryside within easy reach of the sea. This delightful old world cottage with oak beams stands just outside Holditch on the Devon/Dorset/Somerset borders, affording splendid views over beautiful countryside. Charmouth and its sandy beaches seven miles distant. Lyme Regis, with safe bathing and recreational facilities eight miles. The cottage is completely modernised and tastefully furnished with fitted carpets throughout, for up to four people. One twin-bedded room and two single rooms; sittingroom with colour TV; kitchen with dining area; modern bathroom; second toilet; electric cooker, fridge, vacuum cleaner, modern sink unit, immersion heater, night storage heaters throughout (included in terms). Everything supplied except linen. Electricity charged by meter reading. Phone; walled garden; garage. Chard four-and-a-half miles. Terms £130 to £200 weekly. Open all year. Regret no children under 10 years. No pets. All enquiries to **Mrs P.A. Spice, Orchard Cottage, Duke Street, Micheldever, Near Winchester, Hants SO21 3DF (01962 774563).**

LYME REGIS. Mr Stenson, Lyme Bay Holidays (FHG), 44 Church Street, Lyme Regis DT7 3DA (01297 443363; Fax: 01297 445576). ♈♈♈/♈♈♈♈. Country and coastal cottages in and around Lyme Regis, Charmouth and West Dorset. Over 100 properties, all Tourist Board inpected. Phone for our free catalogue or help in selecting the right property for you. Terms on request.

LYME REGIS. Mrs S. Denning, Higher Holcombe Farm, Uplyme, Lyme Regis DT7 3NS (01297 443223).

Working farm, join in. Sleeps 6 plus cot. Completely separate part of farmhouse on the working dairy farm, which was once a Roman settlement. Surrounded by pleasant country walks; golf, fishing, horse riding and safe sandy beaches are all nearby. There are three bedrooms - one double and two twin; two bathrooms; lounge with inglenook fireplace, colour TV; kitchen/diningroom with electric cooker, microwave, fridge, etc; use of washing machine, tumble dryer and dishwasher. Central heating (50p slot meter). Plenty of parking. One mile from village shops and pub, two miles coast of Lyme Regis. Winter Breaks. Linen provided. One pet by arrangement.

LYME REGIS near. Mrs Debby Snook, Westover Farm Cottages, Wootton Fitzpaine, Bridport DT6 6NE

(01297 560451). ꙮꙮꙮ *COMMENDED.* **Working farm. Sleeps 6/7.** Immerse yourself in rural tranquillity. Set in an area of outstanding natural beauty, Wootton Fitzpaine nestles amidst rolling Dorset farmland. Within walking distance of the beaches and shops of Charmouth, world famous for its fossils, and three miles from the renowned Cobb at Lyme Regis. Golf, water sports and riding close by. We have two spacious, comfortable, well-furnished three-bedroomed cottages with open fires, inglenooks, heating and all amenities. Also large secluded, secure gardens with furniture, barbecues, parking. Open all year. Pets and children welcome. Logs and linen available. Guests are welcome to walk our dairy farm. Terms from £175 to £495 per week, winter breaks available.

SHAFTESBURY. Mrs Susan Smart, Hartgrove Farm, Hartgrove, Shaftesbury SP7 0JY (01747 811830

Fax: 01747 811066). Sleeps 2/5. Come and meet Daisey and Tempo our two friendly goats and Whisper the pony. Watch the cows being milked, feed a lamb or collect eggs. All in glorious country with breathtaking views. Four award winning cottages and farmhouse flat, log fires and beams. Tennis court. Games barn. Free local swimming. Lovely village pubs. Open all year. Brochure.
e-mail: smart@hartgrove.demon.co.uk

SHERBORNE. White Horse Farm, Middlemarsh, Sherborne DT9 5QN (01963 210222). Toad Hall

Sleeps 4; Moley's sleeps 2; Ratty's sleeps 2. Set in beautiful Hardy countryside, a small complex of comfortable chalet/bungalows furnished to a high standard and surrounded by three acres of paddock and garden with a small lake. We lie between the historic towns of Sherborne, Dorchester and Cerne Abbas. Delightful coastal attractions are some 30/40 minutes' drive away. Situated next door to an inn serving good food and drink. We are helpful hosts welcoming children, partially disabled guests and pets. Central heating ensures year-round comfort. Electricity, bed linen, towels inclusive. Ample parking. Good value at £140 to £330 per week. Discounted two weeks or more. B&B holidays available in our attractive farmhouse.

STURMINSTER NEWTON. Mrs Sheila Martin, Moorcourt Farm, Moorside, Marnhull, Sturminster Newton DT10 1HH (01258 820271). Working farm. Sleeps

4. Ground floor flat with own entrance and front door key. It is part of the farmhouse, kept immaculately clean and furnished to the highest order. We are a 117 acre dairy farm in the middle of the Blackmore Vale. Guests are welcome to wander round, watch the farm activities and laze in the large garden - we have some garden loungers for your use. We are very central for touring with easy access to New Forest, Longleat Wildlife Park, Cheddar, Stonehenge and the lovely Dorset coast. Accommodation for four people in two double bedrooms, one with a double bed, the other with twin beds. Bathroom, separate toilet. Sittingroom with colour TV and door leading straight onto the back garden. Well equipped kitchen/diner, with fridge/freezer, microwave and washing machine; all utensils colour co-ordinated, matching crockery, etc. Beds made up with fresh linen on arrival. Towels, tea towels, etc provided. Electric heaters in all rooms. Electricity payable by meter, units to be read at the start and finish of your holiday. Sheila creates a friendly atmosphere here "down on the farm" and does her best to make your holiday an enjoyable one. Open April to November. Car essential. Sorry, no pets. Weekly terms from £170 to £270. SAE please.

SWANAGE. Mrs Rosemary Dean, Quarr Farm, Valley Road, Swanage BN19 3DY (01929 480865). ⚭⚭ *APPROVED.* **Sleeps 10 plus cot.** Quarr Farmhouse is a 17th century stone building built in Purbeck marble quarried on farm. The farm is family farmed in a close to nature way. Chickens run free and hatch eggs in barns, while peacocks, cows, calves and horses are much in evidence. You will see chicks and ducks on your lawn, watch steam trains passing through our meadows. The house has four bedrooms, two double rooms (plus one single in each) and two twin rooms; bathroom with shower; large sittingroom with stone walls and 1651-built fireplace with log fire, colour TV; well-equipped kitchen including washer/dryer, dishwasher, microwave, fridge/freezer. Three miles from Swanage and five miles from Studland's sandy beach. Further details available on request.

WAREHAM near. Mrs M.J.M. Constantinides, "Woodlands", Hyde, Near Wareham BH20 7NT (01929 471239). THE MAISONETTE, north wing of secluded house, formerly Dower House of Hyde Estate, stands alone on a meadow of the River Piddle in four-and-a-half acres in the midst of "Hardy Country". The Maisonette comprises upstairs lounge with colour TV; one bedroom (two single beds); downstairs large kitchen/diner, small entrance hall, bathroom; electric cooker (in addition to Aga cooker), refrigerator. Independent side entrance. Extra bedroom (two single beds) on request at £30 per week. Visitors are welcome to use house grounds; children can fish or play in the boundary stream. Pleasant walks in woods and heath nearby. Golf course half-a-mile, pony trekking nearby. All linen included, beds ready made and basic shopping arranged on arrival day. Aga will be lit and maintained on request. Ideal for a quiet holiday far from the madding crowd. Cot and high chair available and children welcome to bring their pets. SAE, please, for terms and further particulars.

LULWORTH COUNTRY COTTAGES
Tel & Fax: 01929 400100

Five family owned properties on historic 1200 acre estate. Coastguard Cottage is approx 400 yards from Lulworth Cove and sleeps seven, East Lodge sleeps four, Home Farm Cottage sleeps seven, St Mary's and Limekiln Farmhouse sleeps 10. All cottages are well equipped with washing machines, tumble dryers, fridge/freezers, colour TV, dishwashers. Central heating, duvets with linen and electricity are inclusive. All properties have gardens and parking. The cottages are situated in an area of exceptional natural beauty. Open throughout the year, short breaks available. Children and pets welcome.

For Brochure contact: Mrs E. S. Weld, Lulworth House, East Lulworth, Wareham, Dorset BH20 5QS

WEST BEXINGTON-ON-SEA. Gorselands Caravan Park, West Bexington-on-Sea DT2 9DJ (01308

897232; Fax: 01308 897239). This attractive, secluded park is set in a coastal valley overlooking Chesil Beach. Choose from fully serviced caravans or self-contained flats and make use of site facilities including a shop, launderette and games room, with a village pub just 100 yards away. It is an ideal base for discovering Dorset's charming villages and Heritage coastline. The beach is a mile, by car or through the meadows, and the fishing is excellent. Pets are most welcome. Please call or write for a brochure, quoting department FHG

DURHAM

CONSETT. The Cottage and Dairy Cottage. Two adjoining self-contained units each comprising

one double and one twin bedroom, kitchen, bathroom and comfortable living area. Colour TV, private garden and patio furniture, heating and linen are all included in the price. We are a working sheep farm just north of the village of Castleside on the A68 heading towards Corbridge and offer easy access to the Roman Wall, Durham City, the Metro Centre, Beamish Museum and lots more. Pass the Fleece Inn Pub on the north side of the village, take a left turn after a short distance, left again down a very steep hill, the road is signposted 'Derwent Grange', follow this and we are the farm on the right. Terms from £150 to £175 Low Season, £175 to £200 High Season. Please contact for further information: **Kay Elliot, Derwent Grange Farm, Castleside, Consett DH8 9BN (01207 508358).** e-mail: ekelliot@aol.com

HARWOOD-IN-TEESDALE. Upper Teesdale Estate, Raby Estate Office, Middleton-in-Teesdale, Barnard

Castle DL12 0QH (01833 640209; Fax: 01833 640963). ꙮ *APPROVED.* HONEY POT AND FROG HALL sleeping four and six respectively, are two former farmhouses remotely situated in completely unspoilt countryside in the heart of the North Pennines area of outstanding natural beauty, with the National Nature Reserve, Cauldron Snout and High Force Waterfalls close by, a haven for walkers, naturalists and fishermen. Ideally situated for touring Durham, Cumbria, the Yorkshire Dales and Lake District. Both cottages have background heating are simply furnished yet fully equipped; fuel for open fires is included in price. Cot and high chair available. Please write for a brochure.

MIDDLETON-IN-TEESDALE. North Wythes Hill Cottage, Lunedale, Middleton-on-Teesdale. Working

farm. Sleeps 6/7. Cosy secluded cottage on the Pennine Way route with large enclosed garden, situated on our working hill farm with sheep, cattle and duck pond. Sleeps six to seven in three bedrooms. Open fire and beamed ceilings. All fuel and linen included in rent. An area of outstanding natural beauty. Brochure available on request. Please contact: **Mrs J. Dent, Wythes Hill Farm, Lunedale, Middleton-in-Teesdale DL12 0NX (01833 640349).**

GLOUCESTERSHIRE

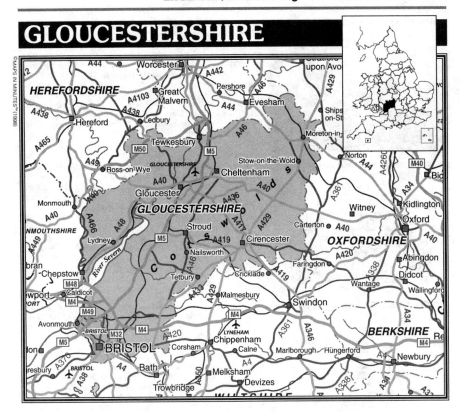

CIRENCESTER. Mrs Tina Barton, 'Flowers Barn', Manor Farm, Middle Duntisbourne, Cirencester GL7 7AR (Tel & Fax: 01285 658145). An attractive listed converted Cotswold stone barn, set in a secluded hamlet in the Duntisbourne Valley. This peaceful setting offers a wonderful view from the lounge window to watch the cows and calves grazing in the meadow or to appreciate the unspoilt countryside offering buzzards to badgers to admire. or walk down to see the ducks on the ford running through the village. The perfect setting for a relaxing holiday. The accommodation offers three bedrooms on the ground floor sleeping 6 to 8 with a well-equipped kitchen with microwave, washing machine and dishwasher. Bed and Breakfast also available in the farmhouse.

DURSLEY. Two Springbank, 37 Hopton Road, Upper Cam, Dursley. ♈♈♈ *COMMENDED*. A recently renovated Victorian mid-terraced cottage, situated in a pleasant rural location one mile from the market town of Dursley where the amenities include a swimming pool and sports centre. Ideal location for keen walkers with the Cotswold Way only a short distance away. On the ground floor accommodation comprises a comfortable sittingroom with colour TV and electric fire. A large archway leads into a dining area with freestanding multi-fuel stove, set in a tiled alcove with oak surround. Through a half door to the rear is a fitted kitchen with fridge/freezer, electric cooker and microwave. A conservatory with washing machine gives access to the rear of the property. Two bedrooms are situated on the first floor, one double and one twin, with a cot and high chair available on request. Terms from £126 to £207 per week. **Mrs F.A. Jones,**

Little Gables, 32 Everlands, Cam, Dursley, Gloucestershire GL11 5NL (01453 543047).

DURSLEY near. Gerald and Norma Kent, Hill House, Crawley Hill, Uley, Dursley GL11 5BH (01453

860267). Sleeps 2. The flat is a separate part of this Cotswold stone house which stands in four-and-a-half acres and is situated on top of a hill with beautiful views of the surrounding countryside. The accommodation consists of double bedroom, kitchen with cooker, microwave, fridge, etc., lounge with TV and video, toilet and shower. Car port and garden area. We supply a comprehensive set of maps and tourist information as well as routes to the many places of interest in the area. Bed linen and towels not supplied. Electricity by meter. Open all year. Sorry, no pets. Non-smoking. Terms from £100 per week. Please telephone, or write, for brochure.

MITCHELDEAN, near. Mrs Appleton, Church Farm, Church Lane, Abenhall, Near Mitcheldean GL17

ODX (01594 541211). Sleeps 2/4. Charming holiday apartments in converted granary. Well-equipped for self-catering, owner supervised. Pets and guests' own horses are welcome - stabling and turnout provided. Direct hacking in the Forest of Dean and excellent equestrian facilities on the farm. Bedroom, lounge with colour TV, well-equipped kitchen, bath and shower. Cot can be supplied. Situated halfway between Ross on Wye and Gloucester. Superb local tourist facilities including walking, cycle tracks, children's activities, etc. Ample parking. Short breaks available. Please call or write for brochure.

WINCHCOMBE. Orchard Cottage, Stanley Pontlarge, Near Winchcombe; TEWKESBURY, Magpie

Cottage, 4 Chance Street, Tewkesbury. ϙϙϙ. ORCHARD COTTAGE, set amid pear trees of orchard on Cotswold escarpment, three miles from Winchcombe. Rural privacy, own access and garden. Four people accommodated in two bedrooms; bathroom; sitting-diningroom (log-coal burning stove); night storage heaters; fully equipped; kitchen with electric cooker, etc. Car essential - parking. Shop one mile. Secluded town cottage at MAGPIE COTTAGE offers holiday accommodation for four people. Sitting-diningroom (log-coal burning fire); two bedrooms; bathroom; small kitchen (electric cooker), everything provided. Car not essential; shops nearby. Children welcome at both properties; pets by arrangement. Open all year. Ideal centres for exploring, walking, sightseeing, alll sports. Stratford-upon-Avon, Cheltenham, other interesting towns and villages within easy reach. Terms: Orchard Cottage from £180 to £300 per week; Magpie Cottage from £150 to £250 per week. Contact: **Mrs S.M. Rolt, Stanley Pontlarge, Near Gretton, Winchcombe GL54 5HD (01242 602594).**

Key to Tourist Board Ratings

     ### The Crown Scheme

The **English Tourism Council** (formerly the English Tourist Board) has joined with the AA and RAC to create a new, easily understood quality rating for serviced accommodation. **Hotels** will receive a grading ranging from **one to five STARS (★)**. Other serviced accommodation such as **guest houses** and **B&B establishments** will be graded from **one to five DIAMONDS (◆)**. These ratings represent Quality, Service and Hospitality not just facilities. *NB.Some properties had not been assessed at the time of going to press and in these cases the publishers have included the old CROWN gradings.*

ϙ   The Key Scheme

The Key Scheme covering self-catering in cottages, bungalows, flats, houseboats, houses, chalets, etc remains unchanged. The classification from **One to Five KEYS** indicates the range of facilities and equipment. Higher quality standards are indicated by the terms APPROVED, COMMENDED, HIGHLY COMMENDED AND DE LUXE.

HAMPSHIRE

LYNDHURST. Penny Farthing Hotel, Romsey Road, Lyndhurst SO43 7AA (02380 284422; Fax: 02380 284488). AA/RAC/ETB ◆◆◆◆.

The Penny Farthing is a cheerful small Hotel ideally situated in Lyndhurst village centre, the capital of the "New Forest". The hotel offers en suite single, double, twin and family rooms with direct dial telephones, tea/coffee tray, colour TV and clock radios. We also have some neighbouring cottages available as hotel annexe rooms or on a self-catering basis. These have been totally refitted, much with "Laura Ashley" and offer a quieter, more exclusive accommodation. The hotel has a licensed bar, private car park and bicycle store. Lyndhurst has a charming variety of shops, restaurants, pubs and bistros and the "New Forest Information Centre and Museum".
website: www.smoothound.co.uk/hotels/pennyf.html

SWAY. Mrs H.J. Beale, Hackney Park, Mount Pleasant Lane, Sway, Lymington SO41 8LS (01590 682049). Properties sleep 4/6. Situated in commanding and tranquil setting two miles from Lymington and Sway village. Delightful residence in own extensive grounds adjoining New Forest Heath with superb walks, rides and drives. Apartments to sleep six (further bedrooms available). Coach House cottage to sleep five. Comfortable and modern, colour TV, bed linen and electricity included. Pets by prior arrangement. First class stables for those wishing to bring own horse and excellent riding facilities within walking distance. Many famous places of interest nearby. Close to Isle of Wight ferry and within six miles of sandy beaches, 15 miles Bournemouth and Southampton. Open all year.

FOR THE MUTUAL GUIDANCE OF GUEST AND HOST

Every year literally thousands of holidays, short breaks and overnight stops are arranged through our guides, the vast majority without any problems at all. In a handful of cases, however, difficulties do arise about bookings, which often could have been prevented from the outset.

It is important to remember that when accommodation has been booked, both parties – guests and hosts – have entered into a form of contract. We hope that the following points will provide helpful guidance.

GUESTS: When enquiring about accommodation, be as precise as possible. Give exact dates, numbers in your party and the ages of any children. State the number and type of rooms wanted and also what catering you require – bed and breakfast, full board etc. Make sure that the position about evening meals is clear – and about pets, reductions for children or any other special points.

Read our reviews carefully to ensure that the proprietors you are going to contact can supply what you want. Ask for a letter confirming all arrangements, if possible.

If you have to cancel, do so as soon as possible. Proprietors do have the right to retain deposits and under certain circumstances to charge for cancelled holidays if adequate notice is not given and they cannot re-let the accommodation.

HOSTS: Give details about your facilities and about any special conditions. Explain your deposit system clearly and arrangements for cancellations, charges etc. and whether or not your terms include VAT.

If for any reason you are unable to fulfil an agreed booking without adequate notice, you may be under an obligation to arrange suitable alternative accommodation or to make some form of compensation.

While every effort is made to ensure accuracy, we regret that FHG Publications cannot accept responsibility for errors, omissions or misrepresentations in our entries or any consequences thereof.

Prices in particular should be checked because we go to press early. We will follow up complaints but cannot act as arbiters or agents for either party.

HEREFORDSHIRE

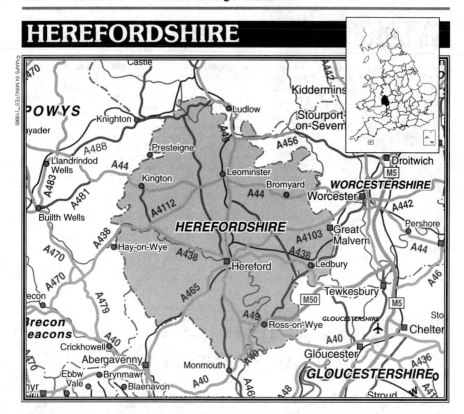

FELTON. Marjorie and Brian Roby, Felton House, Felton, Herefordshire HR1 3PH (Tel & Fax: 01432 820366). The Lodge is a spotlessly clean, cosy, restful cottage in the beautiful grounds of Felton House, the former rectory, just off A417 between Hereford, Leominster and Bromyard. The Lodge has been restored to its Victorian character but with the convenience of electric heating, a modern kitchen, two shower rooms, a dining room and a sitting room with TV. Guests are accommodated in one double, one twin and one single bedroom and a cot is available. Linen may be hired. Children, and pets with responsible owners are most welcome. Private parking, patio and garden. Weekly terms £150 to £250 exclusive of electricity. Brochure available.
website: www.SmoothHound.co.uk/hotels/felton.html

Mainoaks Farm Cottages
Goodrich, Ross-on-Wye

Six units sleeping 2,4,6 & 7. Set in 80 acres of pasture and woodland beside the River Wye in an area of outstanding natural beauty with an abundance of wildlife, this 15th century Listed farm has been converted to form six cottages of different size and individual character. All with exposed beams, pine furniture, heating, fully equipped kitchens (four have microwaves), washer/dryers, colour TV. Private gardens and barbecue area. Linen and towels provided. Cot and high chair on request. An ideal base for touring the local area, beautiful walks including Forestry Commission, fishing, canoeing, pony trekking, bird watching or just relaxing in this beautiful, tranquil spot. Short breaks available throughout the year. Pets by arrangement.

Mrs P. Unwin, Hill House, Chase End, Bromsberrow, Ledbury, Herefordshire HR8 1SE
Telephone (01531 650448) 🛏🛏🛏 *and* 🛏🛏🛏🛏 *Highly Commended.*

HEREFORD. Rose Cottage, Craswall, Hereford. ♈♈♈♈ *APPROVED.* **Sleeps 5.** Rose Cottage is a modernised stone-built cottage, retaining its original character situated at the foot of Black Mountains, on a quiet country road. Hay-on-Wye, Hereford, Abergavenny easily accessible and ideal base for walking and touring. Many churches and castles of historic interest; close to River Monnow where trout fishing is available. Pony trekking, hang gliding nearby. A car is essential and there is ample parking. Rose Cottage is comfortably furnished with full central heating and wood fire (heating and hot water included). Linen and towels provided free of charge. Electricity by meter reading. Two bedrooms, one with double bed, one with three single beds. Cot can be provided. Bathroom, toilet. Kitchen fully equipped with electric cooker, kettle, fridge etc. Sittingroom; diningroom. TV. Dogs are allowed. Available all year round. Terms from £150 to £160. **Mrs M. Howard, The Three Horseshoes, Craswall HR2 0PL (01981 510631).**

HEREFORD. Mrs Rita Price, Folly Farm, Holme Lacy, Hereford HR2 6LS (Tel & Fax: 01432 870259)

♈♈♈♈ *COMMENDED.* **Working farm.** Carey Dene and Rock House, spacious oak-beamed cottages on a working farm, in an area of outstanding natural beauty, overlooking the River Wye. Ideal for a quiet and peaceful holiday. Between Ross-on-Wye and Hereford, and within easy reach of many attractions, castles, stately homes, Malvern Hills and Black Mountains. Both are very well equipped and have colour TV. washing machine, electric cooker, fridge/freezer and microwave. Bed linen, towels, electricity and heating included in rent. Cot and high chair available. Short breaks, children and well behaved pets welcome. Carey Dene sleeps four, Rock Haven sleeps six to eight. Terms from £170 low season to £390 high season.

FREE and REDUCED RATE Holiday Visits!
Don't miss our Readers' Offer Vouchers

HEREFORD. Mrs S. Dixon, Swayns Diggins, Harewood End, Hereford HR2 8JU (01989 730358). This

highly recommended first floor flat is completely self-contained at one end of the main house. The bedroom, sitting room and private balcony all face south with panoramic views over farmland towards Ross and Symonds Yat. The well-equipped kitchen overlooks the garden with grand views towards Orcop Hill and the Black Mountains. Open all year, rental from £120 to £130 per week includes electricity, linen, heating, colour TV. Ideal base for exploring the beautiful Wye Valley, Herefordshire, Gloucestershire and the historic Welsh Marches. There is much to see and do in the area. Write or phone for further particulars.

KINGTON. The Harbour, Upper Hergest, Kington. Properties sleep 5/9. This bungalow is on a good second-class road facing south with beautiful views from its elevated position, across the Hergest Ridge and Offa's Dyke. The Welsh border is a mile away. Shops are two-and-a-half miles away. Kington Golf Club nearby. Accommodation for five/nine in two double rooms (one with extra single bed) downstairs and two double dormer bedrooms; two cots; bathroom, toilet; sittingroom (TV); diningroom; sun porch for relaxing; kitchen with electric cooker, fridge, food store and usual equipment. No linen. Suitable for the disabled. Children and pets welcome. Car essential - parking. Available all year. Also mobile home sleeping two with bathroom and flush toilet. SAE, please, to **Mr A.J. Welson, New House Farm, Upper Hergest, Kington, Herefordshire HR5 3EW (01544 230533).**

LEINTWARDINE. Mocktree Barns Holiday Cottages. ETC up to ↑↑↑ COMMENDED. Small group of barns

now offering comfortable self-catering accommodation around sunny courtyard. Well equipped cottages sleeping between two and six. Friendly owners. Open all year. Short breaks available. Pets and children welcome. Lovely views, excellent walks – direct access to footpaths through farmland and woods. Hereford, Cider Country, Shropshire Hills, Shrewsbury, Ironbridge and the splendid mid-Wales countryside all an easy drive away. Beautiful Ludlow seven miles. Guided walks/tours arranged. Golf, fishing, cycling nearby. Colour brochure. Contact: **Clive and Cynthia Prior, Mocktree Barns, Leintwardine, Ludlow SY7 0LY (01547 540441).**

LEOMINSTER. Mrs E. Thomas, Woonton Court Farm, Leysters, Leominster HR6 0HL (Tel & Fax: 01568

750232) ↑↑↑↑ COMMENDED. MILL HOUSE FLAT: We have recently converted the first floor of an old cider house to provide a high standard of comfort comprising one large double room with washbasin, one smaller bedroom with twin beds (extra accommodation available in the farmhouse, also Bed and Breakfast); comfortable sitting room with colour TV, central heating and panel electric fire; kitchenette with electric cooker, microwave, fridge; bathroom. Patio/Garden. Ample car parking. Children welcome, cot, high chair and babysitting available. Linen provided, electricity included. Terms from £180 to £250 per week. Short Breaks available. Brochure on request. Caravan and camping available nearby.

MUCH COWARNE. Mr and Mrs R.M. Bradbury, Cowarne Hall Cottages, Much Cowarne, Bromyard

HR7 4JQ (01432 820317; Fax: 01432 820093). ↑↑↑↑ HIGHLY COMMENDED. Project supported by the English Tourist Board. A splendid historic Gothic Hall with beams, open fireplaces, arched windows and doorways has been sensitively converted to provide luxurious cottage accommodation. Situated twixt the Malvern Hills and Wye Valley in a network of country lanes passing through rolling countryside. Convenient for the historic towns of Malvern, Bromyard, Ledbury, Hereford and Worcester. The cottages are centrally heated and have a patio, garden and parking. Details supplied of the area's attractions including working farms and vineyards, a Hop Trail, open gardens and National Trust walks. The lanes are ideal for dog walks. Free colour brochure.

ROSS-ON-WYE. Mrs Thelma Green, The Ashe, Bridstow, Ross-On-Wye HR9 6QA (01989 563336).

ооо
ͳͳͳͳ *COMMENDED*. The Ashe is a 15th century sandstone farmhouse and buildings with oak beams and panelling, situated on a 200 acre mixed farm in beautiful countryside, two miles north west of Ross-On-Wye. Stratford-upon-Avon 50 miles. Public transport, garage and shops approximately one mile. Guests have access to walks on farm, an eighteen-hole par three golf course, fishing lakes, barbecue area, a large garden and hard surface tennis court. The Ashe, situated in the beautiful Wye Valley, is ideal for a touring or walking holiday. Golf, fishing, pony trekking, canoeing, bowling and ballooning are all available nearby. Terms on request.

See also Colour Display Advertisement

ROSS-ON-WYE. Langstone Court Farmhouse. 14th Century farmhouse. Lounge and dining room each measure 15 x 18 feet. Farmhouse wing sleeps 18 plus cots, Cidermill flat sleeps 6-8 plus cot or can be let as one unit sleeping up to 26 plus cots. Very popular for hen parties, birthdays and family get-togethers. Two ground floor bedrooms, one double, one single. Central heating, log fires, laundry, payphone, bike storage, dishwashers. Set in beautiful Herefordshire Countryside. Large groups please book early. Short Breaks available all year except August. **Colour brochure: Lesley Saunders, Dales Barn, Langstone, Llangarron, Ross-on-Wye HR9 6NR (01989 770774).**

SYMONDS YAT. Mrs J. Rudge, Hilltop, Llangrove, Near Ross-on-Wye (01600 890279). Sleeps 4. Chalet

bungalow with magnificent views over surrounding countryside. One mile off A40 dual carriageway and within easy reach of Forest of Dean, Monmouth and Black Mountains. The chalet stands in the gardens of a seven-acre smallholding, enjoying peace and quiet, yet close to local shops, public houses and the local attractions. Livingroom with TV. Kitchen and bathroom with all amenities. Two bedrooms, one with two single beds and one with double bed. Patio, sun lounge, garden. Children welcome. No pets. Accommodation particularly suitable for the elderly. No linen supplied. £1 meter. Terms from £175 to £225. SAE, please.

WORMELOW. Old Forge Cottage. Sleeps 4 plus cot. ETB ͳͳͳͳ *COMMENDED*. Detached historic Forge

Forge Cottage

central to Hereford, Monmouth and Ross-on-Wye. Accommodation consists of double bedroom, family bathroom, twin bedroom with en suite shower room. Large open plan lounge, well equipped kitchenette. Central heating, TV, payphone. Linen and towels included. Own driveway, carport, patio and barbecue. Access to grounds of Lyston Smithy. All on one level with wheelchair access. Three-day short breaks available from November to March inclusive. Self catering terms from £165 to £314 all inclusive. For brochure/tariff contact: **Shirley Wheeler, Lyston Smithy, Wormelow, Hereford HR2 8EL (01981 540625).**

Please mention *The Farm Holiday Guide* when enquiring about accommodation featured in these pages.

ISLE OF WIGHT

ISLE OF WIGHT. Island Cottage Holidays. ♙♙♙ *COMMENDED* / ♙♙♙♙♙ *DE-LUXE*. Charming cottages in lovely rural surroundings and close to the sea - situated throughout the Isle of Wight. Beautiful views, attractive gardens, delightful country walks. Dogs and horses welcome at many properties. Some cottages on farms, some with swimming pools, and some only a short walk from lovely sandy beaches. All equipped to a high standard and graded for quality by the Tourist Board. Open all year. Terms from £100 to £750 per week. Short breaks available in low season (3 nights) £85 to £179. For a brochure please contact: **Mrs Honor Vass, The Old Vicarage, Kingston, Corfe Castle, Dorset BH20 5LH (01929 480080; Fax: 01929 481070).** e-mail: ich@cottageholidays.demon.co.uk website: www.cottageholidays.demon.co.uk

TOTLAND BAY. 3 Seaview Cottages, Broadway, Totland Bay. Sleeps 5. ♙♙. This well-modernised cosy old coastguard cottage holds the Farm Holiday Guide Diploma for the highest standard of accommodation. It is warm and popular throughout the year. Four day winter break - £38; a week in summer £242. Located close to two beaches in beautiful walking country near mainland links. It comprises lounge/dinette/kitchenette; two bedrooms (sleeping five); bathroom/toilet. Well furnished, fully heated, TV, selection of books and other considerations. Another cottage is also available at Cowes, Isle of Wight. Non-smokers only. **Mrs C. Pitts, 11 York Avenue, New Milton, Hampshire BH25 6BT (01425 615215).**

LANCASHIRE

LUNE VALLEY. Barbara Mason, Oxenforth Green, Tatham, Lancaster LA2 8P (015242 61784). **Working farm, join in. Sleeps 4 plus cot.** Cottage and static caravan on working farm with panoramic views of Ingleborough and surrounding hills. Central for Lakes, dales and coast. Good walking, fishing and horse-riding nearby. Guests are welcome to watch the day-to-day workings of the farm. Our cottage sleeps four in one double and one twin room with lounge, fitted kitchen, ground and first floor shower rooms. The caravan sleeps four in one double and two bunkbeds, with washbasin, shower, flushing toilet, colour TV. Garden and garden chairs available. Children welcome. One dog welcome. Three-quarters-of-a-mile to nearest pub. Prices from £200 to £270 per week. Caravan from £110 per week.

LUNE VALLEY. Mrs Margaret Burrow, High Snab, Gressingham, Lancaster LA2 8LS (015242 21347). **Working farm. Sleeps 2/4.** ♙♙♙♙ *COMMENDED*. Garden cottage, with private drive and garden, adjoins our farmhouse on a working dairy and sheep farm in a quiet location. Just five miles from junction 35 of the M6. Ideal for touring Lakes, dales and coast. Conservatory and utility room with washer and dryer. Well-equipped kitchen/oak beamed lounge. Two bedrooms – one double, one twin; bathroom with shower; snooker table. Central heating. Cot and high chair. Electricity and linen included. Tourist Board Regional Award Winner. Open March to November. Brochure.

FHG Please mention *The Farm Holiday Guide* when enquiring about accommodation featured in these pages.

MORECAMBE. Mrs G.A. Tamassy, 8 Marine Road, West End, Morecambe LA3 1BS (01524 418249).

Luxury holiday flats overlooking the gardens with a beautiful view of Morecambe Bay and Lakeland Hills. All modern facilities including en suite and colour TV. Open all year. Overnight guests welcome. (Sorry, no children). Reasonable rates. Senior Citizen rates off season. SAE please, for brochure. Member of Morecambe Bay Warmth of Welcome.

LEICESTERSHIRE including Rutland

MOUNTSORREL. Marilyn Duffin, Stonehurst, Bond Lane, Mountsorrel LE12 7AR (01509 413216). This

comfortable, modern, well-equipped family house with five bedrooms, a private garden and barbecue, is attached to Stonehurst Family Farm and Museum, to which free admission is given during stay. Teashop and restaurant on farm. All amenities in the village. The farm is 12 minutes from M1 J21A. Open all year. Children and pets welcome. Terms from £175 - £350.

Other specialised

FHG PUBLICATIONS

• Recommended COUNTRY HOTELS OF BRITAIN   £4 95

• Recommended WAYSIDE & COUNTRY INNS OF BRITAIN   £4.95

• PETS WELCOME!   £5 25

• BED AND BREAKFAST IN BRITAIN   £3 95

• THE GOLF GUIDE Where to Play / Where to Stay   £9.95

Published annually: Please add 55p postage (UK only)
when ordering from the publishers

FHG PUBLICATIONS LTD
Abbey Mill Business Centre, Seedhill, Paisley, Renfrewshire PA1 ITJ

LINCOLNSHIRE

WAINGROVE FARM COUNTRY COTTAGES

Bookings: Mrs Stephanie Smith, Waingrove Farm, Fulstow, Louth LN11 0QX

English Tourist Board
HIGHLY COMMENDED

Tel/Fax: 01507 363704
e-mail: macandstephanie@waingrove.demon.co.uk
Award-winning Country Cottages – detached farmhouse
or single storey courtyard cottages – beautifully presented with pretty interiors,
superbly equipped, carefully maintained. 'A delightful retreat - your holiday
begins the moment you arrive'. Colour brochure. "Just Two" discounts.

Not suitable for children under 10 years. No pets.
COURTYARD COTTAGES FROM £200 TO £345
FARMHOUSE FROM £245 TO £450. "JUST TWO" DISCOUNTS.
SHORT BREAKS.

MABLETHORPE. Mrs Graves, Grange Farm, Maltby le Marsh, Alford LN13 0JP (01507 450267; Fax: 01507 450180). Sleeps 5. Working farm, join in. Situated

five minutes' drive from the Lincolnshire coast and golden beaches is Yew Tree Cottage. Proprietors Ann and Michael Graves warmly welcome visitors to their working farm, renowned for carefree holidays and its friendly, relaxed atmosphere. All rooms are beautifully furnished and modern in style. For those who do not wish to venture into historic Lincoln or nearby market town of Louth, the patio, gardens and fishing lake are ideal to relax and while away the day. Pets welcome.

SKEGNESS. Mr and Mrs K. Bennett, Field Farm, Station Road, Burgh-Le-Marsh PE24 5ES (Tel & Fax: 01754 810372). Sleeps 2-4. Working farm. Self-contained one bedroom farmhouse flat with sofa bed in living area. Fully equipped, fridge freezer, electric cooker, shower room, storage heaters for winter. Features include attractive beams, electric fire, patio doors into large porch entrance. Static caravan sleeps 4/6 available, fully equipped with fridge, gas cooker, shower, etc. The farm is 250 yards from the A158, with plenty of ample safe parking. Conveniently situated between the coast/Fantasy Island (six miles) and attractive Wolds with its many interesting small towns. Abundant fishing lakes. Good migratory bird-watching nine miles. B&B available next door. Terms from £140 per week. Non-smokers only please. No pets.

FHG PUBLICATIONS

FHG publish a large range of well-known accommodation guides. We will be happy to send you details or you can use the order form at the back of this book.

FREE and REDUCED RATE Holiday Visits!
Don't miss our Readers' Offer Vouchers

NORFOLK

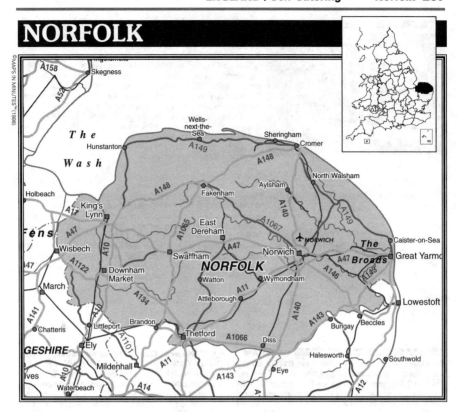

ATTLEBOROUGH. Carleton Cottage. ETB ♀♀♀♀ HIGHLY COMMENDED. Sleeps 6 plus cot. Detached converted farm buildings in grounds (1.6 acres) of main property in rural village. Original beams and inglenook fireplace with log burner. Three bedrooms, bathroom, kitchen, diningroom and lounge. Unfenced pond and small orchard with slide and swing. Pony, chickens, goats etc which children can feed. Well placed for Norfolk and Suffolk attractions. Heating, bedding, towels, etc., welcome pack included. £200 to £400 per week, two day breaks from £90. Bed and Breakfast £20 per person, per night. Please phone or write for further details. **Mrs M. Findlay, Carleton Manor, Carleton Rode, Norwich NR16 1RL (01953 788755).**

BRAMERTON. 'Heron's Reach', Riverside, Hill House Road, Bramerton NR14 7EG. Sleeps 8. Nestling at the foot of a leafy hill in a designated Area of Outstanding Beauty, 'Heron's Reach' is a traditionally built flint cottage, ideally situated to accommodate boat lovers, bird watchers, walkers, artists and daydreamers. 'Heron's Reach' is at the gateway to the Norfolk Broads and within walking distance of nature reserves. Children welcome. Not suitable for pets or smokers. Please telephone **020 8287 1318** for details.

CLIPPESBY. Clippesby Holidays, Clippesby Hall, Clippesby, Near Great Yarmouth NR29 3BL (01493 367800; Fax: 01493 367809). ℓℓ **to** ℓℓℓℓ **up to** *COMMENDED.* ✓✓✓✓ *EXCELLENT.* David Bellamy Gold Conservation Award. IN NORFOLK BROADS NATIONAL PARK between Norwich and Great Yarmouth. Luxury lodges and woodland cottages in a peaceful country setting. Touring, walking, cycling, boating, bird-watching, fishing, exploring local nature reserves and tourist attractions. Short breaks and longer stays all year round. From May to September we have: swimming, lawn tennis, mini golf, family pub. Summertime apartments, award-winning touring park and more. Send for colour brochure.
e-mail: holidays@clippesby.ndirect.co.uk
website: clippesby.ndirect.co.uk

DEREHAM. Carol Mears, Moor Farm and Stable Cottages, Foxley, Dereham NR20 4QN (Tel & Fax: 01362 688523). ℓℓℓ *APPROVED.* Located on a working farm, we have a courtyard of two and three bedroomed self-catering chalets. All are fully equipped and have central heating, which is included in the letting fee. Situated 20 miles from the coast and 15 miles from the Broads on 365 acres of mature woodland adjoining the owners' farm. Ideal area for walking holidays. Fishing available close by. Pets are welcome at a charge of £10. Please contact us for further details.

DEREHAM. Mrs G.V. Howes, Church Farm Cottages, Brisley, Dereham NR20 5LL (Tel and Fax: 01362 668332). ℓℓℓℓ *COMMENDED* Peace and tranquillity in owner supervised cottage between Dereham and Fakenham. Kept to a very high standard of cleanliness and comfort, it has full oil fired central heating, log fires, colour TV, video, washing machine, dishwasher, fridge freezer, microwave, tumble dryer, outside drying etc. It has a lawned garden and plenty of parking space. Open all year. Linen, logs and heating are included in price. Sorry no pets. Weekly price £165 to £321 for two or £185 to £342 for four, £227 to £384 for five. Short breaks available from October to April from £99 for two to £230 for five.

GELDESTON. Hillside, 15 Kells Way, Geldeston, Beccles. Sleeps 4/6. This bungalow situated in small country village, very quiet and near River Waveney, is within easy reach of Great Yarmouth, Norwich, Lowestoft, Southwold and seaside. Accommodates four/six people; one double, one twin bedroom; bed settee in lounge, storage heaters, colour TV, wood burner, beams; diningroom; bathroom/shower, toilet; kitchen, electric cooker, microwave, etc. Carpets throughout. Cot available. Sorry, no pets. Bed linen supplied. Open all year. Car essential - parking. Shops nearby. Terms on request. Special winter rates. **Mrs M. Rolt, "Conifer", 17 Kells Way, Geldeston, Beccles, Suffolk NR34 0LU (01508 518689).**

KINGS LYNN. Mrs Angela Ringer, Sid's Cottage, c/o The Grange, West Rudham, Kings Lynn PE31 8SY (Tel & Fax: 01485 528229). ℓℓℓℓ *APPROVED.* **Sleeps 4.** Sid's Cottage is semi-detached, surrounded by grass but has no enclosed garden. Overlooks a small orchard, patio at rear. Sleeps four in three bedrooms. Linen provided. Gas central heating, open fire, colour TV, microwave, automatic washing machine, dishwasher, fridge/freezer. Cot and high chair available on request. Electricity £1 meter. Carp fishing on farm. Heated indoor swimming pool. Good base for seeing Norfolk. Sandy beach in easy reach. Children welcome. Sorry, no pets. Open all year. Terms from £150 to £500 per week.

SPIXWORTH. Mrs Sheelah Cook, Grange Farm, Buxton Road, Spixworth, Norwich NR10 3PR (01603 898190; Fax: 01603 897176). ꜛꜛꜛꜛ *HIGHLY COMMENDED.*

Delightful 18th century coachman's cottage and award-winning stables conversion and Lodge cottage in seclusion on our farm. Ideal for exploring Norwich, the Broads and the coast. Very well furnished and equipped. Central heating and log fires. Families welcome. Secure garden and space to relax. Barn games room and outdoor play area. Swimming and tennis, walks and fishing available. Short breaks from £120 or weekly from £190 to £550. We offer a warm welcome, please ring or write for further details.

TOFT MONKS. Mrs I.B. Birt, Bay Cottage, Maypole Green, Toft Monks, Near Beccles NR34 0EY (01502 677405). Sleeps 4. Detached 19th-century boarded cottage

on Maypole Green in a scattered rural parish. Open plan beamed lounge with colour TV, fully equipped kitchen/dining area. Shower room which includes washbasin and WC. Upstairs is bedroom with double bed and a second bedroom with full sized bunk beds. Carpeted throughout, electric heaters; table and bed linen supplied. Secluded garden. Pleasant country walks, five miles from Beccles and the River Waveney, 12 miles from Great Yarmouth, 16 miles from Norwich. £110 to £140 weekly. Further particulars on application.

WINTERTON-ON-SEA. Timbers, The Lane, Winterton-on-Sea. Sleeps 5. Comfortable, well-furnished ground floor flat in attractive timber cottage situated in quiet seaside village just eight miles north of Great Yarmouth. Broad sandy beach and sand dunes (nature reserve) for pleasant walks. Three miles from Norfolk Broads (boating and fishing). Flat is carpeted throughout and is fully equipped for self-catering family holidays. Ideal for children, and pets are welcome. One double, one twin-bedded and one single bedroom. Sleeps five plus cot. Bed linen provided and maid service every other day for general cleaning. Beamed sittingroom with colour TV. Secluded garden. Car parking. Available May to September. Terms from £200 to £320 per week. For full details write to **Mr M.J. Isherwood, 79 Oakleigh Avenue, London N20 9JG (020 8445 2192).**

PLEASE MENTION THIS GUIDE WHEN YOU WRITE

OR PHONE TO ENQUIRE ABOUT ACCOMMODATION.

IF YOU ARE WRITING, A STAMPED,

ADDRESSED ENVELOPE IS ALWAYS APPRECIATED.

Visit the **FHG** website
www.holidayguides.com
for details of the wide choice of accommodation
featured in the full range of FHG titles

NORTHUMBERLAND

ALNWICK. Mrs V. Purvis, Titlington Hall Farm, Alnwick NE66 2EB (01665 578253). ♈♈♈♈ *COMMENDED.* **Can sleep parties of 10.** Two lovely country cottages available for holiday lets all year round. They are situated in a quiet and beautiful area with many interesting places just a short drive away. Facilities include central heating, TV, fridge, microwave, washing machine, tumble dryer and linen. Children welcome, pets by arrangement. Prices from £195 to £315 per week

BELFORD. Mrs K. Burn, Fenham-Le-Moor Farmhouse, Belford NE70 7PN (Tel & Fax: 01668 213247). ♈♈♈ *COMMENDED.* A comfortably furnished farm cottage situated in peaceful surroundings on a quiet road half-a-mile from the shore and Lindisfarne Nature Reserve, an Area of Outstanding Natural Beauty, close to Holy Island, Bamburgh and within easy reach of Cheviot Hills. An ideal area for golf, beaches and walking. Electricity, linen and fuel for open fire included in rent. Terms from £190 to £370 per week. Please telephone for further details.

BERWICK-UPON-TWEED. Mrs S. Wight, Gainslawhill Farm, Berwick-upon-Tweed TD15 1SZ (01289 386210).

Well-equipped cottage with own walled garden on mixed farm, three miles from Berwick-upon-Tweed, situated between the Rivers Tweed and Whiteadder (last farm in England). Ideal position for touring north Northumberland and the Border country. Good beaches, golf, riding nearby. Lovely walks along both rivers. Trout fishing. Sleeps six, cot available. Pets welcome. Livingroom with open fire, colour TV, telephone. Three bedrooms (linen provided), kitchen with dining area, fridge freezer, automatic washing machine, microwave oven. Bathroom. Night store heaters. Terms from £250.

CORBRIDGE. Mrs M.J. Matthews, The Hayes, Newcastle Road, Corbridge NE45 5LP (01434 632010).

Cottages ꝸꝸꝸ *COMMENDED*. On the edge of this historic village, and with easy access to the A69 and A1M. Former stables and coach house in extensive grounds of large country house, converted to self-catering cottages sleeping four to five people. Well furnished. Modern kitchen and equipment. Also a caravan. Prices range from £175 to £325 weekly. Full details and brochure on request.
e-mail: MJCT@mmatthews.fsbusiness.co.uk

CORNHILL-ON-TWEED near. Hawthorn Cottage.

In a quiet, rural location on a family farm, this traditional stone-built cottage (formerly two) has a panoramic view and a lovely enclosed garden. It is only 20 minutes' drive to Lindisfarne and the beautiful Northumberland Coast. The cottage is attractively furnished and looked after by the owner. It consists of a spacious living room with dining area, log/coal fire, colour TV and French window looking into the garden. Two double and one single bedrooms; bathroom; kitchen with electric cooker, fridge/freezer and microwave. There are five night storage heaters and three electric heaters. Conveniently situated for touring the Border's many castles, abbeys and stately homes, excellent golf courses and good eating places. Logs and coal are free. One pet only. Available March to November. Brochure on request. Contact: **Mrs D.C.S. Tweedie, Buchtrig, Hownam, Jedburgh TD8 6NJ (01835 840230).**

HALTWHISTLE. Mr J.M. Clark, Featherstone Castle, Haltwhistle NE49 0JG.

I can offer at HALTWHISTLE, two cottages – Horse Close (illustrated) and Greenriggs. Both sleep five to six. Haltwhistle is five miles, Alston 12 miles and Carlisle and Hexham 20 miles. Scottish Borders, Solway Coast, Lake District, Kielder and Durham City all within one hour. Both are traditional stone and slate shepherd's cottages remotely situated above the South Tyne Valley with garden area, sittingroom with log fire and kitchen with electric cooker and open fire, off peak background heating. Horse Close has three small bedrooms, bathroom/WC upstairs and a separate WC downstairs. Greenriggs has two large bedrooms, downstairs bathroom/WC and front and back porch/lobby. TV. Pillows and duvets are provided. Terms £200 to £250 per week. Bookings to **Mr J. Rutherford, Featherstone Castle, Haltwhistle (01434 320202). If no answer ring J.M. Clark's office on 01434 320363.**

FREE and REDUCED RATE Holiday Visits!
Don't miss our Readers' Offer Vouchers

HALTWHISTLE. Mr and Mrs Knox, Close-A-Burn, Near Cawburn, Haltwhistle NE49 9PN (01434 320764). ŤŤŤ *COMMENDED*. **Sleeps 4/5.** Two bedrooms. In whichever season you visit, or for however long your stay, a warm welcome is assured at Close-A-Burn. Set in seven acres of quiet countryside. Excellent touring base. Open January to December. Terms from £150 to £250 per week.

MORPETH. Mr & Mrs A.P. Coatsworth, Gallowhill Farm, Whalton, Morpeth NE61 3TX (01661 881241). ŤŤŤŤŤ *HIGHLY COMMENDED*. **Working farm. Sleeps 4-6.** Relax in our two spacious stone-built cottages. Recently converted and modernised to give you every facility you require. Electric cooker, fridge, freezer, dishwasher, washer/dryer, microwave, colour TV. Located in the heart of Northumberland on a very tidy farm with private gardens. Bolam Lake two miles, Belsay Castle four miles, coast 20 minutes, Hadrian's Wall 30 minutes, to name only a few attractions. All linen, heating, electricity included in price. Sorry, no pets. All children welcome. Brochure on request. Terms £200 to £395.

ROTHBURY. Mrs H. Farr, Lorbottle, West Steads, Thropton, Morpeth NE65 7JT (01665 574672). ŤŤŤŤ *COMMENDED*. **Working farm. Sleeps 5.** Semi-detached newly modernised cottage on 320 acre mixed farm, lying in the beautiful Whittingham Vale, surrounded by peaceful rolling hills and unspoilt countryside, four-and-a-half miles from Rothbury. Double glazed, full gas central heating and fire. Well-equipped modern kitchen. Cooking by electricity (included in price), own parking and back garden. Panoramic views from all windows. Colour TV. Very central and ideal for visiting all parts of Northumbria. Gas by meter reading. Children allowed to look around the farm. Alnwick 15 miles, Border region 25 miles, Kielder Water and Hadrian's Wall 30 miles. All bed linen supplied. Single, twin and double beds. No dogs please (sheep nearby). Details on request.

See also Colour Display Advertisement

SEAHOUSES. Mrs Julie Gregory, Springhill Farm, Seahouses NE68 7RE (01665 720351/720399). ŤŤŤ COMMENDED. Springhill Cottages are peacefully positioned at the side of a winding country lane, which leads three-quarters-of-a-mile to sandy beaches, stretching between the fishing village of Seahouses, gateway to the Farne Island Nature Reserve, and Bamburgh village, which nestles beneath its magnificent castle. We offer a perfect base for exploring Northumberland and the Scottish Borders. Cosy log fires and deserted beaches make our Short Winter Breaks very popular. SPRINGHILL COTTAGE sleeps five, COPYWELL COTTAGE sleeps four. Both have well equipped kitchens with washing machines, electric showers/heating. Bed linen is inclusive in rent. Both cottages are non-smoking. More information available on request.

When making enquiries or bookings, a stamped addressed envelope is always appreciated.

SHROPSHIRE

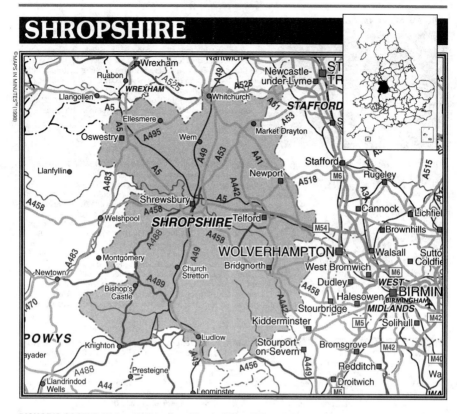

BISHOP'S CASTLE. Walcot Hall, Lydbury North, Bishop's Castle. Flats sleep 4/9. Spacious flats in Stately Home. Secluded location in own grounds; splendid scenery and ideal area for peaceful holiday for young and old. All flats fully furnished and recently decorated and sleep four/nine. Larger parties by arrangement. Village shop half a mile; local market towns, castles, villages and hill country of the Border Counties provide opportunities for exploration and walking. Coarse fishing in pools and lake. Boats and bicycles available, and riding locally. Terms from £182 to £295 weekly. **Mrs M. Smith, 41 Cheval Place, London SW7 1EW (020 7581 2782)**

CRAVEN ARMS. Mrs B. Freeman, Upper House, Clunbury, Craven Arms SY7 0HG (01588 660629).

Welcome to Horseshoe Cottage which is situated in the beautiful gardens of Upper House (17th century Listed) in Clunbury, a village of archaeological interest in a designated area of outstanding natural beauty – A.E. Housman countryside. This private self-catering cottage is completely furnished and equipped; being on one level the accommodation is suitable for elderly and disabled persons. Colour TV. Sleeps four; cot available. Children and pets welcome. Ample parking. This Welsh Border countryside is rich in medieval history, unspoilt villages and natural beauty. Enjoy walking on the Long Mynd and Offa's Dyke, or explore Ludlow and Ironbridge. £135 to £170 per week. Please write or phone for further details.

CRAVEN ARMS. Mrs C.A. Morgan, Strefford Hall, Strefford, Craven Arms SY7 8DE (Tel & Fax: 01588 672383). Set in the lovely South Shropshire countryside surrounded by fields and close to Wenlock Edge. The Coachhouse provides two luxury self-catering units. Swallows Nest on the ground floor is ideal for frail or disabled guests. Wrens Nest is on the first floor. Each consists of double en suite bedroom, fitted kitchen, large sitting/diningroom with colour TV; central heating and linen included. Fitted carpets. Patio area with seating. Ample parking to the side of the Coachhouse. Terms £185 to £250 per week. Also Bed and Breakfast available in the farmhouse.

LUDLOW. Hazel Cottage, Duxmoor, Onibury, Craven Arms. ♔♔♔♔ *HIGHLY COMMENDED.* **Sleeps 4.** Beautifully restored, semi-detached, yet private, period cottage, set in its own extensive cottage-style garden with its own drive and ample parking space. Amidst peaceful surroundings and panoramic views of the countryside, it is situated five miles north of historic Ludlow and one-and-a-half miles from the A49. The cottage retains all its original features and fittings with traditional decorations and is fully furnished as a home, with antiques throughout. It comprises a comfortable living room with a Victorian range for coal and log fire; TV, wireless and telephone; dining room with bread oven; fully equipped kitchen, hall, Victorian bathroom; two bedrooms (one double and one twin-bedded) with period washbasins. Electric central heating throughout. All linen included. Tourist information. Open all year. Short Breaks. No pets. Terms from £150 to £330 per week. **Mrs Rachel Sanders, Duxmoor Farm, Onibury, Craven Arms SY7 9BQ (01584 856342).**

See also Colour Display Advertisement   LUDLOW. **Mrs M. Lowe, Lower Hayton Grange, Lower Hayton, Ludlow SY8 2AQ (01584 861296; Fax: 01584 861371). Sleeps 4.** GRANGE COTTAGES are conversions from 17th century barns, set in the beautiful grounds (four and a half acres) of this period house. Hundreds of trees and shrubs in the peaceful gardens which have a delightful duck pond. Four miles from the pretty market town of Ludlow. Wonderful views all around the area and many attractions and places to visit within a short distance. Quality cottages with quality fittings and outdoor furniture. Central heating, double glazing. All weather tennis court (en-tout-cas). Children and small pets welcome. Three night breaks or longer – arrive any day.

OSWESTRY. Mrs Glenice Jones, Lloran Ganol Farm, Llansilin, Oswestry SY10 7OX (01691 791287). WTB Four Dragons. Working farm. Sleeps 5. A luxury self-catering bungalow on mixed farm in quiet valley. Farm and bungalow are situated over the border in the Welsh hills in Clwyd. Five people accommodated in two double and one single bedrooms; bathroom, toilet; sittingroom, diningroom; colour TV; long kitchen with dining area; automatic washing machine, tumble dryer, dishwasher, microwave, freezer and fridge. Linen supplied. Extra charge for pets. Two and a half miles from the shops. Car essential - parking. Trout fishing on farm; horse riding locally, golf and trekking in surrounding area. Open all year round, the bungalow is suitable for partially disabled guests. Storage heaters, fitted carpets and garden furniture provided. Glass conservatory. Weekly terms from £100. Bed and Breakfast also available with family in house adjoining from £16 per night, Bed, Breakfast and Evening Meal (by arrangement) from £30 per night.

OSWESTRY near. Mr and Mrs Breeze, Lloran Isaf, Llansilin, Near Oswestry SY10 7QX (01691 791376

or 01691 780318). Working farm. Beautiful bungalow set on a working farm in its own valley which has wonderful scenery and walks. Kitchen with microwave, washer/dryer, fridge, cooker; lounge/dining area with colour TV and woodburning stove, small charge for logs; three bedrooms – one twin, one double, one single (duvets supplied but no linen); separate toilet and bathroom. Fitted carpets and electric heating in bedrooms and lounge; barbecue, garden furniture in enclosed garden. One and a half miles from village, wonderful touring area with lots of attractions. Open all year. Pets welcome. Sorry no children. Prices from £80. Electricity by meter reading. 3 Dragon Grade.

SHREWSBURY. Mrs A. Cartwright, Ryton Farm, Ryton, Dorrington, Shrewsbury SY5 7LY (01743

718449). Ryton Farm Holiday Cottages are peacefully situated overlooking the South Shropshire Hills but only half-a-mile from the A49, five miles south of Shrewsbury. There is a choice of traditional cottages with large gardens or recently coverted barns with en suite facilities furnished, equipped and maintained to a high standard. Lovely walking and plenty of interesting places to visit (Ironbridge, gardens, stately homes, steam railways, working farms, castles and so much more) make this an ideal holiday base. Excellent coarse fishing is available in the farm pools and well behaved pets are most welcome. Please write or telephone for further information.

FOR THE MUTUAL GUIDANCE OF GUEST AND HOST

Every year literally thousands of holidays, short breaks and overnight stops are arranged through our guides, the vast majority without any problems at all. In a handful of cases, however, difficulties do arise about bookings, which often could have been prevented from the outset.

It is important to remember that when accommodation has been booked, both parties – guests and hosts – have entered into a form of contract. We hope that the following points will provide helpful guidance.

GUESTS: When enquiring about accommodation, be as precise as possible. Give exact dates, numbers in your party and the ages of any children. State the number and type of rooms wanted and also what catering you require – bed and breakfast, full board etc. Make sure that the position about evening meals is clear – and about pets, reductions for children or any other special points.

Read our reviews carefully to ensure that the proprietors you are going to contact can supply what you want. Ask for a letter confirming all arrangements, if possible.

If you have to cancel, do so as soon as possible. Proprietors do have the right to retain deposits and under certain circumstances to charge for cancelled holidays if adequate notice is not given and they cannot re-let the accommodation.

HOSTS: Give details about your facilities and about any special conditions. Explain your deposit system clearly and arrangements for cancellations, charges etc. and whether or not your terms include VAT.

If for any reason you are unable to fulfil an agreed booking without adequate notice, you may be under an obligation to arrange suitable alternative accommodation or to make some form of compensation.

While every effort is made to ensure accuracy, we regret that FHG Publications cannot accept responsibility for errors, omissions or misrepresentations in our entries or any consequences thereof.

Prices in particular should be checked because we go to press early. We will follow up complaints but cannot act as arbiters or agents for either party.

SOMERSET

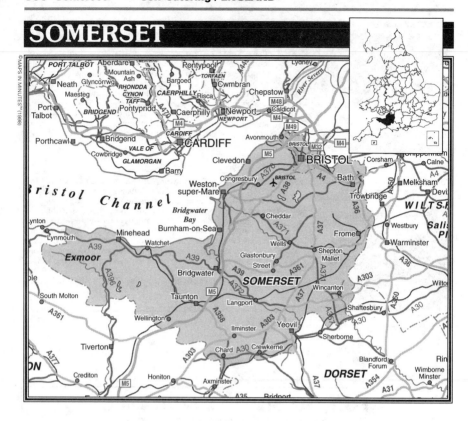

ALLERFORD. The Pack Horse Holiday Flats, Allerford, Near Minehead TA24 8HW (Tel & Fax: 01643 862475). WCTB ♀♀♀ COMMENDED. Close to Porlock for restaurants, inns, freshly baked bread, mini-markets – all you need for a self-catering holiday. Woods and moors within minutes for walkers. Riding stables one mile. Our centrally heated flats are open all year, and ideally suit two/three persons with double bedded and small single room. They overlook the ancient packhorse bridge and small River Aller in National Trust village. Family cottage also available. Walled courtyard ensures safe parking. Coffee, lunches and cream teas served in our garden on fine days. Dogs accepted by arrangement. Terms from £195 to £300. Bed and Breakfast £45 double. Short breaks available. Brochure by return.

BURNHAM-ON-SEA near. Mrs W. Baker, Withy Grove Farm, East Huntspill, Near Burnham-on-Sea TA9 3NP (01278 784471). ♀♀♀ APPROVED. Properties sleep 4/5. Come and enjoy a relaxing and friendly holiday "Down on the Farm" set in beautiful Somerset countryside. Peaceful rural setting adjoining River Huntspill, famed for its coarse fishing. The farm is ideally situated for visiting the many local attractions including Cheddar Gorge, Glastonbury, Weston-super-Mare and the lovely sandy beach of Burnham-on-Sea. Self-catering cottages are tastefully converted and fully equipped including colour TV. Facilities also include heated swimming pool, licensed bar and entertainment in high season, games room, skittle alley. Reasonable rates. Please write or telephone for further details.

CHEDDAR. Sungate Holiday Apartments. In Cheddar village, close to Cheddar Gorge and the Mendip Hills, this Listed Georgian building has been thoughtfully converted into four holiday apartments. Each apartment has lounge with sofa bed, TV, bedroom, bathroom, fully-equipped kitchen plus microwave. Linen supplied. Laundry facilities. Pets welcome with prior approval. Private parking. Swimming and leisure facilities nearby. Competitively priced for a short break, longer holiday or a short-term let. Bookings: **Mrs Fieldhouse, "Pyrenmount", Parsons Way, Winscombe BS25 1BU (01934 842273; Fax: 01934 741411).**

EXMOOR. Mrs Jones, Higher Town, Dulverton TA22 9RX (01398 341272). Our property is set in 80 acres of National Park, half-a-mile from open moorland and visitors are welcome to walk over our beef and sheep farm. The bungalow is situated on its own with lovely views, lawn and parking space. It sleeps six with one bunk-bedded room, double bedroom and one bedroom with two single beds. Bedding, linen and electricity are provided. The bathroom and toilet are separate and the bath also has a shower over. The lounge has an open fire and colour TV, the kitchen has electric cooker, fridge freezer and washer dryer. Centrally heated and double glazed. SAE please for further information.

GLASTONBURY. Mrs A. Coles, Middlewick Farm Holiday Cottages, Wick Lane, Glastonbury BA6 8JW (Tel & Fax: 01458 832351). To ŤŤŤŤ COMMENDED. **Working farm. Sleep 2/6.** Eight delightful cottages with luxury indoor heated swimming pool set in 20 acres of cottage gardens, meadows and apple orchards. The cottages have country style decor with olde worlde charm. The smallest cottage sleeps two, the largest six plus cot. In total, the eight cottages sleep 30 people. The accommodation is set around a courtyard and gardens. They have a wealth of inglenooks and beamed ceilings. Each has its own character and all are cosy and comfortable. Some ground floor accommodation available. Central for many places of interest. Terms from £180 to £585.

GLASTONBURY. Mrs M. Moon, West Town Farm, Baltonsborough, Glastonbury BA6 8QX (01458 850217). Spacious, fully furnished flat in wing of 17th century farmhouse, situated in lovely Somerset countryside. Ideal for touring – Glastonbury, Wells, Cheddar, Wookey, Longleat – and midway between south and north coast seaside resorts. Self contained with own bathroom/toilet/shower. Lounge/diner with TV and electric fire; fitted kitchen with electric cooker and fridge. One bedroom with double and single beds, washbasin; second bedroom with two single beds, washbasin; cot. Central heating. Large walled garden with lawns. Visitors must supply own linen. Children most welcome. Sorry, no pets. Holder of FHG Diploma. SAE for full details, terms and dates available.

MUCHELNEY. South Ham Barn. ŤŤŤŤ COMMENDED. **Sleeps 4**. A barn adjacent to our three-hundred-year-old thatched farmhouse in a medieval village has been converted into cosy well-equipped accomodation with a double room and two twins. Plus occasional sofa bed. Comfortable lounge with wood burner and spacious kitchen and diner. Automatic washing machine and colour TV. Cot and baby sitting service available. Linen, towels and electricity included, and a welcome pack awaits your arrival. Own garden with picnic table and barbecue. Home-made bread available as are fresh eggs from our own free range chickens. Children will enjoy seeing our ducks, horses and sheep. Canoeing, walking and fishing, and bikes are usually available. A wonderful rural location on Somerset Levels, one of the last unspoilt wetlands in England. Terms from £250 to £450. Two nights break from £150. Contact: **Dr Elizabeth Nightingale, South Ham Farm, Muchelney Ham, Near Langport TA10 0DJ (Tel & Fax: 01458 250816.)**

PORLOCK. Lucott Farm, Porlock, Minehead. Sleeps 2/10. Isolated farmhouse on Exmoor, with wood burning fireplaces and all modern conveniences. It lies at the head of Horner Valley and guests will delight in the wonderful scenery. Plenty of pony trekking in the area. Ten people accommodated in four double and two single bedrooms, cot; bathroom, two toilets; sittingroom; diningroom. Kitchen has oil-fired Aga and water heater. No linen supplied. Shops three miles; sea four miles. Car essential - parking. Open all year. Terms (including fuel) on application with SAE please to **Mrs E.A. Tucker, West Luccombe Cottage, Porlock, Minehead TA24 8MT (01643 862810).**

SHEPTON MALLET. Mrs J.A. Boyce, Knowle Farm, West Compton, Shepton Mallet BA4 4PD (01749 890482; Fax: 01749 890405). ♈♈♈♈ *COMMENDED*. **Working farm. Cottages sleep 2/5/8.** Four charming cottages superbly converted from old barns and furnished to a high standard. Pretty gardens to relax in and separate play area for children. Two cottages have kitchen/diner, separate lounge, colour TV, the other two have kitchen, lounge/diner, colour TV. Cot, high chair by prior arrangement. Bed linen supplied; towels by request. Situated in quiet secluded countryside yet close to Wells, Glastonbury, Bath, etc, and approximately five miles from Wells and Mendip Golf Clubs. Area also has a wide selection of family attractions. Sorry no pets. Terms: £170 to £420. Car essential, ample parking. Payphone for guests. Open all year.

SIMONSBATH. Jane Styles, Wintershead Farm, Simonsbath, Exmoor TA24 7LF (01643 831222; Fax: 01643 831628). ♈/♈♈♈♈ *HIGHLY COMMENDED*. Hidden away in that place on Exmoor which you normally only find once you're already on holiday, and can never remember where you saw it! Wintershead offers you the peace and tranquility you need to recharge the batteries after the stresses of everyday life. Five self-catering cottages to suit all your needs. Short breaks available from November to March. Please telephone, fax or write for a colour brochure.

Wintershead

TAUNTON. Mrs Joan Greenway, Woodlands Farm, Bathealton, Taunton TA4 2AH (01984 623271). You can be assured of a warm and friendly welcome on our family-run dairy farm, with a small carp pond. Children are welcome and will enjoy feeding the animals. We are in the heart of beautiful unspoilt countryside within easy reach of the North and South Coasts and Exmoor. The cottage sleeps five people and is furnished to a high standard to enjoy a relaxing holiday. The kitchen has washing machine, microwave, etc. Bathroom with bath and shower. Electricity, central heating and bed linen included in the tariff. Terms from £165 to £295 per week. Please write or phone for colour brochure.

WINSFORD (near Dulverton). Ball Cottage, Winsford. Sleeps 6 plus cot. 17th century cottage in one of the prettiest villages of the Exmoor National Park. The River Exe runs through the large garden. Redecorated and furnished very comfortably for six people plus baby (one double bedroom, one twin, two singles, sittingroom, kitchen/diner, bathroom). All-electric except for an open fire with free logs. Colour TV. Washer/dryer. Excellent village shop but car essential. Own garage. No linen provided, and no pets, please. Open all year round. £212 to £310 per week. **SAE to Mrs Mary Wilkinson, 44 Guildford Road, London SW8 2BU (020 7622 6757).**

STAFFORDSHIRE

LEEK. Edith and Alwyn Mycock, 'Rosewood Holiday Flats', Lower Berkhamsytch Farm, Bottom House, Near Leek ST13 7QP (Tel and Fax: 01538 308213).

ꝗꝗꝗ *COMMENDED*. **Sleep 6 plus cot.** Two cosy flats each with own private entrance on stock rearing farm within walking distance of two pubs serving meals and Little Chef Restaurant. Central to Alton Towers, Potteries and Peak District. Ground floor flat sleeps six in two bedrooms and sofa bed in lounge. First floor flat sleeps seven in two bedrooms plus sofa bed in lounge. Colour TV and microwaves; shower rooms with washbasin and toilet in both flats. Children welcome, cot and high chair available. Play area, patio sitting area. Well behaved pets welcome. Laundry room. Guests are offered a warm welcome by the owners who will do their best to give you an enjoyable holiday. Terms from £120 to £235 per week. Electricity and linen included.

SUFFOLK

HEPWORTH. Mrs K. M. Chapman, Goswell Farm, Clay Lane, Hepworth IP22 2QD (01359 251094).

ꝗꝗꝗꝗ *HIGHLY COMMENDED*. **Sleeps 3 adults plus cot or 2 adults and 2 children.** Property is located on a quiet country lane half-a-mile from the village of Hepworth. Goswell Farm is quarter-of-a-mile from the nearest public house which also provides bar and restaurant meals. 'The Granary' is a detached late 18th century brick and flint building adjacent to the farmhouse. Beautifully restored, the accommodation now comprises - Downstairs: Entrance lobby/hall. Cloakroom with wc, washbasin, shaver-point, washing machine/tumble dryer. Upstairs: Sitting-room with exposed timbers and lovely views to the south and west. Wood burning stove in sitting-room. TV, video and radio are provided. Also all linen and towels. Sofabed in the sitting room. A cot and high chair are available. No smoking. Pets by arrangement. Ample parking available. Nearest PO/General stores 2 miles. Bury St Edmunds and Diss mainline train stations 10 miles. The weekly price is inclusive of electricity. Terms from £174 Low Season, to £208 High Season. Short breaks are available from £40 per day. Open all year. Brochure available.

KESSINGLAND. Kessingland Cottages, Rider Haggard Lane, Kessingland. Sleeps 6. An exciting three-

bedroom recently built semi-detached cottage situated on the beach, three miles south of sandy beach at Lowestoft. Fully and attractively furnished – colour TV and delightful sea and lawn views from floor to ceiling windows of lounge. Accommodation for up to eight people. Well-equipped kitchen with electric cooker, fridge, electric immersion heater. Electricity by £1 coin meter. Luxurious bathroom with coloured suite. No linen or towels provided. Only a few yards to beach and sea fishing. One mile to wildlife country park with mini-train. Buses quarter-of-a-mile and shopping centre half-a-mile away. Parking, but car not essential. Children and disabled persons welcome. Available 1st March to 7th January. Weekly terms from £50 in early March and late December to £195 in peak season. SAE to **Mr S. Mahmood, 156 Bromley Road, Beckenham, Kent BR3 6PG (Tel & Fax: 0208-650 0539).**

SAXMUNDHAM. Mrs Mary Kitson, White House Farm, Sibton, Saxmundham IP17 2NE (01728 660260). Working farm. Sleeps 4/6 adults; 2/4 children. The flat is a self-contained part of late Georgian farmhouse standing in 130 acres of quiet farmland with a variety of livestock. Fishing on farm. Accommodation in three double bedrooms (two double/two single beds) plus cot; livingroom with TV; shower/toilet on first floor. Entrance hall, kitchen/diner on ground floor. Full central heating. Situated one-and-a-half miles from village shops, etc. Ten miles from coast at Dunwich, Minsmere Bird Sanctuary, Snape Maltings. Linen optional. Pets permitted. Car essential - parking. Available all year. Terms from £130 to £180 per week. SAE, please, for further details.

SAXMUNDHAM. David Gray, Park Farm, Sibton, Saxmundham IP17 2LZ (01728 668324). BLUEBELL, BONNY and BUTTERCUP - three delightful converted dairy buildings situated around a flower-decked courtyard, just the place for a barbecue on soft summer evenings. BLUEBELL sleeps two plus cot, BONNY and BUTTERCUP four each plus cot. All have bathrooms, fully equipped kitchens, comfortable living room with TV, video and audio systems. Wide doors for wheelchairs. Laundry and games room. Wonderfully central for Heritage Coast ideal for cycling, walking, bird-watching or simply experiencing "life in the slow lane". Sorry, no pets or smoking.

WALSHAM-LE-WILLOWS. Bridge Cottage, Walsham-le-Willows, Near Bury St. Edmunds. ♙♙♙ *APPROVED.* **Sleeps 5.** Bridge Cottage is illustrated in the book "English Cottages", with introduction by John Betjeman. Built in the 17th century it has been attractively modernised. There are fitted carpets and comfortable beds; centrally heated and well furnished. The kitchen is well equipped with electric cooker and fridge/deep freeze. Plenty of hot water. Children and well-behaved pets are welcome. Electricity and heating included in rent. Colour TV. Tennis court and swimming pool available in summer by arrangement. Walsham-le-Willows is in the centre of East Anglia (11 miles from Bury St. Edmunds) and has shops and post office. Available all year. Terms from £190 to £300. **Mrs H.M. Russell, The Beeches, Walsham-le-Willows, Near Bury St. Edmunds IP31 3AD (01359 259227; Fax: 01359 258206).**

WOLDINGHAM. Mrs J.A. Crux, The White Cottage, Birchwood House, Woldingham Road, Woldingham CR3 7LR (01883 343287; Fax: 01883 348066). Sleeps 4/5 plus cot. ♙♙♙♙ Detached single storey part brick/timber cottage on owners' farm situated in valley on the edge of North Downs. Accommodation comprises lounge with sofa bed, dining room, kitchen, bathroom and two bedrooms (one with double bed and one with two single beds). The cottage is fully furnished including fitted carpets, electric cooker, fridge, washing machine, tumble dryer, colour TV, Sky TV etc. Barbecue and garden furniture. Central heating. Woldingham is a beautiful area, known locally as Little Switzerland. For those wanting country access as well as easy access to London it is ideal. Available all year. Rates from £220 –£240 per week. Brochure available.

SURREY

KINGSTON-UPON-THAMES near. Sunny House. LTB ★★★ An attractive alternative to staying in hotels. Designed to suit the discerning business executive or independent traveller away from home, Sunny House has the appeal of a modern up-market establishment whilst still retaining the charm and characteristics of a well-cared for home. Easy availability of transport to almost anywhere in London, overlooking the quaint surroundings of Royal Bushy Park. All accommodation equipped with en suite facilities, colour TV with satellite, fridge, tea/coffee facilities, direct-dial telephone; use of spacious well-fitted kitchen with dishwasher, washing machine, microwave etc. Also use of beautiful lounge; six-day maid service; full parking facilities. For full details contact: **Chase Lodge Hotel, 10 Park Road, Hampton Wick, Kingston-upon-Thames KT1 4AS (020 8943 1862; Fax: 020 8943 9363).**

EAST SUSSEX

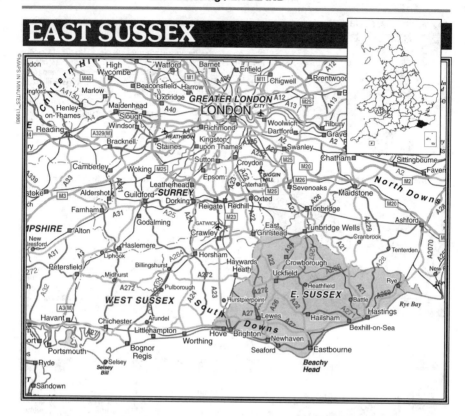

ALFRISTON. Mr and Mrs G. Burgess, Polhills, Arlington, Polegate BN26 6SB (01323 870004).

Idyllically situated on shore of reservoir and edge of Sussex Downs within easy reach of the sea. Fully furnished period cottage (approached by own drive along the water's edge) available for self-catering holidays from April to October (inclusive). Fly fishing for trout can be arranged during season. Accommodation consists of two main bedrooms; tiled bathroom. Lounge with colour TV; large well-fitted kitchen with fridge freezer, electric cooker, microwave, washing machine; dining room with put-u-up settee; sun lounge. Central heating. Everything supplied except linen. Most rooms contain a wealth of oak beams. Children and pets welcome. Car essential. Ample parking. Shops two miles. Golf, hill climbing locally. Sea eight miles. Weekly terms from £195 to £265 (electricity included).

HERSTMONCEUX. Cuckoo Cottage, Chapel Row, Herstmonceux, Near Battle BN27 1RB ETB

HIGHLY COMMENDED. **Sleeps 4 plus cot.** Near Herstmonceux Castle, this newly refurbished period farmworker's cottage is an ideal base for visiting Eastbourne, Battle, Hastings and the market town of Hailsham. Also nearby is the oldest, and most original, inn in Sussex – the 'Kicking Donkey'. The cottage retains its original oak beams, and has a lounge with inglenook fireplace and log fire, colour TV (with Sky), well stocked bookshelves, cloakroom, laundry room and fully equipped kitchen. There are two bedrooms (one double, one twin), luxury bathroom and central heating. The cottage is in a beautiful rural setting on the edge of Herstmonceux village with many beautiful walks, such as the Cuckoo Trail, within easy reach. Large garden with patio area, table and chairs. Children welcome, regret no pets. Rates from £225 to £420 per week. For bookings please contact: **Mr Laurence Gilday, 71 Cornwallis Avenue, Tonbridge, Kent TN10 4ET (01732 770054 or 01323 417174; Fax: 01732 358127; Mobile: 07973 191610).**

WEST SUSSEX

HENFIELD. The Holiday Flat and Cottage, New Hall, Small Dole, Henfield BN5 9YJ (01273 492546). ♙♙♙ *COMMENDED.* New Hall is the manor house of Henfield, it stands in three --and-a-half acres of mature gardens, surrounded by farmland with abundant footpaths. The holiday cottage is the original 1600 AD farmhouse. It has one en suite bedroom with large living room with a folding bed, dining room and kitchen. A door opens into the walled garden. Holiday flat is the upper part of the dairy wing. Its front door opens from a Georgian courtyard. It has three bedrooms sleeping five, lounge/diner, kitchen and bathroom. Both units are fully equipped and comfortably furnished. Children welcome. Open all year. Terms from £140 to £295 per week. Send SAE for details, or phone **Mrs M.W. Carreck.**

STEYNING. Mrs A. Shapland, Wappingthorn Farm, Horsham Road, Steyning BN44 3AA (Tel & Fax: 01903 813236). Working farm. We have two luxury furnished bungalows which we have recently converted from our stables. Each bungalow sleeps two/four with a double sofa bed in the lounge area. Many footpaths surround our 300 acre farm and the market town of Steyning, or relax by our heated outdoor pool and gardens. Overlooking the South Downs, approximately four miles seaside, seven miles Worthing, 12 miles Brighton. All linen/towels provided, washing and drying facilities, cots, babysitting, packed lunches, telephone, taxi service available. From £112 per week. Traditional farmhouse B&B from £18 per person also available. Open all year.

FOR THE MUTUAL GUIDANCE
OF GUEST AND HOST

Every year literally thousands of holidays, short breaks and overnight stops are arranged through our guides, the vast majority without any problems at all. In a handful of cases, however, difficulties do arise about bookings, which often could have been prevented from the outset.

It is important to remember that when accommodation has been booked, both parties – guests and hosts – have entered into a form of contract. We hope that the following points will provide helpful guidance.

GUESTS: When enquiring about accommodation, be as precise as possible. Give exact dates, numbers in your party and the ages of any children. State the number and type of rooms wanted and also what catering you require – bed and breakfast, full board etc. Make sure that the position about evening meals is clear – and about pets, reductions for children or any other special points.

Read our reviews carefully to ensure that the proprietors you are going to contact can supply what you want. Ask for a letter confirming all arrangements, if possible.

If you have to cancel, do so as soon as possible. Proprietors do have the right to retain deposits and under certain circumstances to charge for cancelled holidays if adequate notice is not given and they cannot re-let the accommodation.

HOSTS: Give details about your facilities and about any special conditions. Explain your deposit system clearly and arrangements for cancellations, charges etc. and whether or not your terms include VAT.

If for any reason you are unable to fulfil an agreed booking without adequate notice, you may be under an obligation to arrange suitable alternative accommodation or to make some form of compensation.

While every effort is made to ensure accuracy, we regret that FHG Publications cannot accept responsibility for errors, omissions or misrepresentations in our entries or any consequences thereof.

Prices in particular should be checked because we go to press early. We will follow up complaints but cannot act as arbiters or agents for either party.

WARWICKSHIRE

Warwickshire Farm Holidays

Warwickshire farming families welcome guests into their homes to enjoy the comforts of a traditional English farmhouse and discover the peace of the English countryside. Each home listed has its own unique character and differs in size, style and price, but all offer a high standard of accommodation, good food, a warm welcome and excellent value for money to holidaymakers and business travellers. Most owners are members of the Farm Holiday Bureau, all properties are inspected, classified and graded by the English Tourism Council. Warwickshire, in the heart of England, provides the perfect setting for the perfect holiday. mile upon mile of rolling countryside, picturesque villages and meandering waterways. There are castles, stately homes, theatres, country gardens and some of the prettiest villages to be found.

Places to visit within easy reach include Stratford-upon-Avon, Warwick, Royal Leamington Spa, The Cotswolds, Oxford, Coventry, National Exhibition Centre and National Agricultural Centre.

For further details about Bed & Breakfast or Self-catering cottages, please write, telephone or fax for a free brochure to: Warwickshire Farm Holidays (FHG), Crandon House, Avon Dassett, Leamington Spa CV33 0AA.
Tel: 01295 770652; Fax: 01295 770632 E-mail: warksfarmhols@talk.com

---

ATHERSTONE. Hipsley Farm Cottages, Hipsley Lane, Hurley, Atherstone CV9 2LR (Tel & Fax: 01827 872437) ꞇꞇꞇ/ꞇꞇꞇꞇ *HIGHLY COMMENDED* **Sleeps 2/4.**

Hipsley Farm is situated in beautiful rolling countryside. Very peaceful and quiet yet only three miles from the M42, giving easy access to all the Midlands. The barns and cowshed have been carefully converted into six very comfortable, individually furnished cottages. Fully equipped including gas central heating, colour TV, all bed linen and towels. Laundry facilities and putting green. Ample parking on site. Open all year.

LEAMINGTON SPA. Mrs Christine Whitfield, Furzen Hill Farm, Cubbington Heath, Leamington Spa CV32 6QZ (Tel & Fax: 01926 424791). ꞇꞇꞇ *COMMENDED*.

Furzen Hill is a mixed farm. The Cottage is part of 17th century farmhouse with a large shared garden. Sleeping seven. The Barn and Dairy Cottages, both recently converted, each sleep four. Dairy Cottage has its own small garden. The Barn shares the Cottage garden. All have the use of tennis court. Situated within easy reach of NAC, NEC, Warwick Castle and Stratford. Children welcome and well behaved dogs by arrangement. Open all year. Terms from £120 to £320 per week.

STRATFORD-UPON-AVON. Lilian Court, off Vincent Avenue. Sleeps 4/6. A select development of two-bedroom flats and three chalet-bungalows, half-a-mile from Shakespeare's birthplace. Fully equipped kitchens with washing machine, dishwasher, fridge, freezer and microwave oven. Electric shower. Gas central heating to flats, gas and bungalows. Colour TV. Twin or double beds available. En suite bathrooms in bungalows. Fitted carpets throughout. Linen available. Small landscaped garden to bungalows and patio area to flats, each with barbecue facilities. Adequate car parking. No pets. No smoking. £300 to £500 per week. **Mr Fraser, 21 Vincent Avenue, Stratford-Upon-Avon CV37 6SR (01789 269572).**

Visit the FHG website
www.holidayguides.com
for details of the wide choice of accommodation
featured in the full range of FHG titles

WILTSHIRE

CHIPPENHAM. Mr D. Humphrey, Roward Farm, Draycot Cerne, Chippenham SN15 4SG (01249 758147). ETB ♈♈♈♈ *HIGHLY COMMENDED*. **Sleep 2/4.**

Roward Farm offers two holiday cottages, converted from traditional farm buildings. Overlooking open fields, they provide the perfect base for visiting the Cotswolds and Bath, with Castle Combe, Lacock Abbey and Bowood House all close by. Both cottages are fully-equipped and furnished to a high standard. Laundry facilities are available and bed linen, towel and tea towels are provided. Barbecue facilities also available. One cottage has one double bedroom plus sofa bed in the living room, the other has one double and one twin. Welcome pack on arrival. Non-smoking throughout. Well behaved pets are welcome. Please call or write for brochure and terms.

DEVIZES. Colin and Cynthia Fletcher, Lower Foxhangers Farm, Rowde, Devizes SN10 1SS (Tel & Fax: 01380 828795). Sleep 4/6.

Enjoy your holiday with us on our small farm/marina with its many diverse attractions. Hear the near musical clatter of the windlass heralding the lock gate opening and the arrival of yet another narrowboat. Relax on the patios of our rural retreats – four holiday mobile homes sleeping four/six in a setting close to the canal locks. Bed and Breakfast accommodation in 18th century spacious farmhouse from £19.50 per person. Also available weekly or short breaks with our narrowboat holidays or small camp site with electricity and facilities. Self-catering rates from £170 per week.

MALMESBURY. Mrs Edwards, Stonehill Farm, Charlton, Malmesbury SN16 9DY (01666 823310). ♈♈♈

COMMENDED. Sleeps 2/3. Superbly located on the edge of the Cotswolds in lush rolling countryside. We invite you to stay with us on our family run dairy farm in two comfortable, well equipped cottages, converted from farm buildings and comprising lounge, kitchen/diner, bathroom, bedroom. Tariff includes power, heat and linen. Visit quiet villages, stately homes, market towns, walk in the countryside or stay at the farm and watch the cows being milked. Spend days in Bath, Oxford, Stonehenge or the Cotswold Hills. From £160 to £210 per week.

SALISBURY. Mr G. Gould, The Old Stables, Bridge Farm, Lower Road, Britford, Salisbury SP5 4DY (01722 328954; Fax: 01722 332376). Sleep 5/6.

Newly converted 19th century stable block. Peacefully situated in village close to Salisbury. Three units, traditionally and individually decorated, spiral staircases and exposed beams. Downstairs one en suite double/twin room, upstairs one double, one single and shower room. Ground floor is wheelchair accessible/disabled friendly. Washing machine, microwave, TV, central heating. Bedding provided, payphone available. Own patios, shared garden within chalk thatched wall. Ideal touring base. Stonehenge, Avebury, New Forest, Longleat, Wilton House all within easy reach. Town and Cathedral five minutes' drive. Non-smoking. Open December 1999.

FREE and REDUCED RATE Holiday Visits!
Don't miss our Readers' Offer Vouchers

YORKSHIRE

Terms quoted in this publication may be subject to increase
if rises in costs necessitate

ASKRIGG. Fern Croft, 2 Mill Lane, Askrigg. Sleeps 4. A modern cottage enjoying quiet location on edge

of village with open fields rising immediately behind. Attractive and compact, this Wensleydale village is an ideal centre for Dales, with facilities for everyday needs, including two shops, post office, restaurant and a couple of pubs. Furnished to a high standard for four, ground floor accommodation comprises large comfortable lounge/diner with colour TV and well-equipped kitchen. Upstairs there are two double bedrooms with a double and twin beds respectively, and modern bathroom. Storage heating included, other electricity by meter. Regret no pets. Terms from £115 to £235 weekly. Brochure: **Mr and Mrs K. Dobson (01689 838450).**

ASKRIGG/WENSLEYDALE. Mrs E. Scarr, Coleby Hall, Askrigg, Leyburn DL8 3DX (01969 650216).

Working farm. Sleeps 5 plus cot. Situated in Wensleydale, half-a-mile from Bainbridge and one mile from Askrigg, Coleby Hall is a 17th century gabled farmhouse with stone mullioned windows, the west end being to let. A stone spiral staircase leads to two bedrooms; linen provided. The kitchen is equipped with electric cooker, fridge, crockery, etc., and coal fire. The lounge has an inglenook coal fire and metered TV. Oil-fired central heating throughout. Coleby has lovely views and is an ideal situation for walking, fishing and driving round the Yorkshire Dales. Children and pets welcome. Terms from £170 per week.

COVERDALE. Mrs Caroline Harrison, Hill Top Farm and Livery Yard, West Scrafton, Leyburn DL8 4RU

(01969 640663). ῗῗῗῗ *HIGHLY COMMENDED.* **Working farm. Properties sleep 4/6.** Relax in our recently converted traditional Dales stone barns with panoramic views of Rova Crag and open moorland. This peaceful hamlet nestles in the heart of the Yorkshire Dales National Park, Herriot country. The properties' fully equipped kitchens and modern en suite bathrooms retain much character with original exposed beams and open fireplaces. Facilities include central heating, log fires, colour TVs, dishwashers, automatic washing machines, fridges, deep freeze facilities, microwaves, electric cookers, fitted carpets throughout. Linen provided. Games room. Pets corner with pony. Ideal for children, walkers or relaxing. Livery yard with qualified registered instructor. BHF book of bridleways provided. Fishing, shooting. Comprehensive brochure provided.

EASINGWOLD. Mrs Rachel Ritchie, The Old Rectory, Thormanby, Easingwold, York YO61 4NN

(01845 501417). The Old Rectory's Coach House and Stable have been lovingly converted into two holiday cottages and enjoy a delightful setting in a quiet country lane, just out of the small village of Thormanby (three miles north of Easingwold). It is an excellent base for visiting York (17 miles), the North Yorkshire Moors to the east and Dales to the west. There are many country houses, abbeys and castles in the area. Stable Cottage has one double and one twin-bedded rooms plus cot. The Coach House has one double and two twin rooms plus cot. They are fully equipped. All linen and towels provided. Colour TV, open fires (fuel supplied). Night storage heaters when required. Children and well-behaved pets welcome. Electricity by meter reading. Open all year. From £130 weekly. SAE for brochure.

See also Colour Display Advertisement

EASINGWOLD. Village Farm Holidays 🔑🔑🔑🔑 *HIGHLY COMMENDED*. Situated in a peaceful and picturesque village approximately three miles from the York ringroad and five miles south of Easingwold. Our two holiday cottages are converted from farm buildings and are spacious and well furnished. They are both single storey and suitable for accompanied special needs people. Gas central heating, electricity, linen and towels are included in the rent. Colour TV, video and satellite system (card not provided). Washing machine, microwave, fridge and electric cooker, hi-fi, iron and coffee machine. One double and one twin bedroom. Cot and high chair available. One pet per occupancy. Breakfast service available by prior arrangement. Bed and Breakfast also available. Further details: **Pat and Ernie Huck, Village Farm, Cherry Tree Avenue, Newton-on-Ouse, York YO30 2BN (01347 848064; Fax: 01347 848065).**
website: www.yorkshire.co.uk/stayat/villagefarm

GOATHLAND, near Whitby. Rosedean, Abbot's House Farm, Goathland. Sleeps 2 plus cot. Ground floor studio apartment next to farmhouse. Separate entrance, garden, conservatory, car parking. Electric cooker, microwave, fridge/freezer, colour TV, open fire. Goathland (Aidensfield from YTV Heartbeat series) is situated in the heart of North York moors, a centre for walking, cycling or just relaxing. North York Moors Railway runs through the farm. Pets welcome. Rates from £165 per week include fuel and power, bed linen/towels. The farm is 600 metres from Goathland village. SAE to **Abbot's House Farm, Goathland, Whitby YO22 5NH (01947 896270 or 896026).**

GRASSINGTON near. Mrs Judith M. Joy, Jerry and Ben's, Hebden, Skipton BD23 5DL (01756 752369; Fax: 01756 753370). Properties sleep 3/6/8/9.

Jerry and Ben's stands in two acres of grounds in one of the most attractive parts of the Yorkshire Dales National Park. Seven properties; Ghyll Cottage (sleeps eight); Mamie's Cottage (sleeps eight); Paradise End (sleeps six); Robin Middle (sleeps six); High Close (sleeps nine); Cruck Rise (sleeps six); Raikes Side (sleeps two/three). All have parking, electric cooker, microwave, toaster, fridge, colour TV, electric heating and immersion heater; lounge, dining area, bathroom with shower; cots if required. Fully equipped, including linen if requested. Washing machine and telephone available. Ghyll and Mamie's Cottages now have dishwashers. Well behaved pets accepted. Open all year. Fishing and bathing close by. Terms from £90 to £340. SAE, please for detailed brochure. Suitable for some disabled guests.

HARROGATE. Mrs Hardcastle, Southfield Farm, Darley, Harrogate HG3 2PR (01423 780258). Two well-equipped holiday cottages on a farm in an attractive area between Harrogate and Pateley Bridge. An ideal place to explore the whole of the Dale, with York and Herriot country within easy driving distance. Riverside walks, village shop and post office within quarter-of-a-mile, and local pub one mile away. Each cottage has two bedrooms, one double and one with bunk beds, bathroom and shower. Games room with table tennis and small snooker table. Large lawn for ball games, with garden chairs and barbecue. Pets welcome. Ample car parking. Prices from £150 to £180 low season, £180 to £250 high season.

HAWES. River View, Dyers Garth, Hawes. Sleeps 6. A spacious three-bedroomed terraced Dales cottage situated in a cul-de-sac overlooking "Duerley Beck", and attractive trout stream which runs through Hawes, a market town in the centre of Yorkshire Dales National Park and on the Pennine Way. The cottage is in an ideal location for river walks and high fell walks, fishing and visits to local scenic attractions which include Hardraw Scar, Aysgarth Falls and has the benefit of the owners living next door. Hawes is of course the home of Wensleydale cheese-making and also rope-making. The cottage accommodates six plus baby (cot); three double bedrooms, bathroom, lounge with colour TV and fully equipped kitchen/diner. Storage heaters, open coal fire. Shops 30 yards. Parking space for one car. Terms from £120 to £270 per week. SAE, please, for terms to **Mrs Sheila Alderson, Inverdene, Hawes DL8 3NJ (01969 667408).**

HAWES. Graham and Mary Watts, Gaudy Farmhouse, Gayle, Hawes DL8 3NA (Tel & Fax: 01969

667231). ETC ʔʔ *APPROVED.* **Sleeps 2/6.** Traditional Yorkshire stone barns converted to four spacious self-contained flats sleeping two, four or six. Situated alongside the owners' old farmhouse in 25 acres of sheep grazed pastures with gardens, woodland and stream, the accommodation is in a unique setting on the Pennine Way with magnificent views over Wensleydale, offering privacy, peace and comfort. An ideal location for exploring the Dales, with Hawes just one mile away for shops, pubs, excellent fish and chips and a delightful countryside museum. Children welcome, also well-controlled pets. Group bookings of up to 20 people can be taken and a meeting room in the farmhouse is often available. Reasonable, negotiable rentals all year round from £140 to £285 per week. Please write or phone for our brochure.
email: gaudy@ndirect.co.uk
website: www.wensleydale.org/accommodation/gaudyfarmhouse

Three holiday cottages sleeping two, four and six persons respectively. Each with colour TV, video, washer, dishwasher, microwave. Peaceful rural surroundings on a working farm with pigs, sheep and cattle. Winter and Spring Breaks available. Short Breaks from £80 and High Season weeks up to £440. Bed and Breakfast also available. Please telephone for brochure and further details.

ʔʔʔʔ HIGHLY COMMENDED.

Mrs Sally Robinson, Valley View Farm, Old Byland, Helmsley, North Yorkshire YO6 5LG
Tel: 01439 798221　E-mail: sally@valleyviewfarm.com　Web: www.valley.viewform.com

---

HELMSLEY near. Mrs Rickatson, Summerfield Farm, Harome, Near Helmsley, York YO6 5JJ (01439

748238). Working farm, join in. Sleeps 6. Enjoy walking or touring in North Yorkshire Moors National Park. Lovely area 20 miles north of historic city of York. Modernised, comfortable and well-equipped farmhouse wing; sleeps four/six plus cot. Kitchen equipped with electric cooker, fridge, microwave and automatic washing machine. Sit beside a log fire in the evenings. Linen supplied. Weekly terms from £90 to £210. Mid-week and weekend bookings are possible in winter. Trout stream on farm. For further information send SAE, or phone.

LEYBURN. Park Grange Holiday Farm, Harmby, Leyburn. A working farm situated just a mile from the

picturesque market town of Leyburn, Wensleydale. Relax by an open log fire, after leisurely days spent walking, riding and exploring the Yorkshire Dales, or have a tasty barbecue in the garden on long summer evenings. Farmhouse accommodation comprising two family rooms, one twin room, one double, one single, with extra beds and cots available. Bungalow accommodation comprises two double and one bunk-beds. Children, dogs and horses welcome. Ample parking. Grazing/stabling for horses and ponies. Outside kennels on request. Short breaks available. We cater for special occasions and include a "Yorkshire Welcome" pack for birthdays, honeymoons etc. Contact: **Pam Sheppard, Low Gill Farm, Agglethorpe, Leyburn DL8 4TN (01969 640258).**

FHG Please mention *The Farm Holiday Guide* when enquiring about accommodation featured in these pages.

NIDDERDALE. Mrs M. Watson, High Winsley Farm, Burnt Yates, Ripley, Near Harrogate HG3 3EP (01423 770376). Sleeps 2-5. This spacious, well maintained bungalow is situated in scenic peaceful countryside on the owner's sheep farm. Situated seven miles from and central to Harrogate, Knaresborough, Ripon and Pateley Bridge it makes an ideal base for touring Nidderdale. Local places of interest include Ripley Castle, Brimham Rocks, Fountains Abbey and Studley Park. York and North Yorkshire Moors all within easy driving distance. This comfortable accommodation comprises lounge with open fire, dining room with arch through to well-fitted kitchen with wood burning stove for hot water and radiators. Three bedrooms: one double, one twin and one single. Bathroom and shower. Bed linen and electricity included in rent. Open May until September. Low Season £170, Mid £240, High Season £310. e-mail: hwinsley@aol.com

PICKERING. Mrs Sue Cavill, Badger Cottage, Stape, Pickering YO18 8HR (01751 476108). Comfortable self-catering on small, remote, moorland farm. Seven miles from Pickering on edge of Cropton Forest. Wonderful area for touring, walking, cycling or riding. Accommodation available for guests' horses. Cottage is converted from original stone milking parlours, so all on ground floor. Open plan well equipped kitchen, dining and sitting room with sofa bed and cosy woodburning stove. Spacious bedroom with double and single beds, en suite shower room. Parking space and a garden to sit in. Linen and power included. Terms £120 to £180 per week.

RATHMELL, near Settle. Rosemary Hyslop, Field House, Rathmell, Settle (01729 840234; Fax: 01729 840775). ΨΨΨΨ *HIGHLY COMMENDED.* **Sleep 2-10.** Situated on a working sheep farm, Layhead Farm Cottages are a group of three, with lovely views of rolling countryside and Penyghent in the background. Four miles from busy little market town of Settle we are the ideal base from which to explore the Yorkshire Dales. LAYHEAD FARMHOUSE, recently renovated to a high standard, has oil-fired central heating from Rayburn in kitchen/dining room, open fire in lounge. Attractive garden with furniture and barbecue. CRAGGS and COBBLESTONES are the result of a conversion of an original stone barn into two superb cottages with all modern amenities. Cobbled courtyard with garden furniture and colourful tubs. Pets welcome. Colour brochure available. Prices from £190 to £550. e-mail: rosehyslop@easynet.co.uk

Terms quoted in this publication may be subject to increase if rises in costs necessitate

ROBIN HOOD'S BAY. Ken and Nealia Pattinson, South House Farm, Fylingthorpe, Whitby YO22 4UQ

(01947 880243). Two super detached stone cottages on this 180-acre farm only a short distance walk from the beach at Boggle Hole. Situated in a National Park this is wonderful walking country with the North York Moors all around. The cottages have two and three bedrooms and are fully equipped and centrally heated. Llama and pony trekking nearby. Sorry no pets. Terms from £80 to £350.

SCARBOROUGH. Peter and Maggie Martin, Gowland Farm, Gowland Lane, Cloughton, Scarborough YO13 0DU (01723 870924). ϓϓϓ/ϓϓϓϓ *HIGHLY COMMENDED.* **Sleep 2/7.** Four charming converted stone barns situated within

the beautiful North Yorkshire Moors National Park enjoying wonderful views of Harwood Dale and only two miles from the coast. The cottages have been sympathetically converted from traditional farm buildings, furnished and fitted to a very high standard, retaining the old features as well as having modern comforts. They are fully carpeted, warm and cosy with central heating and double glazing. Electric fires and colour TVs in all lounges. Well equipped kitchens. All linen and bedding provided (duvets). Large garden with plenty of car parking space. Garden furniture and laundry facilities. Sorry, no pets. Open all year. From £100 to £440 per week. Bed, Breakfast and Evening Meal also available from April to October. White Rose Award Self-Catering Holiday of the Year runner-up 1993.

SKIPTON. Mrs Brenda Jones, New Close Farm, Kirkby Malham, Skipton BD23 4DP (Tel & Fax 01729 830240). Sleeps 5. A supa dupa cottage on New Close Farm in

the heart of Craven Dales with panoramic views over the Aire Valley. Excellent area for walking, cycling, fishing, golf and touring. Two double and one single bedrooms; bathroom. Colour TV and video. Full central heating and double glazing. Bed linen and all amenities included in the price. Low Season £225, High Season £275; deposit required. Sorry, no young children, no pets. Non-smokers preferred. The weather can't be guaranteed but your comfort can. Yorkshire and Humberside Tourist Board Member; FHG Diploma Award Winner.

SKIPTON. Anne Pearson, Cawder Hall Cottages, Cawder Hall, Cawder Lane, Skipton BD23 2QQ (01756 791579; Fax: 01756 797036). Sleeps 2/6. ETB ϓϓϓ

- ϓϓϓϓ to *HIGHLY COMMENDED.* Enjoy the peace and quiet of our warm, welcoming cottages just one mile from Skipton, with its thriving street market, medieval castle and church. Surrounded by fields and animals, each cottage is well equipped (colour TV, video, microwave) and is suitable for disabled guests. There is a lawned garden, barbecue, phone, laundry room and children's play area. Linen, gas and electricity are included in the price, as are cots and high chairs. Open all year. Prices from £120 to £340 per week.

FREE and REDUCED RATE Holiday Visits!
Don't miss our Readers' Offer Vouchers

STAITHES. Garth End Cottage, Staithes. Sleep 5/6. Victorian cottage situated on sea wall in this old fishing village in the North Yorkshire Moors National Park. Excellent walking centre. Small sandy beach with numerous rock pools. Cottage has feature fireplace, beamed ceilings, pine panelled room, well equipped kitchen including microwave. Warm, comfortable, well equipped with central heating, electricity and bed linen included in rent. Two lounges, front one with picture window giving uninterrupted panoramic views of sea, harbour and cliffs. Dining kitchen; bathroom with toilet; three bedrooms - one double, one twin, one single (two with sea views); colour TV. Front terrace overlooking the sea. Sorry, no pets. Terms from £200. Apply **Mrs Hobbs (01132 665501).**

TERRINGTON. Mrs S. Goodrick, Springfield Court, Terrington, York YO6 4PX (01653 648370) *COMMENDED*. Come and enjoy comfort and rest in one of our three superb holiday cottages, sleeping two to five people. A peaceful, unspoilt farming village just 14 miles north east of York and within four miles of Castle Howard, Terrington is an ideal position for your discovery of a beautiful area. Terms from £103 to £325 per week. Microwave. Children welcome. Illustrated brochure. SAE for full details.
e-mail: goodrick@terrington10.freeserve.co.uk

★ *Charlcot Lodges* ★

Charlcot offers an ideal base from which to explore The Yorkshire Dales and unwind in peaceful surroundings. Our lodges sleep up to five people in two bedrooms, all have fully-equipped kitchen, shower and bath, colour TV, cot, highchair, heating, duvets and bed linen. Electricity is included in the price. Enjoying a safe and private location, Charlcot is ideal for children and pets. Each lodge has an adjacent parking area and shared barbecue facilities. There are numerous places of interest nearby with the stone-built market town of Masham just a five minute drive away. Activities are available such as golf, coarse fishing, mountain biking, swimming and horse riding. Ideal for walking. Many local inns offering excellent local fare. Terms from £160 to £350 per week, short breaks available. Please write or phone for our full colour brochure.

Contact: Mrs A. Slee, 14 The Horseshoe, York YO2 2LX   Tel: 01904 700200

WHITBY. Nick Eddleston, Greenhouses Farm Cottages, Greenhouses Farm, Lealholm, Near Whitby YO21 2AD (01947 897486). The three cottages have been converted from the traditional farm buildings. The old world character has been retained with the thick stone walls, exposed beams and red pantile roofs typical of North Yorkshire. Set in the tiny hamlet of Greenhouses and enjoying splendid views over open countryside, the cottages offer a very quiet and peaceful setting for a holiday. All the cottages are equipped with colour TV, electric cooker, fridge-freezer, microwave and automatic washing machine. Linen, fuel and lighting are all included in the price. There are ample safe areas for children to play. Sorry, no pets. Prices from £169 to £476 per week. Winter Breaks from £128.

FHG Please mention *The Farm Holiday Guide* when enquiring about accommodation featured in these pages.

WHITBY. Mrs Rhys, Blackmires Cottage, Blackmires Farm, Danby Head, Danby, Whitby YO21 2NN

(01287 660352). ỶỶỶỶ *COMMENDED*. **Sleeps 6.** Stone cottage in quiet situation on Esk Valley Walk, adjacent to Moors in an Area of Outstanding Natural Beauty. Our small farm is three miles from Danby, Castleton and the North York Moors National Park Information Centre. Accommodation consists of lounge/ dining room, kitchen, two bedrooms and bathroom on ground floor with twin bedroom upstairs. Bed linen, towels and electricity included in price. Garden with swing and sandpit. Children welcome, dogs by arrangement. Open all year. Welcome Host Certificate. Terms £225 to £375.

WHITBY near. Mr and Mrs Geoffrey Hepworth, Land of Nod Farm, Near Whitby YO21 2BL (01947 840325). Sleeps 6 plus cot. Attached sandstone bungalow, situated in the clean air, carefree part of North Yorkshire Moors National Park. All five windows face south across pastures, the sittingroom window also faces east across six miles of widening valley to Whitby Abbey Headland. Runswick Bay is three miles northward. The holiday property is separated from the farm house by a dividing passage. There are three compact bedrooms, one of which has two single beds and cot. Modern toilet facilities and shower. Kitchen/diner fully equipped with electric cooker, microwave, fridge; spin dryer, colour TV. Bed linen, electricity included in hire. Small charge for pets. No telephone bookings. No smoking. Owner attended. For availability, enquiries, brochure phone 01947 840325. Rates from £81 Low Season to £159 High Season per week.

YORK. Sunset Cottages, Grimston Manor Farm, Gilling East, York. ỶỶỶỶ *COMMENDED*. **Working**

farm. Six beautiful cottages lovingly converted from the granaries of our family farm. Superbly situated in the heart of the Howardian Hills, on the outskirts of the National Park and only 17 miles north of the historic city of York, Herriot country. With panoramic views, these warm and comfortable cottages retain their original mellow beams and interesting stonework while still providing all the modern comforts you rightfully expect in a well-designed self-catering cottage. Full central heating. Personally supervised by the resident owners, Heather and Richard Kelsey. Sorry, no pets (sheep country). Prices from £150 to £350. Please write, or phone for brochure to **Mr and Mrs R.J. Kelsey, Grimston Manor Farm, Gilling East, York YO62 4HR (01347 888654; Fax: 01347 888347).**

YORK. Orillia Cottages, Stockton-on-Forest, York. Four converted farmworkers' cottages in a courtyard setting at the rear of the 300-year-old farmhouse in Stockton-on-Forest; three miles from York. Golf course nearby, pub 200 yards away serves food. Post office, newsagents and general stores within easy reach. Convenient half-hourly bus service to York and the coast. Fully furnished and equipped for two to eight, the cottages comprise lounge with colour TV, etc; kitchen area with microwave oven, grill and hob. Bedrooms have double bed or twin beds. Gas central heating. Non-smokers preferred. Children and pets welcome. Available Easter to October. Short Breaks may be available. Terms from £150 to £360 weekly includes heating, linen, etc. Contact: **Mike Cundall, Orillia House, 89 The Village, Stockton-on-Forest, York YO3 9UP (01904 400600).**

YORK. Mrs Lazenby, Rossmoor Park Farm, Melbourne, York YO42 4SZ (01759 318410). Sleeps 5/6.

Situated in a park and woodland setting stands this attractive Tudor style farmhouse with a self-contained wing. Recently decorated and furnished to high standards the accommodation offers private enclosed garden, patio and furniture; oil central heating; sittingroom with log fire, colour TV and video; kitchen and dining room. The first floor has one double bedroom with en suite shower room and four-poster bed, twin bedroom and single bedroom plus folding bed. Bathroom. The historic city of York is just a 15 minute drive maikng us the ideal base for the Yorkshire Moors, East Coast, Wolds and Dales. Village shop and pub one mile away. Golf, riding, swimming and fishing all nearby. Welcome tray. Please write or telephone for a brochure.

YORK. Mrs M.S.A. Woodliffe, Mill Farm, Yapham, Pocklington, York YO4 2PH (01759 302172). Three attractive self-catering choices on the farm. 12 miles from York with fine views of the Yorkshire Wolds. WOODLEA, detached house, sleeping five/six people, with fully equipped kitchen, dining area, large lounge with colour TV, bathroom, downstairs cloakroom and three bedrooms. BUNGALOW adjacent to farmhouse sleeps two/four with kitchen, bathroom, lounge/diningroom with colour TV and double bed settee, twin room with cot. Children and pets welcome. STUDIO adjacent to farmhouse, sleeps two. Modern kitchen, lounge/diningroom with colour TV, twin bedroom, bathroom/toilet. Parking for all. Open all year. Shopping and other amenities at Pocklington (two miles). Eating out, stately homes, a variety of activities available locally; coast 28 miles. SAE for details.

WEST YORKSHIRE

HEBDEN BRIDGE. Mrs R. Ryder, Stray Leaves, Wadsworth, Hebden Bridge HX7 8TN (01422 842353).

COMMENDED. Stray Leaves is a bungalow set amidst rural surroundings with panoramic views. It is situated one mile from Hebden Bridge with the Yorkshire Dales, Bronte Country, Leeds, York and Manchester within easy reach. Children are welcome and a high chair and cot are available. All linen and towels provided. Central heating, electricity and water are included; the only extra is the electric fire which is metered (£1). Terms from £95 to £250 per week. Please write or telephone for brochure.

CHANNEL ISLANDS

HOLIDAY · JERSEY · BUNGALOWS

Three bungalows a few metres direct access to beach. Reasonable rates. Electric cooking and heating. Near golf course, shops and bus. Family accommodation with cot. Open most of the year with reduced rates out of season. Well equipped. Jersey is a beautiful place to visit all year round. Plenty to see and do on the island. Excellent restaurants, shops (no VAT) and entertainment. Easy access to the other Channel Islands and France for day trips. Access by air and boat from Poole and Weymouth (both take cars). Please phone **(01534) 853333** early evening, or write to:

Mrs. P. Johnson, 'Mon Repos', Coast Road, Grouville, Jersey C.I. JE3 9FG

ENGLAND

Caravan & Camping Holidays

LOOE. Mr and Mrs G. Veale, Trelay Farmpark, Pelynt, Looe PL13 2JX (01503 220900). ✓✓✓✓ Trelay Farmpark is a small, peaceful, friendly, family-run site. It is quiet, uncommercialised and surrounded by farmland. The park lies on a gentle south facing slope offering wide views of open countryside. Excellent new facilities include hot showers/launderette and disabled suite with wheelchair access. The three acre camping field is licensed for 55 tourers/tents etc. Good access, generous pitches, hook ups. In adjoining area (1.5 acres) are 20 holiday caravans in a garden-like setting. The village of Pelynt which is a half mile away has shops, Post Office, restaurants, pub. Looe and Polperro are both just three miles away. Controlled dogs welcome.

LOSTWITHIEL. Mr Evans, Powderham Castle Tourist Park, Lanlivery PL30 5BU (01208 872277).

✓✓✓✓✓ A quiet select touring park with spacious pitches. Recommended by all relevant national and international touring organisations. Appeal to those who wish to holiday in natural uncommercialised surroundings. Ideally situated for all Cornwall and close to the Eden Project. Seasonal pitches for tourers and all year storage facilities. Occasional vacancies for new holiday homes for personal private use. AA Award for Excellence.

MITHIAN, near St. Agnes. Mrs Jenny Osborne, Mellowvean, Mithian, St. Agnes TR5 0QA (01872 553274). Sleeps 4. This single caravan/chalet is situated in a peaceful spot with its own lawn and garden on a two-and-a-half acre smallholding. Mithian's central location makes it an ideal base for touring the whole of Cornwall. St. Agnes village offers good shops, pub, restaurants, beach, etc. The accommodation comprises a caravan which has been extended to include a separate bedroom, flush toilet with handbasin, and a large porch. All-electric facilities include cooker, fridge, water heater and colour TV. A shower is available and there is ample parking. Terms from £75 to £200 per week including electricity.

PADSTOW. Mrs M.J. Raymont, Trevean Farm, St Merryn, Padstow PL28 8PR (01841 520772).

Small, pleasant site close to several sandy beaches with good surfing and lovely, golden sands. Rural area with splendid sea views. Riding school and golf club within two miles. Village shops one mile. Sea and river fishing nearby. Padstow four miles. Camel Estuary four miles. Three static king-size six-berth caravans with cooker, fridge, mains water supply, flush toilets, showers; milk supplied from farm. Good approach from B road. Children welcome, pets permitted (dogs must be kept on a lead). Tourers and campers welcome. Weekly rates for static vans from £140 to £280 according to season; from £6.00 per night for touring caravans and tents. Open Easter to October.

CUMBRIA

APPLEBY. Mrs A. Balmer, Grassgill, Bleatarn, Appleby CA16 6QB (017683 71528). Three six-berth

caravans with flush toilet and shower on pleasant farm site with excellent views. All have Calor gas cookers and TV. Fully equipped except bed linen. Ideal centre for touring Yorkshire Dales and Lake District and only six miles from Appleby, four miles from Kirkby Stephen and the M6 motorway nearby at Tebay. Water, flush toilet and shower on site.

BROUGHTON-IN-FURNESS. Mrs H. Glessal, Whineray Ground, Broughton-in-Furness LA20 6DS

(01229 716500). Working farm. Private, sheltered yet within easy reach of a whole host of facilities - miniature railway, castles, gardens, beach, museum, fishing, bird watching, fell walking - attractive six-berth, 30' modern static caravan set in its own half acre on a working fell farm. Marvellous views and absolute seclusion can be guaranteed. Two bedrooms (one with bunks, one with double bed), spacious living area and separate kitchen; shower and toilet. Fridge, gas fire and cooker - no additional charge for electricity and gas. Hot and cold water. River Duddon close by, indoor swimming pool, village, shops, pub, restaurant and golfing within two miles. Ulverston market town about ten miles. Further details on request. Terms from £130 weekly, fully inclusive.

CONISTON. Mrs E. Johnson, Spoon Hall, Coniston LA21 8AW (015394 41391). Caravans sleep 6. Three 33ft caravans situated on a 50 acre working hill farm one mile from Coniston, overlooking Coniston Lake. All have flush toilet, shower, gas cookers, fires and water heaters, electric lighting and fridge plus colour TV. Children are welcome. Pets are allowed free. Available all year round. Pony trekking arranged from farm. Weekly terms on request.

CONISTON near. Mrs J. E. Halton, Scarr Head Caravans, Torver, Coniston LA21 8BP (015394

41576/41328). Static caravans for hire, pitches for touring caravans, motor caravans and tents. Very small, quiet site with all modern facilities. Static caravans situated in a private garden with ample parking for visitors' cars. Coniston village three miles; two village inns in Torver serving meals, both within walking distance (10 minutes); pony trekking 500 yards. Scarr Head is a small working farm close to Coniston Old Man, and being in a quieter part of the Lake District is the perfect base for exploring the beautiful surrounding countryside either by car or on foot. Children and pets welcome. Open Easter to October. Please telephone, or write, for full details. RTB Inspected.

MILLOM. Mr Fogg, Butterflowers Holiday Homes, Port Haverigg, Millom LA18 4HB (01229 772880).

Visit our peaceful village in the South Lakes and get away from the bustle of life. On our site we cater for tourers, tents, mobile homes etc., and have available gents and ladies toilets, large kitchen, laundry and indoor swimming pool. Within a quarter of a mile, our sister park is also available to you, for lake fishing, skiing, and model railway.

POOLEY BRIDGE/LAKE ULLSWATER. Parkfoot Caravan and Camping Park, Howtown Road, Pooley

Bridge, Penrith CA10 2NA (017684 86309; Fax: 017684 86041). Family-run park set in magnificent Lakeland scenery. Country Club, licensed bar, restaurant, take-away, games room. Free lake access with boat launching. Car parking. Ideal for watersports, sailing, boating, canoeing, windsurfing and fishing. Tennis court, mountain biking (hire available) and pony trekking from the Park. Private access to Barton Fell for walking. Modern toilets, hot showers, hair dryers, shaver points; fully equipped laundry room. Public telephones. Shop. Adventure playground and children's playgrounds. Camping fields have level and hill sites with views of Lake Ullswater. Grass and hardstanding pitches for touring caravans. Electric hook-ups. Self-catering log cabins and houses for hire. SAE, or telephone, for brochure.

Tanglewood Caravan Park

CAUSEWAY HEAD, SILLOTH-ON-SOLWAY, CUMBRIA CA5 4PE

Tanglewood is a family-run park on the fringes of the Lake District National Park. It is tree-sheltered and situated one mile inland from the small port of Silloth on the Solway Firth, with a beautiful view of the Galloway Hills. Large modern holiday homes are available from March to October, with car parking beside each home. Fully

equipped except for bed linen, with end bedroom, central heating in bedrooms, electric lighting, hot and cold water, toilet, shower, gas fire, fridge and colour TV, all of which are included in the tariff. Touring pitches also available with electric hook-ups and water/drainage facilities, etc. Play area. Licensed lounge with adjoining children's play room. Pets welcome free but must be kept under control at all times. Full colour brochure available.

 TEL: 016973 31253   ★★★

WASDALE. Mrs Ruth Knight, Church Stile Farm, Wasdale, Seascale CA20 1ET (019467 26252). A quiet,

secluded farm park on a working family farm welcoming tents, motor caravans and dormobiles, no touring caravans. It is approximately one-and-a-half-miles to Wastwater Lake and the nearest fells, Scafell is five miles. This is an excellent walking and climbing area with glorious scenery. Nine miles to Muncaster Castle and the Ravenglass and Eskdale Railway. Ideal for touring the rest of the Lake district. Children and pets welcome. Children's play area. Facilities include showers, toilets, washbasins, laundry room, hot and cold water and electricity throughout the toilet block. Two country hotels in the village for either food or drink. Price list supplied on request. Open March to November.

FHG

Visit the FHG website
www.holidayguides.com
for details of the wide choice of accommodation
featured in the full range of FHG titles

DERBYSHIRE

ASHBOURNE. Mrs Louie Tatlow, Ashfield Farm, Calwich, Near Ashbourne DE6 2EB (01335 324279

or 324443). Working farm. Five modern six-berth caravans, fully equipped, each with gas cooker, fridge, TV; overlooks the peaceful Dove Valley and is convenient for the Peak District. The old market town of Ashbourne is only two miles away, with golf course, swimming pool, squash and bowling. Within easy reach of stately homes like Haddon Hall and Chatsworth, with the Potteries and Lichfield 25 miles distant. Uttoxeter is 10 miles away, while Alton Towers Theme Park is under five miles away. Prices and brochure on request. Write or telephone for further information.

BUXTON near. Mr and Mrs J. Melland, The Pomeroy Caravan Park, Street House Farm, Flagg, Near

Buxton SK17 9QG (01298 83259). ✓✓✓ Working farm. This site for 30 caravans is situated five miles from Buxton, in heart of Peak District National Park. Ideal base for touring by car or walking. Site adjoins northern end of now famous Tissington and High Peak Trail. Only nine miles from Haddon Hall and ten from Chatsworth House. Landscaped to the latest model standards for caravan sites; tourers and campers will find high standards here. New toilet block with showers, washing facilities and laundry; mains electric hook-up points. Back-packers welcome. Large rally field available. Children welcome; dogs on lead. We now have six-berth 28ft x 10ft Holiday Van with separate end bedroom; hot and cold water; WC. Fridge, full size gas cooker and fire, TV. Weekly rates only £90 to £120. Fully equipped except linen. Touring rates £6.00 to £6.50 for two people per night. Open Easter to end of October. SAE for brochure please.

DEVON

ASHBURTON. Parkers Farm Holiday Park, Ashburton TQ13 7LJ (01364 652598; Fax: 01364 654004).

A friendly, family-run farm site, set in 400 acres and surrounded by beautiful countryside. 12 miles to the sea and close to Dartmoor National Park. Ideal for touring Devon/Cornwall. Perfect for children and pets with all farm animals, play area and plenty of space to roam, also large area for dogs. Holiday cottages and caravans fully equipped except for linen. Level touring site with some hard standings. Electric hook-up. Free showers in fully tiled block, laundry room and games room. Small family bar, restaurant, shop and phone. Prices start from £90 Low Season to £380 High Season. Good discounts for couples. To find us: From Exeter take A38 to Plymouth till you see "26 miles Plymouth" sign; take second left at Alston Cross signposted to Woodland and Denbury.

BIDEFORD. Mrs J.A. Fox, Highstead Farm, Bucks Cross, Bideford EX39 5DX (01237 431201). Large

and attractive modern caravan on a private farm site with fine sea views nearby. Just off the A39 Bideford/Bude road close to the coast of North Devon and convenient for Clovelly, Bideford and Westward Ho! Luxury accommodation for six adults (sleeping accommodation for up to 11 at extra charge) with bath/shower, separate toilet, fully equipped kitchen including microwave, gas fire and colour TV. Babysitting also available. Pets welcome by arrangement. Linen supplied as extra. Shopping, beaches, local attractions and Moors within easy reach. Car essential but good walking country. Open March to October from £95 weekly low season.

CHITTLEHAMHOLT (North Devon). Snapdown Farm Caravans, Chittlehamholt. 12 only, six-berth

caravans with all facilities in beautiful unspoilt country setting down our quiet lane. Very peaceful, quiet and secluded, and well away from busy roads. Each with hard standing for car and each with outside seats and picnic table. Table tennis. Children's play area in small wood adjoining. Laundry room. PLENTY OF SPACE - field and woodland walks on farm. Lots of wildlife. Help feed and milk the goats. Within easy reach of sea and moors. Well behaved pets welcome. Terms (two types): £85 to £215 and £95 to £230, per caravan per week, both including gas and electricity. Reductions for couples early and late season. Illustrated brochure from **Mrs M. Bowen, Snapdown Cottage, Chittlehamholt, Umberleigh EX37 9PF (01769 540708).**

COLYTON. Mrs S. Gould and Mrs R. Gould, Bonehayne Farm, Colyton EX13 6SG (01404 871416 or

871396). Working farm. Six-berth luxury caravan in secluded spot on farmhouse lawn, overlooking the river, fields and woodlands where wildlife is a common sight. Many animals to make friends with on this 250 acre farm. Good trout fishing available. Caravan contains well fitted master bedroom, twin bedded room with cot rail available, and convertible double in lounge. Kitchen with cooker and fridge freezer. Spacious lounge and dining area. Colour TV. Bathroom with toilet, washbasin, shower and bath, heated towel rail. Fully equipped except linen. All rooms with plenty of cupboard space. Built-in radiators, fully insulated, making it ideal for out of season holidays. Laundry facilities and barbecue available. Milk and eggs obtainable from farmhouse. Colyton two miles, sea four and and a half miles. Brochure available.

CULLOMPTON. Mr A.R. Davey, Pound Farm, Butterleigh, Cillompton EX15 1PH (01884 855 208). Working farm. Sleeps 6. A Pound Farm holiday combines finest English scenery with traditional beauty of village of Butterleigh, half-a-mile away. Enjoy family break from April to November on this 80-acre sheep and beef farm. Spacious comfortable caravan accommodation for six, in grass paddock with paths and parking for two cars. Enter by road. Well-equipped; linen hire by arrangement. Hot and cold water, shower. Electric power points (8). All cutlery, utensils, blankets and pillows. Washroom/Utility room. Adjoining caravan has flush toilet, double drainer, stainless steel sink unit in utility room with shaving point, hot/cold water, electric light and two-bar heater. Farmstead within sight of caravans. Visitors free to walk over the farm. South and North coast 45 to 60 minutes' drive. Four miles from M5, Cullompton, North Devon Link road (A361), Tiverton, Silverton, Bickleigh thatched olde worlde village in heart of beautiful Exe Valley. Pets allowed. Free coarse fishing, no closed season - carp, tench, perch, roach, rudd. Terms from £120 to £175. FHG Diploma Winner.

HONITON. Francis Wigram, Riggles Farm, Upottery, Honiton EX14 0SP (01404 891229). Working farm. Caravans sleep 6. Two beautifully situated caravans on 300 acre beef, sheep, arable farm six miles from Honiton, with easy access to many lovely beaches, moors and local attractions. Visitors welcome on farm, well behaved pets accepted. Children's play area, table tennis, darts. Linen hire, washing machine and dryer. Caravans set in two peaceful acres near farmhouse. Each is fully equipped for two/six people. Two separate bedrooms and spacious living areas. Own bathroom with shower, flush toilet, washbasin. Gas cooker, heater, colour TV, fridge. Terms from £95 to £210 per week (10% reduction for couples, not school holidays). For brochure please write or telephone. e-mail: rigglesfarm@farming.co.uk

KINGSBRIDGE. Mounts Farm Touring Park, The Mounts, Near East Allington, Kingsbridge TQ9 7QJ

(01548 521591). Mounts Farm is a family-run site in the heart of South Devon. On site facilities include FREE hot showers, flush toilets, FREE hot water in washing-up room, razor points, laundry, information room, electric hook-ups and site shop. We welcome tents, touring caravans and motor caravans. Large pitches in level, sheltered fields. No charges for awnings. Children and pets welcome. Situated three miles north of Kingsbridge, Mounts Farm is an ideal base for exploring Dartmouth, Salcombe, Totnes, Dartmoor and the many safe sandy beaches nearby. Please telephone or write for a free brochure. Self-catering cottage also available.

TOTNES. J. and E. Ball, Higher Well Farm and Holiday Park, Stoke Gabriel, Totnes TQ9 6RN (01803 782289). ✓✓✓ A quiet secluded farm park welcoming tents, motor caravans and touring caravans. It is less than one mile from the riverside village of Stoke Gabriel and within four miles of Torbay beaches. Central for touring South Devon. Facilities include toilets, showers, launderette, shop, payphone and electric hook-ups. There are also static caravans to let. Enjoy a delightful relaxing holiday in the beautiful Devonshire countryside. Static caravans from £125 per week or £18 per night.

WOOLACOMBE. North Morte Farm Caravan and Camping, Dept FHG, Mortehoe, Woolacombe EX34

NORTH MORTE
FARM
CARAVAN & CAMPING PARK

7EG (01271 870381). The nearest camping and caravan park to the sea, in perfectly secluded beautiful coastal country. Our family-run park, adjoining National Trust land, is only 500 yards from Rockham Beach, yet only five minutes' walk from the village of Mortehoe with a post office, petrol station/garage, shops, cafes and pubs – one of which has a children's room. Four to six berth holiday caravans for hire and pitches for tents, dormobiles and touring caravans, electric hook-ups available. We have hot showers and flush toilets, laundry room, shop and off licence; Calor gas and Camping Gaz available; children's play area. Dogs accepted but must be kept on lead. Open Easter to end September. Brochure available.

FOR THE MUTUAL GUIDANCE OF GUEST AND HOST

Every year literally thousands of holidays, short breaks and overnight stops are arranged through our guides, the vast majority without any problems at all. In a handful of cases, however, difficulties do arise about bookings, which often could have been prevented from the outset.

It is important to remember that when accommodation has been booked, both parties – guests and hosts – have entered into a form of contract. We hope that the following points will provide helpful guidance.

GUESTS: When enquiring about accommodation, be as precise as possible. Give exact dates, numbers in your party and the ages of any children. State the number and type of rooms wanted and also what catering you require – bed and breakfast, full board etc. Make sure that the position about evening meals is clear – and about pets, reductions for children or any other special points.

Read our reviews carefully to ensure that the proprietors you are going to contact can supply what you want. Ask for a letter confirming all arrangements, if possible.

If you have to cancel, do so as soon as possible. Proprietors do have the right to retain deposits and under certain circumstances to charge for cancelled holidays if adequate notice is not given and they cannot re-let the accommodation.

HOSTS: Give details about your facilities and about any special conditions. Explain your deposit system clearly and arrangements for cancellations, charges etc. and whether or not your terms include VAT.

If for any reason you are unable to fulfil an agreed booking without adequate notice, you may be under an obligation to arrange suitable alternative accommodation or to make some form of compensation.

DORSET

★★★ **MANOR FARM HOLIDAY CENTRE** ♀♀♀

Charmouth, Bridport, Dorset DT6 6QL *Approved*

Situated in a rural valley. Charmouth beach a level ten minutes' walk away.

Luxury 6-berth Caravans for Hire with toilet/shower, refrigerator, full cooker, colour TV, gas fire.

30-acre Tourist Park for touring caravans, dormobiles and tents

Centre facilities include •Toilets •Hotel showers •Licensed bar with family room; Bar Food available
•Amusement room •Launderette •Shop and Off-licence •Swimming pool •Electric hook-up points
•Calor gas and Camping Gaz •Ice pack service
•Chemical disposal unit •Disabled facilities

Send SAE for colour brochure to Mr R. B. Loosmore or Tel. 01297 560226

See also Colour Display Advertisement in this Guide.

LYME REGIS. Mrs C. Grymonprez, Beechfield Cottage, Yawl Hill Lane, Uplyme, Lyme Regis DT7 3RW (01297 443216). Caravans sleep 4/6. Beechfield is a four-acre smallholding situated on Yawl Hill, commanding a truly scenic outlook over Lyme's countryside and the sea. It is conveniently located on the borders of Devon, Somerset and Dorset. To ensure utmost privacy we have a well-kept one acre field, hedge-screened and peaceful, set aside for only two modern caravans. Both are fully equipped (except linen), with fridge, mains electricity and water, inside flush toilet, shower, gas cooker and fire, colour TV. Cleanliness guaranteed. New picnic tables. Well behaved pets welcome. Lyme Regis is only two-and-a-half miles away. Free-range eggs available. SAE appreciated.

LYME REGIS. Mrs J. Tedbury, Little Paddocks, Yawl Hill Lane, Lyme Regis DT7 3RW (01297 443085). Sleeps 6. A six-berth caravan on Devon/Dorset border in a well-kept paddock overlooking Lyme Bay and surrounding countryside. Situated on a smallholding with animals, for perfect peace and quiet. Lyme Regis two-and-a-half miles, Charmouth three-and-a-half miles. Both have safe beaches for children. Easy driving distance to resorts of Seaton, Beer and Sidmouth. The caravan is fully equipped except linen. It has shower room with handbasin and toilet inside as well as flush toilet just outside. Electric light, fridge and TV. Calor gas cooker and fire. Car can be parked alongside. Dogs welcome. Terms from £85. Also fully equipped chalet for two from £70. SAE, please.

See also Colour Display Advertisement

WIMBOURNE. Woolsbridge Manor Farm Caravan Park, Three Legged Cross, Wimborne, Dorset BH21 6RA (01202 826369). AA Three Pennants. ✓✓✓✓. Situated approximately three-and-a-half-miles from the New Forest market town of Ringwood – easy access to the south coast. Seven acres level, semi-sheltered, well-drained spacious pitches. Quiet country location on a working farm, ideal and safe for families. Showers, mother/baby area, laundry room, washing up area, chemical disposal, payphone, electric hook-ups, battery charging. Children's play area on site. Site shop. Dogs welcome on leads. Fishing adjacent. Moors Valley Country Park golf course one mile. Pub and restaurant 10 minutes' walk.

---

*When making enquiries or bookings,
a stamped addressed envelope is always appreciated.*

ESSEX

MANNINGTREE. Mr. Leslie Baxter, Strangers Home Inn, The Street, Bradfield, Manningtree CO11 2US

(01255 870304). A two acre site with 65 level touring pitches, 14 with electric hook-up. Showers, toilets and chemical disposal point. Open March to October. Please write or telephone for further information.

KENT

DOVER. Hawthorn Farm, Martin Mill, Dover CT15 5LA (01304 852658; Fax: 01304 853417).

Beautiful award winning park, Hawthorn Farm is situated at Martin Mill two-and-a-half-miles from St. Margaret's Bay near Dover. It is well signposted when driving along the main A258 from Dover towards Deal. Set in 28 acres of outstanding natural beauty our park offers superb toilet and shower facilities and is an ideal base to discover Kent's White Cliffs Country or as a ferry stopover. Open from 1st March to 31st October. Park shop, gas and launderette. Colour brochure available **Freephone 0800 305070.**

HERNE BAY. Mr D. H. Newman, Braggs Lane Farm Camping Site, Braggs Lane, Herne, Herne Bay CT6 7NP (01227 367261). Conveniently placed in the heart of Kent, on the A291 approximately three miles from the seaside town of Herne Bay with its many tourist attractions and leisure facilities. The site is also close to the Channel Tunnel and ferry ports. In a secluded location, and surrounded by acres of woodland, the site provides miles of enjoyable walks. The village of Herne is one-and-a-half miles away for local shopping and the Cathedral city of Canterbury is six miles away. Sorry, no dogs. Open May to October.

LANCASHIRE

LUNE VALLEY. Mrs Ruth Hartley, Clintsfield, Old Moor Road, Wennington, Lancaster LA2 8PE

(015242 21447). Working farm. Sleeps 4. Large static holiday home on single site in quiet rural setting on working farm. Situated in the beautiful forest of Bowland, on the Yorkshire, Lancashire and Cumbria borders. Extensive views to the Lake District Fells. One double bedroom plus double bed-settee in sitting room; full cooking facilities in all-electric kitchen; electric shower with toilet and handbasin; mains plumbing; central heating. Flat site for tent adjacent. TV and garden area. Children welcome. No smoking or dogs. Price, including bed linen, from £120 per week. Open all year.

LINCOLNSHIRE

MARKET RASEN. Mr Robert Cox, Manor Farm Caravan Site, Manor Farm, East Frisby, Market Rasen

LN8 2DB (01673 878258). A small 15 touring caravan and six tent site ideal for visiting Lincoln and the Lincolnshire Wolds. Set in three acres over two level fields - one for families, the other for solitude. New toilet block for the year 2000. Ideal cycling country neighbouring a Saxon settlement reconstruction. Tents, caravans, caravanettes, trailer tents welcome. Electric hook ups, toilets, hot showers, gas exchange and small animals area. Cycles/tandems for hire. We also have a gypsy-style caravan for hire. Ten miles from Lincoln.

NORFOLK

NORTHUMBERLAND

ALNWICK. Mrs J.W. Bowden, "Anvil-Kirk", 8 South Charlton Village, Alnwick NE66 2NA (01665

579324). Tourist Board *COMMENDED*. One six-berth caravan on single private site. Hard standing and lovely spacious surroundings. Three-quarters of a mile from the A1; six miles north of Alnwick and six miles also from the lovely clean beaches of Beadnell, Seahouses, Craster Village; nine miles from the Cheviot Hills. Many castles nearby – Bamburgh and Alnwick being the largest; wild cattle and bird sanctuaries; Ingram Valley for the hill walker, Berwick and Morpeth markets. Holy Island is a must with its tiny castle and harbour with fishing boats. Many places to eat out within a radius of 10 miles. The caravan has mains water and electricity; electric cooker, fridge, microwave, TV. End bedroom (bunk beds); flush toilet in bathroom. Open Easter to October. Children and pets welcome. Milk and papers delivered daily. Terms from £165 to £195 per week. One Rose Award. SAE, please. Also Bed and Breakfast available in house from £18 to £20 per night.

SHROPSHIRE

CRAVEN ARMS. Mrs S. Thomas, Llanhowell Farm, Hopton Castle, Craven Arms SY7 0QG (01588 660307). Comfortable and well equipped mobile home (30'x10'). Single site with own lawn, located on an upland working family farm. Sleeps four to five in two separate bedrooms, kitchen includes full cooker, fridge and microwave. Lounge area includes colour TV and gas fire. Shower room with all services. Linen included. Local village pubs provide good food. Historic town of Ludlow approximately 14 miles. Booking concessions for two people or less and long lets. 10% deposit required on booking. Prices on application.

LYDBURY NORTH. The Powis Arms, Lydbury North SY7 8PR (01588 680232). Caravan site available at our country pub. Good food from snacks to full à la carte with friendly and professional service available. Parking. Fishing and walking. Ideally situated for exploring Shropshire and the Welsh Borders and mediaeval towns of Ludlow and Shrewsbury. Nearby are the world famous Ironbridge and walking or bicycling country of Offa's Dyke, the Long Mynd, Stiperstones and Wenlock Edge. Self-catering flats and Bed & Breakfast accommodation also available.

SOMERSET

See also Colour Display Advertisement

BRIDGWATER. Mill Farm Caravan and Camping Park, Fiddington, Bridgwater TA5 1JQ. ✓✓✓✓. Attractive, sheltered farm site situated between beautiful Quantock Hills and the sea. Boating, swings, table tennis, TV, tourist informations and large sand pit. Tropical indoor heated pool and two outdoor pools with giant waterslide. Canoes, trampolines and ponies for hire. Caravan storage available. Clean toilets, etc. Laundry room, electric hook-ups, camp shop, good local pubs. Open all year. SELF CATERING HOLIDAY COTTAGE ALSO AVAILABLE. Please write or telephone for brochure. Contact: **M.J. Evans (01278 732286).**

DULVERTON. Mrs M.M. Jones, Higher Town, Dulverton TA22 9RX (01398 341272). Working farm. Caravans sleep 8. Our farm is situated half-a-mile from open moorland, one mile from the Devon/Somerset border and four miles from Dulverton. 80 acres of the farm is in the Exmoor National Park. We let two caravans which are quarter-of-a-mile apart and do not overlook each other, and have lovely views, situated in lawns with parking space. Both are eight berth, with a double end bedroom, bunk bedroom, shower, flush toilet, hot/cold water and colour TV. The caravans are modern and fully equipped except linen. Cot and high chair available. One caravan new for season 1999 with three bedrooms. Visitors are welcome to watch the milking or walk over our beef and sheep farm. Riding and fishing nearby. Open May to October. Price from £70, includes gas and electricity.

FHG Please mention *The Farm Holiday Guide* when enquiring about accommodation featured in these pages.

WIVELISCOMBE. Richard and Marion Rottenbury, Oxenleaze Farm Caravans, Chipstable, Wiveliscombe TA4 2QH (Tel & Fax: 01984 623427). ✓✓✓✓✓ This exceptional site is set in the peace and tranquillity of the Devon/Somerset borders close to Exmoor known for its beautiful countryside. Super Luxury and luxury caravans on a working hill farm. Each caravan has its own shower and flush toilet, hot and cold water, cooker, fridge, fire and colour TV. Parking is available beside each caravan; car is essential. The site, ideal for the "away from it all" holiday, offers a games room, children's play area, sandpit, swings, indoor heated swimming pool, laundry and telephone. A fisherman's paradise for those keen on coarse angling - free fishing on two acre ponds stocked with large carp and tench. No closed season. Early booking advised. Strictly no pets. Open Easter to end October. Prices from £85 to £350 weekly. SAE for colour brochure.

WIVELISCOMBE. Mrs A. Taylor, Waterrow Touring Park, Near Wiveliscombe, Taunton TA4 2AZ (01984 623464; Fax: 01984 624280). ETC ★★, AA Two Pennants. One only three-bedroom holiday home with uninterrupted views across the Tone Valley. The luxury specification includes accommodation for up to six, shower room, fitted galley kitchen, colour TV, linen included. Well behaved dogs welcome. We also have separate facilities for caravans, motorhomes and tents on our touring park bordered by woods and the River Tone. Attractive landscaping with spacious pitches in a peaceful setting where you can relax and watch the buzzards soaring overhead. Excellent touring area close to the Somerset/Devon border and Exmoor with fishing, walking, golf, etc. available locally. Park open all year. Please ring for brochure.
e-mail: taylor@waterrowpark.u-net.com
website: www.waterrowpark.u-net.com

STAFFORDSHIRE

COTTON. Star Caravan Park, Cotton, Near Alton Towers, Stoke-on-Trent ST10 3DW (01538 702256/702219/702564). ✓✓✓.

Situated off the B5417 road, between Leek and Cheadle, within ten miles of the market towns of Ashbourne and Uttoxeter, with Alton Towers just three-quarters of a mile away. A family-run site where your enjoyment is our main concern, Site amenities include large children's play area, shop, toilet block with showers, etc. laundry room with drying and ironing facilities, electric hook-ups, etc. Dogs welcome but must be kept on a leash. Open 1st February to 31st December. £6 per night for two persons. Special rates for groups and parties of campers (Scouts, schools, etc.). AA two star. Brochure and further details available.

SUFFOLK

SUDBURY. Mrs A. Wilson, Willowmere Camping Park, Bures Road, Sudbury CO10 0NN (01787 375559). ✓✓✓✓

This neat little site could be suitable for a weekend or as a touring base for inland Suffolk. It has just 40 pitches, 24 with electric points. Site has single toilet block of good quality and well maintained, with free hot water in the washbasins and showers. No other on-site amenities apart from milk, cold drinks, etc. Village shops half-a-mile away. Open Easter to October. AA, HPA. Terms per unit with two persons from £8.

NORTH YORKSHIRE

WHITBY near. Partridge Nest Farm, Eskdaleside, Sleights, Whitby YO22 5ES (01947 810450). Set in

beautiful Esk Valley, six caravans on secluded site in 45 acres of interesting land reaching up to the moors. Beautiful views. Just five minutes from the sea and the ancient fishing town of Whitby. The North Yorkshire Moors Steam Railway starts two miles away at Grosmont. Ideal for children, birdwatchers and all country lovers. Each caravan has mains electricity, gas cooker, fire, colour TV, fridge and shower/WC. Ideal touring centre. Riding lessons available on our own horses/ponies. Terms from £130. Two double Bed and Breakfast rooms also available from £16 per person.

ENGLAND
Activity Holidays

Edge of Teign Valley Forest

HALDON LODGE FARM
KENNFORD, NEAR EXETER
Tel: (01392) 823312

Delightful modern caravans only five miles Exeter and short distance Dawlish, Teignmouth and Torbay, from £70 to £195 (high season). Lounge (TV), two bedrooms, kitchen, bathroom, (washbasin and toilet). Attractive private grounds in peaceful surroundings, forest walks, famous village inns, three well stocked fishing lakes, farm food and shop nearby. Small private camping site, pony trekking or riding holiday available; special welcome to inexperienced riders also the personal service of a small family-run private site.

RIDING & TREKKING • PETS WELCOME • OPEN ALL YEAR • ENQUIRIES D. L. SALTER

DEVON, ASHBURTON. Parkers Farm Holiday Park, Ashburton TQ13 7LJ (01364 652598; Fax: 01364 654004). SELF CATERING: GENERAL.

A friendly, family-run farm site set in 400 acres and surrounded by beautiful countryside. 12 miles from the sea and close to Dartmoor National Park; ideal for touring Devon/Cornwall. Perfect for children and pets with all farm animals, play area and planty of space to roam, also large area for dogs. Holiday cottages and caravans, fully equipped except for linen. Level touring site with some hard standings. Free showers in fully tiled block, laundry room and games room. Small family bar, restaurant, shop and dining. Prices start from £90 Low Season to £380 High Season. Good discounts for couples. From Exeter take A38 to Plymouth till you see "26 miles to Plymouth' sign; take second left at Alston Cross signposted to Woodland and Denbury.

DEVON, AXMINSTER. Mrs C.M. Putt, Highridge Guest House, Lyme Road, Axminster EX13 5BQ (01297 34037). BOARD: FISHING.

River, fly and coarse fishing – 18 different venues available. We have detailed information on each venue including maps and photos of fish. Ideal for a good day's fishing. All facilities including bait, fridge, drying room. Large lounge, good food, packed lunches available. Pretty gardens with wildfowl and ponds. Terms from £16.50 per night Bed and Breakfast, Evening Meal from £8.50.

SOMERSET, CHEDDAR. Broadway House Holiday Touring Caravan and Camping Park, Cheddar BS27 3DB (01934 742610; Fax: 01934 744950). SELF-CATERING: GENERAL.★★★ Cheddar Gorge - "England's Grand Canyon." A totally unique five star caravan and camping family experience. One of the most interesting inland parks in the West Country. A family business specialising in family holidays. A free cuddle with the llamas a speciality. Prices include the use of the heated outdoor swimming pool and entrance to the Bar/Family room. Activities on the park include archery, abseiling and shooting; mountain bike/tandem hire; table tennis, crazy golf, boules, croquet, skate-board ramps. AA 4 Pennants, RAC Appointed, Rose Award Park.
e-mail: broadwayhouse.uk.com
website: www.enquiries@broadwayhouse.uk.com

THE FHG DIPLOMA

HELP IMPROVE
BRITISH TOURIST STANDARDS

You are choosing holiday accommodation from our very popular FHG Publications.
Whether it be a hotel, guest house, farmhouse or self-catering accommodation, we think you will find it hospitable, comfortable and clean, and your host and hostess friendly and helpful.

Why not write and tell us about it?

As a recognition of the generally well-run and excellent holiday accommodation reviewed in our publications, we at FHG Publications Ltd. present a diploma to proprietors who receive the highest recommendation from their guests who are also readers of our Guides. If you care to write to us praising the holiday you have booked through FHG Publications Ltd. – whether this be board, self-catering accommodation, a sporting or a caravan holiday, what you say will be evaluated and the proprietors who reach our final list will be contacted.

The winning proprietor will receive an attractive framed diploma to display on his premises as recognition of a high standard of comfort, amenity and hospitality. FHG Publications Ltd. offer this diploma as a contribution towards the improvement of standards in tourist accommodation in Britain. Help your excellent host or hostess to win it!

FHG DIPLOMA

We nominate ....

....

Because

Name ....

Address..

....

Telephone No...

SCOTLAND
Board Accommodation

The Black Watch Museum
Balhousie Castle, Perth PH1 5HR

Two-and-a-half centuries of treasures of the 42nd/73rd Highland regiments.
The Museum displays by means of pictures, weapons, uniforms and medals
the 250 year history of Scotland's Senior Highland Regiment.

Admission is FREE — donations to Museum Fund.

Opening Times: *May to September (Monday to Saturday incl. Public Holidays):*
10am to 4.30pm. NB Closed last Saturday of June.
October to April: (Monday to Friday) 10am to 3.30pm.
Closed 23th December to 6th January.

ABERDEEN, BANFF & MORAY

See also Colour Display Advertisement **BALLATER/BRAEMAR. The Administrator, The Estate Office, Balmoral Castle, Ballater AB35 5TB.** The Estate Grounds, Gardens and Exhibitions are open to the public from Monday, 17th April until Monday, 31st July 2000. Open daily from 10am to 5pm (last recommended admission 4pm). The Castle Ballroom Exhibition contains paintings, porcelain, silver and other items of interest from the Castle. The Carriage Hall Exhibition contains some carriages, a Royal Travel display, a commemorative china collection and a display of native wildlife, shown in their natural habitat. Other facilities include modern self-service cafeteria, gift shops, country walks, pony trekking and pony cart rides (when ponies available).

See also Colour Display Advertisement **BRECHIN. Brechin Castle Centre, Haughmuir, by Brechin, Angus (01356 626813).** One of the largest tourist attractions in Angus and a great day out for all the family. High quality Garden Centre and Coffee Shop. Country Park with ornamental lake. Picnic and enjoy the tranquillity, walk around the park to the farm, touch the animals. Summer Events. Brochure on request.

FOCHABERS. Mrs Alexia Shand, Castlehill Farm, Blackdam, Fochabers IV32 7LJ (01343 820351; Fax:

01343 821856). STB ★★ *B&B*. Comfortable accommodation on working farm at edge of forest with panoramic views to Ben Aigen. Lovely trails to walk or cycle. Deer and badgers are some of the woodland's inhabitants in addition to the birdlife. Ideal base for touring, golf, fishing, sandy beaches and old fishing villages locally. The famous Speyside Way, Whisky and Castle Trails are nearby. Accommodation comprises one double room and one family/twin room both with washbasins and tea/coffee facilities, full central heating and electric blankets. Guest lounge with coal fire. After an active day enjoy this peaceful overnight stop. Warm welcome awaits from your welcome host.

KEITH. Mrs Jean Jackson, The Haughs Farm, Keith AB55 6QN (01542 882238). STB ★★★ *GUEST*

HOUSE. AA QQQQ. The Haughs is a traditional mixed farm engaged in rotational cropping and cattle and sheep production. The spacious old farmhouse has a light cheerful dining room with excellent views. Four ground floor bedrooms, three en suite and one with private facilities, all with tea/coffee facilities and colour TV. The farm is situated just half-a-mile outside Keith and off the A96 Inverness road on the Whisky Trail; Falconry Centre eight miles. Open April to October. Bed and Breakfast from £17 to £20; Evening Meal £11.50.

METHLICK. Mrs Christine Staff, Sunnybrae Farm, Gight, Methlick, Ellon AB41 7JA (01651 806456).

STB ★★ *B&B.* **Working farm.** Comfortable accommodation on a working farm situated in a quiet, peaceful location with superb views. Close to Castle, Whisky and Stone Circle Trails. Centrally located for many places of interest. One twin and one double bedroom, both en suite and one single room. All rooms have tea/coffee making facilities. Guest lounge with colour TV. Full central heating. Full farmhouse breakfast. Ample parking space. Open all year. Pets welcome. Bed and Breakfast from £17 to £20; reduced rates for children. A warm welcome awaits all guests.

PETERHEAD. Carrick Guest House, 16 Merchant Street, Peterhead AB42 1DU (Tel/Fax: 01779 470610). STB ★★ *GUEST HOUSE.* Comfortable accommodation centrally situated for all amenities. Two minutes' walk from main shopping centre, harbour and beach. All rooms en suite, colour television, hospitality tray, trouser press, hairdryer. Full central heating. Good car parking. Bed and Breakfast from £20 to £25 per person.

Key to Tourist Board Ratings – Scotland and Wales

The Scottish Tourist Board Star Grading System. This easy-to-understand system tells you at a glance the quality standard you can expect. The gradings range from ★ (Fair and acceptable) to ★★★★★ (Exceptional, world-class) and will also include the type of accommodation eg ★★★ Self-catering or ★★ Hotel.

The Wales Tourist Board also operates the above system for serviced accommodation only. Self-catering properties will continue to show the **Dragon Award Grading** from **One** to **Five** depending on quality and facilities.

Some properties had not been assessed at the time of going to press and in these cases the publishers have included the old Crown Gradings.

ARGYLL & BUTE

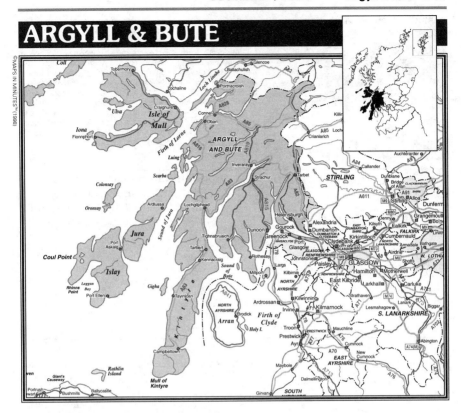

©MAPS IN MINUTES™ (1998)

ARDMADDY, near Oban. Mrs D. Gilbert, Ardshellach Farm, Ardmaddy, By Oban PA34 4QY (01852

300218). Working beef cattle and sheep farm situated on the Ardmaddy road 12 miles from Oban on the B844 to Easdale and approximately one mile before the Bridge over the Atlantic and Ardmaddy Castle Gardens. This quiet accommodation is 400 yards from the sea overlooking Luing and Scarba and comprises one room sleeping two/four. Bathroom with bath and shower adjacent. TV lounge. Children welcome. Bed and Breakfast from £15 includes evening cup of tea. Bar meals available by Atlantic Bridge.

ARROCHAR. Mrs C. Bowen, The Roadman's Cottage, Rest and Be Thankful, By Arrochar G83 7AS

(01301 702 557). STB ★★ *B&B* By itself in breathtakingly beautiful Glen Croe, seven miles from Loch Lomond on the A83 with Inveraray 15 miles. Scenic routes to Campbeltown or Oban, the west coast and islands. Access to easy walks in Argyll Forest Park which is rich in flora and fauna. Hillwalking and climbing on Munros. Adjacent to farmland, good fishing on Loch Long. I bake my own bread and enjoy cooking local produce. Traditional and vegetarian menus are offered. Bed and Breakfast £14 to £15. Dinner £8.50. One double or family room, one twin room.

CARRADALE. Mrs D. MacCormick, Mains Farm, Carradale, Campbeltown PA28 6QG (01583 431216).

STB ★★ *B&B*. **Working farm.** From April to October farmhouse accommodation is offered at Mains Farm, five minutes' walk from safe beach, forestry walks with views of Carradale Bay and Arran. Near main bus route and 15 miles from airport. Golf, sea/river fishing, pony trekking, canoeing locally. Comfortable accommodation in one double, one single, one family bedrooms; guests' sitting/diningroom with coal/log fire; bathroom, toilet. Heating in rooms according to season. Children welcome at reduced rates, cot and high chair available. Pets by prior arrangement. The house is not suitable for disabled visitors. Good home cooking and special diets catered for. Bed and Breakfast from £17.00. Tea making facilities in rooms.

LOCHGOILHEAD. Mrs Rosemary Dolan, The Shorehouse Inn, Lochgoilhead PA24 8AJ (01301 703340). Friendly informal Inn, fully licensed, has seven letting

rooms, central heating and double glazing. There are two family, three twin, one single and one double bedrooms. Residents' lounge, a bar of unusual character and licensed restaurant. Home cooking, bar meals. Formerly the old manse on a historic site with lochside and panoramic views looking southward down Loch Goil, situated in the village on the shore. Local amenities include water sports, fishing, pony trekking, tennis, bowls, golf, swimming pool, curling in winter and a good area for hill walking. Some rooms with private facilities. Fully licensed. One hour travel time from Glasgow. Open all year round. Ideal for winter or summer breaks. Rates from £14 Bed and Breakfast.

OBAN. Mr and Mrs E. Hughes, "Sgeir-Mhaol" Guest House, Soroba Road, Oban PA34 4JF (Tel & Fax: 01631 562650). Family-run guest house situated only

approximately five minutes' walk from town centre, bus/rail stations, main ferry terminal for sailings to the islands of Mull, Iona, Staffa, Coll, Tiree and Colonsay. Bedrooms comprise double, twin and family, all colour co-ordinated and furnished to a high standard with colour TV, tea/coffee makers, etc and most with en suite facilities. The lounge and dining room overlook a pleasant garden and, like the bedrooms, are on the ground floor. There is a spacious private car park within the grounds. Open all year. The area has a wealth of natural beauty with opportunities for walks, golf, fishing, sailing, pony trekking and a sports complex where swimming, tennis, squash and bowling are available. Oban is an excellent base for day trips by coach or car to many places including Campbeltown, Fort William, Glencoe, etc, or for a day's sailing to the Islands. Bed and Breakfast from £19 to £24.

Terms quoted in this publication may be subject to increase
if rises in costs necessitate

AYRSHIRE & ARRAN

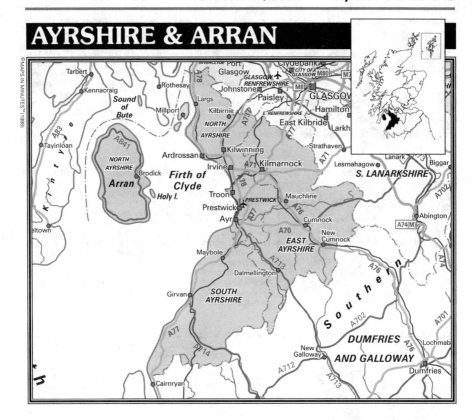

©MAPS IN MINUTES™ (1998)

AYR. Mrs Wilcox, Fisherton Farm, Dunure, Ayr KA7 4LF (Tel & Fax: 01292 500223). STB ★★★ *B&B.*

Traditional stone-built farmhouse on working mixed farm with extensive sea views to Arran. Convenient for golf, walking and Burns Country. Also convenient for Culzean Castle and Prestwick Airport. From Ayr take A719 coast road past Haven, Craig Tara; farm is five miles south of Ayr. Accommodation comprises one double and one twin en suite, ground floor bedrooms with TV and tea/coffee making facilities. Central heating throughout. Children welcome. Pets by arrangement. Please write, telephone or fax for further information. Prices from £18.50 to £20. Also self-catering property. Welcome Host.

DUNLOP. Mrs W. Burns, East Langton Farm, Dunlop KA3 4DS (01560 482978). A warm welcome in peaceful surroundings, close to all amenities. 20 minutes to Glasgow or Prestwick Airport, also 20 minutes from the coast with spectacular views overlooking the Isle of Arran, Dalry and the Kilbirnie hills, and Ben Lomond in the distance. Very quiet, peaceful countryside. One double and two twin rooms, all with private bathroom/shower, TV with Teletext, radio alarms, tea/coffee making facilities and hairdryers. Terms from £18.50 to £22.50 per person.

KILMARNOCK. Mrs M. Howie, Hill House Farm, Grassyards Road, Kilmarnock KA3 6HG (01563 523370). STB ★★★ *B&B*. Enjoy a peaceful holiday on a working dairy farm two miles east of Kilmarnock. We offer a warm welcome with home baking for supper, choice of farmhouse breakfasts with own preserves. Three large comfortable bedrooms with lovely views over Ayrshire countryside, en suite facilities, tea/coffee, electric blankets, central heating; TV lounge, sun porch, dining room and garden. Excellent touring base with trips to coast, Arran, Burns Country and Glasgow nearby. Easy access to A77 and numerous golf courses. Children very welcome. Bed and Breakfast from £17 (including supper). Self catering cottages also available.

KILMARNOCK. Mrs Anna Steel, Laigh Langmuir Farm, Kilmaurs, Kilmarnock KA3 2NU (01563 538270). STB ★★★ *B&B*. Laigh Langmuir is an attractive stone-built farmhouse in lovely surroundings just outside Kilmaurs village. Easily accessible from Glasgow and the South. Perfect stop-over for the Highlands, or stay and golf at Troon or visit the island of Arran, Loch Lomond or South West Scotland. Relax in the evening by a log fire and in the morning enjoy a real farmhouse breakfast made from our own produce, home baking and preserves. All bedrooms have central heating, washbasins, electric blankets, hairdryers and tea making facilities; three rooms with en suite facilities. Children very welcome. Cot, high chair and baby sitting available. Bed and Breakfast from £16. A Scottish Farmhouse of the Year Award Winner. Telephone or write for further details.

WHITING BAY. Peter and Barbara Rawlin, Viewbank House, Golf Course Road, Whiting Bay KA27 8QT (01770 700326). Beautiful privately owned house where you can relax and enjoy super home-cooked fresh food. Large lawned garden with magnificent views across the Clyde. 500 yards down a country lane brings you onto the shore. Seven bedrooms (four of which have private facilities), one on the ground floor. Also new superior three bedroom self-catering bungalow to let. Open most of the year with full central heating and warm atmosphere, Viewbank charms its guests back time and time again. TWICE WINNERS OF FARM HOLIDAY GUIDE DIPLOMAS. Bed and Breakfast from £20 to £24; three-course Dinner with coffee £12 (B.Y.O.B.).

PLEASE MENTION THIS GUIDE WHEN YOU WRITE OR PHONE TO ENQUIRE ABOUT ACCOMMODATION. IF YOU ARE WRITING, A STAMPED, ADDRESSED ENVELOPE IS ALWAYS APPRECIATED.

BORDERS

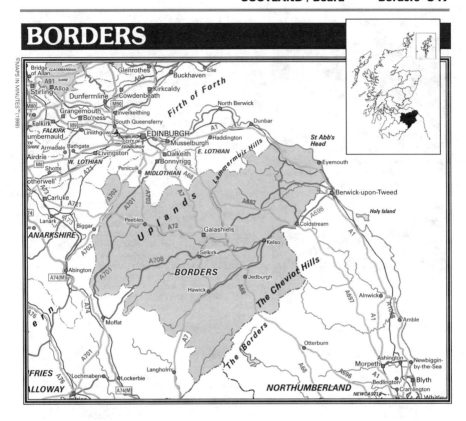

BIGGAR. Mrs Rosemary Harper, South Mains Farm, Biggar ML12 6HF (01899 860226). Working farm.

South Mains Farm is a working family farm, situated in an elevated position with good views, on the B7016 between Biggar and Broughton. An ideal place to take a break on a North/South journey. Edinburgh 29 miles, Peebles 11 miles. Well situated for touring the Border regions in general. A comfortable bed and excellent breakfast provided in this centrally heated and well-furnished farmhouse, which has two double and one single bedrooms. Open all year. Car essential, parking. Terms £15 per night which includes light supper of home-made scones, etc. If you are interested just ring, write or call in. Warm welcome assured.

GREENLAW. Mrs Carruthers, Bridgend House, 36 West High Street, Greenlaw TD10 6XA (01361 810270).

Bridgend is on the scenic A697 road between Newcastle (68 miles south) and Edinburgh (38 miles north). Built in 1816, it retains many original features besides having three en suite bedrooms and one bedroom with private bathroom; lounge with colour TV, books, games and a real fire in winter. Traditional and wholefood breakfasts, home-baking and cooking with local produce in season. Parking available in courtyard. Trout fishing in River Blackadder from the pretty garden. Book one of our Special Weekend Breaks and come and unwind in the beautiful Scottish Borders. Bed and Breakfast from £18 per night.

HAWICK. Mrs Sheila Shell, Wiltonburn Farm, Hawick TD9 7LL (01450 372414; mobile: 07774 192551; Fax: 01450 378098). Working farm. You will be warmly welcomed and cared for as you unwind on our friendly, working mixed hill farm. A spacious farmhouse B&B with log fires and three cosy letting rooms — one family en suite, one double with private bathroom and one twin/double. Your base for walking, riding, fishing, golf, castles or stately homes and gardens. This is tranquillity without isolation in an idyllic valley two miles from Hawick, the centre of Scottish textiles. Our showroom containing designer cashmere knitwear, paintings, jewellery, pretty, hand- painted furniture, and country gifts will make your stay more pleasurable. Bed and Breakfast from £18. Also two self-catering cottages, terms from £100. Private parking. Open all year.

e-mail: shell@wiltonburnfarm.u-net.com
website: www.SmoothHound.co.uk/hotels/wiltonbu.html

INNERLEITHEN. Mrs J. Caird, Traquair Bank, Innerleithen EH44 6PR (01896 830425). Working farm, join in. Comfortable friendly farmhouse with large garden overlooking the hills and the River Tweed. This is a 580 acre stock and arable farm, part of the historical Traquair Estate. Visitors may sometimes participate in farm activities. We have dogs, cats, kittens, hens, chickens, pet lambs and ponies all happy to play, as well as cows and sheep on the farm. Beautiful walking, birdwatching, riding and cycling country; trout fishing, 300 yards, mountain bikes, pony treks, swimming pool six miles. Beaches one hour, golf course two miles and Edinburgh 35 minutes. Bed and Breakfast from £18 Dinner, Bed and Breakfast from £28.

PEEBLES. Mrs A Waddell, Lyne Farm, Peebles EH45 8NR (Tel & Fax: 01721 740255). STB ★★ *B&B* A warm welcome is assured at Lyne Farm, situated in an area of scenic beauty. Located only four miles on the A72 from the picturesque town of Peebles. Guests can walk around the farm, relax in our walled garden or go hill walking up the Black Meldon. The tastefully decorated Georgian Farmhouse accommodation consists of one twin room and two double rooms with tea/coffee making facilities; two bathrooms; diningroom and sittingroom for guests. Also available, spacious cottage which sleeps two to eight persons. Traquair House, Kailzie, Neidpath Castle and Dawyck Botanical Gardens within a few miles. Bed and Breakfast from £17 to £19 per person, reductions for children.

Key to Tourist Board Ratings
Scotland and Wales

The Scottish Tourist Board Star Grading System. This easy-to-understand system tells you at a glance the quality standard you can expect. The gradings range from ★ (Fair and acceptable) to ★★★★★ (Exceptional, world-class) and will also include the type of accommodation eg ★★★ Self-catering or ★★ Hotel.

The Wales Tourist Board also operates the above system for serviced accommodation only. Self-catering properties will continue to show the **Dragon Award Grading** from **One** to **Five** depending on quality and facilities.

Some properties had not been assessed at the time of going to press and in these cases the publishers have included the old Crown Gradings.

DUMFRIES & GALLOWAY

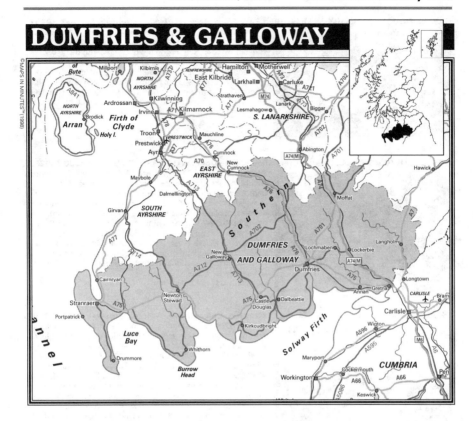

©MAPS IN MINUTES™ (1998)

BEATTOCK. Mrs Freda Bell, Cogries Farm, Beattock, Moffat DG10 9PP (01576 470320). STB ★ *B&B*.

Working farm. Cogries is a 275 acre dairy and mixed farm which lies just under half-a-mile off the A74 (10 miles north of Lockerbie and three miles south of Beattock). The farmhouse has four bedrooms, all with washbasins and tea making facilities. Bath/shower room and separate toilet. Visitors can go salmon and trout fishing, train spotting, bird-watching on the farm, play croquet on the lawn or just relax on the patio. An ideal stopover when travelling north or south, or as a touring base for South West Scotland. Cogries is conveniently situated for Moffat, Dumfries, Glasgow, Edinburgh, Hadrian's Wall, Carlisle and the northern Lake District. Comments from the visitors' book are very favourable, and hopefully yours will be added. Bed and Breakfast from £16.00.

CANONBIE. Mrs Steele, North Lodge, Canonbie DG14 0TA (013873 71409). A warm welcome awaits

you at this small family-run guest house situated approximately one mile south of the village of Canonbie, on the tourist route A7 to Edinburgh. Canonbie village is renowned for its fishing - private fishing on the "Willow Pool" can be arranged. NORTH LODGE is a 19th century cottage set in beautiful gardens and was recently extended to include five double/twin bedrooms, four en suite, the other has private facilities. The ground floor en suite room is suitable for the disabled traveller (Grade 1 classification). Within easy reach of Hadrian's Wall, the Lake District, Carlisle, Dumfries, Moffat, Kielder Dam, Hawick, Gretna and many more interesting places. An ideal touring base. Breaks available. Please telephone for further details.

CASTLE DOUGLAS. Mrs Jessie Shaw, High Park Farm, Balmaclellan, Castle Douglas DG7 3PT (Tel

& Fax: 01644 420298). STB ★★ *B&B* Enjoy a holiday amidst beautiful scenery while staying at our comfortable farmhouse situated by Loch Ken. High Park is a family-run dairy, beef and sheep farm offering accommodation in one family room, one twin bedroom (upstairs), one double bedroom (ground floor); all have washbasins, shaver points, tea/coffee making facilities, colour TV. Central heating, home baking. Comfort, cleanliness and good food guaranteed. Open Easter to October. Bed and Breakfast from £15. Brochure on request.

CASTLE DOUGLAS. Mrs C. Pickup, Craigadam, Castle Douglas DG7 3HU (Tel & Fax: 01556 650233).

Working farm. STB ★★★★ A family-run 18th century farmhouse situated in the hills looking across Galloway. All bedrooms are en suite and there is a lovely oak-panelled dining room which offers Cordon Bleu cooking using local produce such as venison, pheasant, salmon. Oak-panelled billiards room. Come home in the evening to comfort, warmth and good Scottish hospitality. Fish on our own trout loch. The area offers much to the traveller with its lovely beaches, hill and forest walks, sailing, fishing, bird watching, pony trekking, golfing, as well as many places of historic and local interest. Please telephone **Richard or Celia** for further details.
website: www.craigadam.com

CROSSMICHAEL (Galloway). Mr James C. Grayson, Culgruff House Hotel, Crossmichael DG7 3BB

(01556 670230). Culgruff is a former Baronial Mansion standing in its own grounds of over 35 acres, overlooking the beautiful Ken Valley and the loch beyond. The hotel is comfortable, ideal for those seeking a quiet, restful holiday. An excellent position for touring Galloway and Burns country. The hotel is half-a-mile from A713 Castle Douglas to Ayr road, four miles from Castle Douglas and A75 to Stranraer. Many places of interest in the region - picturesque Solway coast villages, gardens, castles (including Culzean), the Ayrshire coast. For holiday activities - tennis, riding, pony trekking, bowls, golf, fishing (salmon, fly, coarse and sea), boating, water ski-ing, windsurfing, swimming etc. Lovely walks. All rooms have washbasins (some en suite), electric blankets, tea/coffee facilities; ample bathroom/toilet facilities. All bedrooms have TVs. Large family rooms available. One of the lounges has colour TV; diningroom. Central heating. Children under 10 years at reduced rates. Cot. Non-smoking accommodation if required. Car advisable, parking. Bed and Breakfast from £12 per person in large family rooms, doubles from £17 per person. Open from Easter to October. Restricted October to Easter. RAC**. Home of author James Crawford.

MOFFAT. Mr and Mrs W. Gray, Barnhill Springs Country Guest House, Moffat DG10 9QS (01683

220580). STB ★★ *GUEST HOUSE.* AA ◆◆◆. Barnhill Springs is an early Victorian country mansion standing in its own grounds overlooking Upper Annandale. Situated half-a-mile from the A74/M, the house and its surroundings retain an air of remote peacefulness. Internally it has been decorated and furnished to an exceptionally high standard of comfort. Open fire in lounge. Accommodation includes family, double, twin and single rooms, some en suite. Open all year. Children welcome; pets welcome FREE of charge. Bed and Breakfast from £20.00; Evening Meal (optional) £14.00.

WHITHORN. Mrs E. Forsyth, Baltier Farm, Whithorn, Newton Stewart DG8 8HA (01988 600241). STB

★★ *B&B*. **Working farm, join in.** Modern stone-built house on dairy farm with large garden and sun room. High position gives fine views over surrounding countryside. Accommodation comprises single, double/twin and family rooms (en suite available). Locally there is an archaeological dig in progress, or you can take a trip to Ireland. Children welcome. Sorry, no pets. Bed and Breakfast from £16 to £20. Room only available. Open March to November.

EDINBURGH & LOTHIANS

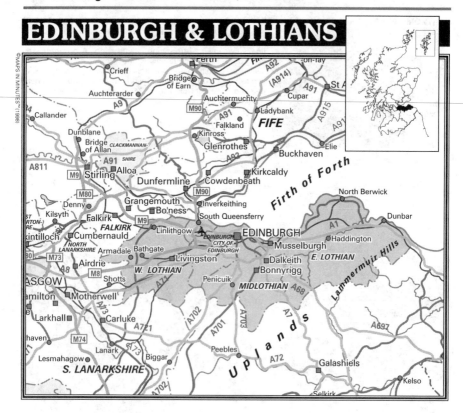

EDINBURGH. Rothesay Hotel, 8 Rothesay Place, Edinburgh EH3 7SL (0131 2254125; Fax: 0131 220 4350). STB ★★ *HOTEL*. **AA ★★.** Within Edinburgh's Georgian New Town, situated five minutes' walk from Princes Street – Edinburgh's shopping and commercial centre. 36 rooms with private bathroom and colour TV, tea/coffee facilites. Elevator. Bar and restaurant where Traditional Scottish Breakfast is served. Children welcome. Reasonable terms, open all year. Contact Mr. Fariday.

E-mail: info@rothesay.hotel.demon.co.uk
Website: http://www.rothesay-hotel.com

EDINBURGH. Kenvie Guest House, 16 Kilmaurs Road EH16 5DA (Tel & Fax: 0131-668 1964). A charming and comfortable Victorian townhouse situated in a quiet and pleasant residential part of the city, about one mile south of the centre and one small block from main road (A7) leading to city via Bypass to all routes. Excellent bus services. We offer for your comfort complimentary tea/coffee, central heating, colour TV and no-smoking rooms. En suite rooms available. A lovely breakfast and lots of additional caring touches. A warm and friendly welcome is guaranteed from Richard and Dorothy.

Southdown Guest House

A warm welcome and personal service is assured at the Southdown Guest House. Conveniently situated on a main bus route in a prime residential area just 10 minutes from Princes Street, The Castle and Holyrood Palace; several golf courses are within easy reach. We have several full ensuite rooms available, while all others have private showers. Cable/Sky TV, tea/coffee making facilities. There is a comfortable residents' lounge with colour TV. Full Scottish Breakfast with home produce our speciality.

Bed and Breakfast from £17.50 (singles from £22.50). Reduced rates for families and groups. Own key access all day. Full central heating and Fire Certificate. Private car park. Cot, high chair and babysitting service available. .

20 Craigmillar Park, Edinburgh EH16 5PS
Telephone: 0131-667 2410   Fax: 0131-667 6056   E-mail: haml20@aol.com

---

INVERESK. 16 Carberry Road, Inveresk, Musselburgh EH21 7TN (0131-665 2107). A lovely Victorian

stone detached house situated in a quiet conservation village seven miles east of Edinburgh, overlooking fields and close to a lovely river walk and seaside with harbour. Buses from door to city, very close to sports centre with swimming pool and within easy distance of many golf courses. Spacious accommodation comprises one family room and two double rooms, all have central heating, colour TV and tea/coffee making facilities. Two large, fully equipped bathrooms adjacent. Parking in quiet side road or in garden if required by arrangement. Full cooked breakfast included from £18 per person per night; reduction for children.

LINLITHGOW. Mrs N. Hay, Belsyde Farm, Lanark Road, Linlithgow EH49 6QE (Tel & Fax: 01506

842098). STB ★★★ *B&B*. This large 18th century farmhouse is situated in large secluded gardens with a superb view over the Forth estuary. Golfing and fishing available close by. All bedrooms have washbasins, tea/coffee-making facilities, colour TV and central heating; one bedroom en suite. Located close to M8, M9 and M90 and to Edinburgh airport. Follow A706 south-west from Linlithgow (one-and-a-half miles); first entrance on left after crossing Union Canal. Open all year except Christmas. AA Listed.

MUSSELBURGH. Inveresk House, Inveresk Village, Musselburgh EH21 7UA (0131-665 5855; Fax:

0131-665 0578). Historic Mansion house and award- winning Bed & Breakfast. Family-run "home from home". Situated in three acres of garden and woodland. Built on the site of a Roman settlement from 150 AD, the remains of a bathhouse can be found hidden in the garden. Three comfortable en suite rooms. Original art and antiques adorn the house. Edinburgh's Princes Street seven miles from Inveresk House. Good bus routes. Families welcome. Off street parking. Telephone first. Price from £35pp. Family room £100 to £120.
e-mail: chute.inveresk@btinternet.com

PATHHEAD. Mrs Margaret Winthrop, "Fairshiels", Blackshiels, Pathhead EH7 5SX (01875 833665)

We are situated on the A68, three miles south of Pathhead at the picturesque village of Fala. The house is an 18th century coaching inn (Listed building). All bedrooms have washbasins and tea/coffee making facilities; one is en suite. All the rooms are comfortably furnished. We are within easy reach of Edinburgh and the Scottish Borders. A warm welcome is extended to all our guests - our aim is to make your stay a pleasant one. Cost is from £16 per person; children two years to 12 years £9.00, under two years FREE.

FIFE

LETHAM. Mrs Susan Jackson, Lindifferon Farm, Letham KY15 7RX (Tel & Fax 01337 810230).

Working farm. A warm welcome awaits you at Lindifferon, a working arable/beef/sheep farm situated in the beautiful Howe of Fife, within easy reach of Perth, St Andrews, Dundee and Edinburgh. An ideal base for touring and golfing. This spacious, tastefully decorated farmhouse with traditional furniture has one double and one family room with large seating areas, tea/coffee making facilities, hair dryers. Home baking. Central heating. Open from Easter to October. Bed and Breakfast from £18.50.

ST. ANDREWS. Mrs Anne Duncan, Spinkstown Farmhouse, St. Andrews KY6 8PN. (Tel & Fax: 01334 473475). STB ★★★★ *B&B*. Working farm. Only

two miles from St. Andrews on the picturesque A917 road to Crail, Spinkstown is a uniquely designed farmhouse with views of the sea and surrounding countryside. Bright and spacious, it is furnished to a high standard. Accommodation consists of double and twin rooms, all en suite and with tea/coffee facilities; diningroom and lounge with colour TV. Substantial farmhouse breakfast to set you up for the day; evening meals are by arrangement only. The famous Old Course, historic St. Andrews and several National Trust properties are all within easy reach, as well as swimming, tennis, putting, bowls, horse riding, country parks, nature reserves, beaches and coastal walks. Plenty of parking available. Bed and Breakfast from £20; Evening Meal £12. AA QQQQ Selected.

GLASGOW & DISTRICT

GLASGOW. Holly House, 54 Ibrox Terrace, Glasgow G51 2TB (0141-427 5609; Fax: 0141-427 5608

or 0850 223500 Mobile). STB ★★★ *GUEST HOUSE*. Situated in an early Victorian tree-lined terrace in the city centre south area, Holly House offers spacious rooms with en suite facility. Room rates include Breakfast. Glasgow Airport and the City Centre are only a short drive away; Ibrox Underground Station two minutes' walk. Other local places of interest include Burrell Collection in Pollok Park, Pollok House, Bellahouston Park and the Ibrox Football Stadium. SECC 10 minutes. Singles £20 to £25; Twins/Doubles £36 to £50. Member of Harry James Appreciation Society: ask for details. Please telephone Peter Divers for further information.
e-mail: stay@hollyhouse.gispnet.com
website: www.gisp.net/hollyhouse/html

GLASGOW. Sally Divers, Kirkland House, 42 St. Vincent Crescent, Glasgow G3 8NG (0141-248 3458; Fax: 0141-221 5174). STB ★★★ *GUEST HOUSE*. City Centre

guest house located in Glasgow's little Chelsea, a beautiful Victorian Crescent in the area known as Finnieston, offers excellent rooms, most with en suite facilities, full central heating, colour TV and tea/coffee makers. The house is located within walking distance of the Scottish Exhibition Centre, Museum/Art Gallery and Kelvingrove Park. We are very convenient to all City Centre and West End facilities and only 10 minutes from Glasgow's International Airport. Room rates: Singles from £30 to £35; Twins/Doubles £60 to £70. Featured in Frommers Tour Guide. Member of Harry James Appreciation Society: details on request.
e-mail: admin@kirkland.gispnet.com
website: www.s-h-systems.co.uk/hotels/kirkland.html

HIGHLANDS

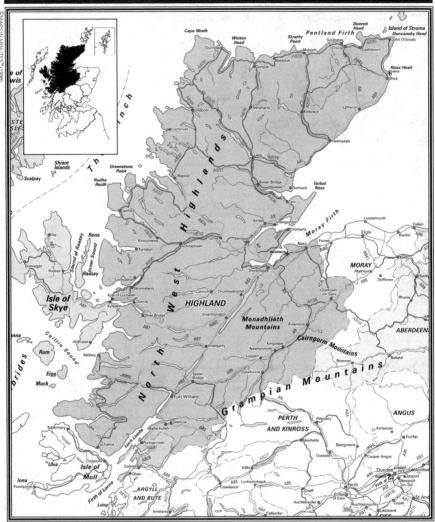

HIGHLANDS (MID)

AULTBEA. Mrs H. MacLeod, The Croft, Aultbea IV22 2JA (01445 731352). Guests are assured of a warm welcome at The Croft, which stands on its own just yards away from the sea and the village of Aultbea, overlooking Loch Ewe and the Torridon Hills. Lots of hill walking and climbing within easy reach and Inverewe sub-tropical gardens are only five miles away. Unrestricted access to house and guests are provided with their own keys. One twin, two double rooms, all with washbasins and tea making facilities; bathroom with shower, toilet; sitting/diningroom. All modern conveniences. Car essential – parking. Open from March to October. Bed and Breakfast from £18.

DUNDONNELL. Mrs A. Ross, 4 Camusnagaul, Dundonnell IV23 2QT (01854 633237). Situated near Anteallach mountain range. Suitable for walkers, birdwatchers and climbers. Gruinard Sands are ten miles away. Inverewe Gardens are 20 miles away. Bed and Breakfast from £16. Evening meals can be obtained from Dundonald Hotel. Caravan and self-catering cottages to let – prices on application.

HIGHLANDS (SOUTH)

DAVIOT. Margaret and Alex Hutcheson, Daviot Mains Farm, Daviot, Near Inverness IV1 2ER (01463 772215; Fax: 01463 772099). STB ★★★★ *B&B.* Comfortable early 19th century listed farmhouse in quiet situation near Inverness. Relax in the warm atmosphere of this friendly home where delicious meals are prepared for you (residential licence). Log fires in sitting and dining rooms. En suite/private facilities. The perfect base for exploring the Scottish Highlands. Selected by 'Taste of Scotland", and recommended by Elizabeth Gundrey's "Staying Off the Beaten Track". and Fodor. Closed Christmas. Bed and Breakfast from £19.

FORT WILLIAM. J. & E. Rosie, Guisachan Guest House, Alma Road, Fort William PH33 6HA (Tel & Fax: 01397 703797). STB ★★★ *GUEST HOUSE.* Delightfully situated in own grounds overlooking Loch Linnhe and Ardgour Hills, yet within five minutes walking of bus and railway stations and town centre, well-placed for day-trips to Inverness, Isle of Skye, Oban, Inveraray, Pitlochry etc. For the more energetic there is excellent walking, climbing and fishing and skiing in winter and early spring. Rooms are en suite with tea/coffee, colour TV, hairdryers and clock radio. A warm welcome awaits you. Open January - December. Prices £18 - £28 per person.

FORT WILLIAM. Norma and Jim McCallum, "The Neuk", Corpach, Fort William PH33 7LR (01397 772244). The Neuk is fully centrally heated and double glazed throughout to ensure maximum comfort of guests. Two family, one twin and one double bedrooms., all en suite and have colour TV and refreshment facilities. Guests' dining room and smoking lounge. Payphone. Situated north-west of Fort William in the village of Corpach offering panoramic views over Mamore Mountains, Ben Nevis and Loch Linnhe. An ideal base for exploring the surrounding area either walking, cycling or motoring. Open all year. Whatever the weather you can always be sure of a warm welcome. Bed and Breakfast from £16 - £40. Evening meal £11. Brochure available.

FORT WILLIAM. Mrs A. Grant, Glen Shiel Guest House, Achintore Road, Fort William PH33 6RW

(01397 702271; Fax: 01397 202271). STB ★★ *GUEST HOUSE.* Modern purpose-built guest house situated near the shore of Loch Linnhe with panoramic views of the surrounding mountains. Accommodation comprises three en suite double bedrooms, one twin-bedded room and one family room, all with colour TV and tea making facilities. Non-smoking accommodation available. Large car park. Garden. Bed and Breakfast from £16 to £20. Directions: on the A82 one-and-a-half miles south of Fort William.

See also Colour Display Advertisement

GRANTOWN-ON-SPEY. Richard and Angela Roulson, Rosegrove Guest House, Skye of Curr, Dulnain Bridge, Grantown-on-Spey PH26 3PA (01479 851335). Situated in the heart of the Spey Valley, Rosegrove is an ideal place for a holiday among the mountains and glens of the Scottish Highlands. We believe a good holiday starts with a comfortable room and good food in a relaxed and friendly atmosphere. Our bedrooms (some en suite) are centrally heated with wash basins, tea making facilities and electric blankets. Watch TV in the lounge in front of a log fire or relax in the sun lounge and patio after the day's activities. Evening meals available; special diets catered for. Ideally situated for visiting Balmoral, Loch Ness, Culloden, Cawdor Castle and the Highland Wildlife Park at Kingussie. Well behaved pets welcome. Open all year. No smoking. Terms from £15. Please telephone for further information.
e-mail: rosegroveguesthouse@tesco.net

INVERGARRY. Caroline Francis, Drynachan Cottage, Invergarry PH35 4HL (01809 501225). STB

★★★ *B&B.* As seen on BBC's 'Summer Holiday' Programme in July 1998, a friendly welcome and comfortable accommodation awaits you all year round at our 17th Century Highland Cottage, visited by Bonnie Prince Charlie in 1746. We offer family, twin or double rooms, (two with en suite bathrooms), cosy sitting room with log fire and colour TV and a separate dining room where breakfast and home cooked evening meals are served. There is a large garden and ample parking. Drynachan is ideal for touring, hillwalking and cycling. B&B £15-£23, DBB £27-£35. Discounts available for bookings of seven nights or more. Please ask for brochure.
E-mail: Drynachan@aol.com

INVERNESS. Mrs E. MacKenzie, The Whins, 114 Kenneth Street, Inverness IV3 5QG (01463 236215). Comfortable, homely accommodation awaits you here 10 minutes' walking distance from town centre, bus and railway stations, Inverness being an excellent touring base for North, West and East bus and railway journeys. Bedrooms have TV and tea-making facilities, washbasins and heating off-season. Bathroom has a shared shower and toilet. Pensioners welcome at slightly reduced rate. Two double/twin rooms from £14 per person per night. Write or phone for full details. Non smoking.

INVERNESS. Mrs A. McLean, Waternish, 15 Clachnaharry Road, Inverness IV3 8QH (01463 230520). Delightful Bungalow in beautiful setting overlooking Moray Firth and Black Isle. On main A862 road to Beauly, just five minutes to Inverness town centre. Ideal touring centre for north and west. Canal cruises and golf course nearby and lovely walks by banks of Caledonian Canal. Loch Ness is just 15 minutes drive. Accommodation comprises three double/twin rooms, one en suite, all with tea/coffee making facilities and colour TV. Comfortable lounge. Full Scottish breakfast. Private car parking. Open March to October. Bed and Breakfast from £14.

MORAR (by Mallaig). Mrs U. Clulow, Sunset Guest House, Morar, by Mallaig PH40 4PA (Tel & Fax: 01687 462259). Situated in the peaceful west coast village of Morar, overlooking the renowned silver sands and the beautiful Inner Hebrides. With the island studded Atlantic in front and backdrop of the mountain wilds of Knoydart, Sunset is superbly placed for those wishing to find the tranquillity, scenic beauty and romantic history for which this part of Scotland is famous. Authentic Thai food is also on the menu to provide some inner warmth after a long and energetic day. Children welcome. Prices from £12.50.
e-mail: sunsetgh@aol.com

LANARKSHIRE

Mrs A. Hodge

Gilkerscleugh Mains Farm, Abington, By Biggar ML12 6SQ
Tel & Fax: 01864 502388

One double, one twin and one family bedroom (all rooms en suite). Ideal base for visiting Edinburgh and Glasgow.

Bed and Breakfast from £16.00 per person; Evening Meal from £10.00 (by arrangement). Reductions for children.

HARTHILL. Mrs H. Stephens, Blair **Mains Farm, Harthill ML7 5TJ (01501 751278).** Attractive farmhouse on small farm – 72 acres. Immediately adjacent to Junction 5 of M8 motorway. Ideal centre for touring, with Edinburgh, Glasgow, Stirling 30 minutes' drive. Fishing (trout and coarse) and golf nearby. One family, two double, two twin and two single bedrooms; bathroom; sittingroom, diningroom; sun porch. Central heating. Children welcome – babysitting offered. Pets welcome. Car essential – parking. Bed and Breakfast from £16; weekly rates available. Reduced rates for children. Open all year.

NETHERBURN. Mrs White, Broomfield Farm, Netherburn ML9 3DH (01698 792929). Broomfield Farm is a luxurious "Red Rose" Victorian farmhouse situated one mile from Junction eight of the M74. In a courtyard setting with formal garden at the rear Broomfield makes the ideal stopover for going either north or south. Peaceful, non-smoking luxurious accommodation. Family bedroom with private lounge; twin, double en suite. Full five-course Scottish breakfast. Renowned cuisine by our resident chef. Dinner from £9. Open fireplaces, antique furniture. Full central heating. Unbelievable value at Bed and Breakfast from £17. Family reductions. Dinner, Bed and Breakfast based on two sharing – six nights £150 per person, two nights £49 per person, three nights £73 per person. Great food, great value, great atmosphere.

STRATHAVEN. Mrs White, Todcastle Farm, Strathaven ML10 6QD (01357 440259). Todcastle Farm is a 'Red Rose' Vistorian farmhouse set in glorious countryside. Leather couches, log fires. Two miles west of Strathaven on the A71. Bedrooms have colour TV and tea/coffee facilities. Ground floor en suite available. Bed and Breakfast from £14, Dinner from £7.50. Full Scottish breakfast. Family reductions. Dinner, Bed and Breakfast - six nights £125, two nights £42, three nights £63, based on two people sharing. Pets and children welcome. Great food, great value, great atmosphere.

PERTH & KINROSS

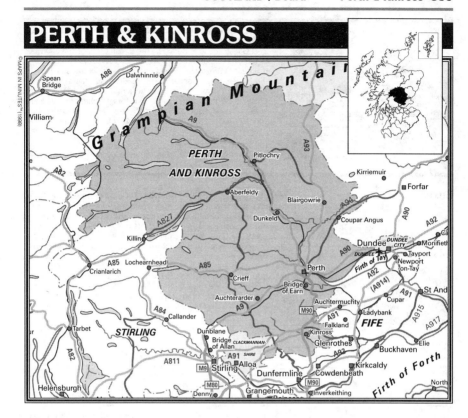

BLAIRGOWRIE. Mrs Morag Houstoun, Glenkilrie, Blacklunans, Blairgowrie (01250 882241). Set in its

own grounds on a working hill farm 13 miles north of Blairgowrie on the main A93 Glenkilrie is an ideal touring base with Perth, Pitlochry, Braemar, Kirriemuir and the Angus Glens all within easy reach. Outdoor activities in the area include hill walking, fishing, pony trekking, hang gliding, skiing and golfing. Accommodation comprises one twin and one double bedroom with shared facilities and one double room with private facilities; residents' lounge with TV and tea making facilities. Prices from £15.

BRIDGE OF CALLY. Mrs Josephine MacLaren, Blackcraig Castle, Bridge of Cally PH10 7PX (01250 886251 or 0131-551 1863). A beautiful castle of architectural

interest situated in spacious grounds. Free trout fishing on own stretch of River Ardle. Pony trekking can be arranged. Excellent centre for hill walking, golf and touring - Braemar, Pitlochry (Festival Theatre), Crieff, Dunkeld, etc. Glamis Castle within easy reach by car. Four double, two twin, two family and two single bedrooms, eight with washbasins; two bathrooms, three toilets. Cot, high chair. Dogs welcome free of charge. Car essential - free parking. Open for guests from 1st July to 7th September. £23.50 per person per night includes full Breakfast plus night tea/coffee and home baking served at 10pm in the beautiful drawing room which has a log fire. Reduced rates for children under 14 years. Enquiries November to end June to **1 Inverleith Place, Edinburgh EH3 5QE.**

CRIANLARICH. Mr & Mrs A. Chisholm, Tigh Na Struith, The Riverside Guest House, Crianlarich FK20 8RU (01838 300235; Fax: 01838 300268). Voted the

Best Guest House in Britain by the British Guild of Travel Writers in 1984, this superbly sited Guest House comprises six bedrooms, each with unrestricted views of the Crianlarich mountains. The three-acre garden leads down to the River Fillan, a tributary of the River Tay. Personally run by the owners, Janice and Sandy Chisholm, Tigh Na Struith allows visitors the chance to relax and enjoy rural Scotland at its best. To this end, each bedroom is centrally heated, double glazed, with colour TV and tea/coffee making facilities. Open March to November. Bed and Breakfast from £18 per person.

DUNKELD. Jo Andrew, Letter Farm, Loch of Lowes, Dunkeld PH8 0HH (Tel & Fax: 01350 724254).

STB ★★★★ B&B. Enjoy the peace and tranquillity of our family run stock farm, set next to the Loch of the Lowes Wildlife Reserve, home to ospreys and otters. It lies three miles east of the historic town of Dunkeld and is central to Perthshire's attractions. Our three bedrooms are spacious and comfortable with en suite bathrooms, and all have tea/coffee making facilities, kingsize beds in double and family rooms and large fluffy towels! We have a guest lounge with log fire and there is full central heating throughout. We are a non-smoking house and offer discounts to children and for long stays. Bed and Breakfast from £20 per person, £25 single. Open May to November.

PERTH. Mrs Mary Fotheringham, Craighall Farmhouse, Forgandenny, Near Bridge of Earn, Perth PH2

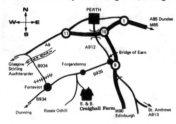

9DF (01738 812415). Working farm. Come and stay in a modern and warm farmhouse with a cheerful, friendly atmosphere situated in lovely Earn Valley, half-a-mile west of village of Forgandenny on B935 and only six miles south of Perth. True Highland hospitality and large choice for breakfast served in diningroom overlooking fields where a variety of cattle, sheep and lambs graze. Farm produce used. Open all year, the 1000 acre arable and stock farm is within easy reach of Stirling, Edinburgh, St. Andrews, Glasgow and Pitlochry. Fishing, golf, tennis, swimming locally. Hill walking amid lovely scenery. All rooms en suite. Tea making facilities. Sitting room. Cot and reduced rates for children. Sorry, no pets. Central heating. Car not essential. Parking. Bed and Breakfast from £19.50. Mid-week bookings taken. AA/RAC Acclaimed.

PITLOCHRY. Mrs Ruth MacPherson-MacDougall, Dalnasgadh House, Killiecrankie, By Pitlochry

PH16 5LN (01796 473237). AA/RAC ◆◆. Attractive country house in grounds of two acres amidst magnificent Highland scenery. Close to National Trust Centre in Pass of Killiecrankie, historic Blair Castle nearby. Only seven minutes from Pitlochry with its famous Festival Theatre. Easy touring distance to Queen's View, Loch Tummel, Balmoral, Braemar, Glamis Castle, Scone Palace and Aviemore. Only six guests accommodated at one time. All bedrooms have washbasins, shaver points, electric blankets and tea/coffee making facilities. Lounge with colour TV. Shower room with toilet and washbasin; bathroom with bath, shower, toilet and washbasin. Centrally heated throughout. Sorry no pets. No smoking. Open Easter to October. Fire Certificate Awarded. Write, telephone or please call in to enquire about terms.

PITLOCHRY. Blair Castle, Blair Atholl, Pitlochry, Perthshire (01796 481207). "A great day inside and out". Blair Castle, Scotland's most visited private Historic House, is where you can experience 700 years of history in one day. Browse through 32 rooms of fascinating treasures. Explore the beautiful grounds. Marvel at our 'Hercules Walled Garden' project. New licensed restaurant. New gift shop. New children's playground. Open daily 10am to 6pm (last entry 5pm) from 1st April to 27th October 2000. Telephone for information, leaflets or party booking information.

STANLEY. Mrs Ann Guthrie, Newmill Farm, Stanley PH1 4QD (01738 828281. STB ★★★ *B&B*.This 330 acre farm is situated on the A9, six miles north of Perth. Accommodation comprises twin, double and family rooms, most en suite; lounge, sitting room, dining room; bathroom, shower room and toilet. Bed and Breakfast from £18; Evening Meal on request. The warm welcome and supper of excellent home baking is inclusive. Reductions and facilities for children. Pets accepted. The numerous castles and historic ruins around Perth are testimony to Scotland's turbulent past. Situated in the area known as "The Gateway to the Highlands", the farm is ideally placed for those seeking some of the best unspoilt scenery in Western Europe. Many famous golf courses and trout rivers in the Perth area.
e-mail: guthrienewmill@sol.co.uk

STRATHYRE. Mrs Catherine B. Reid, Coire Buidhe, Strathyre FK18 8NA (01877 384288). STB ★ *B&B*

FHG Diploma Winner. Run by the longest established hosts in Strathyre, Coire Buidhe sits in the beautiful valley of Strathyre, nine miles from Callander. An excellent base for touring Loch Lomond, Trossachs, Stirling, Edinburgh, with both East and West coasts within easy reach. Two single, two twin, two double (one with en suite bathroom), two family rooms, all with heaters, washbasins, electric blankets, shaver points and tea making facilities; two showers, bathroom, three toilets. Sitting and diningrooms. Open all year. Parking. Regret, no dogs. Children welcome at reduced terms; cot, high chair, babysitting offered. All water sports and shooting available plus trekking, tennis, hill walking, golf and putting. Bed and Breakfast from £15. All food personally prepared, home baking. Special diets catered for. Bar and restaurant meals available within 50 yards. Well recommended. Full Fire Certificate. Reduced weekly terms.

RENFREWSHIRE

LOCHWINNOCH. Mrs Janet Blair, East Kerse Farm, Lochwinnoch PA12 4DU (01505 502400). Working

farm. STB ★★★★ *B&B*. An attractive farmhouse with sun lounge and panoramic views over Kilbirnie Loch. A warm welcome awaits you on this 200 acre family-run dairy farm situated just off the A760 Lochwinnoch to Largs road and just 15 minutes from Glasgow Airport. Nearby are Muirshiel Country Park, RSPB Centre and canoeing at Lochwinnoch. Burns Country is within easy reach, also Kelburn Country Park, many golf courses and fishing in the Maich Burn and Kilbirnie Loch. Accommodation is offered in one double, one twin and one single bedrooms. Bed and Breakfast from £15 to £20.

LOCHWINNOCH. Mrs Amanda Mackie, High Belltrees Farm, Belltrees Road, Lochwinnoch PA12 4JN (01505 842409). 18th century farmhouse offers Bed and

Breakfast on a friendly family-run dairy farm in picturesque rural surroundings. Fully centrally heated with private parking. Three bedrooms are available: one double/family room and two twin rooms all with washbasin, colour TV and tea/coffee facilities. Centrally situated ten minutes from Glasgow Airport and convenient for city centre and SECC. Close by are several golf courses, a RSPB Bird Reserve, and Muirshiel Country Park, and canoeing is available on Castle Semple Loch. Open all year. Children welcome. We look forward to meeting you. Bed and Breakfast from £17.

STIRLING & DISTRICT

BLAIRLOGIE. Mrs Margaret Logan, Blairmains Farm, Manor Loan, Blairlogie, Stirling FK9 5QA

(01259 761338). Working farm. Charming, traditional stone farmhouse set in attractive gardens on a working dairy farm with a herd of pedigree Holstein cattle. Adjacent to a picturesque conservation village and close to the Wallace Monument and Stirling University. Three-and-a-half miles from Stirling. Edinburgh airport is 30 minutes' drive and Glasgow airport 45 minutes. Ideal base for touring and walking. Accommodation is in one double and two twin rooms with shared bathroom. Very comfortable TV lounge. Ample private parking at this non-smoking establishment. Children welcome. Sorry no pets. Bed and Breakfast terms – double or twin £18 to £20; single £20 to £22. Room only £16. A warm Scottish welcome awaits you.

DRYMEN. Mrs Julia Cross, Easter Drumquhassle Farm, Gartness Road, Drymen G63 0DN (01360

660893). STB ★★★ *B&B*. AA ◆◆◆. Join us in this quiet rural setting, with spectacular views. Ideal base for touring Loch Lomond and Central Scotland. Situated on the West Highland Way. Accommodation consists of one double, one twin and one family room, all en suite. Children and pets welcome. Bed and Breakfast from £16.50 to £25. Evening Meal from £10.
e-mail: julia.macx@aol.com

STIRLING. Mrs Moira Johnston, West Plean, Denny Road, Stirling FK7 8HA (01786 812208;

Fax: 01786 480550). STB ★★★ *B&B*. Enjoy warm Scottish farming hospitality in a historic setting, with sweeping lawns, walled garden, extensive woodland walks, surrounded by our mixed farm. We offer quality food, spacious comfort, bedrooms en suite, hot drink facilities and attentive hosts. Riding and fishing can be arranged locally. Located on the A872 Denny Road, two minutes from M9/M80 junction 9. Open Febuary to November. Bed and Breakfast £22.

ISLE OF MULL

DEVAIG. Mrs Lorna Boa, Antuim Farm, Dervaig PA75 6QW (Tel & Fax: 01688 400230). Working farm, join in. Traditional farmhouse on a working farm, just outside the picturesque village of Dervaig. An ideal spot for hill walking, bird-watching and boat trips, and we are only five miles from the white sands of Calgary beach. A two hour drive takes you to the south of the island, from where you can take a five minute boat trip over the isle of Iona - the home of Scottish Christianity. Boat trips can also be arranged to Staffa and the Treshnish Isles, as can wildlife excursions with the possibility of seeing golden eagles, sea eagles and otters. We have one double, one twin and one family room available. Children welcome. Regret, no pets. Bed and Breakfast from £18 to £19.

ISLE OF SKYE

LUIB, by Broadford. Harvey and Gill Willett, Laimhrig, Luib, By Broadford IV49 9AN (01471 822686). With its own access to the sea and magnificent views of the Red Cuillin Hills and the Island of Raasay and Scalpay, this centrally situated bungalow on the shores of Loch Ainort is perfect for exploring Skye. Wlaking, climbing, bird watching, sailing and golf are popular pastimes in this peaceful area. Explore at will or let us help you plan your days to gain the most from your visit. Bed and Breakfast (English or Continental) from £11.50. Three-day breaks (Bed, Breakfast and Evening Meal) from £58. Vegetarians welcome. Sorry, no smoking.

ORKNEY ISLES

KIRKWALL. John D. Webster, Lav'rockha Guest House, Inganess Road, Kirkwall KW15 1SP (Tel & Fax: 01856 876103). STB ★★★★ *GUEST HOUSE*. Situated a short walk from the Highland Park Distillery and Visitor Centre, and within reach of all local amenities. Lav'rockha is the perfect base for exploring and discovering Orkney. We offer high quality accommodation at affordable rates. All our rooms have en suite WC and power shower, tea/coffee tray, hairdryer, radio alarm clock and remote-control colour TV. Those with young children will appreciate our family room with reduced children's rates, children's meals and child minding service. We also have facilities for the disabled, with full unassisted wheelchair access from our private car park. All our meals are prepared to a high standard using fresh produce as much as possible. Bed and Breakfast from £22 per person. Special winter break prices available.
e-mail: lavrockha@orkney.com
website: www.orkneyislands.co.uk/lavrockha/

Key to Tourist Board Ratings – Scotland and Wales

The Scottish Tourist Board Star Grading System. This easy-to-understand system tells you at a glance the quality standard you can expect. The gradings range from ★ (Fair and acceptable) to ★★★★★ (Exceptional, world-class) and will also include the type of accommodation eg ★★★ Self-catering or ★★ Hotel.

The Wales Tourist Board also operates the above system for serviced accommodation only. Self-catering properties will continue to show the **Dragon Award Grading** from **One** to **Five** depending on quality and facilities.

Some properties had not been assessed at the time of going to press and in these cases the publishers have included the old Crown Gradings.

SCOTLAND

Self-catering Accommodation

ABERDEEN, BANFF & MORAY

Bremners of Foggie

Old School, Aberchirder AB54 7XS
Tel & Fax: 01466 780260
or 01466 780510

Two and three bedroomed houses to let in quiet country village. Only 20 minutes' drive from coast at Banff and Portsoy. Weekly terms from £150 to £250; electricity extra. Sleeps 6/8. STB ★★ SELF-CATERING

See also Colour Display Advertisement ABERDEEN. **The Robert Gordon University, Business and Vacation Accommodation, Customer Services Dept, Schoolhill, Aberdeen AB10 1FR (01224 262134; Fax: 01224 262144). STB ★ & ★★** *SELF-CATERING*. Situated in the heart of Aberdeen and offering a wide variety of accommodation to visitors from June through to August. Aberdeen is ideal for visiting Royal Deeside, castles and historic buildings, playing golf or visiting the Malt Whisky Trail. The city itself is a place to discover and Aberdonians are a friendly and welcoming people. Self-catering accommodation available for individuals or groups of people at superb rates. Each flat is self-contained, centrally heated, fully furnished and suitable for children or disabled guests. All have colour TV and some have microwave facilities. Bed linen and cooking utensils are provided, as is a 'welcome pack' of basic groceries. Each residence has laundry facilities and a telephone as well as car parking. ASSC MEMBER.

See also Colour Display Advertisement ELGIN. **Mrs J.M. Shaw, North East Farm Chalet, Sheriffston, Elgin IV30 8LA (01343 842695) STB ★★** *SELF-CATERING*. An "A" frame chalet near Keith and Elgin situated on a working farm. "Habitat" furnished, fully equipped for two to six people, colour TV, bed linen, duvets. Beautiful rural location in Moray - famous for flowers - district of lowlands, highlands, rivers, forests, lovely beaches, historic towns, welcoming people. Excellent local facilities. Moray golf tickets available. From £170 to £300. January to December. ASSC MEMBER.

Tulloch Lodges

Peace, Relaxation and Comfort
in beautiful Natural Surroundings

One of the loveliest self-catering sites in Scotland. Modern, spacious, attractive and beautifully equipped Scandinavian lodges for up to six in glorious woodland/water setting. Perfect for the Highlands and Historic Grampian, especially the Golden Moray Coast and the Golf, Castle and Malt Whisky Trails. £195 - £540 pw.

Brochure: Tulloch Lodges, Rafford, Forres, Moray IV36 2RU
Tel : 01309 673311; Fax: 01309 671515
Web: ww.assc.co.uk/tulloch

See also Colour Advertisement

See also Colour Display Advertisement HUNTLY. Mrs Cruickshank, Logie Newton Farm, By Huntly AB54 6BB (01464 841229; Fax: 01464 841277). STB ★★★★ *SELF-CATERING*. **Sleep 4/6.** A warm welcome awaits you at Logie Newton Farm, a delightful holiday retreat eight miles east of Huntly. Set in the heart of Grampian, Dykeside and Tanaree are charming stingle storey cottages where comfort and Scottish hospitality are priorities. The farm has its own walks, children's lead rein pony rides, stone circles and even the site of a Roman Camp! Both cottages have lounge with open fire, colour TV, video, payphone, hi-fi, books, games and toys. A fully-fitted kitchen, bathrooms, electric blankets and duvets are also provided. Laundry room on site. Cots and highchairs available. Well behaved pets welcome. Large garden with safe children's play area. Locally available eating facilities range from small pubs to country hotels and private castles. Please call or write for our brochure. ASSC MEMBER.

See also Colour Display Advertisement INVERURIE. Mr and Mrs P. A. Lumsden, Kingsfield House, Kingsfield Road, Kintore, Inverurie AB51 0UD (Tel & Fax: 01467 632366). STB ★★★ *SELF-CATERING*. 'The Greenknowe' is a comfortable detached and renovated cottage in a quiet location at the southern edge of the village of Kintore. It is in an ideal situation for touring castles, historic sites and distilleries, or for walking, fishing and even golf. The cottage is all on one level with a large south-facing sitting room overlooking the garden. It sleeps four people in one double and one twin room. a cot is available. Parking adjacent. Open from March to November. Prices from £225 to £350 per week, inclusive of electricity (the cottage is all-electric) and linen. ASSC member.

TOMINTOUL. Mrs Shearer, Croughly Farm, Tomintoul AB37 9EN (01807 550476). STB ★★ *SELF-CATERING*. **Sleeps 4 to 6**. Croughly Farm lies in a peaceful valley, two miles from Tomintoul, with views of the Cairngorm Mountains and surrounding scenery. Whisky and Castle Trails are nearby, the Lecht Ski Centre is only a 15 minute drive away, and fishing can be arranged on the River Avon. The 16th century wing has been renovated and converted into this comfortable self-catering cottage. One double and one twin bedrooms plus extra sofa bed allow for four to six people, with colour TV, fully equipped kitchen, bathroom, utility room and lounge with open fire providing all the necessary comforts. There is ample parking, a private water supply and it is only two miles away from shops and Post Office. Advance ordering of provisions available. Terms from £200 to £280 per week.

See also Colour Display Advertisement TURRIFF. Mrs O.E. Bates, Forglen Holiday Cottages, Forglen Estate, Turriff AB53 4JP (01888 562918/562518; Fax: 01888 562252). The Estate lies along the beautiful Deveron River and our traditional stone cottages (modernised and well equipped) nestle in individual seclusion. Visitors are free to wander and explore one of the ancient baronies of Scotland. The sea is only nine miles away, and the market town of Turriff only two miles, with its golf course, swimming pool etc. Many places of interest including the Cairngorms, Aviemore, picturesque fishing villages and castles, all within easy reach on uncrowded roads. Wildlife haven. See our Highland cattle. Terms from £145 weekly, including VAT and heating. Special winter lets. Ten cottages sleeping six to nine. Children and reasonable dogs welcome. Please telephone for brochure.

ARGYLL & BUTE

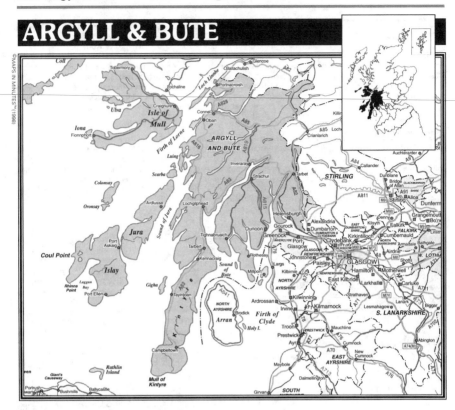

©MAPS IN MINUTES™ (1998)

ACHARACLE. Mrs Chapel, Steading Holidays, Kilchoan, By Acharacle PH36 4LH (01972 510262; Fax: 01972 510337). STB ★★★ *SELF CATERING*. Escape to Ardnamurchan, the most westerly point of the British mainland.. Enjoy sea views, beaches and peace from a well managed and comfortable home. Regular crossings to Tobermory. Fishing and walking are just a few of the attractions. Pets welcome. Open all year. ASSC MEMBER.

APPIN. Ardtur Cottages, Appin. Two adjacent cottages in secluded surroundings on promontory between

Port Appin and Castle Stalker, opposite north end of Isle of Lismore. Ideal centre for hill walking, climbing etc.(Glencoe and Ben Nevis half hour drive). Direct access across the field to sea (Loch Linnhe). Tennis court available by arrangement. Boat hire, pony trekking, fly fishing all available locally. Accommodation in first cottage for eight people in four double bedrooms, large dining/sittingroom/kitchenette and two bathrooms. Second cottage accommodates six people in three twin-bedded rooms, dining/sittingroom/kitchenette and bathroom. Everything is provided except linen. Shops one mile; sea 200 yards. Pets allowed. Car essential, parking. Open March/October. Terms from £165 to £375 weekly. SAE, please for full details to **Mrs J. Pery, Ardtur, Appin PA38 4DD (01631 730223 or 0162 834172)** e-mail: pery@eurobell.co.uk

---

APPIN. Mr and Mrs F.G. Weir, Appin Holiday Homes, Appin PA38 4BQ (01631 730287). STB ★★ *SELF-CATERING*. **Sleep 2/5.** Ideal touring centre with free fishing and boats available. Great for families, or romantic honeymoons, our lodges sleep from two to five people. Special Spring, Autumn and Winter terms. Prices from £155 to £355 per unit weekly. Also eight very private 12' wide holiday residential caravans on lochside. Park graded as Excellent by STB. Licensed inn nearby. Launderette, recreation room and play area on site. Open all year. Plenty to do and see. Free colour brochure from resident proprietors. ASSC MEMBER.
e-mail: appinholidayhomes@tesco.net
website: www.oban.uk

ARDNAMURCHAN. Ockle Holidays, Ardnamurchan. Enjoy the breathtaking beauty of Ardnamurchan, an ideal location for walking, bird watching, fishing, swimming, sailing or simply taking it easy and relaxing. All our houses are situated in their own gardens within a working farm and each is fully equipped. Electricity by meter reading; private water supply, linen and towels £6.50 per person. SRUTHAN RUADH (3 Star) sleeps six persons in two twin bedrooms and one double room, BURNSIDE(3 Star) sleeps four in one twin and one double bedroom. TIGH DOCHIE (2 Star) has one twin and one double bedroom. Kilchoan (nine miles) has a well stocked shop, two hotels serving meals and bar snacks. For reservations or information please contact: **Mrs Sue Cameron, Ockle Holidays, Ockle, by Acharacle PH36 4LG (01972 510321).**

BALLYGRANT. Robolls Cottage, Ballygrant, Isle of Islay. Sleeps 6. Situated in wooded farming surroundings beside the main road, the cottage has two bedrooms, sittingroom/livingroom, kitchenette and bathroom. Bed linen is provided and peat for the open fire. Electricity is by 50p meter. Pets are welcome. Property surrounded by its own hedged garden with Hotel and shop only five minutes' walk away. Golf, pony trekking, swimming pool and numerous beaches nearby. A haven for bird-watchers and walkers. Terms from £50 to £150 per week. Further details from **Mrs Elizabeth Morris, Main Street, Ballygrant, Isle of Islay PA45 7QR (01496 840670).**

Mr & Mrs E. Crawford, Blarghour Farm, Lochaweside, By Dalmally, Argyll PA33 1BW
Tel: (01866) 833246; Fax: (01866) 833338
e-mail: blarghour@aol.com

At Blarghour, a working hill farm on the shores of lovely Loch Awe, the holiday guest has a choice of high quality, well appointed, centrally heated, double glazed accommodation of individual character, each enjoying its own splendid view over loch and mountain in this highly scenic area.

Barn House sleeps two in one ground floor bedroom with twin or zip-linked beds, has a bathroom adjacent to bedroom and open lounge/dining/kitchen on the first floor which is well lit and has a pleasing view.

Stable House accommodates four in two first floor bedrooms with twin or zip-linked bed arangements, has one bathroom and large lounge/dining room with an elegant spiral staircase and full length windows with an oustanding view.

Barr-beithe Bungalow sleeps five in three bedrooms, one twin or zip-linked, one double and one single. There is a bathroom and shower room. The lounge/dining/sun lounge enjoys an outstanding loch view.

Upper Blarghour House sleeps eight in three bedrooms, two with twin or zip-linked beds and one with twin beds and bunk beds. There is a bathroom and shower room on the first floor and a cloakroom on the ground floor. The large lounge/dining/sun lounge overlooks a spectacular views as does the balcony leading from the master bedroom.

All have modern kitchens with fridge/freezer, washer/dryer, microwave and electric cooker and the two larger houses have dishwashers. Cots and high chairs are available in the two larger houses. All have telephones and televisions. Linen and towels are supplied.

Cars may be parked beside each house. Barn and Stable Houses are unsuitable for children under five years. No pets are allowed. Open all year. The area, centrally situated for touring, offers opportunities for walking, bird-watching, boating and fishing. Golf is available at Dalmally and Inveraray.

Colour brochure sent on request.   *See also colour advertisement*

FHG PUBLICATIONS
publish a large range of well-known accommodation guides. We will be happy to send you details or you can use the order form at the back of this book.

DALMALLY by. Mrs E. Fellowes, Inistrynich, By Dalmally PA33 1BQ (01838 200256; Fax: 01838 200253). STB ★★ *SELF-CATERING.*

Three cottages situated on a private estate surrounded by beautiful scenery. Garden Cottage (four bedrooms), Millside Cottage (two bedrooms) and Inistrynich Cottage (two bedrooms). Situated five miles from Dalmally, 11 miles from Inveraray, 28 miles from Oban, the cottages overlook Loch Awe and each has a garden area. They all have convector heaters in all rooms and an open fire in the livingroom. All have electric cookers, microwaves, fridge, immersion heater, electric kettle, iron, hoover, washing machine and colour TV; cot and high chair available on request. Dogs allowed by arrangement. Car essential – ample parking space. Ideal centre for touring mainland and Western Isles. Hill walking, forest walks, fishing, boat trips, pony trekking and golf all within easy reach. Colour brochure available on request.

DUROR OF APPIN. Mrs Elspeth Malcolm, Achadh Nan Sgiath, Cuil Bay, Duror of Appin PA38 4DA (01631 740259). **Working farm, join in. Sleeps 4 adults; 2 children.**

This spacious flat is on the first floor of a large house set in its own grounds at end of side road, one mile from A828 Ballachulish – Oban road. Own private entrance and uninterrupted views of Loch Linnhe. One double and two twin-bedded rooms, all with washbasins; sittingroom, bathroom/ toilet; kitchen/breakfast room – all electric. Linen provided at small extra charge. Three hotels near; village shop one mile, sea 500 yards. Pets allowed. Car essential, parking. Open all year. Sailing, boat hiring and pony trekking nearby and opportunities for climbing, walking and bird watching. Several historical connections of interest. The owners have a small fish smoking business and James Malcolm runs the farm. Weekly terms from £80 to £230 according to season.

See also Colour Display Advertisement **INVERARAY. Bralecken House, Brenchoille Farm, Inveraray PA23 8XN (01499 500662). STB ★★★** *SELF-CATERING.* A mid 19th century stone building carefully restored to provide two comfortable houses situated on private upland farm. Each comprises of sitting room, fully fitted kitchen, two bedrooms, bathroom and shower room. Both are completely private or suitable for two families wishing to holiday together. Large parking area and garden. Children most welcome, but regretfully no pets. Contact **Mr and Mrs Crawford**. ASSC MEMBER.

See also Colour Display Advertisement **LOCHAVICH. Mrs G. H. Dalton, Maolachy, Lochavich, by Taynuilt PA35 1HJ (01866 844212; Fax: 01866 844295). STB ★★** *SELF-CATERING.* **Sleep 2/4.** Warm, comfortable stone cottage sleeping two to four plus cot in a secluded glen 18 miles south of Oban. Within a Regional Scenic Area, it is an ideal base for exploring Argyll and the Islands. Fishing, walking, watersports, golf, pony trekking, bird-watching and gardens all nearby. Price from £162 to £291 per week, discounts for two. Short Breaks. Colour brochure on request. ASSC MEMBER

LOCH AWE. Innis Chonain, Loch Awe, Dalmally (01838 200220). Attractive three bedroom cottage on private 20 acre island (vehicle access by bridge from main A85 road). Superb situation on this beautiful loch with complete privacy, but only half a mile to shops. Ideal touring centre, Inveraray 17 miles, Oban 20 miles. Cottage has three bedrooms sleeping five/six persons. Modern furnishings, colour TV/video, electric heating, gas cooking, washing machine/dryer. Linen not provided. Boat with free fishing on loch. Children welcome, pets with permission. Ample parking. Rates from £195 to £395 per week. Full details from **J.C.D. Somerville, Ashton House, Pattingham Road, Perton, Wolverhampton WV6 7HD (01902 700644).**

See also Colour Display Advertisement **LOCH CRINAN. Poltalloch Estate. STB ★★★★** *SELF-CATERING.* A selection of charming self catering cottages, each unique in its history and character, and enhanced by the natural beauty of Loch Crinan. All have been attractively modernised and furnished, with care taken in the retention of many traditional and historically interesting features. The cottages offer varying accommodation for two to five persons in comfort. Eating out is no problem with many good restaurants in the area. Salmon fishing, hill walking and safe sandy beaches can all be enjoyed on the estate. Terms and further details on application. SAE please. **Susan Malcolm, Duntrune Castle, Kilmartin PA31 8QQ (01546 510283).**

LOCHGILPHEAD. Finchairn Farm, Ederline Estate, Lochgilphead PA31 8RT. STB ★★★ *SELF-*

CATERING. **Sleep 2,6,7.** Ederline is a family-owned working estate situated at the south end of Loch Awe in one of the most historic and picturesque parts of Argyll. The estate has three newly refurbished stone-built cottages with log fires. One cottage has a conservatory. Ederline is a wonderful secluded retreat with numerous activities including wild brown trout fishing in over 20 hill lochs, coarse fishing, walking and within 15 minutes of the seaside. Terms £165 – £390 including VAT and firewood. Brochures available giving full accommodation details from: **Pat Cairns, Finchairn Farm, Lochgilphead PA31 8RJ (01546 810223).**

See also Colour Display Advertisement **LOCHGILPHEAD by. Ellary Estate Office, By Lochgilphead (01880 770232/770209 or 01546 850223). Properties sleep 6/8.** Ellary affords peace and seclusion amidst outstanding scenery, plus complete freedom to pursue holiday pastimes for young and old alike. The range of accommodation is wide - small groups of cottages and chalets on Ellary, and super luxury and luxury caravans at Castle Sween. Cottages accommodate six to eight. All units fully equipped except for linen. The estate, beautiful at all times of the year, is suitable for windsurfing, fishing, swimming, wildlife observation and numerous walks. Further details and brochure on request.

LOCHGOIL. Darroch Mhor, Carrick Castle, Loch Goil, Argyll PA24 8AF (01301 703249/703432).

Sleep 4. Five self-catering chalets on the shores of Loch Goil in the heart of Argyll Forest Park with superb lochside views. Chalets are fully equipped except linen. Colour TV, fitted kitchen, carpeted. Pets very welcome. Open all year. Weekly rates £120-£295; reductions for two people. Short breaks available.

See also Colour Display Advertisement **OBAN. Lagnakeil Highland Lodges, Lerags, Oban PA34 4SE.** Our timber lodges are nestled in seven acres of scenic wooded glen overlooking Loch Feochan, only three-and-a-half miles from Oban - "Gateway to the Highlands". Lodges are fully equipped to a high standard, including linen and towels. Country pub only a short walk away. Senior Citizen discount. Free loch fishing. Special Breaks from £29 per lodge per night, weekly from £135. Our colour brochure will tell lots more. Please phone or write to: **Colin and Jo Mossman (01631 562746; Fax: 01631 570225).** ASSC MEMBER.
e-mail: lagnakeil@aol.com

See also Colour Display Advertisement **OBAN. Highland Hideaways.** Several high quality self-catering properties of individual character in outstanding coastal, town and country locations in Argyll including the Oban area and around Loch Awe. Sleeping two to 12 from £130 to £950 per week. Up to STB 4 Star Grade. For further details please contact: **Highland Hideaways. 5/7 Stafford Street, Oban, Argyll PA34 5NJ (01631 562056; Fax: 01631 566778).** ASSC MEMBER.
e-mail: ADEA@obanestates99.freeserve.co.uk

OBAN by. Mrs H.M. McCorkindale, Scammadale Farm, Kilninver, By Oban PA34 4UU (01852 316282; Fax: 01852 316223). Working farm. Sleeps 7. Wing of old Scottish farmhouse of character with own entrance, it stands in a beautiful position overlooking Loch Scammadale, 13 miles from Oban which has a lively night life and is the starting point for boat trips to the islands. Fishing in loch and river free to residents – includes boat. Furnishings simple and comfortable. Sleeps seven in one family bedroom, one twin-bedded room and a small single bedroom; bathroom/toilet; sitting/diningroom; colour TV. Kitchen has gas cooker and fridge etc. Guests must supply own linen. Sorry, no pets. Shops 13 miles away; sea five miles. Car essential – parking. Garage available. Terms from £130 to £200 weekly, including gas, lights and hot water. Electric fire and TV metered. SAE, please.

See also Colour Display Advertisement

OBAN by. Eleraig Highland Chalets, Kilninver, By Oban PA34 4UX (Tel & Fax: 01852 200225). STB ★★ *SELF-CATERING*. **Sleep 4/7.** Seven well-equipped, widely spaced chalets are set in breathtaking scenery in a private glen 12 miles south of Oban, close to Loch Tralaig, with free brown trout fishing and boating - or bring your own boat. Peace and tranquillity are features of the site, located within an 1800 acre working sheep farm. Walkers' and birdwatchers' paradise. Children and pets are especially welcome (dogs free). Cots and high chairs are available, also free. Gliding, water skiing and other sports pastimes and evening entertainment are available locally. Car parking by each chalet. Open March to October. From £205 per week per chalet including electricity. Colour brochure from resident owners **Anne and Robin Grey**. website: www.scotland2000.com/eleraig

OBAN by. Achnacroish Cottage, Balvicar, Seil, By Oban. Sleeps 2/4. A former stone croft cottage, Achnacroish has been skilfully converted to retain its original character. It is situated 16 miles south of Oban, near the sea, on a croft containing sheep. It sleeps up to four in a double bedroom and an open-plan living area. There are electric radiators, an open fire and well-equipped kitchen. The area offers abundant wildlife and excellent walking, touring, sailing and fishing opportunities. Nearby is the former slate quarrying village of Easdale. Mull and Iona can be visited on day trips. Price, up to £200 per week, includes bed linen and towels but not electricity. Available April to October. Local shop half-mile and restaurants two miles. Easy parking; car essential. Regret no dogs. Member ASSC. Further details: **Dr W. Lindsay, 67 Worcester Road, Sutton, Surrey SM2 6ND (Tel/Fax: 0208 661 1834).**

PORT APPIN. The Cottage, Port Appin. Sleeps 7. Situated on small bay 50 yards from beach. Sheltered position, completely on its own, five minutes from the village. Area offers hill-walking, pony trekking, boating, windsurfing, sea fishing. Ideal for children. Oban and Fort William are within easy reach. Accommodation: four bedrooms (one en suite); dining room; sittingroom, kitchen and bathroom. Sleeps seven. Fully equipped. Electric cooker, fridge/freezer, washing machine, colour TV. No linen. Heating by electricity and coal fires. Available March-September £275 to £350 weekly. For details send SAE to **Mrs A.V. Livingstone, Bachuil, Isle of Lismore, By Oban PA34 5UL or telephone 01631 760256.**

SKIPNESS ESTATE

This unspoilt, peaceful, West Highland estate with its own historic castle, mediaeval chapel and way-marked walks has traditional cottages to let all year round. Each cottage has an open fire and television; some cottages have a rowing dinghy in summer. Laundry facilities are available alongside the Seafood Cabin at Skipness Castle. Properties sleep 4 – 10.

FARM HOLIDAY GUIDE DIPLOMA
STB ★ SELF-CATERING

All cottages have magnificent views and beautiful surrounding countryside and coastline. Safe, sandy beaches can be enjoyed on the estate, with fishing, pony trekking and golf nearby. Local ferries to Arran, Gigha, Islay, Jura and Northern Ireland. PETS WELCOME. Apply for rates and further details:

Sophie James, Skipness Castle, By Tarbert, Argyll PA29 6XU
Tel: 01880 760207; Fax: 01880 760208

See also Colour Display Advertisement   **TARBERT. Dunmore Estate, West Loch Tarbert. STB ★★ to ★★★** *SELF-CATERING.* Luxury Villa and four cottages in architect-designed conversion of home farm all situated on a 1000 acre estate with three miles of shore on West Loch Tarbert. Furnished to the highest standard, all have stone fireplaces for log fires. Bird-watching. sailing, sea fishing, unrestricted walking. Pets welcome. Open all year. Colour brochure. Terms from £165 to £750. Contact: **Meg MacKinnon, Dunmore, Near Tarbert, Argyll PA29 6XZ (01880 820654).** *ASSC MEMBER.*

See also Colour Display Advertisement   **TAYNUILT. Mrs G. H. Dalton, Maolachy, Lochavich, by Taynuilt PA35 1HJ (01866 844212; Fax: 01866 844295). STB ★★** *SELF-CATERING.* **Sleep 2/4.** Warm, comfortable stone cottage sleeping two to four plus cot in a secluded glen 18 miles south of Oban. Within a Regional Scenic Area, it is an ideal base for exploring Argyll and the Islands. Fishing, walking, watersports, golf, pony trekking, bird-watching and gardens all nearby. Price from £162 to £291 per week, discounts for two. Short Breaks. Colour brochure on request. ASSC MEMBER

TAYVALLICH. Cariel and Ternait, Tayvallich, By Lochgilphead. Sleep 7 & 4/8. Two charming, well equipped, modern bungalows with superb view of Tayvallich Bay. CARIEL sleeps seven and TERNAIT sleeps four or eight with annexe. Both have two bathrooms plus showers, games room and open fire. Walk in the woods and hills, picnic on the beach, explore the headlands. Ideally situated to visit the Western Isles. Sample the local seafood at the Tayvallich Inn (two minutes' walk). Terms from £150 to £450 per week. For details telephone **01793 782361 or 0270 5838667** or SAE **Jeanie Wright, Watchfield House, Watchfield, Swindon, Wiltshire SN6 8TD.**

AYRSHIRE & ARRAN

AYR. Mrs Agnes Gemmell, Dunduff Farm, Dunure, Ayr KA7 4LH (01292 500225). STB ★★★★

AA QQQQ *SELECT*. Welcome to Dunduff Farm where a warm, friendly atmosphere awaits you. Situated just south of Ayr at the coastal village of Dunure, this family-run beef and sheep unit of 600 acres is only 15 minutes from the shore providing good walks and sea fishing and enjoying close proximity to Dunure Castle and Park. Accommodation is of a high standard yet homely and comfortable. Bedrooms have washbasins, radio alarm, tea/coffee making facilities, central heating, TV, hair dryer and en suite facilities (the twin room has private bathroom). There is also a small farm cottage available sleeping two/four people. Bed and Breakfast from £23 per person; weekly rate £130. Cottage £230 per week. Colour brochure available.

COLMONELL (Girvan). Knockdolian Estate, Alderside, Colmonell, Girvan KA26 0LB (01465 881237).

Knockdolian Estate is on the edge of Colmonell village on the B634 off the A77 coast road to Stranraer. Situated on the Ayrshire coast with easy access to Burns Country and Culzean Castle. Two houses available for letting with gas central heating, garden. BELHAMIE FARMHOUSE sleeps 10 in five bedrooms: two double (one en suite), three twin (one one ground floor); large sitting room with TV; smaller sitting room; large kitchen with washing machine and microwave. THE LODGE sleeps four in two twin - bedded rooms; sitting room; small kitchen. Children welcome. Pets also welcome but must be kept under strict control. Prices from £250 per week. Sunday to Sunday bookings.

KILMARNOCK. Mrs Mary Howie, Hill House Farm, Grassyards Road, Kilmarnock KA3 6HG (01563

523370). STB ★★/★★★ *SELF-CATERING*. **Working farm. Sleep 6 and 9.** Two properties within half-a-mile of each other situated on a working dairy farm in beautiful open countryside, two miles east of Kilmarnock. Easy access to Ayrshire coast, numerous golf courses, sport and leisure centres. Excellent walking terrain and the cottages provide the ideal base for the holidaymaker who enjoys golf, fishing or relaxing on sandy beaches. Fully equipped, very comfortable accommodation for six and nine people respectively comprising three bedrooms, cot; living room with colour TV, fire; kitchen with electric cooker, fridge freezer, washing machine, etc. Bathroom and shower. Large garden. Telephone. Storage heaters. Linen included. Weekly rates from £150 to £390. Bed and Breakfast available in the farmhouse from £16.

PIRNMILL. Mrs Dale, The Wee Rig, Pirnmill, By Brodick, Isle of Arran KA27 8HP (01770 850228). STB

★★★ *SELF-CATERING.*. Situated on a slightly elevated site, within a spacious garden to the side of the main house, in a unique secluded position flanked by sheltering woodlands but with fine open outlook to panoramic views and sunsets over the Kilbrannan Sound to Kintyre. Across the road the low tide reveals a clean sandy expanse which is habitat to various seabirds. Wider exploration of our unspoiled picturesque island, termed "Scotland in miniature" offers much variety with rugged mountains, rolling farmlands, interesting bird/wildlife, castles, distillery, golf (7 courses), walking, cycling, ponies plus various visitor centres, swimming facilities, etc. An overall sense of peace and relaxation which we warmly welcome you to share with us.

WHITING BAY. Mr and Mrs S. Pairman, 'Seabank', Largiebeg, Whiting Bay, Isle of Arran KA27 8RL

(01770 700301). Sleeps 4. Self-contained red sandstone house two miles south of Whiting Bay, set in peaceful surroundings with own garden overlooking beach and panoramic views across the Firth of Clyde to the Ayrshire coastline. Ideally situated for hill walking, golfing, pony trekking, fishing and bird watching. The house has two double bedrooms; linen supplied but not towels. Sitting/dining room, colour TV/video. Kitchen has electric cooker, fridge/freezer, automatic washing machine. Parking for two cars. Sorry no pets.
e-mail: seabank@freezone.co.uk

BORDERS

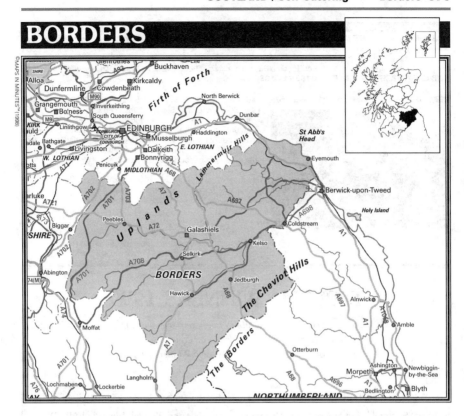

A warm, friendly, spacious farmhouse situated in beautiful surroundings in Lammermuir Hills. Perfect for relaxing, walking and visiting all Scottish Borders attractions. Next door to East Lothian and only one hour from Scotland's capital, Edinburgh. Accommodation comprises one twin, one twin en suite and one double bedrooms (double and twin room can become a family unit). Outdoor heated swimming pool and the hens and ducks keep children amused. Golf course and beautiful beaches within easy reach. Bed and Breakfast from £20; Dinner by arrangement. Special packages available for families, self-catering cottage nearby, sleeping six.

CRANSHAWS HOUSE

Mrs Alison Landale, Cranshaws House, Cranshaws Farm, Near Duns TD11 3SJ
Tel: 01361 890242; Fax: 01361 890295

ETTRICKBRIDGE (by Selkirk). Mrs L. Wilson, Hutlerburn Farm, Ettrick, Selkirk TD7 5HL (01750

52254). STB ★★★ *SELF-CATERING*. **Sleeps 6 plus cot.** This delightful character cottage has a superb location in the picturesque Ettrick Valley with easy access to the family farm. We are a traditional hill farm and have blackface sheep and blue grey cattle. It is central to all Border towns and places of interest. Walking, golfing, fishing, cycling and horse-riding facilities all available in this area. The cottage is tastefully furnished and fully modernised, double glazed and centrally heated throughout. Open log fire for romantic evenings. Children welcome. Pets by arrangement with their own beds. Open all year. Rates from £140 to £290. Please telephone for further details.

JEDBURGH. Mill House, Letterbox and Stockman's Cottages.
STB ★★★★ *SELF-CATERING*. Three recently renovated, quality Cottages, each sleeping four, on a working farm three miles from Jedburgh. Both ideal centres for exploring, sporting holidays or getting away from it all. Each cottage has two public rooms (ground floor available). Minimum let two days. Terms £190–£310. Open all year. Bus three miles, airport 54 miles. Green Tourism Business Award – SILVER. **Mrs A. Fraser, Overwells, Jedburgh TD8 6LT (01835 863020; Fax: 01835 864334).** ASSC member.

PEEBLES. Mrs L. Chisholm, 93 Edinburgh Road, Peebles EH45 8ED (Tel & Fax: 01721 720501). STB

★★★ *SELF-CATERING* **Sleeps 5.** Detached stone-built bungalow adjacent to town. Ideal touring and walking base. Edinburgh 23 miles, bus nearby. Accommodation comprises three bedrooms and two public rooms. Central heating. Linen included. Bungalow available January to December. Prices from £185 to £260. Please write or telephone for further details.

DIPLOMA WINNERS 1999

Each year we award a small number of diplomas to holiday proprietors
whose services have been specially commended by our readers.
The following were our FHG Diploma Winners for 1999.

England

Mr & Mrs Haskell, Borwick Lodge, Outgate, Hawkshead, Cumbria LA22 0PU (015394 36332)

Mrs Val Sunter, Higher House Farm, Oxenholme Lane, Natland, Kendal, Cumbria LA9 7QH (015395 61177)

Mrs Ellis, Efford Cottage Guest House, Milford Road, Everton, Lymington, Hampshire SO41 0JD (015906 42315)

Mrs Melanie Smith, Capernwray House, Capernwray, Via Carnforth, Lancashire LA6 1AE (01524 732363)

Mrs D. Cole, Hillcrest House, Barrasford, Hexham, Northumberland NE48 4BY (01434 681426)

Mrs J. Hartsilver, Perhams Farm, Templecombe, Somerset BA8 0NE (01963 371123)

Scotland

Mr Ewan, Glen Lyon Lodge, Nairn, Nairnshire IV12 4RH (01667 452780)

Mr Sutton, Linnhe Caravan and Camping Park, Corpach, Fort William, Inverness-shire PH33 7NL (01397 772376)

Wales

Mrs Hazel Davies, Caebetran Farm, Felinfach, Brecon, Powys LD3 0UL (01874 754460)

Mrs Bronwen Prosser, Upper Genffordd Guest House, Talgarth, Brecon, Powys LD3 0EN (01874 711360)

DUMFRIES & GALLOWAY

©MAPS IN MINUTES™ (1998)

CASTLE DOUGLAS. Cala-Sona, Auchencairn, Castle Douglas. Sleeps 6. A stone-built house in centre of Auchencairn village, near shops, post office and garage. To let, furnished. Equipped for six persons. Linen supplied. Two bedrooms (one double bed; two single beds); cot available. Bathroom, bedroom with double bed, livingroom and kitchenette with electric cooker, fridge and geyser. Auchencairn is a friendly seaside village and you can enjoy a peaceful holiday here on the Solway Firth where the Galloway Hills slope down to the sea. Many places of historic interest to visit, also cliffs, caves and sandy beaches. A haven for ornithologists. SAE brings prompt reply. Car essential – parking. **Mrs Mary Gordon, 7 Church Road, Auchencairn, Castle Douglas DG7 1QS (01556 640345).**

See also Colour Display Advertisement **DRUMMORE. Harbour Row. STB ★★★★ SELF-CATERING. Sleep 4/6.** Tom Gray the Edinburgh architect has created his third holiday complex for prestige self-catering holidays in the form of a row of fishermen's cottages with a semi-detached house to finish off the row and effectively end the old village as seen from the sea. Each cottage has been named after an island off the west coast of Scotland and has tartan carpets in the lounge and dining area. French windows at the rear open onto a patio where the southerly aspect affords the best of the sunshine to those using the garden furniture. The village is within easy walking distance and has several shops and two licensed hotels. There is also a bowling green and play park. Car parking. Please send for our colour brochure, terms and further information. **Mrs S. Colman, Cailiness Road, Drummore DG9 9QX (01776 840631). ASSC MEMBER.**

See also Colour Display Advertisement **DUMFRIES. David and Gill Stewart, Gubhill Farm, Ae, Dumfries DG1 1RL (01387 860648).** Listed farm steading flats in peaceful, pastoral valley surrounded by wooded hills and forest lanes. Two bedrooms each plus sofa bed and cot. TV, linen and central heating provided. Electricity metered. Outside facilities include drying room, bicycle shed, stable, dog run, barbecue and picnic area. Management is eco-sound and nature friendly. Lower flat and forest walks are wheelchair compatible. Village shop: one-and-a-half miles, Thornhill one mile, Dumfries 15 miles, riding four miles, fishing and mountain bike course two miles. Queensberry (697 metres) five miles. ASSC MEMBER.
e-mail: stewart@creaturefeature.freeserve.co.uk

PORTPATRICK. Mr A. D. Bryce, Commercial Inn, Portpatrick DG9 8JW (01776 810277). Sea front situation with unrestricted views of harbour and boats, overlooking small sandy beach with safe bathing. Golf, bowling, tennis and sea angling, scenic cliff walks and ideal country roads for touring. Shops and restaurants nearby. Area is of great historical and archaeological interest and enjoys a mild climate. Self-catering flats, three bedrooms; cottage, two bedrooms. Electric heating,cooking etc. Prepayment coin meter. Terms from £150 to £200 per week. Parking at door. Please write or telephone for further details.

DUNDEE & ANGUS

Glenprosen Cottages · Angus

Glenprosen is one of the lovely, secret, Glens of Angus, foothills of the Cairngorms, and one of the most accessible, yet least spoilt parts of the Scottish Highlands. Only 40 minutes from Dundee, and 1 1/2 hours from Edinburgh, the hills reach to over 3000' and the glen is exceptionally rich in wildlife. Birds and animals of the river, moorland, upland and woodland abound. Look for black grouse and red squirrels. Peter Pan was conceived in these hills, James Barrie, spent his best holidays here.

See also colour advertisement.

A wide range of completely individual self-catering cottages, and houses. All traditionally stone built, but fully modernised and comfortable. Wide range of size (2-8) from shepherd's cottage, to Georgian Mansion Flat. Prices to suit all pockets (£165 - £560) per week.

• Pony trekking, fishing, walking, cycling, trampoline all on site. •

Visit our website or ring for brochure 01575 540302. ***www.glenprosen.co.uk***

BROUGHTY FERRY. Kingennie Fishings and Holiday Lodges, Kingennie, Broughty Ferry DD5 3RD (01382 350777; Fax: 01382 350400). STB ★★★★ SELF-CATERING. The four modern Lodges provide luxury self-catering holiday accommodation; all have colour TV and are well insulated and centrally heated. Set in secluded woodland, they enjoy views over the fishing ponds below, where experts and beginners alike can try their skills. GLENCLOVA, sleeping up to seven has been specially designed for disabled visitors, GLENISLA and GLENESK, sleeping four to six, both enjoy lovely views. THE BARD'S NEUK is situated in a quiet secluded corner site. The nearby towns, villages, beaches and countryside around the area provide many fascinating and enjoyable trips all of which can be covered within a day.
e-mail: kingennie@easynet.co.uk
website: kingennie-fishings.com

KIRRIEMUIR, Mrs M. Marchant, Welton Farm, The Welton of Kingoldrum, By Kirriemuir, Angus DD8 5HY (Tel & Fax: 01575 574743). STB ★★/★★★ *SELF-CATERING.* Three luxurious self-catering properties (two with en suite facilities) on a secluded 275 acre working farm, situated in a spectacular setting with superb panoramic views at the gateway to the glorious Angus Glens. Peaceful and relaxing with abundance of birds and wildlife. Ideal for hillwalking and birdwatching. An excellent base for outdoor pursuits including fishing, riding, skiing, shooting, golf, and touring the glens, coast and castles (including Glamis). Many visitor attractions in the area. A wide variety of comfortable, high standard accommodation, sleeping 2/4. Central heating, hot water, linen and ironing facilities, microwave, electric cooker, fridge freezer, dishwasher, colour TV, cot, bed settee, electric blankets, radio alarm, hairdryer, garden furniture, parking. Open all year. Short breaks available. Welcome Host. ASSC Member. Prices £150 to £320.
website: www.angusanddundee.co.uk/members/562.htm

EDINBURGH & LOTHIANS

Hunter Holiday Cottages
Rosewell, Edinburgh

Hunter Holiday Cottages offer a range of cottages in beautiful countryside only eight miles from Edinburgh city centre. These superior cottages are recently renovated, have all modern facilities and sleep six to eight plus. They provide the ideal base for the perfect Scottish holiday from their location in Midlothian's historic countryside. There is easy access to Scotland's capital and the major routes to the rest of Scotland. For more information visit our website. Also B&B, £20-£25 per night

Contact Duncan Hunter   Tel: 0131-448 0888 Fax: 0131-440 2082
E-mail: hunter@holidaycottages.demon.co.uk   Website: www.holidaycottages.demon.co.uk

WEST CALDER by. Mrs Geraldine Hamilton, Crosswoodhill Farm, By West Calder EH55 8LP (01501 785205 Fax: 01501 785308). STB ★★★ to ★★★★ *SELF-CATERING.* **3 Properties Sleep 4/6.** Imagine the best of both worlds... two stunning cities, Edinburgh and Glasgow, within an hour's drive and... midway... Crosswoodhill, a haven of rural tranquillity. Situated on the A70, just 18 miles from the heart of historic Edinburgh, our 1700 acre livestock farm is perfectly placed for exploring Fife, the Borders, Rob Roy and Braveheart Country. Visit castles, stately homes, museums, galleries, fine shops; enjoy leisure pursuits close by. Or simply relax; it's a perfect place to unwind. Choose between Midcrosswood, a gem of a cottage on the scenic Pentland Hills, Steading Cottage or a self-contained wing of our handsome 200 year-old farmhouse with its own garden. Comfort, charm, warmth, tradition and a friendly welcome await you. All properties are superbly equipped, including colour TV, video, electric cooker, microwave, washing machine, tumble dryer, dishwasher, fridge, freezer, pay-phone, all bed linen and towels. Bath and power shower. Central heating. Extras: home-grown peat/coal for multi-fuel stoves, oil (cottages only), electricity by meter reading. Dogs by arrangement (sheep country). Own transport essential. From £250 to £550 weekly. Telephone or SAE for brochure. ASSC.
e-mail: crosswd@globalnet.co.uk
website: www.users.globalnet.co.uk/~crosswd/index.htm

FIFE

See also Colour Display Advertisement **NEWPORT-ON-TAY. Mr and Mrs Ramsay, Balmore, 3 West Road,Newport-on-Tay DD6 8HH (01382 542274; Fax: 01382 542927). STB ★★★** *SELF- CATERING* . **Sleeps 5-6.** Situated on the southern shore of the Tay Estuary, Thorndene is the secluded and self-contained west wing of a large Listed house situated in a three acre walled garden. On the ground floor, it has entry through a paved courtyard, and has its own garden. It is bright and sunny, equipped to a high standard, carpeted throughout, with central heating. There are two double bedrooms – one with a shower en suite, a single bedroom, large sitting room, dining room, sun lounge, tiled bathroom with bath and shower, fitted kitchen with washing machine, dishwasher, microwave and breakfast bar. Terms from £160 to £350. Brochure available. ASSC MEMBER.

HIGHLANDS

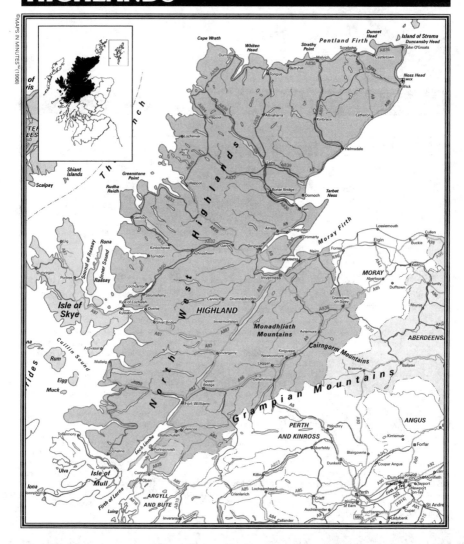

HIGHLANDS (NORTH)

DORNOCH. Mrs E.A. Dunlop, Cluaine Lodge, Evelix, Dornoch IV25 3RD (Tel & Fax: 01862 810276). STB ★★ *SELF-CATERING.* **Sleeps 4.** Comfortable modern bungalow within a secluded private garden of two acres, and surrounded by mature woodland. One-and-a-half miles to Dornoch. One double and one twin bedded room. Living room with open fire, coal/logs provided. Well equipped fully-fitted kitchen. Full electric central heating using night storage heaters. Bedding, towels provided. Colour TV, radios in bedrooms. Open all year. Pets by arrangement. Tariff: October to April from £170 to £200, June to September £210 to £250. NO SMOKING PLEASE. ASSC MEMBER.

LOCHCARRON. The Cottage, Stromecarronach, Lochcarron West, Strathcarron. Working farm, join in. Sleeps 2. The small, stone-built Highland cottage is fully equipped and has a double bedroom, shower room and open plan kitchen/livingroom (with open fire). It is secluded with panoramic views over Loch Carron and the mountains. River, sea and loch fishing are available. Hill walking is popular in the area, and there is a small local golf course. Nearby attractions include the Isle of Skye, Inverewe Gardens, the Torridon and Applecross Hills and the historic Kyle Railway Line. Visitors' dogs are welcome provided they are kept under control at all times. For full particulars, write or telephone **Mrs A.G. Mackenzie, Stromecarronach, Lochcarron West, Strathcarron IV54 8YH (01520 722284).**

LOCHINVER. Clashmore Holiday Cottages, Lochinver. STB ★★★ *SELF-CATERING.* **Sleeps 2-5.** Our three croft cottages at Clashmore are the ideal base for a holiday in the Highlands. They are cosy and fully equipped, with linen provided, Nearby there are sandy beaches, mountains and lochs for wild brown trout fishing. Children welcome, but sorry – no pets. Open all year. Terms from £160 to £320. Contact: **Mr and Mrs Mackenzie, Lochview, 216 Clashmore, Stoer, Lochinver, Sutherland IV27 4JQ (Tel & Fax: 01571 855226).** ASSC MEMBER.
e-mail: clashcotts@aol.com

HIGHLANDS (MID)

AULTBEA. Mrs Peggy MacRae, 'Cove View', 36 Mellon Charles, Aultbea, Wester Ross IV22 2JL (01445

731351). Wester Ross is ideal for a quiet, restful holiday. Detached chalet has two small bedrooms, sitting room, bathroom and mini kitchen. Ideal for two or three persons. Terms from £150 to £175 per week. Pet is welcome. Bed and Breakfast also available from £15. Open April to September. Your dog is welcome at £4 per night.

FORTROSE. Scorrielea, Ness Road, Fortrose, Black Isle. STB ★★★ Sleeps 6 plus cot. Scorrielea is a well equipped traditional detached farm cottage situated in a large garden with parking for three cars surrounded by open farmland near to a sandy beach and 18 hole golf course. Accommodation on two floor consists of two twin bedrooms and shower room on upper, one double bedroom, lounge, fully fitted kitchen, sun lounge and additional WC on ground floor. Ideal base for exploring the Highlands (Inverness only half-an-hour), observing dolphins, seals and other wildlife - dolphin viewpoint within one mile. Local walks, Pictish history. Open March to November. Terms from £130 to £400 per week. Brochure available. Contact: **Mrs L. Grant, Fasgadh, Ness Road, Fortrose IV10 8SD (01381 620367).** ASSC MEMBER.

POOLEWE. Mr F.M. Hughes, Innes-Maree Bungalows, Poolewe IV22 2JU (Tel & Fax: 01445

781454. STB ★★★★ *SELF CATERING.* Situated in the village of Poolewe only a few minutes' walk from the world-famous Inverewe Gardens in magnificent Wester Ross, Innes-Maree is a purpose-built complex of six superb modern bungalows, all equipped to the highest standards of luxury and comfort. Each bungalow sleeps six with main bedrooms en suite. Open plan kitchen, diningroom and lounge has electric cooker, microwave, fridge/freezer, washing machine/tumble dryer and TV. Centrally heated. Ample provisions can be bought locally and there are a number of hotels and restaurants nearby. Children and pets welcome. Terms from £175 to £425 inclusive of bed linen and electricity. Brochure available.
e-mail: innes-maree@lineone.net
website: www.assc.co.uk/innesmaree

TORRIDON. 11 Diabaig, Torridon. Holiday cottage in quiet location overlooking Diabaig Bay with glorious views

out to Skye. The cottage is well-equipped and sleeps six in two double and one twin-bedded rooms. Kitchen with electric cooker, automatic washing machine and fridge, etc; livingroom with electric fire and colour TV. All linen supplied. Pets welcome. Car parking beside house. Open January to December. Prices from £160 to £220 per week. The area around Loch Torridon offers a wide range of outdoor activities, from low-level walks to spectacular hill climbing. Fishing and sailing are also well catered for, with local boat hire available. Permit-free brown trout fishing on the hill lochs and permits for salmon fishing are also available. Contact: **.Mrs Christine Duncan, Hazelbank, Diabaig IV2 2HE (01445 790259).**

ULLAPOOL near. Broomview & Sunset. STB ★★★★ *SELF-CATERING.* Located in the peaceful hamlet of

Rhiroy, 12 miles from Ullapool, where you will find shops and various tourist attractions. BROOMVIEW (ground floor-suitable for disabled):two double bedrooms and one single roon: utility room with auto washer and tumble dryer, spacious kitchen/dining room; lounge with colour TV and video. SUNSET (upper floor): double room and single room: shower room, utility with auto washer and tumble dryer, well equipped kitchen, lounge with colour TV and video. Ideal base for touring; experience for yourself unsurpassed Highland scenery, hill walking, rock climbing, bird watching, photography, forest walks, sandy beaches, etc. Broomview from £250 to £360; Sunset from £195-£285. Sorry, no pets. For colour brochure and further information contact: **Mrs Linda Renwick, Spindrift, Keppoch Farm, Dundonnell, By Garve, Ross-shire IV23 2QR (Tel & Fax: 01854 633269).**

Key to Tourist Board Ratings – Scotland and Wales

The Scottish Tourist Board Star Grading System. This easy-to-understand system tells you at a glance the quality standard you can expect. The gradings range from ★ (Fair and acceptable) to ★★★★★ (Exceptional, world-class) and will also include the type of accommodation eg ★★★ Self-catering or ★★ Hotel.

The Wales Tourist Board also operates the above system for serviced accommodation only. Self-catering properties will continue to show the **Dragon Award Grading** from **One** to **Five** depending on quality and facilities.

Some properties had not been assessed at the time of going to press and in these cases the publishers have included the old Crown Gradings.

When making enquiries or bookings,
a stamped addressed envelope is always appreciated.

HIGHLANDS (SOUTH)

ARISAIG. Achnaskia Croft, Ach na skia, Arisaig PH39 4NS (Tel & Fax: 01687 450606). STB

★★★/★★★★ *SELF-CATERING.*. Three beautiful cedar chalets and cottages set on our croft. Panoramic views to the isles of Eigg, Rum and Skye, with hills behind. One mile from the small village of Arisaig, with its shops, restaurant, hotel, cafe, station and harbour, from where you can take day trips to the Small Isles. Double glazed, well insulated accommodation, cosy at any time of year. In walking distance of sandy beaches. Ideal location for walking, exploring the many unspoilt beaches, mountains and lochs, boating, golf. Volleyball and boules for our guests. Prices from £180 to £390 per week.
email: achnaskia@hotmail.com

See also Colour Display Advertisement **AVIEMORE.** Aviemore – Heart of the Scottish Highlands. For that special vacation enjoy the stunning beauty of the Highlands and the Cairngorm Mountains from our choice of cosy lodges and superbly appointed villas. Great locations; peaceful and relaxing setting. Sky TV, video, payphone, barbecue. Pets welcome. Mini breaks. Many activities available; leisure pool and restaurants nearby. Open all year. Free brochure from: **Premier Vacations - telephone 07000 200099; Fax: 07000 777577.** ASSC MEMBER. e-mail: reservations@premiervacations.net
website: www.premiervacations.net

See also Colour Display Advertisement **BEAULY. Dunsmore Lodges, Beauly, IV4 7EY.** In the Heart of the

Highlands. Superb Lodges set well apart in six acres of woodland, each with its own private garden, surrounded by glorious glens, noted for their scenic splendour. You'll find a warm welcome with advice always on hand to help you explore this beautiful area, whether you prefer touring, hillwalking, golf, etc or nature and wildlife. or relax in the peace and comfort of the Lodges; why so many guests return year after year. Contact: **Mrs Inghammar (01463 782424; Fax: 01463 782839).** ASSC MEMBER.
e-mail: inghammar@cali.co.uk
website: www.cali.co.uk/dunsmore

See also Colour Display Advertisement **DALCROSS. Bob and Margaret Pottie, Easter Dalziel Farm Holiday Cottages, Dalcross IV2 7JL (Tel & Fax: 01667 462213). STB up to ★★★** *SELF-CATERING*. Three cosy, traditional stone-built cottages in a superb central location, ideal for touring, sporting activities and observing wildlife. Woodland and coastal walks. The cottages are fully equipped including linen and towels. Pets by arrangement. Terms from £130 low season to £415 high season per cottage per week. Recommended in the Good Holiday Cottage Guide. Open all year for long or short breaks. Brochure on request. ASSC MEMBER.

FORT WILLIAM. Great Glen Holidays, Torlundy, Fort William PH33 6SW (01397 703015: Fax 01397

703304) STB ★★ *SELF CATERING*. **Sleeps 4/6.** Eight timber chalets situated in woodland with spectacular mountain scenery. These spacious two bedroom lodges are attractively furnished with linen provided. On working Highland farm. Riding, fishing and walking on farm. Ideal for family holidays and an excellent base for touring; four miles from town. Prices from £250 to £420 per week.

Visit the FHG website
www.holidayguides.com
for details of the wide choice of accommodation
featured in the full range of FHG titles

FORT WILLIAM. Mr Hugh Campbell, Rowanlea Holiday Homes, Corpach, Fort William PH33 7LX (01397 772586). Rowanlea Holiday Homes are situated on a working croft, three miles out of Fort William on the Mallaig road (A830), overlooking the Caledonian Canal with a good view of Ben Nevis and Loch Linnhe. Central position for touring, and a good area for all types of fishing. The self-catering properties are fully-equipped with linen, all electric, colour TV, microwave etc. Please call for further details.

INVERGARRY. Mrs Willison, 1/2/3 Nursery Cottages, Invergarry PH35 4HL (01809 501285). Self-catering unit sleeping four people - two bedrooms. Shower room, toilet; fully equipped kitchen including fridge, microwave, washing machine, electric cooker, iron, etc. Colour TV, video. Barbecue. Double glazing and fully insulated. Electricity and bed linen included in price. One of the Highland's most central locations for visitor attractions and scenic tours. Loch Ness and Fort Augustus seven miles, ski slopes 20 miles. Fort William 25 miles. Skye, etc. 50 miles; Glen Garry, Glen Quoich and Kinloch Hourn close by. Open all year. Ample off street parking. Pets welcome by prior arrangement. Brochure on request.

INVERGARRY. High Garry Lodges, Invergarry. STB ★★★ *SELF-CATERING.* Four Scandinavian lodges set in an elevated position with superb views. Double glazed, electric central heating. One twin, two double bedrooms, lounge with breakfast bar and well equipped kitchen and bathroom. Terms from £160 to £440. Also one newly converted cottage nestling at a lower level within the confines of this small working farm. One double and one twin bedroom, tastefully renovted to a high standard. Terms from £190 to £470. Visitors may participate at feeding times on the farm. Ideal for touring the West Highlands. Fishing, walking, golf and bird-watching nearby. Brochure available. Contact: **Mr and Mrs Wilson (01809 501226; Fax: 01809 501307).** ASSC MEMBER.

Taigh An Lianach

Modern self contained bed-sit in the heart of the Great Glen overlooking Loch Oich. Secluded and peaceful. Sleeps 2.

Aberchalder Lodge

Traditional Highland shooting lodge set in spacious grounds. Spectacular views of Loch Oich. Extensively modernised giving a high standard of comfort whilst retaining character and charm. Sleeps 12

Leac Cottage

Secluded cottage in scenic Highland setting, retaining its old world charm whilst still providing a high standard of comfort. Sleeps 3.

All three locations are ideal for hill walkers and country lovers. Salmon, trout fishing, deer stalking available. Regretfully no pets.

For further details send an SAE to Miss J. Ellice, Taigh-an-Lianach, Aberchalder Estate, Invergarry PH35 4HN or telephone 01809 501287

KINCRAIG. Loch Insh Chalets, Kincraig PH21 1NU (01540 651272; Fax: 01540 651208). Set in 14 acres of woodland surrounded on three sides by forest and rolling fields, overlooking scenic Loch Insh. Aviemore seven miles and Kingussie six, offer shops, restaurants and entertainment. Kincraig Village is a short ten minute stroll. Free watersports hire and bank fishing daily (set times). Many leisure facilities. Access to sauna, minigym. Lochside restaurant. Telephone or fax for colour brochure. ASSC MEMBER.

PLEASE MENTION THIS GUIDE WHEN YOU WRITE OR PHONE TO ENQUIRE ABOUT ACCOMMODATION. IF YOU ARE WRITING, A STAMPED, ADDRESSED ENVELOPE IS ALWAYS APPRECIATED.

KIRKHILL (near Inverness). Mr M. R. Fraser, Reelig House, Reelig Glen, Kirkhill, Near Inverness IV5 7PP (01463 831208; Fax: 01463 831413). STB ★/★★ *SELF-CATERING.* **Properties sleep 4/5.** Holiday cottages and chalets in secluded woodland positions only eight miles from Inverness, capital of the Highlands. People staying here have enjoyed the freedom and the solitude; the tall trees and water of the Fairy Glen; the countryside with all the untrammelled joys of nature is at the door, butterflies find what butterflies need. Yet they have been glad of the nearness to shops, the pleasures of Inverness and of Beauly only 10 minutes' drive away. Pony trekking, sandy beaches and organised pastimes not far off. Central for touring West Coast to North, Central Highlands, Glen Affric, Culloden, Aviemore, Speyside and Moray Firth coast. The holiday homes are fully equipped except for linen and towels (unless these are specially asked for), with electric fires, night storage heater, fridge, four-ring cooker, microwave, shaving socket and colour TV. Reduced rates spring and autumn. Please ask for brochure and booking details.
e-mail: reelig@aol.com

NAIRN. Laikenbuie Holidays, Near Nairn. Watch deer and osprey on our tranquil croft with a beautiful outlook over the Loch amid birch woods. Free range hens, cows, sheep, fishing. Warm chalets and two residential caravans provide luxury accommodation by the Moray Firth and its dolphins. Excellent holiday centre four miles from Nairn with low rainfall, plenty sunshine and sandy beaches. Near Loch Ness, Cairngorm Mountains, Cawdor Castle. All that's missing is you! No smoking inside, Pets by arrangement. Chalets from £112 to £468, Caravans from £112 to £300. For colour brochure: **Mrs Therese Muskus, Laikenbuie, Grantown Road, Nairn IV25 5QN (01667 454630).** ASSC MEMBER.
e-mail: www.bigfoot.com/~muskus

NETHY BRIDGE (Spey Valley). Dell of Abernethy Cottages, Nethy Bridge PH25 3DL. STB ★★★ *SELF-CATERING.* **Sleep 2/8.** Warm, comfortable stone-built cottages maintained to modern standards and regularly inspected by Scottish Tourist Board. Dell of Abernethy Cottages are of individual character set in two- and- a-half acres of lawn and mature woodland, one mile from Nethy Bridge amidst farmland and on the edge of the Abernethy RSPB Nature Reserve. This area is ideal for walking, cycling, pony trekking, golf, fishing, tennis and as a centre for touring the countryside and heritage of the Scottish Highlands. Fresh air and wide open spaces make Speyside a holiday area for all the family and it is easily accessible from the south on good roads. For colour brochure contact **John F. Fleming on 01463 224358 or 01479 821643.** ASSC MEMBER.
website: www.nethybridge.com/dellofabernethy.htm

See also colour advertisement

Crubenbeg Farm Steading

Scottish TOURIST BOARD · SELF CATERING

Delightful conversion of an 18th Century steading into seven self-catering cottages. Just five miles south of Newtonmore in beautiful countryside is this centrally situated holiday complex. It comprises a games room, fitness room, sauna, solarium and children's play area. Pets welcome.

Newtonmore, Inverness-shire PH20 1BE
Tel: 01540 673566 • Fax: 01540 673509

E-mail: enquiries@crubenbeg.netlineuk.net • Website: www.newtonmore.com/crubenbeg/

SPEAN BRIDGE. David and Joan Bennet, Riverside Lodges, Invergloy, Spean Bridge PH34 4DY (Tel & Fax: 01397 712684). STB ★★★ *SELF-CATERING.* Pleace and quiet are synonymous with Riverside, where our three identical lodges each sleep up to six people. Accessible from the A82, but totally hidden from it, our 12 acres of woodland garden front on to Loch Lochy. Cots, linen, boat, fishing tackle, barbecue, all for hire. Pets welcome. There is a nominal charge for fishing on our stocked lochan or you can fish free from our shingle beach on Loch Lochy. Brochure gladly provided on request. ASSC MEMBER.
E-mail: d.bennet@dial.pipex.com
Website: http://ds.dial.pipex.com/town/plaza/ykm09

WHITEBRIDGE. Mr and Mrs Allen, Wildside Highland Lodges, Whitebridge, Inverness IV2 6UN (01456 486373). STB up to ★★★★ *SELF- CATERING.* The lodges are at South Loch Ness, set on the banks of a rocky river deep in the countryside amidst spectacular scenery. Accommodation ranges from cosy studio units built for two, to well appointed stone and cedar lodges for up to six people. Spacious grounds and private lawns, free central heating and large picture windows. Country pub nearby and a choice of places to eat out. Open all year, mini breaks available. Pets welcome. See our colour brochure or visit our website.before you choose your special holiday. ASSC member.
e-mail: patricia@wildside-lodges.demon.co.uk
website: www.wildside-lodges.demon.co.uk

LANARKSHIRE

BIGGAR (Clyde Valley). Carmichael Country Cottages, Carmichael Estate Office, Westmains, Carmichael, Biggar ML12 6PG (01899 308336; Fax: 01899 308481; STB ★★/★★★★ *SELF-CATERING.* **Working farm, join in. Sleep 2/7.** These 200-year-old stone cottages nestle among the woods and fields of our 700-year-old family estate. Still managed by the descendants of the original Chief of Carmichael. We guarantee comfort, warmth and a friendly welcome in an accessible, unique, rural and historic time capsule. We farm deer, cattle and sheep and sell meats and tartan - Carmichael of course! Children and pets welcome. Open all year. Terms from £180 to £480. FHB Member. ASSC Member. 15 cottages with a total of 32 bedrooms. We have the ideal cottage for you. Private tennis court and fishing loch; cafe, farm shop and visitor centre. Pony trekking. Off-road driving course.
e-mail: chiefcarm@aol.com
website: www.carmichael.co.uk/cottages

Other specialised

FHG PUBLICATIONS

- Recommended COUNTRY HOTELS OF BRITAIN   £4 95

- Recommended WAYSIDE & COUNTRY INNS OF BRITAIN   £4.95

- PETS WELCOME!   £5 25

- BED AND BREAKFAST IN BRITAIN   £3 95

- THE GOLF GUIDE Where to Play / Where to Stay   £9.95

Published annually: Please add 55p postage (UK only)
when ordering from the publishers

FHG PUBLICATIONS LTD
Abbey Mill Business Centre, Seedhill,
Paisley, Renfrewshire PA1 ITJ

Visit the   website

www.holidayguides.com

for details of the wide choice of accommodation
featured in the full range of FHG titles

PERTH & KINROSS

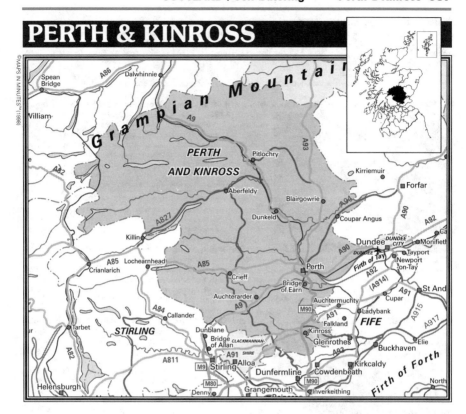

ABERFELDY. Loch Tay Lodges, Acharn. STB ★★★★ *SELF-CATERING.* **Lodges sleep 2/8.** These lodges are in a recently converted stone-built terrace listed as of special historic and architectural interest, situated on a farm on the outskirts of the picturesque Highland village of Acharn on the shores of Loch Tay. There is free trout fishing on the loch; salmon and other fishing by arrangement. Special facilities for sailing: many scenic walks. Golf at Taymouth one and a half miles and five other courses within 20 miles. The lodges are fully equipped to the highest modern standard, including colour TV. Four of the units have log fires. Open all year, with terms from £175 to £460. For free brochure, please apply to **Mrs F. Millar, Remony, Acharn, Aberfeldy PH15 2HR (01887 830209; Fax: 01887 830802).**
e-mail: remony@btinternet.com

See also Colour Display Advertisement

ABERFELDY. Mrs J.M. McDiarmid, Mains of Murthly, Aberfeldy PH15 2EA (01887 820427). STB ★★★ *SELF-CATERING.* **Sleeps 3/5.** Two beautifully situated holiday cottages overlooking Aberfeldy on a working farm, one-and-a-quarter miles from town. Fully equipped for three to five persons. Dining/sittingroom, kitchen, bathroom with shower and bath. Everything supplied except linen. Hire service available. Children welcome. Pets accepted. Ample parking. Fishing available on private stretch of River Tay. Golf courses nearby and new recreation centre with swimming pool in Aberfeldy. Available all year, with terms from £150. SAE please for further details. ASSC MEMBER.

ABERFELDY. Mrs M. McDiarmid, Castle Menzies Farm, Aberfeldy PH15 2LY (01887 820260; Fax: 01887 829666). STB ★★★/★★★★ *SELF-CATERING*. **Sleep 3/5**. Situated in the heart of Highland Perthshire, close to historic Castle Menzies. Two very comfortable stone-built cottages located separately on arable farm two miles west of Aberfeldy. Open all year. Fully equipped 3-5 persons. £150 to £500 per week. Short Breaks available low season. Colour brochure on request. ASSC member.
E-mail: DDMcD@farmline.com
websites: members.farmline.com/castlemenzies/   www.assc.co.uk/castlemenzies/index.html

BANKFOOT. Mrs C. MacKay, Blair House, Main Street, Bankfoot, Near Perth PH1 4AB (Tel & Fax: 01738 787338). STB ★★ *SELF-CATERING*. MYRTLE COTTAGE is situated in a nice quiet location eight miles north of Perth off A9. Fully equipped including linen. Cottage comprises two double bedrooms, lounge, kitchenette/dinette and bathroom with shower. Colour TV and video, telephone, microwave, fridge/freezer, dishwasher, automatic washing machine, tumble dryer, toaster, cooker, iron and drying green at rear. Electricity paid for on departure. Pets welcome. Car parking. Central for touring. SAE appreciated. Bed and Breakfast also available.

See also Colour Display Advertisement | **BLACKFORD. Kingslynn, Stirling Street, Blackford PH4 1QG. STB ★★★** *SELF-CATERING*. **Sleeps 4.** Traditional cottage comprising double bedroom, lounge with bed settee, kitchen/dinette, sun porch and toilet/shower. Colour TV. Fridge freezer. Cot and babychair. Large south facing garden. Post office/shop, hotel, inn and cafe/takeaway in village. Shops and services in Auchterarder. Excellent for easy access to touring, cycling, fishing and golf. Full details in cottage. Open June to September only. **Contact: J.M. Ellis, 15 Riccarton Crescent, Currie, Midlothian (Tel & Fax: 0131 449 2953).** ASSC MEMBER.

BLAIRGOWRIE. Mrs K.A.L. Saddler, Inverquiech, Alyth, Blairgowrie PH11 8JR (01828 632463). STB ★★★ *SELF-CATERING.* **Working farm. Cottage sleeps 4.** Recently refurbished farm cottage with oil-fired central heating. Everything essential for self-catering including colour television, microwave, electric cooker, fridge and vacuum, bath and shower. Farm is bordered by River Isla and Alyth Burn. Free fishing allowed. There are two bedrooms, one double with twin beds and one smaller with bunk beds. Electric blankets, duvets, linen and towels provided. Small garden and double garage with washing machine and tumble dryer. Pets welcome. Golfing, riding, walking, fishing and skiing nearby. Terms £155-£230 includes electricity, oil, coal and logs for open fire. Brochure available.

FREE and REDUCED RATE Holiday Visits!
Don't miss our Readers' Offer Vouchers

DUNKELD by. Laighwood Holidays, Butterstone, By Dunkeld PH8 0HB (01350 724241). STB ★★★/★★★★ *SELF-CATERING*. **Properties sleep 2-8**. A de luxe detached house, comfortably accommodating eight, created from the west wing of a 19th century shooting lodge with panoramic views. Two popular cottages sleeping four, situated on our hill farm with beautiful views. Two well-equipped apartments adjoining Butterglen House near Butterstone Loch. Butterstone lies in magnificent countryside (especially Spring/Autumn), adjacent to Nature Reserve (ospreys). Central for walking, touring, historic houses, golf and fishing. Private squash court and hill loch (wild brown trout) on the farm. Sorry no pets. Terms: House £384 to £570; Cottages and Apartments £130 to £275. ASSC MEMBER.

KILLIN. Springwood. STB ★★★ *SELF-CATERING*. Springwood is a modern bungalow set on a private road

overlooking the River Lochay. It is in a secluded position on the edge of the village yet within walking distance of shops and local facilities. Furnished to a high standard throughout, extras include dishwasher, microwave, automatic washer. There are well laid out gardens to the front and rear, with patio and garden furniture. Prices, which include bedding, towels and electricity, range from £210 per week. Offering a truly relaxing holiday. Details from **Mrs C.A. Campbell, Ledcharrie, Luib, Crianlarich FK20 8QT (Tel & Fax: 01567 820532).**

METHVEN. Cloag Farm, Methven, Perthshire. Three family-run farm cottages with extensive views. Seven miles west of Perth, within walking distance of Methven village in Perthshire is a good base for visiting east and central Scotland. Two bedrooms, sleeps four. Washing and ironing facilities. Fully equipped kitchen with microwave. Pets by arrangement. Open all year. Contact: **David and Moyra Smythe, Cloag Farm, Methven PH1 3RR (01738 840239; Fax: 01738 840156).** ASSC MEMBER.
e-mail: cloagfarm1@cs.com
website: www.destination-scotland.com/cloagfarm

PITLOCHRY near. Mrs E. M. Burns, Milton of Kincraigie, Blair Atholl, Near Pitlochry PH18 5TU

(01796 481278). STB ★★ *SELF CATERING*. **Sleeps 2/6.** Relax in comfortable and well-equipped self-catering accommodation (cottage, bungalow and caravans) on a hill farm in tranquil Glen Fender, overlooking picturesque Blair Castle and Atholl Valley. Panoramic views of surrounding hills from which endless hours of walking in the bracing mountain air can be enjoyed, either at a leisurely pace or while you "bag" a few Munros. An ideal centre for many historic places of interest, working distilleries, golf, fishing, mountain biking, theatre going, forest walks or observing nature. Open/electric fires, duvets, electric blankets. TV/video all available. Terms from £160 to £275. Caravan £90 to £105. Open all year.

RANNOCH. Mrs N. Robertson, Camusericht Farm, Bridge of Gaur, Rannoch, By Pitlochry PH17 2QD (01882 633219 or 01882 633277). Sleeps 5. Situated in the rugged and romantic hills of Scotland where River Gaur runs into Loch Rannoch: Bothy Cottage. Contains livingroom with multi-fuel stove; kitchenette; shower and toilet; two bedrooms with one single and two double beds. Fully furnished except linen. Children welcome. Tariff £120 per week, excluding electricity. Plenty of swimming and fishing. SAE for futher details.

STRATHTAY. Carnish, Strathtay. Sleeps 4. Modern semi-detached bungalow, comfortably furnished, on edge of small village. Aberfeldy five miles, Pitlochry nine miles; near golf course. Sleeps four in two double bedrooms; electric blankets; duvets; fully equipped except linen; fridge; all-electric; parking. Utility room with washing machine and freezer. No children, no pets. Weekly terms plus electricity. **Mrs Kidd, Eiriostadh, Strathtay, Pitlochry PH9 0PG (01887 840322).**

RENFREWSHIRE

HOWWOOD. Mrs Lesley Hay, Mid Risk Farm, Beith Road, Howwood PA9 1DN (Tel & Fax: 01505 842127). Working farm.

Situated on the A737, seven miles from Glasgow Airport, the cottages are a recent conversion of redundant buildings on a fully working farm. We are centrally situated for the North Ayrshire Coast and Glasgow and there are facilities for wind surfing, dinghy sailing, rowing, mountain biking and walking within easy reach. Aspen, Beech and Cedar all have two double rooms, bathroom with shower and a spacious lounge/kitchen area. The kitchen is fully equipped with fridge, washing machine, microwave, etc, electric cooking and water heater. All bed linen and towels are included. The cottages are heated by off peak storage heaters which is included in the rent. All other electricity is paid for by a £1 coin meter. Please phone or fax for price details.

STIRLING & DISTRICT

See also Colour Display Advertisement **PORT OF MENTEITH. Christopher Nairn, Lochend Chalets, Port of Menteith FK8 3JZ (01877 385268; Fax: 01877 385240).** Situated on the shores of the Lake of Menteith with trout fishing, swimming, rowing or sailing right on your doorstep. The Chalets, which feature on the BBC Summer Holiday programme, are furnished to the highest standard and are ideally placed for touring this area of Scotland. Tennis, laundry, play area, games room and mountain bikes on site. No pets. Prices from £160 to £650. Brochure available. Welcome Host. ASSC MEMBER.
e-mail: info@lochend-chalets.com
website: www.lochend-chalets.com

THORNHILL. Mr Willie Brewster, Wester Borland Farm, Thornhill FK8 3QL (01786 850636). Sleeps 8.

Sitting on the edge of Flanders Moss and enjoying panoramic views of surrounding hills this spacious modern farmhouse makes a peaceful retreat. Part of a working dairy and beef cattle farm located just off the main Aberfoyle to Stirling road, making an ideal base for touring this scenic and historic part of Scotland. Accommodation comprises spacious lounge with open coal fire, modern, fully-equipped fitted kitchen, sun porch with furniture. Four bedrooms, one en suite; bathroom with shower, toilet and basin. Calor Gas and electric central heating; bed linen and towels included. Parking. Please write or phone for further information.

Key to Tourist Board Ratings – Scotland and Wales

The Scottish Tourist Board Star Grading System. This easy-to-understand system tells you at a glance the quality standard you can expect. The gradings range from ★ (Fair and acceptable) to ★★★★★ (Exceptional, world-class) and will also include the type of accommodation eg ★★★ Self-catering or ★★ Hotel.

The Wales Tourist Board also operates the above system for serviced accommodation only. Self-catering properties will continue to show the **Dragon Award Grading** from **One** to **Five** depending on quality and facilities.

Some properties had not been assessed at the time of going to press and in these cases the publishers have included the old Crown Gradings.

ISLE OF COLONSAY

See also Colour Display Advertisement   **ISLE OF COLONSAY. Isle of Colonsay Lodges, Argyll PA61 7YR (01951 200320; Fax: 01951 200242). Sleep 2-5.** Modern and comfortable self-catering chalets on a beautiful and unspoiled Hebridean island. All towels and bed linen included, open all year, in low season rent from as little as two nights. Convenient to ferry, shop, church and licensed hotel. The island is simply outstanding for beauty and wildlife, enjoy golf, fishing, rambling amid a wealth of historic sites and numerous deserted sandy beaches. From £145 to £520 weekly. Colonsay is very special -- please ask for full details. ASSC MEMBER.
e-mail: chalets@colonsay.org.uk

ISLE OF ISLAY

BRIDGEND. Blackpark Croft House. Situated in a stunning location with breathaking views, near to safe sandy beaches, ideal for family holidays. The house is exceptionally well-appointed and has a wonderfully presented interior. It sleeps eight people, and consists of one family, and two double bedrooms; two bathrooms with shower facility; large kitchen with all mod cons and a large sittingroom with open fire, which heats the entire house. Bed linen and towels are provided. Price £400 per week. Also, two self-catering apartments situated in the idyllic village of Port Charlotte, with all mod cons. All enquiries to **Mrs M. Shaw, 10 An-Creagan Place, Port Charlotte (01496 850355).**

ISLE OF MULL

See also Colour Display Advertisement   **AROS. Mr Graham Ellis, Puffer Aground, Smiddy House, Salen, Aros PA72 6JB (01680 300389/300472; Fax: 01680 300595). STB ★★★★** *SELF-CATERING.* **Sleep 2/4.** Sunny aspect not far from the Sound Of Mull. Two ground-floor studio flats in the Old Smiddy and Blacksmiths House. Tastefully converted, homely and comfortable with well equipped kitchens. Parking available on site. Smiddy flat has no steps. Each property sleeps two plus studio couch. All towels and bed linen are included. Central island location makes ideal exploration base. Available weekly from Easter to end December. Please telephone or write for more information. ASSC MEMBER.

FREE and REDUCED RATE
Holiday Visits!
Don't miss our
Readers' Offer Vouchers

Visit the **FHG** website
www.holidayguides.com
for details of the wide choice of accommodation
featured in the full range of FHG titles

ORKNEY ISLES

DEERNESS. Mrs M. Eunson, Staye, Deerness KW17 2QH (01856 741240). STB ★★★ *SELF-CATERING.*

Sleeps 8. Farmhouse, situated in a quiet, rural area, with sandy beaches nearby and only 10 miles from Kirkwall. Five minutes' walk to shop and post office, with ferry 25 miles away, and airport seven. Four bedrooms - one king-size, one double and two twin, with cot also supplied. Fully equipped kitchen/ diningroom. Oil central heating, electricity charged at 7p per unit. All bed linen supplied. Ample parking. Sorry, no pets. Terms from £200 to £320 per week.

HOY. Rackwick Hostel, Hoy KW16 3NJ. Sleeps 8. The hostel accommodates up to eight people in two dormitories, each sleeping four. It lies in the Rackwick valley with magnificent cliff scenery, only two miles from the Old Man of Hoy. The area is of special interest to climbers, botanists, ornithologists and geologists. No linen. Cooking is by gas, with cooking utensils, cutlery and crockery provided; one toilet/ shower room. Limited camping is available with use of hostel amenities. Terms from £4.70 per person per night for hostel, from £1.60 per night camping. Sorry, no dogs (except Guide Dogs). Open March to September (special out of season opening for groups can be arranged). **The Department of Education & Recreation Services, Orkney Islands Council, School Place, Kirkwall KW15 1NY (01856 873535 ext.2404; Fax: 01856 876327).**

ORKNEY
ISLANDS COUNCIL

ORPHIR. Mrs J Craigie, Hall of Clestrain, Orphir KW16 3HB (01856 850365). STB ★★★ *SELF-CATERING.*

Working farm. Sleeps 5. Fully equipped farm cottage on working farm. Quiet situation. Scenic views overlooking Hoy and Stromness. Short walk to beach with seals and a variety of sea birds. Centrally situated for exploring Orkney. Small garden. Within three miles of pub with good food at reasonable rates. Oil central heating, solid fuel heater in sittingroom, washing machine, fridge and microwave. Power shower and bath. Bed linen and towels provided, cot available on request. Sorry, no pets. Prices from £80 to £250. Open from May onwards.

PUBLISHER'S NOTE

While every effort is made to ensure accuracy, we regret that FHG Publications cannot accept responsibility for errors, omissions or misrepresentations in our entries or any consequences thereof. Prices in particular should be checked because we go to press early. We will follow up complaints but cannot act as arbiters or agents for either party.

SCOTLAND
Caravan & Camping Holidays

ARGYLL & BUTE

ACHARACLE. Fiona Sinclair, Resipole Farm Caravan & Camping Park, Loch Sunart, Acharacle

(01967 431235; Fax: 01967 431777). On the beautiful Ardnamurchan Peninsula this spacious family run park is situated on the shores of Loch Sunart. A haven for a wide range of wildlife, the park is centrally positioned for exploring this remote and peaceful area. The superb facilities include an excellent restaurant, slipway for boat launching, a nine hole golf course, and laundry. Luxury Thistle award-winning caravan holiday homes for hire and for sale. Lodges and a beautifully furnished cottage are for hire throughout the year. Touring caravans, motor homes and tents can enjoy the wonderful views down Loch Sunart. Pets are welcome. Calor gas available. Please write or phone for a full colour brochure or visit our website.
website: www.resipole.co.uk
email: info@resipole.co.uk.

ARISAIG. Mr A.A. Gillies, Kinloid Farm, Arisaig PH39 4NS (01687 450366; Fax: 01687 450611). ✓✓✓

APPROVED. **Working farm. Caravans sleep 6.** Eight caravans (six berth) available for hire from Easter to October. Attractively situated occupying an elevated position at Kinloid Farm, a five-minute car run from wonderful sands. The caravans are new models and have hot and cold water, showers, fridges, electric lighting, flush toilets and are completely self-contained. Each van commands magnificent and extensive views across Arisaig to the sea and islands of Skye, Rhum and Eigg. Sea cruises from Arisaig to the Islands. Toilet block with hot and cold showers, washbasins, shaver points, laundry rooms. Shops in Arisaig village. Children welcome. Well-behaved pets are allowed. Weekly terms from £160. Huge reductions early/late season. SAE, please.

---

caolasnacon
Caravan & Camping Park, Kinlochleven PA40 4RS

There are 20 static six-berth caravans for holiday hire on this lovely site with breathtaking mountain scenery on the edge of Loch Leven — an ideal touring centre. Caravans have electric lighting, Calor gas cookers and heaters, toilet, shower, fridge and colour TV. There are two toilet blocks with hot water and showers and laundry facilities. Children are welcome and pets allowed. Open from April to October. Milk, gas, soft drinks available on site; shops three miles. Sea loch fishing, hill walking and boating; boats and rods for hire, fishing tackle for sale.

Weekly rates for vans from £180; 10% reductions on two week bookings.
Tourers from £7.50 nightly. 7½ acres for campers — rates from £5.25 nightly.

For details contact Mrs Patsy Cameron — 01855 831279

OBAN. Mrs Violet McKellar, Seaview Caravan & Camping Park, Seaview, Keil Crofts, Benderloch, Oban PA37 1QS (01631 720360).

Sea View Caravan & Camping Park. Small, quiet, friendly ★★ Park, beautifully situated overlooking the Firth of Lorne and Tralee sandy beach. Delightful views and surroundings. Sheltered by the wood alongside the caravans making it a sun haven. Benderloch village one mile with shop/post office, tearoom and petrol station. Oban, Gateway to the Isles, 7 miles for boat trips to the many islands. Ideal centre from which to explore this lovely part of Scotland. Fort William and Ben Nevis 32 miles. Ardmucknish Bay is a paradise for divers. Forest and beach walks nearby. Restaurant with table licence short walk. All facilities, seasonal stances available. Touring vans, motorvans, tents and walkers all very welcome. Also caravan sleeps four, fully equipped.

OBAN. Brian and Sylvia Thompson, Oban Caravan and Camping Park, Gallanachmore Farm, Oban PA34 (01631 562425; Fax: 01631 566624).

✓✓✓✓ In an area of outstanding scenic beauty and graded as "Very Good", Gallanachmore Farm is situated on the seafront overlooking the Island of Kerrera. The Park provides excellent toilet and shower facilities, a well-stocked shop, launderette, children's play area and lends itself superbly for boating, fishing, windsurfing and scuba diving holidays. Also our static park has modern caravans for hire, all with sea views. Situated two-and-a-half miles south of Oban; from roundabout in the centre of the town, follow signs to Gallanach. Terms from £7.00 to £9.00 per night (two persons in touring van).

DUMFRIES & GALLOWAY

NEWTON STEWART. Whitecairn Farm Caravan Park, Glenluce, Newton Stewart DG8 0NZ (01581 300267).

✓✓✓✓✓ Peacefully set by a quiet country road, one-and-a-half-miles from the village of Glenluce with panoramic views over the rolling Galloway countryside to Luce Bay. Rated "Excellent" under the British Graded Holiday Parks Scheme, this family-run park offers a choice of three different caravan types sleeping up to six, all of a high standard and fully equipped except for linen. Amenities include shop, children's play area, launderette, telephone, toilet blocks and shower rooms. Electric hook-ups on touring pitches. Open from March to October, the six acre site offers freedom for children of all ages and dogs are welcome under strict control. Colour brochure available.

STRANRAER. Adam and Liz Mackie, Galloway Point Holiday Park, Portpatrick, Stranraer DG9 9AA (01776 810561).

✓✓✓✓ This family owned and managed park offers panoramic views over the Irish Sea and has a plethora of historic sites and gardens in the area for you to visit. Galloway Point makes an ideal base for touring the area, walking, golf and fishing holidays. We also have luxury Thistle Award caravan holiday homes for hire and a small selection for sale. This STB quality graded park is an excellent choice for short breaks as well as main holidays in Bonnie Galloway. A warm family welcome awaits you. RAC, AA 3 Pennants. David Bellamy Silver Award. British Holiday & Home Parks Association.

HIGHLANDS NORTH

DUNBEATH. Mrs Joyce Polanska, Knockinnon, Dunbeath KW6 6EH (01593 731347). Working farm,

join in. Two caravans on quiet croft site on A9, half-a-mile north of Dunbeath village. Willerby Berwick six-berth with bedroom, bathroom with toilet and shower facilities and water heater; gas cooker, heater. Electric lighting, fridge, kettle, toaster, power points. Atlas Aztec has similar facilities. Both sleep six and are fully equipped (except bed linen). Children and pets welcome. Parking space. Picturesque coastal area. Pony trekking nearby. Charges from £90 per week.

HIGHLANDS MID

ACHNASHEEN. Mr A.J. Davis, Gruinard Bay Caravan Park, Laide, By Achnasheen, Wester Ross IV22

2ND (Tel & Fax: 01445 731225). ✓✓✓✓. An invitation to the most beautiful part of North West Scotland. Situated just a stone's throw from the beach, Gruinard Bay Caravan Park offers the perfect setting for a holiday or a stopover on the West Coast of Scotland. Family owned and operated, the park boasts magnificent views across the Bay, and from the beach you can take in the breathtaking views of the mountains of Coigach, the Summer Isles and Gruinard Island. Limited number of static vans available for hire, all fully serviced and equipped (including duvets and linen) with no additional charge for gas and electricity. For up-to-the-minute availability and tariff information please telephone and we will be pleased to advise you.

HIGHLANDS SOUTH

ARISAIG. Mrs Simpson, Camusdarach, Arisaig PH39 4NT (01687 450221). STB ★★★★. Bronze Green

Tourism Award. AA Four Pennants. Camusdarach has a 42 pitch site for touring vans (11 electric points) and tents (no static vans). Situated on protected, undulating grassy fields, a three minute stroll from glorious sandy beaches, it is served by an immaculate, modern toilet and shower facility, with laundry and drying machines, washing-up areas and facilities for the disabled and babies. Easy ferry access to Eigg, Rum, Muck and Skye and marvellous walks all around. Self-catering apartments, cottage and Bed and Breakfast rooms in the lodge are also available.
e-mail: camdarach@aol.com
website: road-to-the-isles.org.uk/camusdarach

Please mention *The Farm Holiday Guide* when enquiring about accommodation featured in these pages.

PERTH & KINROSS

COMRIE. West Lodge Caravan Park, Comrie PH6 2LS (01764 670354). ✓✓✓✓. Two to six berth static caravans with gas cooker, running water, toilet, electric fridge, lighting, colour TV and gas fire. Crockery, cutlery, cooking utensils, blankets and pillows are provided. Sheets and towels can be hired. Most caravans also have showers. Two modern shower blocks on site, complete with washing machine, tumble dryer, showers and hot and cold running water; shop. Fishing, golf, tennis, bowling, hill-walking and canoeing all within easy reach. Watersports available on nearby Loch Earn. Ideal for touring, 23 miles north of Stirling and 23 miles west of Perth. Terms from £20 to £30 nightly, £100 to £220 weekly; electricity and gas included.

DUNKELD. ☎ Kilvrecht Caravan Park, Inverpark, Dunkeld PH8 0JR (01350 727284; Fax: 01350 728635). Secluded campsite on a level open area in quiet and secluded woodland setting. Close by is the Black Wood of Rannoch, a remnant of the Ancient Caledonian Forest which once blanketed Scotland. There is fishing available for brown trout on Loch Rannoch and there is nothing to beat a sunny day on the shores of the loch for those who wish to relax. There is a Forest Park centre and shop at the Queen's View where you will find full details of walks and activities. Several trails begin from the campsite. Please write, fax or telephone for further information.

FOR THE MUTUAL GUIDANCE
OF GUEST AND HOST

Every year literally thousands of holidays, short breaks and overnight stops are arranged through our guides, the vast majority without any problems at all. In a handful of cases, however, difficulties do arise about bookings, which often could have been prevented from the outset.

It is important to remember that when accommodation has been booked, both parties – guests and hosts – have entered into a form of contract. We hope that the following points will provide helpful guidance.

GUESTS: When enquiring about accommodation, be as precise as possible. Give exact dates, numbers in your party and the ages of any children. State the number and type of rooms wanted and also what catering you require – bed and breakfast, full board etc. Make sure that the position about evening meals is clear – and about pets, reductions for children or any other special points.

Read our reviews carefully to ensure that the proprietors you are going to contact can supply what you want. Ask for a letter confirming all arrangements, if possible.

If you have to cancel, do so as soon as possible. Proprietors do have the right to retain deposits and under certain circumstances to charge for cancelled holidays if adequate notice is not given and they cannot re-let the accommodation.

HOSTS: Give details about your facilities and about any special conditions. Explain your deposit system clearly and arrangements for cancellations, charges etc. and whether or not your terms include VAT.

If for any reason you are unable to fulfil an agreed booking without adequate notice, you may be under an obligation to arrange suitable alternative accommodation or to make some form of compensation.

While every effort is made to ensure accuracy, we regret that FHG Publications cannot accept responsibility for errors, omissions or misrepresentations in our entries or any consequences thereof.
Prices in particular should be checked because we go to press early. We will follow up complaints but cannot act as arbiters or agents for either party.

THE FHG DIPLOMA

HELP IMPROVE
BRITISH TOURIST STANDARDS

You are choosing holiday accommodation from our very popular FHG Publications.
Whether it be a hotel, guest house, farmhouse or self-catering accommodation, we think you will find it hospitable, comfortable and clean, and your host and hostess friendly and helpful.

Why not write and tell us about it?

As a recognition of the generally well-run and excellent holiday accommodation reviewed in our publications, we at FHG Publications Ltd. present a diploma to proprietors who receive the highest recommendation from their guests who are also readers of our Guides. If you care to write to us praising the holiday you have booked through FHG Publications Ltd. – whether this be board, self-catering accommodation, a sporting or a caravan holiday, what you say will be evaluated and the proprietors who reach our final list will be contacted.

The winning proprietor will receive an attractive framed diploma to display on his premises as recognition of a high standard of comfort, amenity and hospitality. FHG Publications Ltd. offer this diploma as a contribution towards the improvement of standards in tourist accommodation in Britain. Help your excellent host or hostess to win it!

FHG DIPLOMA

We nominate ....
....

Because

Name ....
Address..
....
Telephone No..

WALES
Board Accommodation

ANGLESEY & GWYNEDD

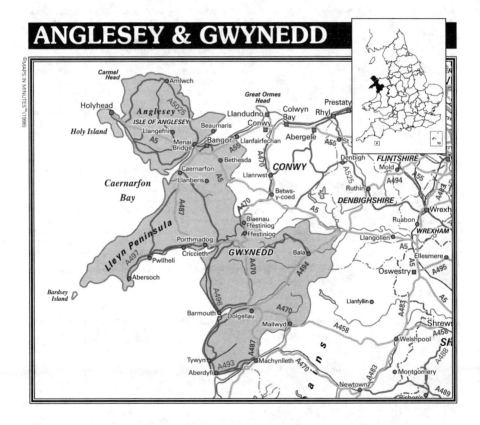

FHG PUBLICATIONS

publish a large range of well-known accommodation guides. We will be happy to send you details or you can use the order form at the back of this book.

ABERDARON. Barbara and David Marshallsay, Carreg Plas, Aberdaron, Pwllheli LL53 8LH (01758

760308). WTB ★★ *GUEST HOUSE.* 17th century manor house of historic interest in sheltered position on north west side of Lleyn Peninsula, set in five acres of secluded wooded grounds, surrounded by National Trust land. Only half a mile from the well-known Whistling Sands Beach, and two miles from the picturesque village of Aberdaron. Lovely coastal scenery and sandy beaches nearby. Seven bedrooms available with washbasins and tea-making facilities, five en-suite or with private bath/shower room. Central heating throughout. Large lounge; separate TV lounge; two diningrooms. Cots, high chairs provided, children especially welcome (reduced rates). Pets by arrangement. Ample car parking. Open all year. Bed and Breakfast from £20 to £26; Evening Meal, Bed and Breakfast from £32. Guests requested not to smoke in house.

ABERDOVEY. Jim and Marion Billingham, Preswylfa, Aberdovey LL35 0LE (01654 767239; Fax:

01654 767983) WTB ★★★ *COUNTRY HOUSE.* Preswylfa is a non-smoking very attractive Edwardian family home, private and secluded with a lovely mature garden filled with old-fashioned fragrant flowers and safe car parking area. A footpath leads down to the old fishing village of Aberdovey, also famous for its sailing, walking and golf. All three luxury en suite bedrooms have full facilities, two of which enjoy breathtaking views over Cardigan Bay. A relaxing guest lounge with period furniture and grand piano awaits you, the dining room beyond leading into the garden. Evening meals are available by arrangement. Excellent cuisine and a warm welcome guaranteed.
E-mail: preswylfa@cwcom.net.

ANGLESEY. Nia Bown, Tre-Wyn, Maenaddwyn, Llanerchymedd, Anglesey LL71 8AE (01248

470875). Working farm. Lovely spacious farmhouse, set on a 240 acre working beef, sheep and arable farm. From the front of the house the view is towards Bodafon Mountain, with lovely walks in the vicinity. Peacefully located in an area of outstanding natural beauty, in a central location providing easy access to all tourist attractions. We have three comfortable en suite bedrooms with colour TV, radio/alarm, hairdryer, tea/coffee making facilities. There is a log fire in the relaxing lounge, and a spacious diningroom with separate tables. Children welcome. Sorry, no pets. Full central heating. Non-smoking. Bed and Breakfast from £21 to £23.00 per person.

BALA. Mrs C. A. Morris, Tai'r Felin Farm, Frongoch, Bala LL23 7NS (01678 520763). WTB ★★ *FARM.*

Working farm. Tai'r Felin Farm is a working farm, situated three miles north of Bala (A4212 and B4501). Double and twin bedrooms available with beverage tray and clock radio. Beamed lounge with colour TV and log fire when the weather is cooler. Excellent base for touring Snowdonia National Park, watersports, walking, fishing, etc. National White Water Centre is nearby. Hearty breakfast, with packed lunches and snacks available on request. Recommended for excellent cooking and friendly atmosphere. Relax and enjoy a homely welcome. Bed and Breakfast from £16 to £18. Reductions for longer stays.

BALA. Mrs S.E. Edwards, Bryn Melyn, Rhyduchaf, Bala LL23 7PG (01678 520376). WTB ★★ *FARM.*
Working farm. Bryn Melyn, Rhyduchaf is situated in the beautiful countryside of Bala, and offers accommodation all year. The house is stone-built and stands on 56 acres of mixed farmland. Home cooking and home produced food makes this a real home from home. Two double and one twin bedrooms, all with washbasins; two bathrooms, toilet; sittingroom; diningroom; central heating. With tea and coffee facilities. Children welcome at reduced rates. Sorry, no pets. A car is necessary to ensure that visitors derive all the pleasure that this region offers. Parking space. Sea 28 miles. Good recreation facilities in the area. Evening Dinner, Bed and Breakfast from £170 weekly or Bed and Breakfast £15 per person, with Dinner £25. No smoking. Mrs Edwards is a Farm Holiday Guide Diploma winner.

BALA near. Mrs J. Best, Cwm Hwylfod, Cefn-Ddwysarn, Bala LL23 7LN (Tel & Fax: 01678 530310).

WTB ★★★ *FARMHOUSE*. **Working farm.** Remote, peaceful 400-year-old farmhouse on working sheep farm. Beautiful countryside and wonderful views. Two double rooms, one large family room, all with washbasins and tea making facilities. Two bathrooms; clothes washing and drying machines. Guest lounge with colour TV. Full central heating. Cot, high chair available. Parking space. All meals are home cooked. Special diets catered for. Ideal centre for touring, walking, fishing, pony trekking and watersports. Bala Lake 10 minutes by car. Snowdon and many beaches can be reached in 40 minutes. Bed and Breakfast from £16 to £18. Reductions for long stays and children under 10 years. Brochure available. Children most welcome.

BEDDGELERT. Colwyn, Beddgelert, Gwynedd LL55 4UY. WTB ★★ *GUESTHOUSE*. Welcome to Colwyn.

Warm, small and friendly our 18th century cottage guesthouse, with its original stone fireplace in the low beamed lounge, is restful and cosy. Old fashioned (but modernised of course), most rooms en suite with white linen, warm duvets and central heating. Colwyn overlooks the river in the centre of picturesque Beddgelert, probably the most popular and unspoilt village in the area, lying in a National Trust valley right at the foot of Snowdon with lakes, streams and forests all around. Spectacular scenery both winter and summer, a perfect base for the whole National Park. There are small shops, inns and cafes in the village. Bed and Breakfast from £19 to £23. Also small cottage available, sleeping two £180, sleeping four £340. Wet pets and muddy boots welcome. Early booking advisable. **Telephone: 01766 890652.**

CAERNARFON. Gwyndaf and Jane Lloyd Rowlands, Pengwern, Saron, Llanwnda, Caernarfon LL54

5UH (Tel & Fax: 01286 831500; 07778 411780 mobile), WTB ★★★★ *FARM*. Charming, spacious farmhouse of character, situated between mountains and sea. Unobstructed views of Snowdonia. Well-appointed bedrooms, all en suite. Set in 130 acres of land which run down to Foryd Bay. Jane has a cookery diploma and provides excellent meals with farmhouse fresh food, including home-produced beef and lamb. Excellent access. Children welcome. Open February to November. Bed and Breakfast from £20 to £25; Evening Meal from £12. AA QQQQQ.

See also Colour Display Advertisement **CAERNARFON. The Stables Hotel, Llanwnda, Caernarfon LL54 5SD (01286 830711; Fax: 01286 830413).** Relaxing comes easy at 'The Stables', set in 15 acres of beautiful countryside on the edge of the Llyn Peninsula amid the magnificent backdrop of Snowdonia. The area offers easy access for sailing, riding, fishing, tennis, climbing, walking and safe bathing from outstanding beaches. Ideal for pet owners. 18 en suite bedrooms, all ground floor, with colour television, intercom, direct-dial telephone and tea/coffee making facilities. Lounge bar and "Starving Rascal" carvery restaurant. Facilities for private functions and conferences. Helipad. Holiday cottages also available.

CRICCIETH. Mrs S.A. Reynolds, Glyn-y-Coed, Porthmadoc Road, Criccieth LL52 0HL (Tel: 01766 522870; Fax: 01766 523341). WTB ★★ *HOTEL*. Lovely Victorian family Hotel facing sea, mountains and two castles. Full central heating, cosy bar, private parking. Highly recommended home cooking with most diets catered for. All bedrooms en suite (one ground floor bedroom; some with four-posters) with colour TV and tea-making facilities. Moderate rates. Also Snow White cottage in grounds, sleeps two and self-catering accommodation sleeping two to 10, in own grounds. Parking. Just two minutes from beach and four minutes from shop and pub. Terms: Bed and Breakfast from £20 to £26 per person per night; Self Catering accommodation from £130 per week.

FHG Please mention *The Farm Holiday Guide* when enquiring about accommodation featured in these pages.

CRICCIETH near. Charlotte Lowe, Tyddyn Iolyn, Pentrefelin, Near Criccieth LL52 0RB (Tel & Fax: 01766 522509). WTB ★★★ *FARM*. Perfectly placed for exploring Snowdonia, Portmerion and the Llyn Peninsula, this restored and secluded 16th century oak-beamed farmhouse is set in idyllic farmland with breathtaking views of Snowdonia and the coastline. Five en suite bedrooms, one with four-poster, all with beverage trays. Traditional cooking, candelit dinners, homemade jams. Bed and Breakfast from £20-30, evening meal from £13. Farm Tourism award. Members of Heart of Snowdonia Farm Group. AA rated. No smoking. Closed Christmas.
e-mail: tiol@nildram.co.uk

DOLGELLAU. Mrs Griffiths, Llwyn Tal Cen, Brithdir, Dolgellau LL40 2RY (01341 450276). WTB ★ *GUEST HOUSE* Situated in an acre of rhododendron and azalea gardens, Llwyn Tal Cen offers a warm welcome, outstanding views, together with peace and quiet. Our location, about four miles east of Dolgellau, makes an ideal centre for hill walkers and nature lovers. We offer good fresh food, organic whenever possible. Traditional and vegetarian fare are both available. Bed and Breakfast from £17.50 to £20; Evening Meal £11. En suite rooms available. Reduced rates are available for children. Ample parking. To find us take narrow lane from the centre of the village of Brithdir (telephone box) past the village hall and wooden houses for about half-a-mile until you reach a crossroads, turn right, Llwyn Tal Cen is on the right in the trees after about 200 yards.

DOLGELLAU. Mrs E. Price, Glyn Farm, Dolgellau LL40 1YA (01341 422286). Glyn Farm is a holding of 150 acres which we farm, together with another 600 acres near Cader Idris. The old farmhouse stands on a hill overlooking the beautiful Mawddach Estuary. Dolgellau, which is one mile away, can be reached on foot along a riverside path,and the bus route runs along the bottom of the drive. Children and dogs are welcome, and most years there is a pet lamb to be fed, while the chickens and the family pet terrier give a farmyard welcome. Mountain bike network of tracks nearby at Ganllwyd; safe bike storage. We have one double en suite, one double with very small single next door, let as a family room, and one twin bedded room. All (except the single) have washbasin, TV, teatray, hairdryer and central heating. Bed and Breakfast from £16, open Easter to November. A cot is available. Ample parking.

DOLGELLAU. Mr and Mrs J.S. Bamford, Ivy House, Finsbury Square, Dolgellau LL40 1RF (01341 422535). WTB ★★ *GUEST HOUSE*. A country town Guest House offering a welcoming atmosphere and good food. Guest accommodation consists of six double rooms, three with en suite toilet facilities, all with TV and tea/coffee making. In the evening the dining room is open to non-residents as well as residents offering an extensive menu of HOME-MADE FOOD including many vegetarian dishes. There is a bar in the cellar. The lounge has tourist information literature and there are maps available to borrow. Dolgellau is an ideal touring and walking centre in the Snowdonia National Park. Bed and Breakfast from £18.50
e-mail: ivy.hse.dolgellau@i.c24.net

HARLECH. Mrs G.M. Evans, Glanygors, Llandanwg, Harlech LL46 2SD (01341 241410). This detached house with two acres of land is situated 400 yards from sandy beach, and has beautiful views of the mountains. It is one-and-a-half miles from Harlech Castle, golf club and swimming pool, and within a quarter-mile of train station. Ideal place for bird-watching. Presenting good home cooking in a homely and relaxed atmosphere and run by a Welsh-speaking family. Open all year. Central heating and electric blankets for Winter months. Accommodation comprises two double, one twin and one family bedrooms, all with washbasins, TV and tea-making facilities; bathroom, toilet; TV lounge and diningroom. Reduced rates for children and Senior Citizens. Bed and Breakfast from £16 per night; Evening Meal optional. Caravan to let.

LLANFACHRETH. Raymond Ivor and Lorna Myfanwy Gear, Ty Isaf, Llanfachreth, Near Dolgellau LL40 2EA (01341 423261). WTB ★★★ *GUEST HOUSE*, **AA**

◆◆◆◆. Take a little break - retreat, relax and revive in our lovely 17th century Welsh Longhouse nestling in a gentle valley in the Welsh Hills and where our llamas wander on the adjoining meadow. Excellent home-cooked food with traditional Welsh fare and free-range eggs from our hens. A kindly atmosphere and cosy en suite bedrooms. Comfortable guest lounge with TV and video, books and games; a peaceful study with views of the encircling mountains where you will find a selection of writings to inspire the heart! A perfect base for walking, hiking, bird-watching, cycling or exploring the beautiful beaches, rivers, lakes and castles in the surrounding area. Please contact us for our brochure and tariff. Welcome Host Gold Award, "Which?" and Good Hotel Guide 2000, 'Taste of Wales'
e-mail: raygear@tyisaf78.freeserve.co.uk

TRAWSFYNYDD. Penny Osborne and Margaret Roberts, The Old Mill Farmhouse, Fron Oleu Farm, Trawsfynydd LL41 4UN (Tel & Fax: 01766 540397). In the heart of Snowdonia National Park midway between Porthmadog and Dolgellau, Fron Oleu Farm offers plenty of wide open space to roam amongst a variety of safe, friendly animals, with beautiful views over the lake to the mountains beyond. Bedrooms are situated adjacent to the farmhouse, each with individual front door, private bathroom, TV, tea making facilities and heating. A two bedroomed family suite is available, as well as double, twin and family rooms. Ideal base for visiting mountains, lakes, rivers, castles, slate and copper mines and National Park properties; plenty of nearby sporting activities. Please telephone for further information.

TYWYN. Mrs Gweniona Pugh, Eisteddfa, Abergynolwyn, Tywyn LL36 9UP (01654 782385; Fax: 01654 782228). WTB ★★★ *B&B*. Eisteddfa offers you the comfort of a newly built bungalow on the Tan-y-coed Ucha Farm, situated adjacent to the farmhouse but with all the benefits of Bed and Breakfast accommodation. The bungalow which has been designed to accommodate disabled guests is conveniently situated between Abergynolwyn and Dolgoch Falls with Talyllyn Narrow Gauge Railway running through the farmland. Three bedrooms, two en suite and the third with a shower and washbasin suitable for a disabled person. The toilet is located in the adjacent bathroom. Tea/coffee tray and TV are provided in the bedrooms as are many other extras. We also cater for Coeliac Diets.

NORTH WALES

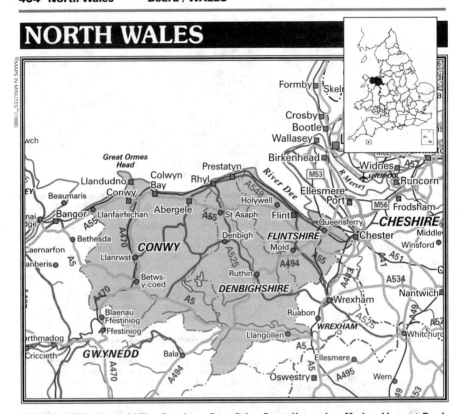

©MAPS IN MINUTES™ (1998)

BETWS-Y-COED. Jim and Lilian Boughton, Bron Celyn Guest House, Lon Muriau, Llanrwst Road, Betws-y-Coed LL24 0HD (01690 710333; Fax: 01690 710111). WTB ★★★ *GUEST HOUSE.* A warm welcome awaits you at this delightful guest house overlooking the Gwydyr Forest and Llugwy/Conwy Valleys and village of Betws-y-Coed in Snowdonia National Park. Ideal centre for touring, walking, climbing, fishing and golf. Also excellent overnight stop en-route for Holyhead ferries. Easy walk into village and close to Conwy/Swallow Falls and Fairy Glen. Most rooms en suite, all with colour TV and beverage makers. Lounge. Full central heating. Garden. Car park. Open all year. Full hearty breakfast, packed meals, snacks, evening meals - special diets catered for. Bed and Breakfast from £19 to £25, reduced rates for children under 12 years. Special out of season breaks.

BETWS-Y-COED. Mrs E. Jones, Maes-y-Garnedd Farm, Capel Garmon, Llanrwst, Betws-y-Coed (01690 710428). Working farm. WTB ★ *FARM.* This 140-acre mixed farm is superbly situated on the Rooftop of Wales as Capel Garmon has been called, and the Snowdonia Range, known to the Welsh as the "Eyri", visible from the land. Two miles from A5. Surrounding area provides beautiful country scenery and walks. Safe, sandy beaches at Llandudno and Colwyn Bay. Salmon and trout fishing (permit required). Mrs Jones serves excellent home-produced meals with generous portions including Welsh lamb and roast beef. Gluten-free and coeliacs' wheat-free diets can be arranged. Packed lunches, with flask of coffee or tea. One double and one family bedrooms with washbasins; bathroom, toilet; sittingroom, dining room. Children welcome; cot, high chair and babysitting available. Regret, no pets. Car

essential, ample parking. Open all year. Bed and Breakfast; Evening Meal optional. SAE brings prompt reply with details of terms. Reductions for children. Bala Lakes, Bodnant Gardens, Ffestiniog Railway, slate quarries, Trefriw Woollen Mills nearby. Member of AA.

BETWS-Y-COED. Mrs H. Hughes, Cwmanog Isaf Farmhouse, Betws-y-Coed LL24 0SL (01690 710225). Working farm.

This traditional Welsh farmhouse with its tranquil, homely atmosphere is set on a small working farm nestling amid the spectacular scenery of Snowdonia, one mile from the picturesque village of Betws-y-Coed. Accommodation comprises two double rooms en suite (one ground floor) and one twin/three-bedded room with private bathroom. All are comfortably furnished and have beverage making facilities, radio/alarm and hairdryer. Non smoking. A guests' lounge has TV and log fire. Home cooked farmhouse cuisine prepared from home-grown and local produce. The varied menu includes vegetarian dishes. Children over 14 years welcome.

BETWS-Y-COED. Mrs Florence Jones, Maes Gwyn Farm, Pentrefoelas, Betws-y-Coed LL24 0LR (01690 770668). WTB Listed *HIGHLY COMMENDED.*

Maes Gwyn is a mixed farm of 90-97 hectares, situated in lovely quiet countryside, about one mile from the A5, six miles from the famous Betws-y-Coed. The sea and Snowdonia Mountains about 20 miles. Very good centre for touring North Wales, many well-known places of interest. House dates back to 1665. It has one double and one family bedrooms with washbasins and tea/coffee making facilities; bathroom with shower, toilet; lounge with colour TV and diningroom. Children and Senior Citizens are welcome at reduced rates and pets are permitted. Car essential, ample parking provided. Good home cooking. Six miles to bus/railway terminal. Open May/November for Bed and Breakfast from £15. SAE, please, for details.

See also Colour Display Advertisement

BETWS-Y-COED near. Mrs Eleanore Roberts, Awelon, Plas Isa, Llanrwst LL26 0EE (01492 640047). Awelon once formed part of the estate of William Salisbury, translator of the New Testament into Welsh in the 16th century. With three-foot thick outer walls, it has now been modernised and is an attractive small guest house. Three bedrooms with en suite available; colour TV and teamakers; cosy lounge; central heating ensures a comfy stay. Private parking. Llanrwst, a busy market town at the centre of the beautiful Conway Valley, is close to Snowdonia, Bodnant Gardens and North Wales coast. A warm Welsh welcome awaits all guests. Bed and Breakfast from £16, en suite from £18.50 per person. A good choice of hotels, pubs and cafes in Llanrwst for evening meals. All home cooking. Children and pets welcome. Recommended by "Which?" Magazine.

CORWEN. Mr Bob Wivell, Pen-y-Bont Fawr, Cynwyd, near Corwen LL21 0ET (01490 412663).

WTB ★★ *B&B*. Pen-y-Bont Fawr is situated on the outskirts of Cynwyd village, near Corwen. Convenient for the A5, with Llangollen, Bala, Betws-y-Coed and Snowdonia all nearby. An ideal area for walking, cycling, fishing and watersports in Bala. Horse riding can be arranged and you can be assured of the legendary Welsh hospitality. Converted barn has a choice of twin or double bedroom, each with vanity unit. Shared toilet and shower facilities. Shared dining and livingroom. Tea and coffee facilities available. Children welcome. Regret, no pets. Evening meal optional, special diets catered for. Bed and Breakfst from £12.50 to £15.00. 3 nights break Bed & Breakfast and evening meal £63.00 per person.

MACHYNLLETH. Mrs Lynwen Edwards, Bryn Sion Farm, Cwm Cywarch, Dinas Mawddwy, Machynlleth SY20 9JG (01650 531251).

A very warm welcome awaits you when you visit Bryn Sion Farm, situated in the quiet, unspoilt valley of Cywarch at the foot of Arran Fawddwy (3000 ft). We are within reach of the beach and fishing and shooting are available on the farm. Bryn Sion is a mixed farm of 708 acres offering a variety of good farmhouse breakfasts and bedtime tea/coffee. Log fire in sittingroom in the evenings. Central heating throughout. One twin en suite and one double en suite with TV, tea making facilities and shaving points. Car essential - parking. Open April to November for Bed and Breakfast from £18 per person. SAE, please with enquiries.

RUTHIN. Mrs Wilkinson, Pant Glas Canol, Bontuchel, Ruthin LL15 2BS (01824 710241). WTB ★★★

FARM. Pant Glas Canol is a 15th century timber-framed farmhouse which was completely renovated in 1990. The farm is situated within easy reach of the market town of Denbigh and medieval town of Ruthin and is convenient for visiting Chester, Snowdonia and the North Wales coast. The house has central heating and is decorated and furnished to a high standard throughout. There are three letting rooms - one family, one double and one twin. A warm welcome to all visitors throughout the year. Children welcome. Caravan to let also available on farm. Directions: take A525 from Ruthin to Denbigh, at Rhewl village go over the bridge, travel for approximately half-a-mile, turn left. Turn left again at junction and farm is second on right.

Terms quoted in this publication may be subject to increase if rises in costs necessitate

CARDIGANSHIRE

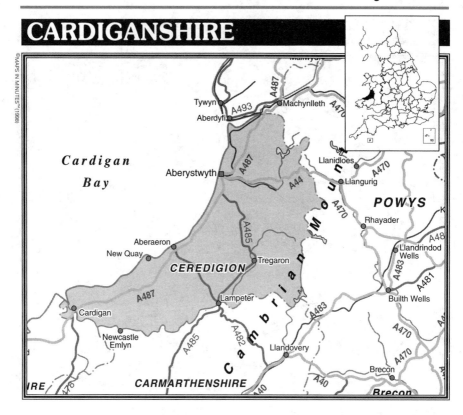

©MAPS IN MINUTES™ (1998)

ABERAERON. Mrs Christine Jones, Frondolau Farm Guest House, Heol Llain Prysg, Llanon SY23 5HZ (01974 202354). WTB ★★ *B&B*. WELCOME HOST AWARD. Frondolau is a period house in a quiet location and is part of a working dairy farm. Situated five miles north of Aberaeron and ten miles south of Aberystwyth we are ideally placed for visiting Ceredigion's many beautiful beaches and mountains. Bedrooms have tea/coffee facilities, clock radio, double glazing and central heating. A large sitting room with wood fire is available for your use. Relax and enjoy being a welcome guest with home-produced food from the farm and garden. B&B from £15 per person with special rates available for short breaks (five days plus). Open all year. Brochure available.

LLANDYSUL. Carole and Allen Jacobs, Broniwan, Rhydlewis, Llandysul SA44 5PF (Tel & Fax: 01239 851261). Broniwan welcomes you to the far West of Wales. Our grey stone house with ancient ivy growing round the porch is situated overlooking the Preseli Hills. Ten minutes' drive from the coast, seven miles from the River Teifi. We offer accommodation in two pretty double bedrooms with en suite or private facilities. A single bedroom is also available. Books, paintings, flowers and country antiques furnish the cosy sitting room and the separate dining room, where guests can watch birds come to the feeder outside the window. Meals are varied, with vegetarian choices. Soups, cakes and marmalade all home-made. Terms from £22.50 to £24 per person Bed and Breakfast, Dinner from £12.50. Reduced weekly rate available.
e-mail: 101535.2310@compuserve.com

CARMARTHENSHIRE

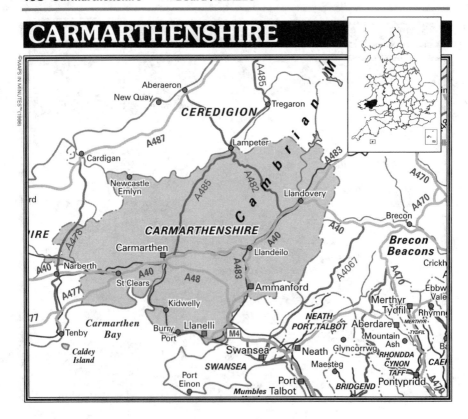

CARMARTHEN. Mrs Heather E. Rodenhurst, Glôg Farm, Llangain, Carmarthen SA33 5AY (01267 241271). WTB ★★ *B&B*. **Working farm**. Welcome Host. Glôg is a working farm, a traditional Welsh longhouse set in the lovely Dylan Thomas countryside. Five miles from the market town of Carmarthen and five miles from beach and castle at Llanstephan. Open all year Glôg offers a warm welcome. We have four bedrooms, all en suite with tea/coffee making facilities. Separate TV lounge and dining room. Wide breakfast choice, evening meal by arrangement. All home cooking. Central heating throughout, log fires in colder months. Children welcome. Ideal base offering peace and tranquillity. Bed and Breakfast £20 per person. AA QQQ.

CARMARTHEN. Mrs C.F. Whittle, Cilcrug Farm, Trawsmawr, Carmarthen SA33 6NA (01267 281682).

WTB ★★ *FARMHOUSE*. A warm welcome assured on our working stock farm situated on the site of an Iron Age settlement and surrounded by traditional farm buildings. There is a cottage garden, woodland walks, scenic views and interesting wildlife. Five miles north of Carmarthen, we are within easy reach of a variety of tourist attractions including the gardens at Aberglasny and the new National Botanic Garden at Middleton Hall. Accommodation consists of twin room with en suite shower and hot drink facilities. £20 per person. Single room also available and family accommodation at reduced rates. Lounge with Sky TV, log fire. Evening meal offered with home grown produce.

CARMARTHEN. Mrs Margaret Thomas, Plas Farm, Llangynog, Carmarthen SA33 5DB (Tel & Fax: 01267 211492). WTB ★★★ *FARM*. **Working farm**. Welcome

Host. Situated six miles west of Carmarthen town along the A40 towards St. Clears. Quiet location, ideal touring base. Working farm run by the Thomas family for the past 100 years. Very spacious, comfortable farmhouse. En suite rooms available, all with tea/coffee making facilities, colour TV and full central heating. TV lounge. Evening meals available at local country inn nearby. Good golf course minutes away. Plas Farm is en route to Fishguard and Pembroke Ferries. Bed and Breakfast from £18 per person. Children under 16 years sharing family room half price. Special mid-week breaks available. A warm welcome assured.

PEMBROKESHIRE

©MAPS IN MINUTES™ (1998)

New Qua

Strumble
Head

Cardigan

Newcastle
Emlyn

A485

Fishguard

St David's

A487

PEMBROKESHIRE

CARMARTHENSH.

Ramsey
Island

A478

Carmarthen

*St Brides
Bay*

A40

Haverfordwest

A40

Narberth

St Clears

A40

A48

A483

*Skomer
Island*

A477

Kidwelly

Milford
Haven

Neyland

A477

*Skokholm
Island*

Pembroke
Dock

Tenby

*Carmarthen
Bay*

Burry
Port

Llanelli

M4

Sw

Pembroke

*Caldey
Island*

SWANSE

*St Govan's
Head*

Port
Einon

M

FISHGUARD near. Heathfield Mansion, Letterston, Near Fishguard SA62 5EG (01348 840263).

WTB ★★★ *GUEST HOUSE.* A Grade II Listed Georgian country house in 16 acres of pasture and woodland, Heathfield is the home of former Welsh rugby international, Clive Rees and his wife Angelica. This is an ideal location for the appreciation of Pembrokeshire's many natural attractions. There is excellent golf, riding and trout fishing in the vicinity and the coast is only a few minutes' drive away. The accommodation is very comfortable and two of the three bedrooms have en suite bathrooms. The cuisine and wines are well above average. This is a most refreshing venue for a tranquil and wholesome holiday. Bed and Breakfast from £20 to £24 per person per night; Dinner by prior arrangement.

GOODWICK. Mrs M.P. Miller, Siriole Guest House, 2 Siriole, Quay Road, Goodwick SA64 0BS (01348 872375).

Beautifully run Bed and Breakfast with spacious accommodation overlooking Fishguard Bay and the Preseli Hills. In a quiet location with ample parking and close to Goodwick village and a short walk to the main ferry terminal to Rosslare - ideal for day trips to Ireland. We are centrally located for walks along the splendid Pembrokeshire National Coastal Path and numerous attractions. All rooms are en suite with shower/toilet, tea/coffee facilities and colour TV; some have sea views. Children and pets welcome. Prices range from £14 to £18 per person. Reductions for longer stays. Open all year.

HAVERFORDWEST Mrs M.E. Davies, Cuckoo Mill Farm, Pelcomb Bridge, St. David's Road,

Haverfordwest SA62 6EA (01437 762139). WTB ★★★.
Working farm. This farm is situated in central Pembrokeshire, two miles out of Haverfordwest on St. David's Road. It is within easy reach of many beaches and coastline walks. There are peaceful country walks on the farm, also a small trout stream. Children are welcome at reduced rates and cot, high chair and babysitting provided. The house is cosy with open fires and welcomes guests from January to December. Car is not essential, but parking available. Home-produced dairy products; poultry and meats all home-cooked. Mealtimes arranged to suit guests. Well appointed, warm, comfortable bedrooms with washbasins and tea-making facilities. Pets permitted. Evening Dinner/Meal, Bed and Breakfast or Bed and Breakfast only. Rates also reduced for Senior Citizens.

HAVERFORDWEST. Mr and Mrs Patrick, East Hook Farm, Portfield Gate, Haverfordwest, Pembroke

SA62 3LN (01437 762211). WTB ★★★ *FARMHOUSE.*
Howard and Jen welcome you to their Georgian Farmhouse surrounded by beautiful countryside, four miles from the coastline and three miles from Haverfordwest. Double, twin and family suite available, all en suite. Pembrokeshire produce used for dinner and breakfast. Dinner £14 per person. Bed and Breakfast from £20 to £22 per person.

HAVERFORDWEST. Mrs B. Devonald, Penygraig Farm, Penygraig, Puncheston, Haverfordwest SA62

5RJ (Tel & Fax: 01348 881277). WTB ★★ *GUEST HOUSE.*
Working farm situated at foot of Preseli Hills. Ideal base for exploring unspoilt North Pembrokeshire. Two bedrooms, one en suite. Non-smoking. Children and pets welcome. Open Easter to October. Bed and Breakfast £17 to £19 per person per night.

HAVERFORDWEST. Joyce Canton, Nolton Haven Farm, Nolton Haven, Haverfordwest SA62 1NH

(01437 710263). The farmhouse is beside the beach on a 200 acre mixed farm, with cattle, calves and lots of show ponies. It has a large lounge which is open to guests all day as are all the bedrooms. Single, double and family rooms; two family rooms en suite, four other bathrooms. Pets and children most welcome, babysitting free of charge. 50 yards to the beach, 75 yards to the local inn/restaurant. Pony trekking, surfing, fishing, excellent cliff walks, boating and canoeing are all available nearby. Riding holidays and short breaks all year a speciality. Colour brochure on request.

MARTINS HAVEN/MARLOES. Mrs Christina Chetwynd, East Hook Farm, Marloes, Haverfordwest SA62 3BJ (01646 636291). Farm on Pembrokeshire Coast Path offering Bed and Breakfast, camping, caravans, horse and pony riding, cycle hire, sea fishing, bird watching and walking. Convenient for boat trips to Skomer and Skokholm Islands and next to Marloes Mere Nature Reserve. 110 acres of natural unspoilt beauty. Bedrooms with washbasins, TVs and tea/coffee making facilities available. Reception room on site. Collection service offered from Haverfordwest. Also transport to Martins Haven for boat trips, diving and Marine Nature Reserve. Bed and Breakfast £16 per person per night. Children welcome.

AA
♦♦♦

HIGHLAND GRANGE Robeston Wathen, Narberth SA67 8EP   WTB ★★★ FARM

Make this delightful farm guesthouse in central South Pembs your destination at all times of the year. Spacious quality accommodation, some en suite. Excellent touring location

on A40, scenic countryside with panoramic views bordering National Park. Country Inn, walks and castle nearby; half hour to sandy beaches, National Trust, mountains, Irish ferry ports. One hour – National Botanical Garden of Wales, St David's Cathedral. Guest lounge, delicious meals, fully licensed, child-friendly environment, Shetland ponies. Welcome Host Certificate.

Proprietor: Naomi Jones. Tel/Fax: 01834 860952
website: www.highlandgrange.co.uk

PEMBROKE. Mrs Mathias, Bangeston Farm, Stackpole, Pembroke SA71 5BX (Tel & Fax: 01646 683986). WTB ★★★ *FARM.* A warm and friendly welcome awaits you at Bangeston, a working 350 acre dairy farm, peacefully situated within the Pembrokeshire Coast National Park. Countryside and sea views. Lawned and shrub gardens. Ample parking. The Grade II Listed 17th century farmhouse is tastefully furnished. Spacious double, twin and single bedrooms all have washbasins, tea facilities, central heating, shaving points and towels. Guests' bathroom has a bath, shower and toilet. Also a separate toilet. Guests lounge with TV, diningroom with separate tables. Excellent breakfasts with home-made preserves a speciality. Three course evening meals optional. Bed and Breakfast £16 per night, £105 per week, Evening Meal £10. Bike hire also available.

PENYBONT-FAWR. Mrs Anne Evans, Glanhafon, Penybont-Fawr, Oswestry SY10 0EW (01691 860377). WTB ★★ *FARM.* **Working farm, join in.** Secluded farm-house in the Upper Tanat Valley, ideal for a peaceful break. Glanhafon is a working sheep farm with hill walks on the farm. Bordering the Berwyn Mountains, it is a wonderful area for walking, bird-watching, or touring, with Lake Vyrnwy. RSPB Centre, and Pistyll Falls - one of the seven wonders of Wales- just seven miles away. Many other places of interest within easy reach, including Powys and Chirk Castle, Snowdonia, Erddig and the market towns of Shrewsbury and Oswestry. There are three attractive bedrooms, all en suite, with tea making facilities. Guests' own sittingroom. Ample parking. Children and pets welcome. Open Easter till October. Bed and Breakfast from £16.

SAUNDERSFOOT. Mrs Joy Holgate, Carne Mountain Farm, Reynalton, Kilgetty SA68 0PD (01834 860546). Working farm. We warmly welcome you to our lovely 200-year-old farmhouse set amidst the peace and tranquillity of the beautiful Pembrokeshire countryside. Distant views of Preseli Mountains, yet only three-and-a-half miles from Saundersfoot. Pretty, picturesque bedrooms with colour TV, washbasins, tea/coffee tray, central heating. Dining room with interesting plate collection, and attractive beamed sitting room with books and maps. Delicious traditional farmhouse breakfast; vegetarians very welcome. Let the strain and stress slip away as you enjoy the peaceful atmosphere and friendly farmyard animals. Bed and Breakfast from £16.00. Welcome Host and Farmhouse Award. Quality six-berth caravan also available in pretty, peaceful setting from £100 per week. SAE please.

Terms quoted in this publication may be subject to increase
if rises in costs necessitate

Key to Tourist Board Ratings
Scotland and Wales

The Scottish Tourist Board Star Grading System. This easy-to-understand system tells you at a glance the quality standard you can expect. The gradings range from ★ (Fair and acceptable) to ★★★★★ (Exceptional, world-class) and will also include the type of accommodation eg ★★★ Self-catering or ★★ Hotel.

The Wales Tourist Board also operates the above system for serviced accommodation only. Self-catering properties will continue to show the **Dragon Award Grading** from **One** to **Five** depending on quality and facilities.

Some properties had not been assessed at the time of going to press and in these cases the publishers have included the old Crown Gradings.

POWYS

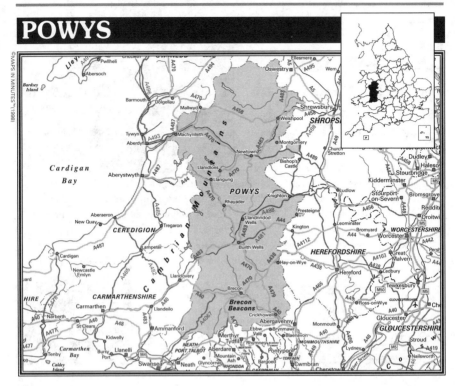

BRECON. Mrs Eileen Williams, Upper Farm, Llechfaen, Brecon LD3 7SP (01874 665269). Working farm.
A modernised farmhouse offering Bed and Breakfast only, situated just off the A40 Brecon to Abergavenny road, two miles from Brecon town. A 64-acre dairy farm in the heart of the National Park directly facing Brecon Beacons. Ideal for touring, with golf, trekking and fishing nearby and many Welsh craft shops to visit. Two double and one family bedrooms with washbasins and tea/coffee facilities; bathroom, toilet; sittingroom; diningroom. Cot, babysitting, reduced rates for children. Open all year. Car essential - parking. No pets.

BRECON. Mrs Jean Phillips, Cwmcamlais Uchaf, Cwmcamlais, Sennybridge, Brecon LD3 8TD (Tel

& Fax: 01874 636376). WTB ★★★ *FARM.* Cwmcamlais Uchaf is a working farm situated on the route of a popular walk in the Brecon Beacons National Park, one mile off the A40 between Brecon and Sennybridge. Our 16th century farmhouse has exposed oak beams and stonework, inglenook firepace and three tastefully decorated bedrooms – two double en suite and one twin with private shower room. Tea/coffee making facilities. The River Camlais with its waterfalls flows through our farmland. A warm Welsh welcome awaits you at our farm. Open all year except Christmas. Bed and Breakfast £20 to £21.

BRECON. Mrs A. Harpur, Llanbrynean Farm, Llanfrynach, Brecon LD3 7BQ (01874 665222).

Llanbrynean is a fine, traditional, Victorian farmhouse peacefully situated on the edge of the picturesque village of Llanfrynach, three miles south-east of Brecon. We are in an ideal spot for exploring the area - the Brecon Breacons rise behind the farm and the Brecon/Monmouth canal flows through the fields below. We are a working family sheep farm with wonderful pastoral views and a large garden. The house is spacious and comfortable with a friendly, relaxed atmosphere. We have two double en suite bedrooms and one twin with private bathroom. All have tea/coffee facilities. There is a sitting room with log fire. Bed and Breakfast from £18 per person. Excellent pub food within easy walking distance.

BRECON. Mrs Pamela Boxhall, The Old Mill, Felinfach, Brecon LD3 0UB (01874 625385). WTB ★★★

B&B. Welcome Host. A 16th century converted corn mill peacefully situated in its own grounds. Inglenook fireplace, exposed beams, en suite rooms, beverage trays, TV lounge. Ideal for country pursuits or just relaxing. Within easy reach of Brecon Beacons, Black Mountains, Hay-on-Wye and local pubs within walking distance. Packed lunches by arrangement. Children welcome. Terms: double room from £16.50 per person; twin en suite room from £18 per person, single from £20 per person. Reductions for weekly stays.

BRECON. Nicola and Bob Atkins, Cambrian Cruisers, Ty-Newydd, Pencelli, Brecon LD3 7LJ (01874 665315). WTB ★★ *FARMHOUSE.* **AA ◆◆◆◆** Our

farmhouse, built in 1720 and three miles south of Brecon, offers excellent accommodation for people wishing to enjoy the Brecon Beacons National Park. We are adjacent to the Mon and Brec Canal and also have a modern fleet of narrow boats for daily and weekly hire. We have very comfortable rooms, all en suite with superb views from every window - all with TV, central heating and tea making facilities. Guests have their own entrance, breakfast room and conservatory. For the comfort and safety of our guests we do not permit smoking or pets. We are open March to October and B&B is from £20 per person.
e-mail: cambrian@talk21.com

BRECON. Mrs M.J. Mayo, Maeswalter, Heol Senni, Near Brecon LD3 8SU (01874 636629). Maeswalter

is a 300-year-old farmhouse in the mountainous Brecon Beacons National Park. There are three tastefully decorated bedrooms: one double en suite, one standard double and a family room sleeping three. The comfortable lounge/dining room features exposed timbers. Visitors can roam freely through the grounds where there are seats to sit and admire the scenery and wildlife. Also private apartment (en suite double bedroom and private sitting room) with basic cooking facilities. The apartment and all bedrooms have colour TV and beverage trays with tea/coffee/ chocolate and biscuits. Rates per room: en suite double £39 per night, standard double £36, family room £50; reductions for longer stays.

BRECON near. Gwyn and Hazel Davies, Caebetran Farm, Felinfach, Brecon LD3 0UL (Tel & Fax: 01874 754460). Working farm, join in. "Welcome Host". A warm

welcome, a cup of tea and home-made cakes await you when you arrive at Caebetran. Visitors are welcome to see the cattle and sheep on the farm. There are breathtaking views of the Brecon Beacons and the Black Mountains and just across a field is a 400 acre Common, ideal for walking, bird-watching or just relaxing. Ponies and sheep graze undisturbed, while buzzards soar above you. The farmhouse dates back to the 17th century and has been recently modernised to give the quality and comfort visitors expect today. There are many extras in the rooms to give that special feel to your holiday. The rooms are all en suite and have colour TV and tea making facilities. The dining room has separate tables, there is also a comfortable lounge with colour TV and video. Caebetran is an ideal base for exploring this beautiful, unspoilt part of the country with pony trekking, walking, birdwatching, wildlife, hang gliding and so much more. For a brochure and terms please write, telephone or fax. "Arrive as visitors and leave as our friends". Winners of the 'FHG Diploma' for Wales 1998 and 1999.

BRECON/LLYSWEN. Mrs Mary Gittoes, Bryndu Farm, Llandefalle, Brecon LD3 0NF (01874 754227).

17th century working farm, close to picturesque village of Llyswen. Enjoy the scenery and wildlife. Situated close to the Brecon Brecons, Black Mountains, Brecon and Hay-on-Wye. Excellent location for a variety of energetic or sedate activities - walking, golfing, gliding, pony trekking, or cruise down the canal. The accommodation comprises double/family room en suite, double/twin room with private bathroom. Colour TV, residents' lounge and dining room. Peace and tranquillity are assured here. For more details, a brochure and terms, please write or telephone.

BUILTH WELLS. Mrs B. Williams, Dollynwydd Farm, Builth Wells LD2 3RZ (01982 553660). This 17th

Century farmhouse is situated beneath the Eppynt Hills in the Wye Valley one-and-a-half miles from Builth Wells on the B4520. Outstanding area for walking, birdwatching (red kite) and touring. Within easy reach of Brecon Beacons, Elan Valley and the bookshops of Hay-on-Wye. Many activities available nearby including sauna, gym, heated swimming pool, sports centre, golf, fishing, tennis and horse riding. The house is very comfortable with central heating, log fire and oak beams. There are four bedrooms – one en suite, one double, one twin and one single, plus two further bathrooms. Non-smoking. Private parking. Hairdryer available, also facilities for ironing and drying clothes. Lock-up garage for bikes.

BUILTH WELLS. Mrs N.Jones, Ty-Isaf Farm, Erwood, Builth Wells LD2 3SZ (01982 560607).

Ty-Isaf is a mixed working farm in the Wye Valley, with cattle, sheep, ponies and plenty of dogs. All bedrooms have washbasins, tea/coffee facilities and full central heating. It is situated just off the A470 near Erwood village, and is an ideal spot from which to tour Mid-Wales, being within easy reach of Elan Valley, the Black Mountains and Brecon Beacons, Llangorse Lake and Hay-on-Wye, famous for its bookshops, including what is claimed to be the largest second-hand bookshop in the world. Bed & Breakfast or Bed & Breakfast and Evening Meal with good home cooking. Terms on request.

BUILTH WELLS near. Mrs Margaret Davies, The Court Farm, Aberedw, Near Builth Wells LD2 3UP

(01982 560277). Non-smokers please. We welcome guests into our home on a family-run livestock farm situated away from traffic in a peaceful, picturesque valley surrounded by hills. Lovely walking, wildlife area, central to Hay-on-Wye, Brecon Beacons, Elan Valley and very convenient for Royal Welsh Showground. We offer comfort, care and homeliness in our spacious stone-built farmhouse with traditional cooking using home produce where possible. Bedrooms have adjustable heating, hospitality trays and electric blankets. En suite or private bathroom available. Guests lounge with TV. Good food at nearby village inn. Bed and Breakfast from £18.

GLADESTRY. Mrs M.E. Hughes, Stonehouse Farm, Gladestry, Kington, Herefordshire HR5 3NU (01544 370651). Working farm. Large Georgian farmhouse, modernised whilst retaining its character, situated on Welsh border with Offa's Dyke Footpath going through its 380 acres of mixed farming. Beautiful unspoiled area for walking. Many places of interest within driving distance such as Elan Valley Dams, Devil's Bridge, Llangorse Lake, Kington golf course. Guests are accommodated in one double and one twin-bedded rooms, with washbasins; bathroom, two toilets; sitting and diningroom. TV. Homely informal atmosphere with home produced food and home cooking. Vegetarian meals on request. Good food available nearby at village inn. Children welcome. Babysitting available. Pets also welcome. Bed and Breakfast from £15; Evening Meals by arrangement.

HAY-ON-WYE. Annie and John McKay, Hafod-y-Garreg, Erwood, Builth Wells LD2 3TQ (01982

560400). A late medieval farmhouse, nestling on a wooded hillside in an Area of Special Scientific Interest, well off the beaten track, above, reputedly, the most picturesque part of the River Wye. A short drive from Hay-on-Wye 'Town of Books', and Brecon and the Beacons National Park. Alternatively, leave your car and step through our gate into a walkers' paradise, steeped in ancient Celtic history. Drink spring water from the tap, and have an enormous breakfast with our free-range eggs. Enjoy a delicious candlelit supper with log fires in the massive inglenook. Bed and Breakfast from £17.50.

LLANDRINDOD WELLS. Mrs Ruth Jones, Holly Farm, Howey, Llandrindod Wells LD1 5PP (01597

822402).AA ◆◆◆◆/WTB ★★★ *FARM*. Holly Farm, set in beautiful countryside, offers guests a friendly welcome. Situated one-and-a-half miles south of the spa town of Llandrindod Wells, it is an excellent centre for exploring lakes and mountains and for bird-watching. Rooms are en suite, with TV and beverage trays. There is a TV lounge with log fire; in the dining room, which has separate tables, superb meals are served using home produce. Safe car parking. Brochure on request. Bed and Breakfast from £18 to £22; Bed, Breakfast and Evening Meal £28 to £32; £185 to £210 per week.

LLANIDLOES. Mrs L. Rees, Esgairmaen, Y Fan, Llanidloes SY18 6NT (01686 430272). "Croeso Cynnes"

a warm welcome awaits you at Esgairmaen, a working farm one mile from Clywedog reservoir where fishing and sailing can be enjoyed, an ideal base for walking, bird watching and exploring nearby forests. The house commands magnificent views of unspoilt countryside, only twenty-nine miles from the coast. One double and one family room, both en suite with tea/coffee facilities. Central heating. Open April to October. Children and pets welcome. Camping also available from £5 per unit. We offer peace and tranquillity.

LLANWRTHWL. Gaynor Tyler, Dyffryn Farm, Llanwrthwl, Llandrindod Wells LD1 6NU (01597 811017;

Fax: 01597 810609). WTB ★★ *FARM*. Idyllically situated amidst the magnificent scenery of the Upper Wye Valley, Dyffryn, dating from the 17th century, is an ideal base from which to explore this unspoilt area of 'Wild Wales' with its wonderful walking, cycling, pony-trekking, bird-watching and fishing. The beautiful Elan Valley is close by. Slate floors, beams, stone walls and woodburning stoves all add their charm to this serene old house. We have two double and one twin bedrooms, en suite facilities and a lovely relaxing hayloft lounge. A cosy self-catering cottage is also available. Enjoy our wholesome food and a warm welcome. No smoking. Bed and Breakfast from £18. Brochure available.
e-mail: dyffrynfm@cs.com

See also Colour Display Advertisement

MACHYNLLETH near. Mrs P. Jesse, Braich Goch Inn and Restaurant, Corris, Near Machynlleth SY20 9RD (Tel & Fax: 01654 761229). Set in beautiful surroundings in the foothills of Snowdonia on the A487. Ideally situated for touring, steam train enthusiasts, bird-watching, rambling, fishing. Golf, horse riding and clay pigeon shooting all well catered for. World famous Centre for Alternative Technology and King Arthur's Labyrinth (new attraction) close by. Bedrooms en suite or with private facilities; licensed restaurant with extensive menu; cheerful beamed bar is a meeting place for friendly locals. Pets most welcome. Bed and Breakfast £21 to £25 per person (double or twin). Autumn and Winter Breaks - phone for details.

MONTGOMERY. Ceinwen Richards, The Drewin Farm, Churchstoke, Montgomery SY15 6TW (Tel &

Fax 01588 620325). AA ◆◆◆◆. A family-run mixed farm set on hillside overlooking panoramic views of the most beautiful countryside. The Drewin is a charming 17th century farmhouse retaining much of its original character with oak beams and large inglenook fireplace, separate lounge; twin and family rooms, both en suite and all modern amenities with colour TV. Full central heating. A games room with snooker table in converted granary. Offa's Dyke footpath runs through the farm - a wonderful area for wildlife. Ideal base for touring the many beauty spots around. Good home cooking and a very warm welcome await our visitors. Bed and Breakfast from £20; Bed, Breakfast and Evening Meal from £30. Featured in The Travel Show. Holder of Essential Food Hygiene Certificate and Farmhouse Award from Wales Tourist Board. Open April to October.

RHAYADER. Carl and Ann Edwards, Beili Neuadd, Rhayder LD6 5NS (Tel & Fax: 01597 810211). WTB

★★★★. Beautifully situated in quiet, secluded countryside with delightful views and its own stream, trout pools and woodland, Beili Neuadd is only two miles away from the smalll market town of Rhayder. The stone-built farmhouse, parts of which date back to the 16th century, has been sensitively restored to retain its original charm and character with exposed beams, polished oak floors, log fires and pretty furnishings. Single, double and twin bedded rooms with private shower and bathrooms, central heating, tea and coffee making facilities. Self- catering bunk house accommodation available in our recently converted stone barn. Special facilities for wheelchair users and families as well as for the outdoor enthusiast.
e-mail: ann-carl@thebeili.freeserve.co.uk

See also Colour Display Advertisement   **TALGARTH. Mrs Bronwen Prosser, Upper Genffordd Farm Guest House, Talgarth LD3 0EN (01874 711360). AA ◆◆◆** AA QQQQ. Set amongst the most spectacular scenery of the Brecon Beacons National Park, Upper Genfford Farm is an ideal base for exploring the Black Mountains, Wye Valley and the Brecon Beacons, an area of outstanding beauty, rich in historical and archaeological interest, with Roman camps and Norman castles. Picturesque mountain roads will lead you to reservoirs, the Gower coast with its lovely sandy beaches and Llangorse Lake - well known for all kinds of water sports. The charming Guest House accommodation includes one double and one twin-bedded room, both with en suite facilities. they are beautifully decorated and furnished, including tea/coffee making facilities, central heating, colour TV and hairdryer. the cosy lounge has a wealth of personal bric-a-brac, maps and paintings. Very much a home from home, with colour TV and books. Guests are made welcome with home-made cakes and tea on arrival. The local pub and restaurant is nearby and Hay-on-Wye, 'The Town of Books', is a short distance away. bed and Breakfast from £18 to £20 per person. Also fully equipped self-catering cottage. Ample parking on attractive patio adjacent to cottage. Play area for children, also a friendly pony. terms from £150 to £180 weekly. Awarded Plaque of Recommendation from the Welsh Tourist Board. Nominated "Landlady of the Year" 1999. Winner of FHG Diploma.

Key to Tourist Board Ratings – Scotland and Wales

The Scottish Tourist Board Star Grading System. This easy-to-understand system tells you at a glance the quality standard you can expect. The gradings range from ★ (Fair and acceptable) to ★★★★★ (Exceptional, world-class) and will also include the type of accommodation eg ★★★ Self-catering or ★★ Hotel.

The Wales Tourist Board also operates the above system for serviced accommodation only. Self-catering properties will continue to show the **Dragon Award Grading** from **One** to **Five** depending on quality and facilities.

Some properties had not been assessed at the time of going to press and in these cases the publishers have included the old Crown Gradings.

Visit the FHG website
www.holidayguides.com
for details of the wide choice of accommodation
featured in the full range of FHG titles

SOUTH WALES

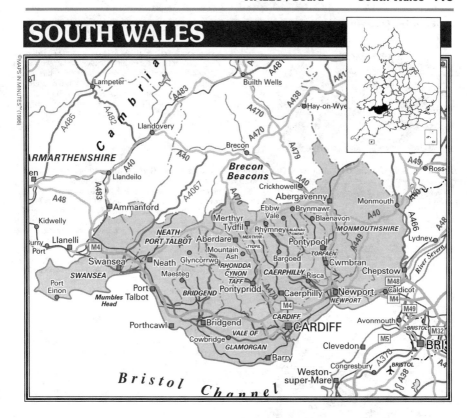

©MAPS IN MINUTES™ (1998)

COWBRIDGE near. Mrs Sue Beer, Plas Llanmihangel, Llanmihangel, Near Cowbridge CF71 7LQ

(01446 774610). WTB ★★ *GUEST HOUSE.* Plas Llanmihangel is the finest medieval Grade I Listed manor house in the beautiful Vale of Glamorgan. We offer a genuine warmth of welcome, delightful accommodation, first class food and service in our wonderful home. The baronial hall, great log fires, the ancient tower and acres of beautiful historic gardens intrigue all who stay in this fascinating house. Its long history and continuous occupation have created a spectacular building in romantic surroundings unchanged since the sixteenth century. A great opportunity to experience the ambience and charm of a past age, featured in "Distinctly Different." Guests are accommodated in three double rooms. Bed and Breakfast from £28. High quality home-cooked Evening Meal available on request.

MONMOUTH. Mrs Solveig Preece, Grange Farm, Newcastle, Near Monmouth NP25 5NX (01600

712636). WTB ★ *FARMHOUSE.* 16th century farmhouse situated in quiet countryside within easy reach of South Wales and the Forest of Dean. Bed and Breakfast from £15, Evening Meal available from £10. Self catering accommodation also available in Old Cider Mill Cottage, sleeping two. Children and pets welcome. No smoking.

MONMOUTH. Rosemary and Derek Ringer, Church Farm Guest House, Mitchel Troy, Monmouth

NP25 4HZ (01600 712176). WTB ★★ *GUEST HOUSE.* AA QQQ. A spacious and homely 16th century former farmhouse with oak beams and inglenook fireplaces, set in large attractive garden with stream. An excellent base for visiting the Wye Valley, Forest of Dean and Black Mountains. All bedrooms have washbasins, tea/coffee making facilities and central heating; most are en suite. Own car park. Colour TV. Non-smoking. Terrace and barbecue area. Bed and Breakfast from £19 to £23 per person. Evening Meal by arrangement. We also offer self-guided Walking Holidays and Short Breaks. Separate "Wysk Walks" brochure on request.

NEATH. Mrs S. Brown, Green Lantern Guest House, Hawdref Ganol Farm, Cimla, Neath SA12 9SL

(01639 631884). WTB ★★★ *B&B.* West Glamorgan's only AA QQQQQ Premier Selected family-run 18th century luxury centrally heated farmhouse, set in its own 45 acres with beautiful scenic views over open countryside. Close to Afan Argoed and Margam Parks; 10 minutes from M4; one mile from birthplace of Richard Burton. Ideal for walking, cycling, horse riding from farm. Colour TV. Tea/coffee facilities in all rooms, en suite availability. Pets welcome by arrangement. We offer luxury accommodation at an affordable price. Safe off-road parking. Central for Swansea, Neath and Port Talbot. Want to be impressed, try us. Terms from £20, reductions for children.
e-mail: stuart.brown7@virgin.net
website: http://freespace.virgin.net/stuart.brown7/

PONTYPOOL. Mr and Mrs Jayne, Mill Farm, Cwmafon, Near Pontypool NP4 8XJ (Tel & Fax: 01495

774588). WTB ★★★★ *FARMHOUSE.* AA ◆◆◆◆. Welcome Host. Caroline and Clive Jayne welcome you to experience complete tranquillity in their 15th century farmhouse situated in 30 acres of gardens, grounds and woodlands. Enjoy the comfort of rooms furnished with antiques, with breakfast until noon. Relax in the indoor heated pool situated in the large comfortable lounge. Ideal centre for walking, touring, visiting historic sites. Bed and heartYWelsh Breakfast £22.50 to £25 per person.

TINTERN. Anne and Peter Howe, Valley House, Raglan Road, Tintern, Near Chepstow NP6 6TH

(01291 689652). WTB ★★ *GUEST HOUSE.* AA ◆◆◆, RAC Acclaimed. Valley House is a fine Georgian residence situated in the tranquil Angidy Valley 800 yards from the A466 Chepstow to Monmouth road and within a mile of Tintern Abbey. Numerous walks through picturesque woods and valleys right from our doorstep. The accommodation is of a very high standard; all rooms are en suite, have tea/coffee making facilities and colour TV, whilst the guests' lounge and diningroom have a unique arched stone ceiling. Numerous places to eat nearby. Bed and Breakfast from £21 per person. Open all year. Non-smoking.

WALES

Self-Catering Accommodation

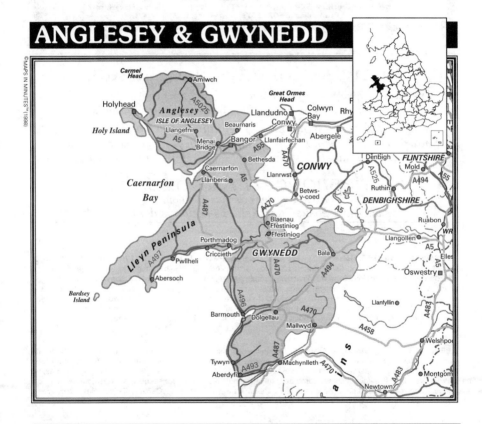

ANGLESEY & GWYNEDD

ABERDARON. Mrs M.P. Roberts, "Ty Fry", Aberdaron, Pwllheli LL53 8BY (01758 760274). Sleeps 5. Completely modernised and fully furnished with linen supplied, this Welsh cottage has exclusive views over Aberdaron Bay. Private drive from main road and ample parking space. Convenient for many sandy beaches and coves, including the famous Whistling Sands. Mountain walks where the sea views literally surround you on the extreme tip of the Lleyn Peninsula. Accommodation to let furnished without attendance. Two bedrooms, sleeping five, cot available; bathroom; immerser; large lounge (TV); kitchen/diner with electric cooker, fridge, microwave; metered electricity. Pets welcome. Bookings from March to October. For prompt reply SAE, please.

ABERSOCH. Quality Cottages. Around the magnificent Welsh coast. Away from the madding crowd. Near safe sandy beaches. A small specialist agency offering privacy, peace and unashamed luxury. Wales Tourist Board 1989 Award Winner. Residential standards - dishwashers, microwaves, washing machines, central heating, log fires, no slot meters. Linen provided. Pets welcome free. All in coastal areas famed for scenery, walks, wild flowers, birds, badgers and foxes. Free colour brochure. **S.C. Rees, Quality Cottages, Cerbid, Solva, Haverfordwest, Pembrokeshire SA62 6YE (01348 837871).**

BALA near. Rhyd Fudr, Llanuwchllyn, Near Bala. Sleeps 6. Stone farm cottage set in an isolated position with views of five mountain peaks and Bala Lake. Accommodation comprises three bedrooms, plus cot; two sitting rooms; sun room; kitchen; bathroom. Garage. Multi-fuel burning stove and most modern conviences but no TV. Fully-equipped including washing machine and telephone. Linen not supplied. Mountain stream and lovely walks on the doorstep. Sea, 45 minutes by car; Snowdon, one hour. Children welcome. Terms from £180. Apply: **Mrs J.H. Gervis, Nazeing Bury, Nazeing, Essex EN9 2JN (0199 289 2331) or Mrs G.E. Evans, Pant-y-Ceubren, Llanuwchllyn, Bala (01678 540252).**

BEDDGELERT. Beudy Coed, Oerddwr, Beddgelert. Sleeps 4. Beautifully renovated shepherd's cottage one mile from Aberglaslyn Pass, situated in a secluded, elevated position overlooking the River Glaslyn. The views towards the mountain ranges are breathtaking. Ideal central location for exploring Snowdonia, walking, fishing, horse riding, yet only four miles away from Porthmadog's sandy beaches. Perfect setting for relaxing amongst the scenery. Accommodation to sleep four persons in double and twin-bedded rooms. Linen supplied. Lounge/diner with stone fireplace, colour TV, fitted carpets. Fully equipped kitchen; shower room. Patio area in enclosed garden with table and benches. Ample car parking. Pets welcome. Contact: **Mrs Madge Williams, Berllan, Borth-y-Gest, Porthmadog, Gwynedd LL49 9UE (01766 513784).**

BEDDGELERT. Bron Eifion, Rhyd Ddu, Beddgelert. Sleeps 6. Attractive semi-detached house on edge of small village in National Park at foot of Snowdon. Splendid mountain, valley and pass walks from village including path up Snowdon. Lakes nearby. Excellent centre for seaside, historic castles and houses, riding, fishing and touring. Three bedrooms; two living rooms; bathroom; modern kitchen, fridge, airing cupboard, heaters. Well equipped. Mountain view, terrace, rough garden. Inn (serving meals) nearby. Cot. Sorry, no pets. High season £150 to £270 per week; low season £60 to £140 per week. Short Breaks by arrangement. Open all year. Apply: **Johnson, 12 Chatsworth Way, London SE27 9HR (0208 670 6455)**

See also Colour Display Advertisement

CAERNARFON. Beach Holiday Homes, West Point, The Beach, Pontllyfni, Caernarvon LL54 5ET (01286 660400). ✓✓✓ and ✓✓✓✓. Beach Holiday Homes offers bungalow, chalet and caravan accommodation in areas of outstanding natural beauty, all with sea views. Nearby restaurants, bar snacks, takeaways, most leisure activities including sea/river fishing, golf, rambling, pony trekking. Ideal for touring Snowdonia. Personal attention. Brochure available.

CAERNARFON. Mrs Eleri Carrog, Bryn Beddau, Bontnewydd, Caernarfon LL54 7YE (01286 830117/673795; Fax: 01286 675664). Sleeps 5. Cosy stone-built stable cottage with views of mountains and sea. Excellent centre for walks, touring, lovely beaches and Snowdonia. Secluded setting yet only 3 miles from Caernarfon. Lovely gallery bedroom with graceful arch windows, twin room, cot. Ideal for families or that romantic break. Spacious beamed lounge of great character and many books. Patio, barbecue. "Croeso Cymreig". Open all year. Terms from £80 to £375. e-mail: elericarrog@virgin.net.

CHURCH BAY. Mrs Lindy Wood, The Lobster Pot Cottage, Church Bay, Holyhead, Anglesey LL65 4EY (01407 730241/730588; Fax: 01407 730598). 11 miles from Holyhead, the ferry port to Ireland, The Lobster Pot cottage/flat is above a renowned seafood restaurant in picturesque Church Bay, with working lobster tanks. The flat is small but cosy, well equipped with electric cooker, microwave, fridge, percolator, etc. It sleeps four in one double and one twin-bedded room. Use of washing machine and tumble dryer and all linen included in tariff. Lawned gardens with barbecue. Well behaved pets welcome. Ideal for coastal walks, boating, bathing, bird watching. Nearby trout fishing, horse riding and golf. Terms from £110 to £240. Also The Anchorage, spacious house sleeping eight, ideal for two families. Rates from £208 to £360 per week. SAE please.

CRICCIETH. Quality Cottages. Around the magnificent Welsh coast. Away from the madding crowd. Near safe sandy beaches. A small specialist agency offering privacy, peace and unashamed luxury. Wales Tourist Board 1989 Award Winner. Residential standards - dishwashers, microwaves, washing machines, central heating, log fires, no slot meters. Linen provided. Pets welcome free. All in coastal areas famed for scenery, walks, wild flowers, birds, badgers and foxes. Free colour brochure. **S.C. Rees, Quality Cottages, Cerbid, Solva, Haverfordwest, Pembrokeshire SA62 6YE (01348 837871).**

CRICCIETH. Mrs M. Williams, Gaerwen Farm, Ynys, Criccieth LL52 0NU (01766 810324). Sleeps 7.

This 200 acre dairy/mixed farm is situated four-and-a-half miles inland from Criccieth and beaches. An ideal centre for enjoying climbing, fishing, pony trekking and quiet country walks with extensive views of Snowdonia and Cardigan Bay. Within easy reach of various historic places nearby. Accommodation is self-contained in furnished farmhouse, comprising TV lounge with inglenook fireplace and oak beams, electric fire; fitted kitchen with electric cooker, automatic washing machine, fridge/freezer and microwave; dining room; two double bedrooms, one twin-bedded room and one single bedroom, with duvets and bed linen; bathroom/shower with washbasin and toilet. Children most welcome, cot and babysitting available. Pets welcome. Car essential. Electricity provided. Weekly terms from £125 to £320. Short Breaks offered. SAE, please, for more details.

CRICCIETH. Mrs L. Hughes Jones, Tyddyn Heilyn, Chwilog LL53 6SW (01766 810441). Freshly renovated but keeping its antique features, charming, very cosy stonebuilt farm cottage in tranquil, unspoilt countryside with sea on either side, sheltered by Snowdonia Mountains in distant background. Comfortably sized kitchen full of electrical gadgets, microwave, washing machine; spacious lounge with colour TV. Capricorn bathroom suite has full size Twingrip bath and shower. Victorian furnished bedrooms have new mattresses with choice of duvets and blankets. As well as flower and shrub beds, there is an olde worlde character to the front and back courtyards - ample parking space here. Also, but not in cottage vicinity, furnished home sleeping up to six persons. Passing through this farmland, the renowned Lon Goed walk has six mile roadway of oak and ash trees and in the flowered hedgerows too there are species of rare birds.

Llanystumdwy, the home village of Earl Lloyd George with its commemorative museum, two fishing rivers, riding school, pets and rabbit farm, the church, cafes and a pub, is one mile away. Write or phone for the moderate terms of the two holiday accommodation properties. No pets. Let anytime of the year. Highly Commended.

CRICCIETH. Betws-Bach & Rhos-Dhu, Ynys, Criccieth LL52 0PB (Tel & Fax: 01758 720047; 01766 810295). Wales Tourist Board Grade 5. A truly romantic, memorable and special place to stay and relax in comfort. Old world farmhouse and period country cottage. Situated just off the B4411 road in tranquil surroundings. Equipped with washing/drying machines, dishwashers, microwaves, freezers, colour TV, old oak beams, inglenook with log fires, full central heating. Snooker table, pitch 'n' putt; romantic four-poster bed; sauna and jacuzzi. Open all year – Winter Weekends welcomed. Ideal for couples. Sleep two–six plus cot. Own fishing and shooting rights, wonderful walks, peace and quiet with Snowdonia and unspoilt beaches on our doorstep. For friendly personal service please phone, fax or write to **Mrs Anwen Jones.**

website: www.criccieth.co.uk/rhos
email: cottages@rhos.freeserve.co.uk

DYFFRYN ARDUDWY. Mr O.G. Thomas, Bron Foel Uchaf, Dyffryn Ardudwy LL44 2HZ (01341 247570).

Bron Foel is a spacious 18th century farmhouse full of character with outstanding views of Cardigan Bay and beyond. The lounge is spacious with oak beams and inglenook fireplace with wood supplied. Modern fitted kitchen with oil-fired Aga; three bedrooms – a double, a twin and a family room, all tastefully decorated. The house is set amidst ample grounds, in an elevated position to give privacy from the working farm. We are one and a half miles from the village of Dyffryn with Barmouth and Harlech a short distance away. Small pets and children welcome. Terms from £225

LLANBEDR. Mrs Beti Wyn Jones, Pensarn Farm, Llanbedr, Gwynedd LL45 2HS (01341 241285). Working farm. Sleeps 4 adults, 2 children. Self-catering, semi-detached cottage in beautiful surroundings, ideal for a peaceful and relaxing holiday. The accommodation consists of modern kitchen, lounge/diner, two bedrooms, bathroom and toilet on ground floor; one bedroom, shower/toilet upstairs. Night storage heaters. Ample parking space and garden. Children and pets welcome. It is situated one mile from the picturesque village of Llanbedr, quarter-of-a-mile off the main Barmouth to Harlech road. Convenient for beach, mountains, golf course, fishing and pleasant walks up the River Artro to the Nantcol and Cwm Bychan Valleys. Terms from £130 to £190 per week.

LLANBEDR. Mrs O. Evans, Werngron Farm, Llanbedr, Merioneth LL45 2PF (01341 241274). Working

farm. Pleasant bungalow on working farm, set in own grounds and enjoying open views of unspoilt countryside. Llanbedr two miles, Harlech three, Barmouth 10. Good touring centre for north and mid Wales; within easy reach of sandy beaches, golf course, indoor swimming pool, pony trekking, freshwater and coarse fishing, sea fishing, various tourist attractions and lovely country and mountain walks. Sleeps six, plus cot, in three bedrooms - double, twin and bunks - all with own washbasins. Sittingroom with colour TV; diningroom; well equipped, all electric fitted kitchen; spacious sun lounge; bathroom/shower. Fitted carpets throughout, electric fires, oil central heating. Bed linen provided. Open all year. Terms from £190 to £250 per week plus heating and electricity.

LLANBEDROG. Mrs L.O. Williams, Bodwrog, Llanbedrog, Pwllheli LL53 7RE (01758 740341). WTB 4 Dragons Standard. Modernised all-electric farmhouse accommodation to let without attendance although occasional free babysitting may be arranged. The 80 acre mixed farm offers stupendous views over the bays and headlands towards Snowdonia. Lleyn Peninsula is exceptionally mild - ideal for out of season holidays. Shooting is available on farm. Double glazing. Three double bedrooms accommodating six (cot provided); lounge, colour TV; kitchen/dining room with mahogany units, microwave, Parker Knoll suite. Bathroom and toilet. Linen supplied. Cleanliness assured. One house-trained pet welcome. Car preferable, ample concreted parking area. Shopping less than one mile away. Also available, six-berth private 32ft Galaxy Kingsley caravan (shower, flush toilet, fridge, colour TV, microwave, etc). SAE for prompt reply. Glorious sandy beach one- and-a-half miles away by car but only one mile across fields. Village pub with Les Routiers listed restaurant three-quarters of a mile, leisure centre five miles. Farmhouse terms from £130 weekly inclusive of electricity and bed linen. Mid-week or weekend bookings accepted during winter period and possibly March to May and in October. Caravan from £110 per week inclusive of electricity, gas and pillowcases.

See also Colour Display Advertisement

PORTHMADOG (Snowdonia). Felin Parc Cottages. Discover this idyllic 17th century riverside millhouse and charming wool manager's cottage in superb waterfall valley between Porthmadog and Beddgelert. Mill (WTB 4 Dragons) with large character beamed livingroom, period furnishings, wood stove, central heating, colour TV. Luxury kitchen, modernised bathroom/cloakroom. Sleeps eight/ten in four bedrooms and self-contained annexe Secluded terraces (barbecue/floodlighting) adjoin Mill pool and falls. Cottage (WTB 3 Dragons) sleeping four/six in two bedrooms, and self-contained gable annexe with similar facilities, is delightfully situated overlooking ancient fording bridge. Superb local scenery with Snowdon, Portmeirion, Ffestiniog Railway all nearby. Cottage Terms £175 to £390 and Mill £200 to £700 weekly. Brochure, photographs:- **Mr and Mrs O. Williams-Ellis, San Giovanni, 4 Sylvan Road, London SE19 2RX (020 8653 3118).**

PWLLHELI. Mrs C.A. Jones, Rhedyn, Mynytho, Pwllheli LL53 7PS (01758 740669) Sleeps 4. Rhedyn  is a small farm overlooking the beautiful Nanhoran Valley, and the farm cottage, accommodating four people, is offered for hire between April and November. It is two miles from Llanbedrog and Abersoch, both noted for their safe bathing. Children are made especially welcome. The house has two double bedrooms; bathroom and toilet; combined sitting/diningroom with TV; kitchen with immersion heater, washing machine, microwave oven. Calor gas stove and fridge. Linen supplied. Pets permitted. One mile from shops and two from the sea. Car essential, ample parking. SAE, for further details and terms.

PWLLHELI. Mrs M. Adams, Cae'r Ferch Uchaf, Pencaenewydd LL53 6DJ (01766 810660). Cedarwood chalet on a secluded smallholding consisting of three bedrooms, all with fitted wardrobes; large lounge with colour TV; luxury shower room with WC, additional WC in boiler room; kitchen/diner. The chalet is double glazed, centrally heated and open all year. The area is superb for walking and cycling, with quiet country roads throughout. The area is good for photography also. We are very central for all beaches and just a few miles from Snowdon. Charges are from £180 to £240 according to season. 50p power meter. Dogs by arrangement only . Please write or ring for details.

SNOWDONIA. Meillionen, Beddgelert. Farmhouse situated in the heart of Snowdonia within one mile of picturesque village. Large house divided into two separate units. One consists of large kitchen/livingroom with colour TV, electric cooker, fridge and Rayburn; stone staircase leading to two double bedrooms and bathroom. Other unit consists of sittingroom, open fireplace; colour TV; kitchen with fridge, electric cooker and microwave; downstairs bathroom; three double bedrooms and single bed. Bed and table linen not provided. Storage heaters in winter. Electricity on meter. Fishing, pony trekking and sports facilities nearby, also beaches within easy reach. SAE to **Mrs S.H. Owen, Cwm Cloch, Beddgelert, Caernarfon LL55 4UY (01766 890241).**

TYWYN. Coastal House, Tywyn, Gwynedd. Two minutes' walk to sandy beach. Two minutes' walk to pub/bar meals. Fully equipped as own home. Garden front and rear. Garage. Eight doors from the home bakery. Tal-y-Llyn Steam Railway walking distance. Pets welcome FREE OF CHARGE. Three bedrooms. Sleeps five Terms £164-£214 per week. Enquiries: **Mr Ian Weston, 18 Elizabeth Road, Basingstoke, Hampshire RG22 6AX (01256 352364; Evenings: 01256 412233).** e-mail: ianweston@iname.com

Key to Tourist Board Ratings – Scotland and Wales

The Scottish Tourist Board Star Grading System. This easy-to-understand system tells you at a glance the quality standard you can expect. The gradings range from ★ (Fair and acceptable) to ★★★★★ (Exceptional, world-class) and will also include the type of accommodation eg ★★★ Self-catering or ★★ Hotel.

The Wales Tourist Board also operates the above system for serviced accommodation only. Self-catering properties will continue to show the **Dragon Award Grading** from **One** to **Five** depending on quality and facilities.

Some properties had not been assessed at the time of going to press and in these cases the publishers have included the old Crown Gradings.

FREE and REDUCED RATE Holiday Visits!
Don't miss our Readers' Offer Vouchers

NORTH WALES

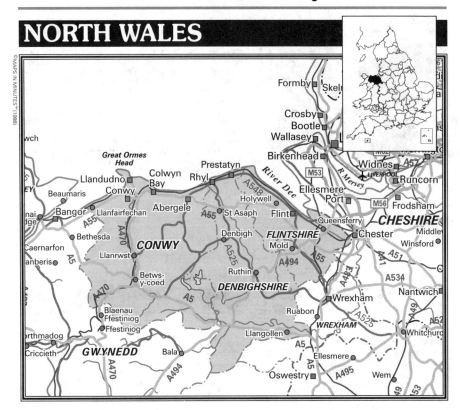

BETWS-Y-COED. Jim and Lilian Boughton, Bron Celyn, Lôn Muriau, Llanrwst Road, Betws-y-Coed LL24 0HD (01690 710333; Fax: 01690 710111). Our cosy 200-year-old converted coach house has been tastefully refurbished and offers accommodation for up to four persons. Upstairs: one double room with space for a cot, and one bunk-bedded room with full length/width bunk beds. All bed linen is provided but not towels. Kitchen with fridge, electric cooker, microwave, toaster and water heater. Electric storage heaters fitted throughout. Metered electricity (read arrival/departure). Open all year. Ideal centre for walking, climbing, fishing or simply just relaxing! Terms £120 to £300 per week. Short Breaks available.
e-mail: broncelyn@talk21.com
website: www.betws-y-coed.co.uk/broncelyn/

BETWS-Y-COED. Mrs E. Thomas, Bryn Farm, Nebo, Llanwrst LL26 0TE (01690 710315).Sleeps 2. Self-contained fully equipped farmhouse flat, sleeps two, on a beef and sheep farm. Situated in the Snowdonia National Park and approximately five miles from Betws-y-Coed and with rural views. The accommodation comprises smalll double bedroom and large bathroom upstairs. Downstairs has a kitchen/diner/lounge including microwave, fridge/freezer and TV. Central heating in winter. Small patio with garden furniture at front of property. Ideally situated for peace and quiet. Excellent base for country walks. Sorry no pets. Terms from £80 to £150 including electricity and bed linen. Short breaks available out of season. Open all year except Christmas and New Year.

See also Colour Display Advertisement   **CORWEN. Mr and Mrs J. Hughes, Tyddyn Hendwr, Llandrillo, Corwen LL20 0SN (01490 440210; Fax: 01490 440730).** The self- catering bungalows are situated in picturesque parkland at the foot of the Berwyn Mountains, four miles from Corwen. They are made of solid timber – in summer they are cool and airy, while in winter they are warm and cosy. Each has electric heating and is fully furnished with three bedrooms (one double and two twin), bathroom, fitted kitchen with electric cooker, fridge and breakfast bar. Spacious lounge with colour TV and opening onto a veranda. Celebrated Welsh lamb, all sorts of fare plus day to day essentials are all stocked in our farm shop, which also serves the farm's caravan park.

LLANGOLLEN. Min-yr-afon, Llanarmon Dyffryn Ceiriog, Llangollen. Llanarmon Dyffryn Ceiriog is a

beautiful village set in breathtaking countryside, with the Berwyn Mountains rising to almost 3000ft to the west. Not only famous for fishing, shooting and walking, it was the home of Welsh lyric poet John Ceiriog Hughes, born about 150 years ago. Nestling in this haven of Welsh beauty is Min-yr-afon a three bedroomed cottage. Carpeted throughout. Accommodation for six in one double, one single and one family bedrooms, with cot. Separate lounge with colour TV, downstairs bathroom and shower; dining room. Fully equipped kitchen (electric cooker, fridge, toaster, kettle, cooking utensils, crockery, cutlery). Also washing machine, iron and ironing board. Linen not provided. Car parking available. Weekly terms from £100 to £195. Available January to December. Enquiries to **Mrs C. Edmonds, Laburnum Cottage, West Hoathly, West Sussex RH19 4QN (01342 810908; mobile: 07711 452998).**

CARDIGANSHIRE

ABERPORTH. Quality Cottages. Around the magnificent Welsh coast. Away from the madding crowd. Near safe, sandy beaches. A small specialist agency offering privacy, peace and unashamed luxury. Wales Tourist Board 1989 Award Winner. Residential standards - dishwashers, microwaves, washing machines, central heating, log fires, no slot meters. Linen provided. Pets welcome free. All in coastal areas famed for scenery, walks, wild flowers, birds, badgers and foxes. Free colour brochure. **S.C. Rees, Quality Cottages, Cerbid, Solva, Haverfordwest, Pembrokeshire SA62 6YE (01348 837871).**

CARDIGAN near. Quality Cottages. Around the magnificent Welsh coast. Away from the madding crowd. Near safe sandy beaches. A small specialist agency offering privacy, peace and unashamed luxury. Wales Tourist Board 1989 Award Winner. Residential standards - dishwashers, microwaves, washing machines, central heating, log fires, no slot meters. Linen provided. Pets welcome free. All in coastal areas famed for scenery, walks, wild flowers, birds, badgers and foxes. Free colour brochure. **S.C. Rees, Quality Cottages, Cerbid, Solva, Haverfordwest, Pembrokeshire SA62 6YE (01348 837871).**

LLANGRANNOG. Quality Cottages. Around the magnificent Welsh coast. Away from the madding crowd. Near safe, sandy beaches. A small specialist agency offering privacy, peace and unashamed luxury. Wales Tourist Board 1989 Award Winner. Residential standards - dishwashers, microwaves, washing machines, central heating, log fires, no slot meters. Linen provided. Pets welcome free. All in coastal areas famed for scenery, walks, wild flowers, birds, badgers and foxes. Free colour brochure. **S.C. Rees, Quality Cottages, Cerbid, Solva, Haverfordwest, Pembrokeshire SA62 6YE (01348 837871).**

See also Colour Display Advertisement

MYDROILYN. Hillside Cottages, Blaenllanarth, Mydroilyn, Lampeter SA48 7RJ (01570 470374). Stone farm buildings, recently converted into four cottages, providing a modern standard of comfort in a traditional setting. Sleep two to three (terms £95 to £190), or sleep four to eight (terms £155 to £320). Gas, electricity and linen included in price. All have shower-room and fully-equipped kitchen. Colour TV; shared laundry-room; facilities for children. Special terms for Short Breaks. Open Easter to October. Situated in a secluded rural area abundant with wildlife. Only five miles from sandy beaches and picturesque harbours of Cardigan Bay. Within easy reach of National Trust coastal footpaths, sites of historic and cultural interest, steam railways, castles and breathtaking mountain scenery. Bird watching, fishing and pony trekking nearby. AA Approved. Full details from **Gil and Mike Kearney.**

PEMBROKESHIRE

©MAPS IN MINUTES™ (1998)

Strumble Head
Cardigan
Newcastle Emlyn
Fishguard
St David's
Ramsey Island
PEMBROKESHIRE
A487
A40
CARMARTHENS
Carmarthen
St Brides Bay
Narberth
Haverfordwest
A40
St Clears
A48
Skomer Island
Milford Haven
A477
Kidwelly
Skokholm Island
Neyland
A477
Pembroke Dock
Carmarthen Bay
Burry Port
Llanelli
Pembroke
Tenby
Caldey Island
St Govan's Head
Port Einon
SWAN

BOSHERTON. Quality Cottages. Around the magnificent Welsh coast. Away from the madding crowd. Near safe sandy beaches. A small specialist agency offering privacy, peace and unashamed luxury. Wales Tourist Board 1989 Award Winner. Residential standards - dishwashers, microwaves, washing machines, central heating, log fires, no slot meters. Linen provided. Pets welcome. All in coastal areas famed for scenery, walks, wild flowers, birds, badgers and foxes. Free colour brochure. **S.C. Rees, Quality Cottages, Cerbid, Solva, Haverfordwest, Pembrokeshire SA62 6YE (01348 837871).**

GOODWICK. Mrs Rosemary Johns, Carne Farm, Goodwick SA64 0LB (01348 891665). Working  **farm, join in.Sleeps 6.** Stone cottage adjoining farmhouse sleeps six in three bedrooms, also a spacious residential caravan for six with two bedrooms, each with its own garden where children can play safely. In peaceful countryside on 350 acre dairy and sheep farm between Fishguard and Strumble Head, three miles from the sea. Within easy reach of many beaches by car, ideal for walking and bird-watching. No linen supplied. Children welcome. Washing machine in cottage. TV, microwave, cots, highchairs. Baby sitting available. You can be sure of a warm welcome and visitors are invited to join in farm activities.

HAVERFORDWEST. Saddle House, Trewilym, Hayscastle, Haverfordwest. WTB 4 Dragon Award. The Saddle House, completely self-contained part of Trewilym Farm House, on a working farm. Surrounded by Pembrokeshire National Park with sandy beaches and coastal walks. Pub/restaurant two miles. The accommodation consists of ground floor: lounge, kitchen/dining. First floor: three bedrooms – double, compact twin and single. Bathroom with shower over bath, toilet and basin. Services: Economy 7 heating, electric fire in lounge. All power and bed linen included; colour TV, electric cooker, fridge/freezer, microwave, washing machine. Cot and highchair available. Attractive garden. Sorry no pets. Available March - December. Price £200 to £295. Contact **Mrs E. M Thomas, Trewilym, Hayscastle, Haverfordwest SA62 5AA (01348 831381).**

HAVERFORDWEST. Haven Cottages, Whitegates, Little Haven, Haverfordwest SA62 3LA (Tel & Fax:  **01437 781552). WTB 4 Dragons. Sleep 2/12.** Situated 200 yards' level walk from beautiful sandy beach in the old village of Broad Haven, close to shops and pubs. On Coastal Path, ideal for walkers, bird watchers, windsurfers and family beach holidays. Linen provided. TV. Laundry room. Pets welcome. Available all year. Organic poultry and ostriches reared. Special rates for breaks available. Bed and Breakfast also available in farmhouse. Details on request.

WEST LAMBSTON

Near. Portfield Gate, Haverfordwest, Pembrokeshire. SA62 3LG
Charles & Joy Spiers • Tel & Fax: 01437 710038

Non-working farm centrally positioned for beautiful coastal walks and many sandy beaches. Sleeps four in two bedrooms and cot. Autowasher, electric and microwave cookers. Fridge/Freezer, and ironing equipment. Cosy window seat and charming oak beamed inglenook. TV and video. Pets by arrangement. Linen inclusive. Open all year. Special rates for short breaks. October to March.

Terms from £150 to £390

NEWGALE. Quality Cottages. Around the magnificent Welsh coast. Away from the madding crowd. Near safe, sandy beaches. A small specialist agency offering privacy, peace and unashamed luxury. Wales Tourist Board 1989 Award Winner. Residential standards - dishwashers, microwaves, washing machines, central heating, log fires, no slot meters. Linen provided. Pets welcome free. All in coastal areas famed for scenery, walks, wild flowers, birds, badgers and foxes. Free colour brochure. **S.C. Rees, Quality Cottages, Cerbid, Solva, Haverfordwest, Pembrokeshire SA62 6YE (01348 837871).**

NORTH PEMBROKESHIRE. Mrs T. Jones, Penbanc, Tegryn, Llanfyrnach SA35 0BP (01239 698279). Working family farm with sheep, cows, calves, ponies, free range hens, ducks and geese; sometimes pigs. Traditional stone-built farmhouse accommodation sleeps six plus cot; bathroom; kitchen; sittingroom with colour TV and woodburner, dining room. Small garden with picnic table. Plenty of books and games for wet days, also old piano. Petrol, stamps, milk and pub meals one mile; village stores two miles. Centrally based for trekking, walking, touring, swimming, golf; coast 20 minutes by car (essential). Fishing – river, reservoir, sea or farm pool. Sandy beaches, rocky coves, coastal path. Island to visit. Plenty to do – castles, woollen mills, nature reserves, museums, crafts, leisure centres, theme park, zoo. Available May to September. Also seven-berth caravan available.

ST. DAVID'S. Ffynnon Ddofn, Llanon, Llanrhian, Haverfordwest. WTB 4 Dragons *APPROVED.* Luxury

cottage in quiet lane between St. David's and Fishguard, with panoramic views over many miles of this spectacular coastline. Ideal for walking; rocky coves and safe sandy beaches nearby. The cottage is fully carpeted, warm, comfortable and very well equipped, sleeping six in three bedrooms, plus cot. Washing machine, tumble dryer, freezer, microwave and video. Games room with table tennis and snooker, children's toys, lovely garden with swing. Perfect for early or late holidays, with central heating and double glazing. Parking beside cottage. Shop one mile. Footpath to beach. Pets welcome. Open all year. Terms from £220, including heating and electricity. Brochure on request. **Mrs T.A. Rees White, Brickhouse Farm, Burnham Road, Woodham Mortimer, Maldon, Essex CM9 6SR (01245 224611).**

ST. DAVID'S. Quality Cottages. Around the magnificent Welsh coast. Away from the madding crowd. Near safe sandy beaches. A small specialist agency offering privacy, peace and unashamed luxury. Wales Tourist Board 1989 Award Winner. Residential standards - dishwashers, microwaves, washing machines, central heating, log fires, no slot meters. Linen provided. Pets welcome free. All in coastal areas famed for scenery, walks, wild flowers, birds, badgers and foxes. Free colour brochure. **S.C. Rees, Quality Cottages, Cerbid, Solva, Haverfordwest, Pembrokeshire SA62 6YE (01348 837871).**

SOLVA. Quality Cottages. Around the magnificent Welsh coast. Away from the madding crowd. Near safe sandy beaches. A small specialist agency offering privacy, peace and unashamed luxury. Wales Tourist Board 1989 Award Winner. Residential standards - dishwashers, microwaves, washing machines, central heating, log fires, no slot meters. Linen provided. Pets welcome free. All in coastal areas famed for scenery, walks, wild flowers, birds, badgers and foxes. Free colour brochure. **S.C. Rees, Quality Cottages, Cerbid, Solva, Haverfordwest, Pembrokeshire SA62 6YE (01348 837871).**

SOLVA. Sarah Griffiths, Llanddinog Farm Cottages, Solva, Haverfordwest SA62 6NA (01348 831224).

WTB 4/5 Dragon Award. Sleep 4/6. Delightful luxury cottages grouped around farm courtyard, only three miles from sandy beaches and coastal paths. Fully equipped, centrally heated. Plenty to do and see: fishing, riding, watersports, golf, island trips, bird watching, seals and puffins. Colour TV, barbecue, large flower garden, swings and small animals. Meals available some nights by arrangement. Cot, highchair provided. Pets welcome. Short Breaks available. SAE, please, for brochure.
e-mail: sarahg@solvagp.demon.co.uk

TENBY. Quality Cottages. Around the magnificent Welsh coast. Away from the madding crowd. Near safe, sandy beaches. A small specialist agency offering privacy, peace and unashamed luxury. Wales Tourist Board 1989 Award Winner. Residential standards - dishwashers, microwaves, washing machines, central heating, log fires, no slot meters. Linen provided. Pets welcome free. All in coastal areas famed for scenery, walks, wild flowers, birds, badgers and foxes. Free colour brochure. **S.C. Rees, Quality Cottages, Cerbid, Solva, Haverfordwest, Pembrokeshire SA62 6YE (01348 837871).**

See also Colour Display Advertisement

WHITLAND. Mrs Angela Colledge, Gwarmacwydd, Llanfallteg, Whitland SA34 0XH (01437 563260; Fax: 01437 563839). Gwarmacwydd is a country estate of over 450 acres, including two miles of riverbank. Come and see a real farm in action, cows being milked, newborn calves and lambs. Children are welcomed. On the estate are five character stone cottages, Tourist Board Grade 4. Each cottage has been lovingly converted from traditional farm buildings, parts of which are over 200 years old. Each cottage is fully furnished and equipped with all modern conveniences. All electricity and linen included. All cottages are heated for year-round use. Colour brochure available.

POWYS

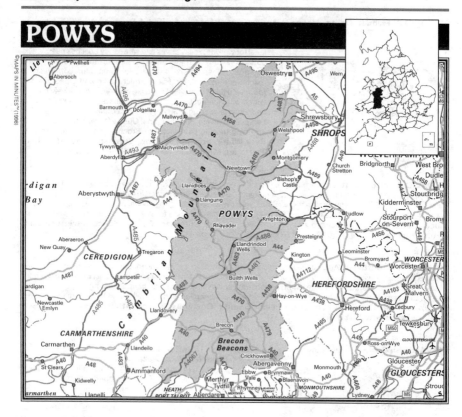

©MAPS IN MINUTES™ (1998)

BUILTH WELLS. Mrs E. Bally, Lane Farm, Painscastle, Builth Wells LD2 3JS (01497 851605; Fax: 01497 851617). 4 Dragons. Set in the heart of Kilvert country close to the border town of Hay-on-Wye (famous for books). Wonderful walking and riding, open country, with part of the farm as a Site of Special Scientific Interest. Two self-contained, self-catering flats overlooking the deer park and lakes. THE OLD STABLES has one family room and one twin-bedded room, two bathrooms, large living room with additional sofa bed and well-equipped kitchen. Wood burning stove. THE GRANARY has one double bedroom and one with three single beds, plus one landing bedroom; bathroom; large living room with additional sofa bed and well-equipped kitchen. Visitors have use of washing machine and tumble dryer. Bed linen and towels provided; cot and high chair available. Pets welcome; horses' stabling available. Both flats centrally heated.

NEWTOWN. Mrs D. Pryce, Aberbechan Farm, Newtown SY16 3BJ (01686 630675). Working farm, join in. Sleeps 6. This part of quaint Tudor farmhouse with its lovely oak beams is situated in picturesque countryside on a mixed farm with trout fishing and shooting in season. Newtown three miles, Welshpool, Powis Castle and Llanfair Light Railway, 14 miles; 45 miles to coast. The accommodation sleeps six persons in four double and two single bedrooms, also cot. Two bathrooms, two toilets. Sitting/diningroom with colour TV. Fully fitted kitchen with fridge, electric cooker, washing machine and dishwasher. Log fires and off-peak heaters. Electricity on meter. Large lawn with swing. Everything supplied for visitors' comfort. Linen available for overseas guests at extra cost. Car essential to obtain the best from the holiday. Farm produce available in season. Village shop one-and-a-half-miles away. Open all year. SAE please.

See also Colour Display Advertisement   TALGARTH. **Mrs Bronwen Prosser, Upper Genfford Farm Guest House, Talgarth LD3 0EN (01874 711360). AA ◆◆◆.** AA QQQQ. Set amongst the most spectacular scenery of the Brecon Beacons National Park, Upper Genfford Farm is an ideal base for exploring the Black Mountains, Wye Valley and the Brecon Beacons, an area of outstanding beauty, rich in historical and archaeological interest, with Roman camps and Norman castles. Picturesque mountain roads will lead you to reservoirs, the Gower coast with its lovely sandy beaches and Llangorse Lake - well known for all kinds of water sports. The local pub and restaurant is quarter-of-a-mile away and Hay-on-Wye, "The Town of Books" is a short distance away. Our self-catering cottage is fully equipped with fridge freezer, electric cooker, microwave and oil-fired Rayburn for cooking. There is a cosy, comfortable lounge with colour TV, open log fire (logs provided), pretty bathroom and two attractive bedrooms (one with two single beds, the second with one double and one single). Ample parking in attractive patio adjacent to the cottage. Play area for children, also a friendly pony. terms from £150 to £180 weekly. Also charming Guest House accommodation, beautifully decorated and furnished. Home-made cakes and tea on arrival. Bed and Breakfast £18 to £20 per person. Awarded Plaque of Recommendation from the Welsh Tourist Board. Nominated "Landlady of the Year" 1999. Winner of FHG Diploma.

SOUTH WALES

ABERGAVENNY near. Mrs Ann Ball, Upper Cwm Farm, Brynderi, Llantilio, Crossenny, Abergavenny

NP7 8TG (01873 821236; Fax: 01873 821236). WTB 4 Dragons. We have two self-catering properties available for let each accommodating up to six persons. THE GRANARY, situated on the upper floor, has three bedrooms, one double and two with twin beds, open-plan lounge with dining and kitchen area, bathroom and toilet, shower over bath and shaver point. THE COACH HOUSE which is situated on the ground floor has the same layout. Sevices in both properties include central heating, electric cooker and hob, microwave, refrigerator, toaster and colour TV. All fuel is included in rent. Cot and high chair available (cot linen not provided). Ample parking. Paved patio with seating. Pets, under strict control, by arrangement only.

ABERGAVENNY. Court Barn Holiday Cottage, Llanfair Green, Abergavenny. WTB 5 Dragons. Enjoy

magnificent panoramic views over to Sugar Loaf, Skirrid and Black Mountains from our recently converted stone barn set amidst unspoilt countryside. Perfect for watching wildlife, walking and exploring nearby castles. Ideal family holiday with sporting facilities in the area. Furnished to the highest standards with beautiful oak beams, fully fitted kitchen, shower room and separate toilet, two double bedrooms and one room with bunk beds. Garden with furniture, patio and barbecue. Garage facilities. Many beautiful and ineresting areas to explore. For more details please contact: **Mrs F. Chandler, Cefn Clytha, Llangattock Lingoed, Abergavenny NP7 8NT (Tel & Fax: 01873 821303).**

WALES

Caravan & Camping Holidays

ANGLESEY & GWYNEDD

BALA. Mrs S.E. Edwards, Bryn Melyn, Rhyduchaf, Bala LL23 7PG (01678 520376). Sleeps 6. One six-berth caravan available on Bryn Melyn, a 56 acre mixed farm in the village of Rhyduchaf, two miles from Bala situated in beautiful countryside. The caravan has a bathroom, inside flush toilet, hot and cold water, electric light, gas cooker, gas heater, fridge, colour TV. Fully equipped with blankets, microwave, etc. Children welcome. Sorry, no pets allowed. Open from April to September. Electricity on slot meter (£1). Weekly terms £85. Bed and Breakfast and Evening Meals available. SAE please for further details.

CAERNARFON. Eleanor Pierce, Glanrafon Farm, Pontrug, Caernarfon LL55 1UB (01286 673207). This six-berth 35 foot static caravan offers a superb panoramic view of Snowdonia Mountains and the River Seiont which runs through the field on the farm. Let the sound of the river drift through your open door this summer. The kitchen is well supplied to make your holiday catering easy. Two double bedrooms, one en suite. The caravan is ideally situated for those who love walking, climbing and fishing. Visit historic Caernarfon and shop at Bangor city or drive across to Anglesey and visit its beautiful beaches all within ten minutes. The caravan has its own entrance, private parking and garden with barbecue and patio set. A big Welsh Welcome awaits!

DOLGELLAU. Mrs S.J. Lane, Llwyn-Yr-Helm Farm, Brithdir, Dolgellau LL40 2SA (01341 450254). Situated on a minor road half a mile off B4416 which is a loop road between A470 and A494, this is a quiet, small working farm site, four miles from Dolgellau in beautiful countryside, ideal for walking. Many places of interest in the area including slate mines, narrow gauge railways, lakes and mountains and nine miles from sandy beaches. Toilet block with free showers and hot water; shaving points and plug. Caravans, Dormobiles and tents; electric hook-ups. Pets welcome. Open Easter to November.

NORTH WALES

ABERGELE. Mr and Mrs T.P. Williams, Pen Isaf Caravan Park, Llangernyw, Abergele LL22 8RN (01745 860276). This small caravan site in beautiful unspoilt countryside is ideal for touring North Wales and is situated 10 miles from the coast and 12 miles from Betws-y-Coed. The eight-berth caravans are fully equipped except for linen and towels and have shower, flush toilet, hot and cold water, Calor gas cooker, electric light and fridge. Fresh eggs and milk can be obtained from the farm on which this 20 caravan site is situated. Children especially will enjoy a holiday here, there being ample space and facilities for fishing and pony riding. Pets are allowed but must be kept under control. Open March to October. Terms on application with SAE, please.

RHYL. Palins Holiday Park, Morfa Avenue, Kinmel Bay, Rhyl LL18 5LE (01745 342672; Fax: 01745

344110). ✓✓✓✓. Palins Holiday Park is situated between Rhyl and Abergele on the A548 Towyn Coast Road. You are assured of the warmest welcome, all our staff are totally committed to ensuring that your holiday will be one you remember and hopefully you will decide to visit again and again. Heated indoor pool with waterchute and toddlers' area, children's play area, cabaret club, bingo and disco. Tudor Lounge with full size snooker table, pool, darts and colour TV. Mexican Theme Wine Bar and Restaurant, supermarket, fish and chip shop, cafe and launderette. All holiday homes have two or three bedrooms all equipped to the highest standard; bed linen and towels not provided. Dogs by arrangement only. Families only. Palins Holiday Park is a superb place from which to explore North Wales and its many attractions.

CARDIGANSHIRE

ABERPORTH. Mrs S. Jones, Manorafon Caravan Park, Sarnau, Llandyssul SA44 6QH (01239 810564). Sleeps 6. Quiet, peaceful site of 11 caravans, fully equipped except linen, all six-berth with end bedrooms. All essential facilities provided. Bathroom facilities with hot water on tap in each van; Calor gas cooker, electric lighting and heating. Toilets and washbasins, showers, shaving points. Calor and Camping Gaz sold. Available Easter to October. Children welcome. Dogs must be kept on lead. Only half-a-mile from the pleasant Penbryn beach and nine miles from the market towns of Cardigan and Newcastle Emlyn. One-and-a half-acres for campers and tourers.

FHG PUBLICATIONS

publish a large range of well-known accommodation guides. We will be happy to send you details or you can use the order form at the back of this book.

FREE and REDUCED RATE Holiday Visits!
Don't miss our Readers' Offer Vouchers

PEMBROKESHIRE

BROAD HAVEN near. Sandra Davies, Barley Villa, Walwyns Castle, Near Broad Haven, Haverfordwest

SA62 3EB (01437 781254). Our comfortable, two-bedroomed caravan is sited in the attractive, peaceful countryside of Walwyns Castle, which hosts a small nature reserve and several public footpaths. It is an ideal base for touring Pembrokeshire's beautiful coastline, visiting our famous bird islands and beautiful sandy bays ideal for swimming, surfing or sailing, all within easy reach by car. Ample shared parking and storage for bicycles. The caravan has a double and twin room, shower/toilet; full size cooker, fridge; lounge and dining room with gas fire and colour TV. Bed linen is provided, beds made up for arrival. Terms from £90 to £175 fully inclusive of gas, electricity and linen.

HAVERFORDWEST. Mrs W. Evans, Castle Farm Caravan Park, Castle Farm, Keeston, Haverfordwest

SA62 6ED (01437 710988). Enjoy a peaceful holiday on our working farm situated three miles from the market town of Haverfordwest and just five minutes from the coast. Our small park has just four caravans on site, so is perfect for those who really want to get away from the hubbub of everyday life. It is also an ideal location from which to explore all the delights of Pembrokeshire and beyond. All caravans are six-berth and are fully equipped with colour television, gas cooker, fridge etc. Terms from £130 to £220 per week. Pets welcome at no extra charge. Farmhouse B&B also available.

LLANTEG. Mrs A.H. James, Rose Park Farm, Amroth Road, Llanteg SA67 8QJ (01834 831203). Working farm. A touring camping and caravan park in a rural setting with views of Caldey Island. Situated near attractions and within easy reach of all the beautiful beaches in Pembrokeshire. Private parking, hook-ups. Advance booking in peak times. Play area and showers. Motor vans, tents and caravans welcome. Short breaks. Dogs allowed.

SOUTH WALES

MERTHYR TYDFIL. Grawen Caravan and Camping Park, Grawen Farm, Cwm-Taff, Cefn Coed,

Merthyr Tydfil CF48 2HS (01685 723740). ✓✓✓ Clean modern facilities. Picturesque surroundings with forest, mountain, reservoir walks from site. Reservoir trout fishing. Ideally located for touring, visiting places of historic interest and enjoying scenic views. Available April to October. Easy access A470 Brecon Beacons road, one-and-a-half miles Cefn Coed, three-and-a-half miles Merthyr Tydfil, two miles from A456 known as the Heads of the Valleys. Pets welcome. Terms from £6 per night. 16 electric hook-ups.

Terms quoted in this publication may be subject to increase
if rises in costs necessitate

THE FHG
DIPLOMA

HELP IMPROVE
BRITISH TOURIST STANDARDS

You are choosing holiday accommodation from our very popular FHG Publications.
Whether it be a hotel, guest house, farmhouse or self-catering accommodation, we think you will find it hospitable, comfortable and clean, and your host and hostess friendly and helpful.

Why not write and tell us about it?

As a recognition of the generally well-run and excellent holiday accommodation reviewed in our publications, we at FHG Publications Ltd. present a diploma to proprietors who receive the highest recommendation from their guests who are also readers of our Guides. If you care to write to us praising the holiday you have booked through FHG Publications Ltd. – whether this be board, self-catering accommodation, a sporting or a caravan holiday, what you say will be evaluated and the proprietors who reach our final list will be contacted.

The winning proprietor will receive an attractive framed diploma to display on his premises as recognition of a high standard of comfort, amenity and hospitality. FHG Publications Ltd. offer this diploma as a contribution towards the improvement of standards in tourist accommodation in Britain. Help your excellent host or hostess to win it!

FHG DIPLOMA

We nominate ....

....

Because

Name ....

Address..

....

Telephone No...

NORTHERN IRELAND
Board Accommodation

Co. DOWN

DOWNPATRICK. Mrs Myrtle McAuley, Havine Farm, 51 Ballydonnell Road, Downpatrick BT30 8EQ (028 4485 1242). ★★★. AA LISTED. Georgian farmhouse. Home cooking. Convenient to all local amenities.From Downpatrick take A25 for Newcastle, left Tyrella signpost, one mile past cross roads. Clough take Downpatrick Road. Right at Tyrella sign. One mile past crossroads on left. Three bedrooms, all with tea and coffee. Home from home hospitality. Supper provided. Bed and Breakfast £15.50 to £17.50.

Co. FERMANAGH

ENNISKILLEN. Mrs M. Love, View Point, 5 Mullnaskea Road, Garvary, Enniskillen BT74 4JQ (Tel & Fax: 028 6632 7321). Just off the B80, about three miles from Enniskillen, View Point is ideally situated to allow easy access to a wide range of Fermanagh tourist attractions. Within minutes of Enniskillen, tourists can relax in the quiet rural setting, amid beautiful countryside while enjoying an extensive breakfast and dinner menu. Two rooms en suite; one twin standard and one double with handbasin and shower. Three rooms have TV, all have central heating, hairdryer, and tea/coffee making facilities. Places of interest within easy reach include Ardhowen Theatre, Belleek Pottery, Castle Coole, Devenish Island and Enniskillen Castle. Castle Archdale Country Park and Carrybridge; boating, water skiing, etc nearby. Children welcome. Bed and Breakfast from £16.50 to £18; single supplement £3. NITB Approved.

FHG PUBLICATIONS

FHG publish a large range of well-known accommodation guides. We will be happy to send you details or you can use the order form at the back of this book.

Co. TYRONE

OMAGH. Mrs M. Montgomery, Clanabogan House, 85 Clanabogan Rd, Omagh BT78 1SL (028 8224

1171). A warm welcome awaits you at Clanabogan House. Situated 3 miles from Omagh off the A32, recently restored Clanabogan House is a listed building (recently restored) in 5 acres of woodland and gardens. Our spacious rooms have colour television and tea/coffee making facilities. We have two sitting rooms and two diningrooms excusively for residents. There is also an enclosed paved courtyard. Adjoining facilities include pony trekking, a golf driving range and licensed bar. Clanabogan House is an ideal base for touring Northern Ireland and is only a few miles from The Ulster History Park, Ulster American Folk Park, Gortin Glens and Fermanagh lakes.
e-mail: robert&mary@clanaboganhouse. freeserve.co.uk

Visit the FHG website
www.holidayguides.com
for details of the wide choice of accommodation
featured in the full range of FHG titles

NORTHERN IRELAND

Self-catering accommodation

Co. DOWN

CASTLEWELLAN. Maria Murray, Coast View Cottage, 41 Ballywillwill Road, Castlewellan BT31 9LF

(028 4377 8006). Sleeps six. Escape from everyday life and enjoy the peace and tranquillity of Coast View Cottage. set in the foothills of Slieve Croob with panoramic view of the County Down coastline. The perfect location to indulge in pastoral pleasures, a virgin territory of hills and glens await your discovery. Activities arranged by request – pony trekking, golfing, bicycle hire, hill walking, fishing and forest parks. Perfect for families, with private parking, garden with barbecue and furniture. Two bedrooms, sleeping up to six, modern kitchen, bathroom with electric shower and bath. Living and dining room with TV and video. Linen supplied. Laundry facilities. Central heating and log fires. £225 per week.

Co. FERMANAGH

See also Colour Display Advertisement

LISBELLOW. John and Eileen Bannon, Farm Cottage, Tattygar, Lisbellaw BT94 5AA (028 6638 7415). Sleeps 7. Spacious two storey house, with oil central heating and open fire. Only half-a-mile from Llisbellaw, six miles from Enniskillen. Easy access to fishing, caves, golf course, theatre and leisure centre. One hour scenic drive to beautiful Donegal beaches. Accommodation comprises three double and one single room. Fitted kitchen with gas cooker, automatic washing machine and frodge. Also two large lawns with swings and sandpit on site. Ample parking space. Children and pets welcome. Prices from £150 to £250 per week. Weekend breaks available - except July and August - from £80.

Terms quoted in this publication may be subject to increase
if rises in costs necessitate

NORTHERN IRELAND

Caravan & Camping Holidays

Co. TYRONE

See also Colour Display Advertisement

DUNGANNON. Dungannon Park Caravan and Camping, Dungannon.✓✓✓✓. Set in 70 acres of beautiful parkland surrounding an idyllic stillwater lake, the caravan park is situated in the heartland of Ulster, less than one miles away from the motorway to Belfast, and is within easy walking distance of the town of Dungannon. Relax and enjoy the many facilities available - up to three miles of scenic park walks, barbecue site and picnic area and children's play area. We have twelve fully serviced caravan sites and access for up to eight tents.Stillwater Raidbow Trout fly fishery. Terms: Caravans £8 per night, Tents £6. For more informations contact: **Dungannon District Council (028 8772 7327; Fax: 028 8772 9169). AA 3 Pennants.**

PLEASE MENTION THIS GUIDE WHEN YOU WRITE

OR PHONE TO ENQUIRE ABOUT ACCOMMODATION.

IF YOU ARE WRITING, A STAMPED,

ADDRESSED ENVELOPE IS ALWAYS APPRECIATED.

REPUBLIC OF IRELAND

Board Accommodation

Co. CORK

BANTRY. Mrs Agnes Hegarty, Hillcrest Farm, Ahakista, Durrus, Bantry (00 353 27 67045). Seaside dairy farm. Charming old-style farmhouse, newly renovated, retaining traditional character. Situated in picturesque peaceful setting overlooking harbour and Dunmanus Bay, quarter-of-a-mile from Ahakista village on the Sheep's Head Peninsula. Magnificent sea and mountain scenery; swimming, fishing, boating and five minutes' walk to the sea. Irish pubs and restaurants close by. Bantry 12 miles, Durrus six miles. Ideal centre for touring the Peninsulas of West Cork and Kerry. Signposted in Durrus. Four guest bedrooms, three with bath/shower en suite, one with washbasin; two are family rooms. Ground floor room available. Tea/coffee making facilities and electric blankets in all bedrooms. Bathroom. Spacious dining room with stone walls; sittingroom with old world fireplace and log fire. Play/games room, antiques, swing, lovely garden with mature trees. Warm hospitality. Fresh farm vegetables and home baking. Babysitting. On new Sheeps Head Way walking route. Bed and Breakfast from (Ir)£17 to £19; Dinner (Ir)£14, High Tea (Ir) £11. 25% reductions for children sharing with parents. Extensive breakfast menu. Award Winner of Farmhouse of the Year 1991/2. Also to let, modern seaside bungalow for self catering. Fully equipped and in superb location, from (Ir)£130 to (Ir)£350 per week. Available all year.

CLONAKILTY. Mrs Beechinor, Liscubba House, Rossmore, Clonakilty (00 353 233 8679). Old style farmhouse off the beaten track on 130 acre beef and tillage farm near Rossmore village. Quiet, rural area. Landscaped garden, fresh farm produce. All home baking and cooking. Four bedrooms, all with washbasin. Pets welcome. Pottery and craft tuition arranged. Children welcome. Warm, family welcome assured. Fishing on nearby rivers. Bed and Breakfast from £16; part board £180 weekly. Children's 50% reduction.

DUBLIN

SUTTON CROSS. Mr Hugh Moore, Mourne Grange Bed & Breakfast, 178 Howth Road, Sutton Cross, Dublin 13 (00353 1832 1342 Fax: 00353 1839 3329). On Howth Peninsula, seven miles north of Dublin city centre, 20 minutes drive from Dublin airport, half-an-hour's drive from car ferry. 20 minute train journey to Dublin's famous nightlife. Five minutes drive to the following golf courses: Howth, Deer Park, Sutton, Malahide, Portmarnock, St Anne's, Royal Dublin, Clontarf. Accommodation: one double room, one triple, one twin.
e-mail: mariemoore@esatclear.ie

Co. GALWAY

ORANMORE. Mrs Cannon, Cartroon Farm, Galway Coast Road, Oranmore (00 353 91 794345). Spacious farmhouse in scenic surroundings overlooking Galway Bay. Situated one mile west of Oranmore and four-and-a-half miles east of Galway City just off N18 and N6 roads. Ideal base for touring Connemara, Burren, Cliffs of Moher and indeed the whole of the West of Ireland. Galway City and Airport eight minutes' drive. Galway Bay Golf and Country Club five minutes, also horse riding, fishing and sailing locally. Dairy farm, other farm animals and domestic poultry also kept. Good food and accommodation in four bedrooms, all en suite. Bed and Breakfast from IR£16 per person; single supplement IR£5; Dinner IR£15.

Co. KILDARE

CASTLEDERMOT. Mr G.D. Greene, Kilkea Lodge Farm, Castledermot (00 353 50345112). Kilkea Lodge has belonged to the Greene family since 1740. Set in 260 acres of prime tillage and rolling parklands this tranquil setting offers guests the opportunity to relax in the comfort of log fires and traditional Irish hospitality. Accommodation comprises two double and one twin-bedded rooms en suite, and one single room and one family suite. First class traditional home cooking. Riding Centre on site run by Marion Greene and offering a variety of instructional and fun holidays under qualified supervision. Children welcome. French spoken. Open all year round except Christmas. Bed and Breakfast from £30; single supplement £5. Dinner from £15 to £20. Advance booking essential. Brochure available.

REPUBLIC OF IRELAND

Self-catering accommodation

Co. CORK

BANTRY. Mrs Sheila O'Shea, Ard-na-Greine, Adrigole, Bantry (00 353 2760018). Ard-na-Greine is a furnished holiday house to let on private ground including a field suitable as childrens' playground. Situated in the Beara Peninsula overlooking Bantry Bay and within 200 yards of the shore of the peaceful sea inlet of Adrigole Harbour. Adrigole is adjacent to the Healy Pass on the Ring of Beara and is an ideal centre for touring; it is within easy reach of Gougane Barra, Glengarrif, the Lakes of Killarney, Ring of Kerry and the fishing town of Castletownbere. Adrigole lies at the foot of Hungry Hill (highest peak in the Caha Mountains) with their fishing lakes, waterfall and numerous walks. Accommodation consists of five bedrooms, bathroom with electric shower, sittingroom with colour TV, diningroom, modern kitchen/breakfast room with electric cooker, fridge, automatic washing machine. microwave. Open fire, electric fires and off peak storage heating. Meter read on arrival. Linen not supplied. Terms from £150 to £300. Reply coupon please.

CASTLETOWNBERE. Mrs Margaret O'Dwyer, Toormore Bungalow, Toormore, Castletownbere, Bantry (027 70598; from UK 00 353 27 70598 after 10am.) Comfortable double glazed bungalow in West Cork overlooking the fishing port of Castletownbere, Bere Island and Bantry Bay. Situated amongst peaceful surroundings with superb views of sea and mountains. One mile from town and sea. Ideal base for touring around the scenic Ring of Beara, Ring of Kerry, Killarney, Blarney, Glengarriff, etc. Golf, fishing, boating, sailing, swimming, cycling, horse riding, mountain climbing, water sports and shooting available locally. Four double rooms; sittingroom with open fire, livingroom with colour TV, bathroom with shower; oak kitchen with all modern conveniences. Baby-sitting available. Oil and solid fuel central heating. Weekly from £150 to £350. Telephone or write. Small pet allowed.

Visit the **FHG** website
www.holidayguides.com
for details of the wide choice of accommodation featured in the full range of FHG titles

---

Terms quoted in this publication may be subject to increase
if rises in costs necessitate

Co. KERRY

ANNASCAUL. Mrs M. Sayers, Kilmurry Farm, Minard Castle, Annascaul (066 57173; from UK 00 353

6657173). Dingle Peninsula. Self-catering accommodation available. House sleeps 6. Three bedrooms. All modern conveniences. Overlooking Dingle Bay. Within walking distance to sandy beach. Pub and shops close by. Dingle town 5 miles, renowned for the famous Dingle Dolphin. Weekly terms: April-May £150; June £160; July-August £250; September £150; October £120. Rest of the year on request. Pets £10. Electricity extra. International Reply coupon please.

LAURAGH. Creveen Lodge Caravan and Camping Park, Healy Pass Road, Lauragh (00 353 64 83131;

from Ireland 064 83131). Attractive two-storey dormer-style farmhouse attached to proprietors' residence, 200 yards from roadside, with magnificent views of sea and countryside. The 80-acre mixed farm is conveniently situated for fishing, mountain climbing, Derreen Gardens, shops and old Irish pub: 16 miles south of Kenmare. Accommodation for six/eight persons in three double and one single room, all with washbasins; cot. Sittingroom with large stone fireplace, TV; separate diningroom. Kitchen has gas cooker; full oil-fired central heating and storage heating; washing machine and dryer. Everything supplied including linen. Children and pets welcome; high chair, and babysitting arranged. Car essential - parking. Available all year. April, May, June and September £140 per week; July and August £250 per week; rest of the year by arrangement. Gas and electricity extra.

REPUBLIC OF IRELAND

Caravan & Camping Holidays

Co. KERRY

See also Colour Display Advertisement KILLORGLIN. West's Caravan Park, Killarney Road, Killorglin **(066 61240; from UK 00 353 66 9761240).** Caravan holiday homes to hire. Situated on the Killorglin/Killarney road, one mile from Killorglin on Ring of Kerry with Ireland's highest mountain in background, on the banks of River Laune renowned for trout and salmon fishing. On park facilities include circular children's swimming pool, tennis, river fishing (racquets and rods for hire), hairdryers, table tennis, pool table, colour TV lounge, babysitting service, shop, payphone, etc. Central site for touring Kerry. Open Easter to end October. Further details on request. Ferry and static caravan prices; Mobile homes from £109 to £349.

ONE FOR YOUR FRIEND 2000

FHG Publications have a large range of attractive holiday accommodation guides for all kinds of holiday opportunities throughout Britain. They also make useful gifts at any time of year. Our guides are available in most bookshops and larger newsagents but we will be happy to post you a copy direct if you have any difficulty. We will also post abroad but have to charge separately for post or freight. *The inclusive cost of posting and packing the guides to you or your friends in the UK is as follows:*

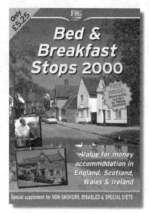

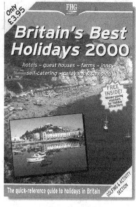

FARM HOLIDAY GUIDE
England, Scotland, Wales and
Channel Islands.
Board, Self-catering, Caravans/
Camping, Activity Holidays.
£5.60 inc p&p

BED AND BREAKFAST STOPS.
Over 1000 friendly and
comfortable overnight stops.
Non-smoking, Disabled and
Special Diets Supplements.
£5.60 inc p&p.

BRITAIN'S BEST HOLIDAYS
A quick-reference general guide
for all kinds of holidays.
£4.20 inc p&p.

SELF-CATERING HOLIDAYS
in Britain
Over 1000 addresses throughout
for Self-catering and caravans
in Britain.
£5.00 inc p&p.

Recommended
WAYSIDE AND COUNTRY INNS
of Britain
Pubs, Inns and small hotels.
£5.00 inc p&p.

Recommended
COUNTRY HOTELS OF BRITAIN
Including Country Houses, for
the discriminating
£5.00 inc p&p

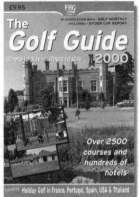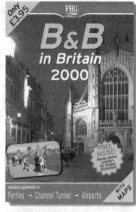

GOLF GUIDE –
Where to play. Where to stay.
In association with GOLF
MONTHLY.Over 2500 golf courses
in Britain with convenient
accommodation. Holiday Golf in
France, Portugal, Spain,USA and
Thailand.
£10.50 inc p&p.

The FHG Guide to CARAVAN &
CAMPING HOLIDAYS
Caravans for hire, sites and
holiday parks and centres.
£4.30 inc p&p.

BED AND BREAKFAST
in Britain
Over 1000 choices for touring
and holidays throughout Britain.
Airports and Ferries Supplement.
£4.20 inc p&p.

CHILDREN WELCOME! Family Holidays and Attractions guide.
Family holidays with details of amenities for children and babies.   £5.00 inc p&p.

PETS WELCOME!
The unique guide for holidays for pet owners and their pets.   £5.60 inc p&p.

Tick your choice and send your order and payment to

FHG PUBLICATIONS, ABBEY MILL BUSINESS CENTRE,
SEEDHILL, PAISLEY PA1 1TJ
(TEL: 0141-887 0428; FAX: 0141-889 7204).

FHG

Deduct 10% for 2/3 titles or copies; 20% for 4 or more.

Send to: NAME...

                 ADDRESS ....

                 ....

                 ....

                 POST CODE ....

I enclose Cheque/Postal Order for £...

                 SIGNATURE ....DATE ....

Please complete the following to help us improve the service we provide. How did
you find out about our guides?:

☐Press   ☐Magazines   ☐TV/Radio   ☐Family/Friend   ☐Other